Custom Textbook Prepared for
Department of Industrial Engineering and Operations Research
Columbia University

Includes Materials from:

Professor Soulaymane Kachani for
IEOR E4403 & IEOR E4003, Columbia University

Financial Accounting: A Valuation Emphasis
Hughes – Ayres – Hoskin

Advanced Engineering Economics
Park – Sharp – Bette

and

Applied Corporate Finance: A User's Manual
Second Edition
Damodaran

This custom textbook includes materials submitted by the Author for publication by John Wiley & Sons, Inc. The material has not been edited by Wiley and the Author is solely responsible for its content.

To order books or for customer service please, call 1-800-CALL WILEY (225-5945).

Printed in the United States of America

ISBN-13   978-0-471-76971-2
ISBN-10   0-471-76971-1

10 9 8 7 6 5 4 3 2 1

Preface

New York, May 2nd, 2005

Dear student,

For several years, students in my Industrial Economics (IEOR E4003), and my Advanced Engineering & Corporate Economics (IEOR E4403) courses at Columbia University's Department of Industrial Engineering and Operations Research have been requesting a textbook that better covers the broad range of topics discussed in these courses.

Unfortunately, such textbook does not exist. This custom book is an attempt to cover most of these topics using four different sources: "Financial Accounting, A Valuation Emphasis" by Hughes, Ayres and Hoskin; "Advanced Engineering Economics" by Park and Sharp-Bette; "Applied Corporate Finance" by Damodaran; and finally a small subset of the lecture slides that I developed here at Columbia University, and that leverage my experience at McKinsey & Company.

I would like to thank Alan Most and Melissa Franks at Wiley for helping me through this process. I would also like to thank my former students for their feedback.

I look forward to your suggestions as, together, we continue to improve these courses and this custom book.

Sincerely,

Soulaymane Kachani

Table of Contents

Part I: Interpreting Financial Statements

- Lecture slides on financial analysis   3
- Chapters 1, 2, 3, 4, 5 and 6 of "Financial Accounting, A Valuation Emphasis" by Hughes, Ayres and Hoskin   31

Part II: Evaluating Economic Performance of Companies and Projects

- Lecture slides on ratio analysis, discounted cash flows and transform techniques   245
- Chapters 2 and 3 of "Advanced Engineering Economics" by Park and Sharp-Bette   265
- Lecture slides on figures of merit   359
- Chapters 6 and 7 of "Advanced Engineering Economics" by Park and Sharp-Bette   371

Part III: Corporate Finance

- Lecture slides on dividend policy, debt policy, WACC and optimal capital structure   451
- Chapters 7, 8, 9 and 10 of "Applied Corporate Finance" by Damodaran   469

Part IV: Additional Topics

- Lecture slides on deterministic capital budgeting   655
- Chapter 8 of "Advanced Engineering Economics" by Park and Sharp-Bette   663
- Lecture slides on utility theory   715
- Chapter 9 of "Advanced Engineering Economics" by Park and Sharp-Bette   723
- Chapter 13 of "Advanced Engineering Economics" by Park and Sharp-Bette   751

Outline

Part I: Interpreting Financial Statements

▪Lecture slides on financial analysis

▪Chapters 1, 2, 3, 4, 5 and 6 of "Financial Accounting, A Valuation Emphasis" by Hughes, Ayres and Hoskin

The Big Picture

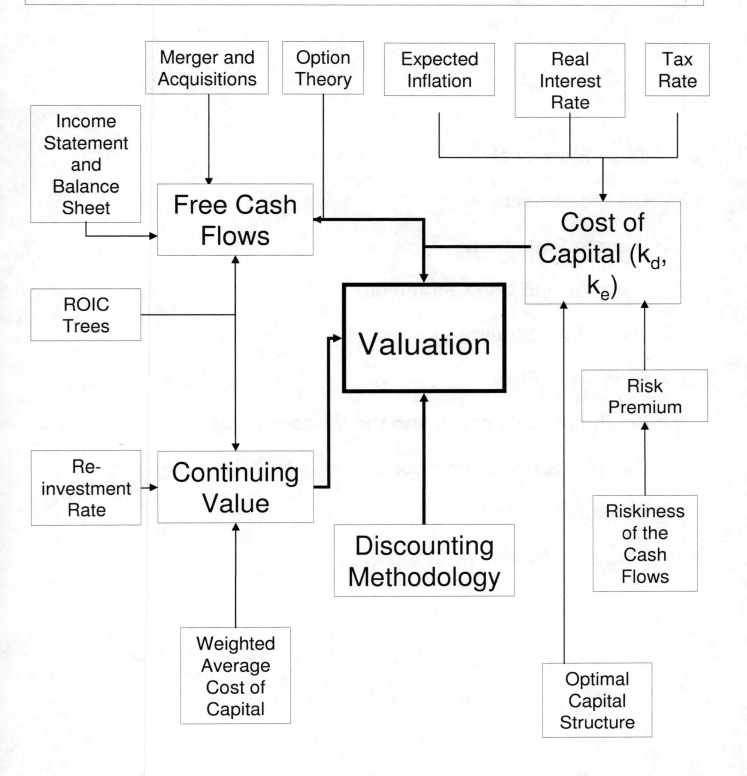

Interpreting Financial Statements

- ➢ **Cash Flow Cycle**

- ➢ **Balance Sheet**

- ➢ **Income Statement**

- ➢ **Sources and Uses Statement**

- ➢ **Cash Flow Statement**

- ➢ **Free Cash Flow**

- ➢ **Financial Statements and the Value Problem**

- ➢ **Balance Sheet Decomposition**

- ➢ **Sustainable Growth**

- ➢ **Financial Statement Footnotes**

Interpreting Financial Statements

Key Concepts

1. **Understand the difference between financial accounting (governed by generally accepted accounting principles) and management accounting (governed by the needs of a particular company)**

   - **GAAP: U.S.**

   - **German accounting system**

   - **IAS (International Accounting System)**

Interpreting Financial Statements

Key Concepts

➢ Financial accounting:

  ✓ **Not for managerial decision making**

  ✓ **Invented by bankers in Spain some 400 years ago**

  ✓ **External accounting**

➢ Management/Cost accounting:

  ✓ **For managerial decision making (sunk cost, opportunity cost)**

  ✓ **Internal accounting**

  ✓ **Company decides cost accounting systems**

  ✓ **Management information systems**

Interpreting Financial Statements

Key Concepts

2. The financial accounting rules differ from a country to another. We will concentrate on major principles that are similar across all countries

3. We have to understand the difference between financial reporting (straight line) and tax reporting (accelerated)

4. Purpose of doing all of this: understand how to determine expected cash flows for business units and company valuation

Interpreting Financial Statements

Three Main Accounting Principles

1. Realization principle / Accrual accounting

➤ **When is a sales revenue recognized in accounting?**

1. Order received

2. Service delivered

3. Invoice sent

4. Payment received

➤ **Can we estimate the market value of a company from financial statements?**

No.

Interpreting Financial Statements

2. Matching principle

> Cost must be recognized when we have recognized the corresponding revenue

> Problems with depreciation and future costs of guarantees

3. Principle of prudence

> Do not overestimate your profits (you are allowed to underestimate your profits)

✓ R&D cost goes to the income statement: because you are not sure you are getting these benefits in the following years

Interpreting Financial Statements

Cash Flow Cycle

> ➤ **Close interplay between company operations and finances**

> ➤ **Property 1:** *Financial statements are an important reflection of reality*

> ➤ **Property 2:** *Profits do not equal cash*

Interpreting Financial Statements

➢ **Financial snapshot, at a point in time, of all the assets a company owns and all the claims against these assets**

Assets = Liabilities + Shareholders' equity

Question: If a company is short in cash, can it spend some of its shareholders' equity? Why?

Interpreting Financial Statements

Assets

- Liquid assets
- Accounts receivable
- Inventories
- Net Fixed assets
- Other assets

Liabilities+S.E.

- Short term borrowing
- Accounts payable
- Net accruals
- Long-term debt
- Owners equity
  - Paid-in capital
  - Retained earnings

Interpreting Financial Statements

Standard Balance Sheet

Assets

➤ **Liquid assets**
- Cash, Market securities
- Belongs to shareholders
- Companies need to justify why they are holding to high levels of liquids assets

➤ **Accounts receivable**
- FIFO, LIFO
- Financed by LTD

➤ **Inventories**
- Financed by AP and STB

➤ **Net Fixed assets**
- Financed from OE

➤ **Other assets**

Intangible assets:
- Patents
- Trademarks
- Human capital
- Goodwill

Financing

➤ **Short term borrowing**

➤ **Accounts payable**
- Unpaid raw materials

➤ **Net accruals**
- Unpaid energy bills and admin bills

➤ **Long-term debt**

➤ **Owners equity**
- How much owners have invested in the company
- Book value: may not include a lot of important value: e.g. trademark value (e.g. Coca Cola), human capital

➤ **Paid-in capital**
- Paid for by owner: investment

➤ **Retained earnings**
- Invested by owners instead of taking them in their pocket

Interpreting Financial Statements

Income Statement

➤ **A record of flow of resources *over time* commonly divided into two parts:**

- **Operating segments**
- **Non-operating segments**

➤ **At least 5 issues associated with Earnings (Net Income) reported in an income statement:**

- **Accrual accounting**
- **Inventory methods: FIFO, LIFO, Average method**
- **Depreciation methods: Straight-line vs. Accelerated depreciation**
- **Taxes**
- **Research and Marketing, creation of trademarks and patents in the balance sheet**

Interpreting Financial Statements

Standard Income Statement

Net Sales

Gross Profit

Operating Profit

Earnings Before Interest & Taxes (EBIT)

Earnings Before Taxes (EBT)

Earnings After Taxes (EAT) or Net Income

Interpreting Financial Statements

Net Sales

- Cost of Good Sold (COGS)

Gross Profit

- Administrative & Selling Expenses (SG&A)

- Depreciation

Operating Profit

+/- Extraordinary Gain/Loss

+ Other Income

Earnings Before Interest & Taxes (EBIT)

- Interest Expenses

Earnings Before Taxes (EBT)

- Provision for Income Taxes

Earnings After Taxes (EAT) or Net Income

Interpreting Financial Statements

➢ **Answers two questions:**

▪ **Where does a company get its cash?**

▪ **How does a company spend its cash?**

➢ **Two-step approach:**

▪ **Place two balance sheets for different dates and note all the changes in accounts**

▪ **Segregate the changes in those that generate cash** *(reduce an asset or increase a liability)* **and those that consume cash** *(increase an asset account or reduce a liability account)*

Sources = Uses

➢ **Question:** *Is "Increase in cash" a source or a use of cash? Why?*

Interpreting Financial Statements

➢ **Expands the Sources and Uses Statement, placing each source and use into 1 of 3 *(4)* categories**

> ▪ **Cash flows from operating activities**
>
> ▪ **Cash flows from investing activities**

▪ **Cash flows from financing activities**

▪ **Effect of exchange rate changes on cash**

Interpreting Financial Statements

Statement of Cash Flows

Net Income

Adjustment to net income:

1. + Depreciation

2. Changes in Working Capital
   1. **- Increase in Accounts receivable**
   2. **- Increase in Inventory**
   3. **+ Increase in Accounts Payable**
   4. **+ Increase in Accrued Liabilities**

3. Cash flow from investing
   1. **- Capital Expenditures**
   2. **- Increase in Other Assets**

Total Cash Flow from Operations and Investing

1. - Dividends and Stock Repurchases

2. + Increase in Short Term Debt

3. - Increase in Marketable Securities

4. + Increase in Long Term Debt

Total Cash Flow from Financing

Increase in Cash

Interpreting Financial Statements

Consolidation

> **Practically speaking, all large companies own other companies. To fully understand the impact of these ownership structures on companies' financial health, companies are required to publish consolidated financial statements. Typically, we divide the companies into three groups with respect to ownership levels:**

- **Ownership > 50% (control the other company): these companies are fully consolidated and are called subsidiaries**

- **50% ≥ Ownership ≥ 20% (include joint ventures): these companies are often called equity affiliates and they are accounted for by the equity method**

- **Ownership < 20%: these companies are treated as financial investments**

Interpreting Financial Statements

Free Cash Flow

> ➤ **Fundamental determinant of the value of a business**

Free Cash Flow = **Total cash available for distribution to owners and creditors after funding all worthwhile investment activities**

= **EBIT (1 – Tax rate) + Depreciation – Capital Expenditures - Increases in Working Capital**

Interpreting Financial Statements

Statement of Free Cash Flow

EBIT.(1-Tax Rate)

Adjustment to EBIT.(1- Tax Rate):

1. + Depreciation

2. Changes in Working Capital
   1. **- Increase in Accounts receivable**
   2. **- Increase in Inventory**
   3. **+ Increase in Accounts Payable**
   4. **+ Increase in Accrued Liabilities**

3. Cash flow from investing
   1. **- Capital Expenditures**
   2. **- Increase in Other Assets**

Free Cash Flow

Interpreting Financial Statements

The Value Problem

➤ **Issues in using accounting data for financial decision making:**

- **Market Value vs. Book Value**

  ✓ Original costs vs. current values
  - Relevant & subjective vs. irrelevant & objective

  ✓ Forward-looking vs. backward-looking
  - Exception: Goodwill

- **Economic Income vs. Accounting Income**

  ✓ Realized vs. unrealized income

  ✓ Cost of equity

Interpreting Financial Statements

> ➢ **This tool starts by dividing both investments and financing methods of a company into two parts**

- ▪ **Investments**
  - ✓ Investments in fixed assets
  - ✓ Investments in the operating cycle = Working Capital Requirement

- ▪ **Financing**
  - ✓ Short-term financing
  - ✓ Long-term financing

Interpreting Financial Statements

Balance Sheet
Decomposition

➤ **Using the four elements we identified, we can divide the balance sheet into 3 separate blocks which affect each other**

- **Net Long-term Financing (NLF)**

  - ✓ Long-term Financing – Fixed Assets

  - ✓ Should be positive (cushion)

  - ✓ Bigger NLF: more conservative financing strategy (low risk) but more expensive

- **Working Capital Requirement (WCR)**

  - ✓ Accounts Receivable + Inventories – Accounts Payable – Net Accruals

  - ✓ Money needed to run the company day to day

- **Net Short-term Borrowing (NSB)**

  - ✓ Short-term Financing – Liquid Assets

WCR = NLF + NSB

Interpreting Financial Statements

Liquid Assets

Short-term Financing

NSB

Receivables

Inventories

Payables

Net Accruals

WCR

Fixed Assets

Long-term Financing

NLF

Interpreting Financial Statements

➢ **What is the maximum growth rate, if no external financing sources exist?**

➢ **More precisely, sustainable growth computes the maximum growth rate a company can sustain without financial difficulties assuming that:**

- **The company cannot raise new equity financing**
  - ✓ Most applicable to small and medium size companies as well as government-owned companies

- **The company (or the banker) does not want to increase the financial risk of the company**
  - ✓ D/E ratio is constant

- **The operational efficiency of the company is constant**
  - ✓ Sales/Assets ratio is constant

Interpreting Financial Statements

➢ **Financial statements are not complete without footnotes which typically explain at least 3 different types of information**

- **Explanations how the company has interpreted different financial accounting principles**

- **More detailed information of income statement and balance sheet numbers**

- **Off-balance sheet items which do not show up in the balance sheet such as:**
  - ✓ Operating leases
  - ✓ Pending lawsuits
  - ✓ Executive stock options
  - ✓ Financial instruments

Outline

Part I: Interpreting Financial Statements

- Lecture slides on financial analysis

- Chapters 1, 2, 3, 4, 5 and 6 of "Financial Accounting, A Valuation Emphasis" by Hughes, Ayres and Hoskin

CHAPTER 1

Financial Reporting: The Institutional Setting

LEARNING OBJECTIVES

After reading this chapter you should be able to:

1 Identify the types of business activities of publicly traded corporations reflected in financial accounting reports.

2 Explain the process governing the regulation of financial reporting and setting of Generally Accepted Accounting Principles (GAAP).

3 Describe the role of independent audits in monitoring compliance of financial reports with GAAP.

4 Recognize the economic consequences of accounting choices, and the link between owners' and managers' wealth and financial statement information.

5 Understand that a potential relationship exists between the value of a firm's stock and the information contained in financial reports, particularly the firm's statement of earnings.

During the day of August 25, 2000, the stock price of Emulex, a computer technology company, drastically dropped (see Exhibit 1.1) following an Internet story that it was under investigation by the Securities and Exchange Commission (SEC). The story also indicated that Emulex would restate its earnings downward as a result of the investigation. The stock quickly rebounded later that same day when investors learned that the story had been a hoax.

This event suggests that both earnings *per se*, and the credibility of that number are relevant to the stock market's assessment of a firm's value. Several questions come to mind: What are earnings? How are earnings linked to the market value of a company's stock? What role do the SEC and other institutions play in determining the reliability of reported earnings? These and many other questions pertaining to the construction of financial accounting information, and how that information relates to the value of the firm and the expectations of investors, lay at the heart of this text.

Exhibit 1.1

THE REAL WORLD

Emulex

Emulex Stock Price Movement. The Vertical Bars Reflect the Range of Price Movement on the Day Shown. The Horizontal Bars Show the Closing Price for the Day.

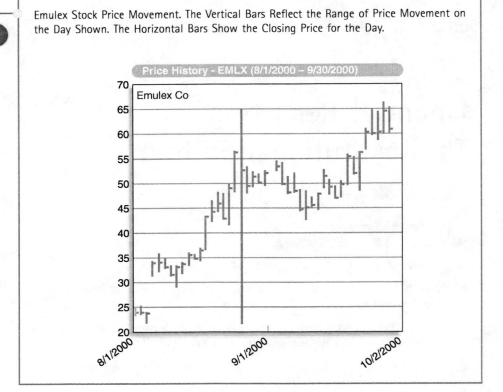

In this book, we focus on the presentation of accounting information for business entities (firms) and its interpretation by external decision makers, such as investors, financial analysts, and government regulators. Firms prepare periodic reports that are made available to such external parties. A key component of these reports consists of financial information generated from the firm's accounting system. This information is summarized in a set of financial statements and related notes. The false report on Emulex referred to one of these statements, the Earnings Statement.

The **earnings statement** for a firm reports its revenues and expenses for a given period of time. **Revenues** are the amounts collected, or relatively certain to be collected, from customers in return for providing goods or services. **Expenses** are the amounts paid, or expected to be paid, to vendors in return for resources that go into the production and marketing of goods or services (such as materials, salaries, and utilities). You may also see earnings referred to as *profits* or *net income*.

EARNINGS = REVENUE – EXPENSES

Although all types of business entities prepare financial statements, we will focus on corporations in this text. **Corporations** are distinguished from other business types (we provide a more complete description of various business types in Chapter 2) by the issuance of shares of **stock,** which represent ownership in the company. When companies initially form, investors (owners) exchange cash for shares of stock in the company. As an example, when Jeff Bezos formed Amazon.com, Inc. in the state of Washington on July 5, 1994, he invested $10,000 in exchange for 1,700,000 shares. Owners then profit from their investment by increases in the value of their shares or by receiving dividends from the company. **Dividends** can typically only be paid if the company has positive earnings on a cumulative basis and may be viewed as returning part of the earnings of the company to the owners. In Amazon.com's case, the company has not produced a profit yet and therefore has paid no dividends. The value of the shares has, however, fluctuated considerably over the life of the company consistent with changes in investors' expectations of the future earnings of Amazon. At the time of this writing Amazon's share price was $40.21 a share. As of April 4, 2003, Jeff Bezos owned almost 108 million shares of Amazon.

Because of their significance in our economy, we specifically focus on **publicly traded corporations,** which are those corporations whose shares trade in a public stock exchange, such as the New York Stock Exchange. Emulex is one example of a publicly traded corporation. Some other more recognizable publicly traded corporations include Starbucks, Nike, and Coca Cola. For publicly traded corporations, financial analysts make buy-and-sell recommendations to investors wishing to purchase or sell shares of stock. These buy-and-sell recommendations may influence investors' purchases and sales, and indirectly, the price of stock. For example, the incorrect Emulex story prompted some analysts to recommend that investors sell their stock. The increase in investors wishing to sell their stock, along with the decrease in those willing to buy the shares, led to price declines. Upon learning of the false report, the situation reversed, causing the price to adjust upward.

As evidenced by investors and analysts' reaction to the news that Emulex would have to restate its earnings, information about a company's earnings plays a key role in assessing a firm's value. For this reason, companies periodically make announcements (typically on a quarterly basis) about their most recent performance. See the announcement of Pepsico in Exhibit 1.2. Further, analysts routinely report their forecasts of earnings and ratios related to earnings, such as the *price-to-earnings ratio (P/E ratio),* which factor significantly into their assessment of the firm's value. For example, in July 2003, the P/E ratio for Pepsico was approximately 21:1, based on the current estimate for the following

> Because the return on investment to a firm's owners (stockholders) comes from future dividends and changes in share value and estimates of both are often based on earnings, earnings are of considerable importance to investors as they make decisions about whether to buy or sell shares of stock.

PEPSICO Q1 EARNINGS PER SHARE INCREASES 17 PERCENT TO 45 CENTS

Worldwide volume grew 3 percent
Division net revenues grew 5 percent, and 6 percent on a currency neutral basis
Division operating profits grew 7 percent, and 8 percent on a currency neutral basis, following 14 percent growth in Q1 2002
Total net income grew 13 percent

Note the prominence of earnings in this disclosure. Also note that because Pepsico has worldwide operations, many of its accounting numbers are influenced by currency differences around the world. Therefore, the company includes data both as reported and after some adjustment for currency differences.

Exhibit 1.2
First Quarter 2003 Performance Announcement by Pepsico

THE REAL WORLD

Pepsico

year's earnings and the current stock price at the time. The P/E ratio can be viewed as the amount investors are willing to pay for each dollar of forecasted earnings. When the earnings in the ratio are the forecasted earnings, the ratio is more specifically known as the *forward* P/E ratio. If, instead, the calculation is based on the last reported earnings (i.e., the actual earnings) then the ratio is called the *trailing* P/E. We will discuss the interpretation of the P/E ratio later in the book.

As will become clearer as you progress through the book, earnings provides a measure of the value added to the owners' wealth as a result of the firm's activities. We describe next those firm activities captured by the accounting process.

REPORTING ON THE ACTIVITIES OF THE FIRM

When assessing a firm's value, most analysts begin by reviewing the economic activities of the firm. All business firms engage in three basic kinds of activities: financing, investing, and operating. **Financing activities** are those activities directed at raising funds for the firm. Firms raise funds (sometimes called **capital**) from two basic sources: owners (*equity capital*) and lenders (*debt capital*). To raise funds from owners, corporations issue shares of stock. To raise funds from lenders, firms typically issue to the lenders a written promise indicating how the money will be repaid as well as the interest rate associated with the loan. There are many types of lenders, but one common lender would be a bank. For example, Skechers USA, Inc. was incorporated in 1992 and by the end of 2001 had $18,498,000 in loans payable to two banks.

A firm generally uses the funds obtained from its financing activities to engage in investing and operating activities. **Investing activities** typically consist of the firm's purchase of property and equipment to enable the company to make products or provide services. Firms may also purchase shares of stock of other companies. These purchases are also considered investing activities. **Operating activities** include those relatively short-term activities that the firm engages in to make and sell products and services. Representative of these activities are the collection of sales dollars from customers, the payment of salaries to employees, and the payment of utility costs.

The accounting process captures the financial effects of these activities. Individual economic events that affect the accounting system are called *transactions*. Financial statements are then constructed from the combined results of the transactions that occur during a particular period of time (e.g., a month, a quarter, a year). These statements reflect the transactions that have been recorded to date and, as such, form a historical record of the firm's activities. The challenge for analysts and investors is to utilize this historical record to assist in forecasting the future economic events that will, in turn, affect the firm's future earnings and hence its value.

Financial statement users make many significant decisions based on the information included in these reports. As a result, the information needs to be as accurate and comprehensive as possible. To ensure this, firms need to follow specific regulations when reporting their main activities. In the next section, we discuss the institutional environment in which accounting regulations are formulated and the key characteristics that are considered in setting accounting standards.

REGULATION OF FINANCIAL REPORTING

Many financial statement users lack the influence to force a company to release information that they might need to make effective decisions. For instance, in the United States, large publicly traded corporations are owned by numerous individuals. The shareholders in these large companies typically do not work for the company and thus have little firsthand information about its day-to-day activities. They therefore rely upon the periodic financial statements issued by the company's management to obtain knowledge about the firm's activities. To ensure that owners or potential owners of public companies get relevant, reliable, and timely information regarding those companies, laws and regulations dictate much of the content of these reports.

The ultimate authority for regulating financial reports of publicly traded companies in the United States rests with the **Securities and Exchange Commission (SEC).** Prompted by the 1929 stock market crash, the U.S. Congress established the SEC to administer the 1933 Securities Act and 1934 Securities and Exchange Act. That is, Congress empowered the SEC with the legal authority to set disclosure and accounting standards that all publicly traded firms are obliged to follow.

To provide adequate disclosure, the SEC created a reporting structure (SEC's Regulation S-X and S-K) that all public companies must follow. For example, the regulations require an annual report (10K), quarterly reports (10Q), and a report of significant events (8K). The 8K report is often used to disclose earning announcements or public meeting with analysts. For instance, on August 6, 2003, American Express issued an 8K report that contained the Chief Executive Officer's presentation to the financial community regarding the company's second quarter results. All of the reports filed with the SEC are available electronically via the electronic filing site of the SEC known as EDGAR.

Although the SEC retains its authority over the disclosures of publicly traded firms, it delegates the primary responsibility for creating accounting standards to the **Financial Accounting Standards Board (FASB).** The FASB consists of individuals from the private sector, principally professional accountants. Since its inception in 1973, the FASB has generated several *Statements of Financial Accounting Concepts (SFACs),* putting forth broad objectives for financial reports (known as the FASB's *conceptual framework*), and many **Statements of Financial Accounting Standards (SFASs)** that address specific valuation and income measurement issues.

On occasion, the SEC intervenes in setting standards, through two series of publications: *Financial Reporting Releases (FRRs)* and *Accounting and Auditing Enforcement Releases (AAERs).* In addition, SEC staff issue a series of bulletins, known as *Staff Accounting Bulletins (SABs),* that reflect their opinion and interpretation of other releases. Congress may also become involved when it deems necessary. Collectively, the body of accounting concepts, standards, guidelines, and conventions governing the construction of financial statements and related disclosures are referred to as **Generally Accepted Accounting Principles (GAAP).**

International Accounting Standards

The development of accounting standards has, in general, been a country-specific process. Each country has developed its own standards, which reflect its political, social, and economic environment. With the development of world markets for both products and capital, however, countries need a greater consensus with regard to financial reporting. To meet this need, the International Accounting Standards Committee (IASC) has been actively formulating international accounting standards.

The IASC is an independent, private-sector body that is funded by donations from accounting organizations around the world. Effective March 2001, a new organization emerged from the IASC, the International Accounting Standards Board (IASB). The IASB now establishes international accounting standards; as of 2002, the IASC/IASB issued 41 International Accounting Standards (IAS). The IASB will issue new standards known as International Financial Reporting Standards (IFRS). To promote the development of international accounting standards, the IASB developed relationships with the primary standard-setting bodies in numerous countries, including the FASB within the United States. In late 2002 the FASB and the IASB agreed to make their standards compatible with one another by January 1, 2005.

DETERMINING GENERALLY ACCEPTED ACCOUNTING PRINCIPLES

Recognizing that it cannot set accounting standards for every economic event that might occur, the FASB developed the conceptual framework (FASB, SFAC No. 2, 1980) that serves as a guide for both standard setting and practice. The conceptual framework seeks to define the desirable characteristics of accounting information. Qualitatively, a number of characteristics shape the financial statement disclosures required under GAAP. Some of the key characteristics are:

- **Relevance**   The information is capable of making a difference in a decision. Relevant information may derive value from its role in predicting future performance (*predictive value*) or in assessing past performance (*feedback value*).

- **Reliability**   The information faithfully represents the economic events it is intended to portray. Reliable information is accurate, neutral (unbiased), and verifiable (see *Verifiability*).

- **Verifiability**   Independent measurers using the same methods reach the same results. Verifiable information allows independent observers to agree on what a reported amount represents.

- **Neutrality**   The information conforms to standards that are independent of the interests of any particular constituency. Neutral information is not withheld or modified to serve the company's or users' objectives.

- **Comparability**   The information can be compared across firms in a meaningful manner. Comparable information does not distort similarities or differences as a consequence of how the company uses accounting methods.

- **Consistency**   The information is determined under the same accounting methods from one period to the next. Consistent information is free of the effects of changing methods in its determination.

Exhibit 1.3
Qualitative Characteristics of
Accounting Information

PRIMARY QUALITIES

Relevance	Reliability
Understandability	Decision Usefulness
Predictive Value	Verifiability
Feedback Value	Neutrality
Timeliness	Representational Faithfulness

SECONDARY QUALITIES

Comparability	Consistency

Trade-offs exist when applying these qualities to a particular economic event. Two of the primary qualities highlighted in Exhibit 1.3, relevance and reliability, are often the focus of these trade-offs. For example, the most relevant information about a company that sells a product in high demand but limited supply may be the number of backorders of the product. This information may be very *relevant* to assessing current firm value as a forecast of future sales, but may not be a very *reliable* measure of future sales. For example, a competitor may be able to supply the same or similar product in a more timely manner which would result in the backorder being cancelled. As a case in point, in mid-2002, Palm, Inc. was having difficulties providing sufficient quantities of a very popular color model of its handheld product. The major distributors (those who had the backorders) found that their customers would not wait and sought alternative distribution channels to get the model. One distributor was quoted in a press release saying "if we can't support our customers in a timely manner, the customer goes and finds the product online." As a result of these trade-offs, in determining specific accounting standards, such as when to recognize backorder sales of a product, the FASB must consider all of the qualities of the information and seek to determine an acceptable solution. In general, backorders are not recognized as sales under GAAP because they generally fail to meet the reliability criteria. However, backorders are still a very relevant piece of information and are often disclosed by firms in their press releases.

An ill-defined concept that also influences the content of financial statements is **materiality.** Materiality means that firms can use a flexible accounting approach for insignificant amounts. For example, firms should account for the purchase of an electric stapler, office equipment, as a long-term asset. However, most firms simply treat the stapler as an expense rather than as an asset. GAAP allows this simpler accounting treatment because treating the stapler cost as an expense would not (materially) affect our view of the firm's assets or expenses.

Financial statement users need to monitor how firms handle the materiality concept when assessing a firm's value and compliance with GAAP. In recent years, the SEC has been concerned that some firms misuse the concept of materiality by deciding that as long as an item is less than a certain percentage of income or assets that it is immaterial (5 percent is often quoted as a rule of thumb). In response, the SEC issued SAB 99 (in 1999), which states that misstatements are not considered immaterial simply because they fall beneath a certain threshold. Firms must consider many other aspects of the misstatement in determining whether to correct it or not. For instance, in SAB 99 two other factors that must be considered are (1) whether the misstatement has the effect of increasing management's compensation say, by satisfying requirements for the award of bonuses or other forms of incentive compensation (see our discussion concerning economic consequences later in this chapter for more information about this factor) and (2) whether the misstatement involves concealment of an unlawful transaction.

Finally, although not a quality explicitly sought under GAAP, financial statements tend to reflect conservatism. **Conservatism** indicates a firm's tendency to anticipate losses, but not gains; carry assets at values that are often low by comparison with current market prices or appraisal values; recognize liabilities in anticipation of obligations that may or may not arise; and delay recognition of revenues until uncertainties have been resolved. For example, under current GAAP, many construction companies recognize the profits from a long-term construction project over the period of construction. However, if they anticipate that there will be a loss on the overall contract at the end of the construction period, they recognize the loss immediately. To illustrate, Foster Wheeler LTD (a construction company specializing in petroleum processing facilities) reported this type of policy in their annual report:

> The Company has numerous contracts that are in various stages of completion. Such contracts require estimates to determine the appropriate cost and revenue recognition. However, current estimates may be revised as additional information becomes available. If estimates of costs to complete long-term contracts indicate a loss, provision is made currently for the total loss anticipated.

Note, however, that the conceptual framework explicitly states that firms must avoid misusing conservatism to understate assets or overstate liabilities.

At times, however, the conceptual framework fails to provide enough guidance. The FASB then moves to adopt a more specific standard for a particular economic event. To do this, the FASB follows a very public process of determining a new standard, encompassing three main stages:

1. The FASB analyzes the issue using the conceptual framework and other relevant existing standards. It then prepares a Discussion Memorandum laying out the alternatives with their pros and cons. The FASB elicits feedback of the Discussion Memorandum from interested parties such as investors, financial analysts, government regulators, corporate executives, and professional accountants.

2. After assessing the responses to this document, the FASB deliberates on the alternatives and issues an Exposure Draft of its proposed pronouncement. The FASB makes the Exposure Draft available for further public comment.

3. In the last step, the FASB incorporates any additional comments and then issues its pronouncement in the form of a Statement of Financial Accounting Standards (SFAS).

The process the FASB uses to set accounting standards is essentially political and subject to override by the SEC or the U.S. Congress. For example, during the oil crisis in the 1970s, the FASB issued SFAS 19 that eliminated certain accounting practices used by oil and gas producers. The new standard would have resulted in more volatile reported earnings for smaller companies engaged in significant exploration activities. Some opponents of the new standard argued that with more volatile earnings, smaller producers might be unable to raise capital to continue exploration, inconsistent with the national interest in encouraging exploration. The political pressures subsequently brought to bear resulted in the FASB rescinding the pronouncement it had originally issued (SFAS 52).

GAAP provides the framework and the specific rules for how the various activities of the firm should be recorded in their accounting system. However, if the firm does not follow these rules or they apply them inappropriately, investors and other readers of the financial statements could be misled about the performance of the firm. For this reason all publicly traded firms are required to present audited statements in their reports. The auditors provide the reassurance that the firm has appropriately applied GAAP. In the next section, we discuss the nature of the audit.

INDEPENDENT AUDITS OF FINANCIAL STATEMENTS

All publicly traded companies must provide a report by independent auditors (see the report for Hasbro, Inc. in Exhibit 1.4). This report attests to the fairness of presentation (that the statements fairly represent the results of the

Exhibit 1.4
Hasbro, Inc. Auditors' Report

THE REAL WORLD
Hasbro, Inc.

The Board of Directors and Shareholders
Hasbro, Inc.:

We have audited the accompanying consolidated balance sheets of Hasbro, Inc. and subsidiaries as of December 29, 2002 and December 30, 2001 and the related consolidated statements of operations, shareholders' equity and cash flows for each of the fiscal years in the three-year period ended December 29, 2002. These consolidated financial statements are the responsibility of the Company's management. Our responsibility is to express an opinion on these consolidated financial statements based on our audits.

We conducted our audits in accordance with auditing standards generally accepted in the United States of America. Those standards require that we plan and perform the audit to obtain reasonable assurance about whether the financial statements are free of material misstatement. An audit includes examining, on a test basis, evidence supporting the amounts and disclosures in the financial statements. An audit also includes assessing the accounting principles used and significant estimates made by management, as well as evaluating the overall financial statement presentation. We believe that our audits provide a reasonable basis for our opinion.

In our opinion, the consolidated financial statements referred to above present fairly, in all material respects, the financial position of Hasbro, Inc. and subsidiaries as of December 29, 2002 and December 30, 2001 and the results of their operations and their cash flows for each of the fiscal years in the three-year period ended December 29, 2002 in conformity with accounting principles generally accepted in the United States of America.

As discussed in note 1 to the consolidated financial statements, effective December 31, 2001, the first day of the Company's 2002 fiscal year, the Company adopted the provisions of Statement of Financial Accounting Standards No. 142, "Goodwill and Other Intangibles."

/s/ KPMG LLP

Providence, Rhode Island
February 12, 2003

economic events that have affected the firm) and compliance of those statements with GAAP. **Auditors** are professional accountants who meet certification requirements set by states (i.e., Certified Public Accountants, or **CPA**s for short). Auditors must also follow procedures under the oversight of the American Institute of Certified Public Accountants (AICPA). The AICPA sets Generally Accepted Auditing Standards (GAAS) that define the auditor's responsibilities.

In addition to assessing compliance with GAAP, auditors also examine the firm's internal controls, verify its principal assets, review for unusual changes in its financial statements, inquire with outside parties concerning the firm's exposure to losses, and determine the firm's ability to continue as a going concern. The term **going concern** means that the auditor expects that the firm will continue to operate into the foreseeable future; in other words, they do not expect the company to go out of business or file for bankruptcy. Investors and others might view the value of a company quite differently if they assumed it would soon quit operating. Auditors also consider the existence or prospect of fraud, though the firm's management has primary responsibility for its detection.

Auditors also apply the concept of materiality in their work. They typically limit their responsibility to material items when they state in their audit opinions that financial statements "present fairly, *in all material respects,* the financial position, results of operations, and cash flows" of a client firm.

Finally, auditors issue one of several types of reports. In an *unqualified opinion* the auditor expresses no reservations concerning the fairness of the financial statements and conformance with GAAP. A *qualified opinion* includes an exception to the conclusion of fairness or conformance with GAAP. Exceptions commonly relate to a deviation from GAAP or a limitation in the scope of the auditor's procedures under GAAS. An *adverse opinion* states that the financial statements do not fairly present the company's financial position and results of operations in conformity with GAAP. Under a *disclaimer,* the auditor does not express an opinion on the financial statements.

Firms appoint auditors and pay their fees. As a result, controversy exists on the independence of auditors whose fees are paid by the client. To help resolve these concerns, the accounting profession devised the *AICPA Code of Conduct* and a *peer review* process to monitor compliance with performance standards. In 2002, the U.S. Congress passed the Sarbanes-Oxley Act (SOX) to address these and other concerns about the auditing profession, partly in response to the Enron failure and the subsequent demise of Arthur Andersen (see Exhibit 1.5). The SOX created a Public Company Accounting Oversight Board that monitors auditing, quality control, and independence standards, and rules. For example, oversight of the public accountant must be done through the firm's audit committee, which must be composed of members who are independent of the company.

Independent audits help to ensure that the financial statements reflect those qualities of accounting information we discussed earlier. Owners, lenders, and managers face economic incentives in their interaction with a firm that may influence accounting decisions. In the next section, we discuss the economic consequences to owners, lenders, and managers from the accounting choices made by the firm. As illustrated by the Enron example, these consequences can be very significant.

> The auditor's opinion is important when using valuation techniques as it provides at least some level of assurance that the data being used to forecast future results are comparably prepared by companies.

Exhibit 1.5

THE REAL WORLD

Enron

In October, 2001 the SEC requested information from Enron Corporation regarding a set of transactions with several related parties. The transactions had the approval of Enron's auditors, Arthur Andersen. By the end of the month, the inquiry had turned into a formal SEC investigation. In an 8K filing (recall that 8K filings detail the occurrence of any material events or corporate changes that should be reported to investors or security holders) with the SEC on November 8, 2001, Enron agreed to restate its financial statements for 1997 through 2001 to record the effects of the related party transactions. The net effect: Enron reduced its owners' equity section by $1.2 billion. On December 2, 2001, Enron filed for protection from its creditors under Chapter 11 of the U.S. bankruptcy laws. In its continuing investigation the SEC requested audit working papers from Arthur Andersen (AA). The SEC then discovered that several individuals at AA had shredded documents related to the Enron audit. The government eventually filed an indictment for obstruction of justice against AA, and the company suffered the loss of numerous clients. AA was ultimately found guilty of obstructing justice and agreed not to audit publicly traded companies.

The loss in credibility of Enron's reported earnings, both past and present, along with the revelation of losses and exposure of business risks led investors to conclude that the stock was overvalued. As a result, Enron suffered such severe declines in its stock price and future prospects that the company was forced to declare bankruptcy.

ECONOMIC CONSEQUENCES OF ACCOUNTING PRACTICES

Although GAAP places restrictions on accounting choices, firms still enjoy considerable flexibility in their selection and application of accounting methods. As a result, managers can and do affect the amounts reported in the financial statements. Allowing flexibility is a two-edged sword. On one hand, it makes it possible for financial statements to better reflect economic reality in the sense that one size does not fit all. On the other hand, it may provide the opportunity for firm owners or managers to manipulate information.

For example, lenders closely monitor a firm's activities to ensure that they will be repaid. One common way for owners to provide assurances to lenders and for lenders to protect themselves is to put restrictions into their lending contracts. These restrictions, called *covenants*, typically set minimums for certain accounting numbers or ratios that the firm must meet. The agreements typically state that the lender can make the loan immediately due if the firm violates these covenants. If a company found itself in danger of violating a covenant, there might be enough incentive to either change accounting methods or misreport transactions to avoid the violation. A mitigating factor on this behavior is that lenders often find it in their best interests to work with firms to restructure debt when violations occur (see Exhibit 1.6 regarding Cogent Communications Group).

As another example, compensation arrangements for a firm's management often include bonuses based on achieving a targeted amount of earnings. Under GAAP, managers commonly have sufficient discretion over accounting policies to significantly influence the recognition of revenues and expenses. In order to meet bonus targets, therefore, managers may advance the recognition of revenues or delay expenses as a means of reporting higher earnings. Other forms of discretion might include relaxing credit requirements customers must satisfy

Exhibit 1.6
Cogent Communications
Group, Inc.—10K Report, April,
2003

THE REAL WORLD

Cogent
Communications
Group

Breach of Cisco Credit Facility Covenant. We have breached the minimum revenue covenant contained in our credit facility from Cisco Systems Capital. This breach permits Cisco Capital, if it wishes, to accelerate and require us to pay approximately $262.7 million we owed to Cisco Capital as of March 28, 2003. Should Cisco Capital accelerate the due date of our indebtedness, we would be unable to repay it. If it accelerates the indebtedness, Cisco Capital could make use of its rights as a secured lender to take possession of all of our assets. In such event, we may be forced to file for bankruptcy protection. We are currently in active discussions with Cisco Capital to restructure the Company's debt.

Note that violation of the covenant in this lending agreement had the potential to impose significant economic consequences to Cogent. You can imagine the pressure that this situation might exert on management to misstate revenues to be in compliance with the covenant. By June, however, Cogent had restructured its debt.

(to produce more revenues), postponing repairs and maintenance on equipment (to reduce expenses), and selling assets or retiring debt on which gains will be recorded (to increase income). These types of actions may actually reduce the firm's value. Although managers benefit by receiving a higher bonus, they do so at the expense of stockholders (lower firm value).

In compensation arrangements, firms try to design contracts that align the economic interests of managers with those of stockholders. One example is to provide some amount of a manager's compensation in the form of stock in the company. The idea is that managers will behave more like owners when managers' compensation includes stock. Stock could be awarded to managers directly. More frequently managers are given the option to buy shares of stock at a fixed price under what are called *stock option plans*, discussed later in the book. Often management compensation arrangements provide a combination of incentives, some based on earnings and some on stock price. For example, Intel compensates its executive managers with a combination of a base salary, a cash bonus tied to meeting an individual earnings performance target, a cash bonus tied to overall company earnings, and a stock option plan.

Other incentives to manipulate earnings may relate to lawsuits, labor negotiations, compliance with bank or insurance company regulations, and trade disputes with foreign rivals. For example, a firm facing litigation might prefer to ignore the likelihood of losing a lawsuit (by not recording a liability in advance of a settlement), thereby giving a false impression of the firm's value.

Many opportunities and incentives therefore exist for manipulating financial reports. One reason for allowing these opportunities to exist is that it may be too costly both to incorporate the level of detail required to set more stringent standards and to monitor compliance with those details. Another reason may be that allowing managers to select from a menu of accounting policies may provide an efficient means of communicating (*signaling*) information about the firm's future prospects when the economic consequences of a given policy depend on those prospects. For example, suppose that there are two companies in the same industry with similar debt agreements (including a restriction in their debt agreement that earnings must remain above $100,000). One firm has very good future sales prospects, and the other firm has very poor future sales prospects. If they both were faced with a decision about voluntarily (i.e., it was not a mandated change) adopting a new accounting policy that would reduce reported earnings in the future, the firm with good prospects would have little problem in adopting this policy as it expects to have good future earnings which would not force the company to violate its debt restrictions (even though it would reduce their future reported earnings due to the policy change). However, the firm with bad prospects would likely not adopt the new policy as it already is in a position to potentially violate the debt restriction (due to its poor future sales prospects) and the change in policy will make it even more likely. Therefore, by observing their decisions about the choice of accounting policy lenders might be able to infer the future prospects of companies and set the interest rates that they require accordingly.

Another economic consideration that managers face in the determination of accounting methods is the effect of the decision on the taxes paid by the company. All corporations pay taxes to the federal government (*Internal Revenue Service* or *IRS*) based on their earnings. The accounting rules for reporting earnings to the IRS are determined by the tax code and in some cases differ from GAAP. The company's objective in choosing its accounting policies for tax purposes is usually to minimize or delay its tax payments. In contrast, the company's objective in choosing its accounting policies for financial reporting purposes is to comply with GAAP. Although the norm is for firms to use different accounting methods for tax and financial reporting purposes, there is at least one case (LIFO inventory accounting) in which the method chosen for tax purposes is only permitted if that same method is used for reporting purposes. Accordingly, there may be a tax incentive that influences an accounting choice.

FINANCIAL REPORTING AND VALUATION

As the discussion in this chapter suggests, financial accounting disclosures, especially earnings, provide information upon which financial analysts and investors at large may project a firm's future cash flows that, in turn, determine firm value. The central role of earnings as an important factor in determining firm value is evidenced by the prominence of earnings forecasts by financial analysts in the financial press and a vast empirical literature by academics that documents stock price reactions to information conveyed by changes in those forecasts, earnings announcements *per se,* and other related disclosures.

In the chapters that follow, we will seek to further an appreciation of the role that financial statements play in arriving at estimates of firm value. Our efforts in this regard culminate in Chapter 14 with the presentation of two principal approaches for mapping information contained in what are called *pro-forma financial statements* (statements based on forecasts of future operating, investing, and financing activities) into value estimates; specifically, *discounted cash flow (DCF)* analysis and *residual income (RI)* analysis. At this point, it is sufficient for you to begin to think of a firm's financial accounting disclosures as a starting point in assessing its future cash flow prospects.

SUMMARY AND TRANSITION

As should be clear by now, accounting information, particularly earnings, plays a key role with investors in guiding their decisions to buy or sell stock. Analysts who advise investors also make significant use of accounting information in estimating the value of a share of stock as a basis for their buy or sell recommendations to investors. The reliability and relevance of accounting information are enhanced by a standard setting process involving both public (SEC) and private (FASB) sector bodies. Auditors provide additional assurance to investors that the accounting information is prepared in compliance with those standards.

Within the framework of generally accepted accounting principles, managers have considerable discretion over accounting policies adopted by the firm. Often managers' choices have economic consequences for themselves, their stockholders, and lenders. The nature of the consequences is driven by the contracts written between managers, stockholders, and lenders.

In the remainder of the book we will continue to visit valuation issues and to examine economic consequences issues as they arise. The next few chapters explain the construction of the financial statements contained in financial accounting reports and describe the major concepts underlying this construction. Considerable attention is given to the principal concepts used in the determination of earnings. These chapters are followed by an initial exposure to the techniques of financial analysis with a focus on the use of financial statements in assessing past performance and forecasting future performance. Later chapters consider a comprehensive set of valuation and income measurement issues in depth. The final chapter of the text provides basic introduction to the forecasting of financial statements and the two major approaches for valuing the firm based on components from those statements.

END OF CHAPTER MATERIAL

KEY TERMS

Auditors	Financial Accounting Standards Board (FASB)
Capital	Financing Activities
Conservatism	Generally Accepted Accounting Principles (GAAP)
Corporation	Going Concern
Dividends	Investing Activities
Earnings Statement	Materiality
Expenses	Operating Activities

Publicly Traded Corporations

Revenue

Securities and Exchange Commission (SEC)

Statement of Financial Accounting Standards (SFAS)

Stock

ASSIGNMENT MATERIAL

REVIEW QUESTIONS

1. Describe and illustrate the three major types of activities that firms engage in.

2. Discuss the meaning of Generally Accepted Accounting Principles, and describe the organizations that establish these principles.

3. What is the purpose of an auditor's opinion, and what types of opinions can auditors render?

4. Identify at least three major users of corporate financial statements, and briefly state how they might use the information from those statements.

5. List and briefly describe the major qualitative characteristics that accounting information should possess, according to the FASB concepts statements.

6. Discuss how materiality is used in the choice of accounting methods.

7. Describe what is meant by economic consequences of accounting practices and provide an example of how accounting choices can affect the welfare of parties with an interest in the firm.

8. How might differences in accounting standards across countries affect the analysis done by an analyst in predicting stock prices?

9. Describe what conservatism means in the construction of the financial statements of the firm.

APPLYING YOUR KNOWLEDGE

10. For a manufacturing company, list two examples of transactions that you would classify as financing, investing, and operating.

11. The AMAX Company purchased land several years ago for $60,000 as a potential site for a new building. No building has yet been constructed. A comparable lot near the site was recently sold for $95,000.

    a. At what value should AMAX carry the land on its balance sheet? Support your answer with consideration for the relevance and reliability of the information that would result.

    b. If AMAX wanted to borrow money from a bank, what information about the land would the bank want to know?

12. You are the accounting manager for a U.S. company that has just been acquired by a German company. Helmut, the CEO of the German company, has just paid you a visit and is puzzled why American companies report on two different bases, one for reporting to their stockholders and another to the taxing authority, because in Germany these are one and the same. Draft a memo explaining to Helmut why there are two different bases

and a brief explanation for why they might involve different accounting rules.

13. Harmonization of accounting standards has been proposed on a global basis. As a CEO of an American company, what would you see as advantages and disadvantages of having the same set of standards across countries?

14. Suppose that the FASB proposed that inventory be accounted for at its current market price (i.e., what you could sell it for) rather than its historical cost. Provide an argument that supports or opposes this change on the basis of relevance and reliability.

15. Suppose that you started your own company that assembles and sells laptop computers. You do not manufacture any of the parts yourself. The computers are sold through mail order. Make a list of the information that you consider relevant to assessing your firm's performance. When you are through, discuss how you would reliably measure that performance.

16. Suppose that you own and operate your own private company. You need to raise money to expand your operations, so you approach a bank for a loan. The bank loan officer has asked for financial statements prepared according to GAAP. Why would the loan officer make such a request and, assuming that your statements were prepared according to GAAP, how could you convince the banker that this was so?

17. In order for a company's stock to be listed (i.e., traded) on most stock exchanges, the company's financial statements are required to be audited by a CPA firm. Why?

18. As a manager, suppose that you are responsible for establishing prices for the products your division sells. Under GAAP your firm uses a method of inventory costing called LIFO that means that the costs of the last units purchased are the first ones that are reported in the statement of earnings. Consequently, the costs that remain in inventory are those associated with the first purchases. Because inventory can build up over the years, some of these costs may be very old. How relevant would these old costs attached to ending inventory be to you as you decide how to price inventory in the coming year? If they are not relevant, what piece of information would be more relevant to you?

19. From time to time there have been calls from the user community for management to disclose their own forecasts of future results such as net income. As an external user of the financial statements, discuss the relevance and the reliability of this type of information.

20. Suppose a company decides to change accounting methods such that it reports its revenues sooner than it previously did. Discuss how this might effect investors' evaluation of the company's stock.

USING REAL DATA

21. Amazon.com, Inc. has operated at a net loss since its formation, yet its stock has a positive value. Explain why investors would value the shares of Amazon at a positive value.

22. In early February 2001 Emulex Corporation revised its quarterly sales estimates downward. Prior to the revision Emulex had been expecting a 28 percent sales increase over the previous year and had shown 40 percent increases in sales annually for the last five years. Upon hearing this news, investors drove the price of Emulex down from $77.50 per share on a Friday to $40.25 on the following Monday. Explain why the valuation of Emulex dropped given this announcement.

23. In early February 2001 CISCO announced that it was missing its first quarter sales estimates. This was the first time since July 1994 that it had come in under its sales estimates, and it was the first time in more than three years that it had failed to beat its sales estimates. As an investor, how might you react to this news and how might this announcement affect the valuation of the company's shares?

BEYOND THE BOOK

The Beyond the Book problems are designed to force you to find and utilize resources found outside the book.

24. Familiarize yourself with the resources that are available at your university to acquire information about corporations. Most universities have an electronic database that contains financial statement information. The following is a short list of resources that may be available:

    LEXIS/NEXIS Database This is an incredibly large database that contains all sorts of news and financial information about companies. It contains all of the SEC filings including the 10-K, 20-F (foreign registrants), and Proxy Statements. The financial information is in full text form.

    CD-Disclosure This database contains full text financial footnote information for thousands of companies but does not contain full text of the major financial statements.

    EDGAR Filings The EDGAR filings are electronic forms of the SEC filings that are included in the Lexis/Nexis database but are also accessible through the internet (www.sec.gov).

    ABI Inform (UMI, Inc.) This database contains full text information from numerous business periodicals.

25. Go to the FASB's website (www.fasb.org), locate the project activities section, and list the titles of the projects on its projects update list.

26. For a publicly traded company of your choosing, answer the following questions:

    a. What are the products (or product lines) and/or services that your company sells? Please be as specific as possible.

    b. Who are the customers of your company? Please be as specific as possible.

    c. In what markets, domestic and global, does your company sell its products and/or services?

    d. Who are the major competitors of your company?

    e. What are the major inputs your company needs to manufacture its products? Who are the suppliers of these inputs?

f. Are any of the items listed in the questions above changing substantially? Use a two-year time span as a window to address this question.

g. What has happened to the stock price of your company over the last two years?

To answer these questions it will be useful to collect a series of articles concerning your company over the most recent two-year period. Try to find at least five reasonably sized articles. Use these as references to write a two- to three-page background paper about your company.

CHAPTER 2

Financial Statements: An Overview

LEARNING OBJECTIVES

After reading this chapter you should be able to:

1. Understand the differences in the major forms of business organization, as well as some of the relative pros and cons for choosing a particular form of business.

2. Identify the nature of information contained in the main general-purpose financial statements: Statement of Financial Position, Statement of Earnings, Statement of Cash Flows, and Statement of Changes in Stockholders' Equity.

3. Explain the connection between statements of financial position at points in time and changes in financial position over time.

4. Describe the types of supplemental disclosures accompanying financial statements in a firm's annual report.

On October 12, 2001, Polaroid Corporation filed for protection from creditors under Chapter 11 of the U.S. bankruptcy laws. This action resulted from the financial difficulties that Polaroid faced when its sales declined significantly, starting in the fourth quarter of 2000. As Exhibit 2.1 shows, the value of the company's stock began its downward slide late in the first quarter of 2000. Note that the S&P 500 (Standard and Poor's) is an index of how the stock market performed overall during this same period. This correspondence between declining quarterly sales and relative stock price suggests that investors rely on information contained in financial statements. In this chapter, we begin to explore this relationship by describing the contents of those statements.

Polaroid's stock price movement relative to the S&P Index and trading volume from March 1999 through April 2002.

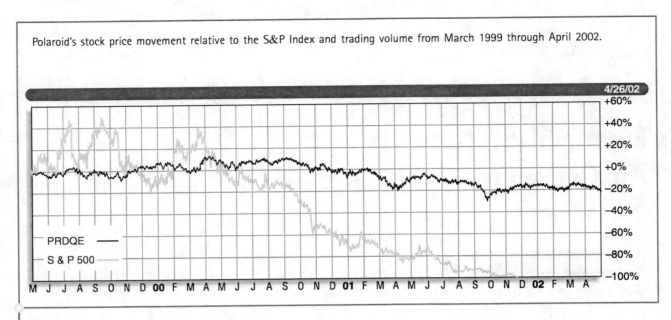

Exhibit 2.1

THE REAL WORLD

Polaroid

The changes in company value are very evident for a publicly traded corporation such as Polaroid since its stock price is published daily. This is not true for all forms of business. While we intend to focus on publicly traded corporations we would like to spend a little bit of time describing other forms of business so that you understand why the corporate form of business is the dominant one in the U.S. economy.

FORMS OF BUSINESS ORGANIZATION

The corporate form of business is by far the most popular for large publicly traded firms. This popularity stems from three principal features:

- Limited liability for its capital suppliers
- Ease of transferring ownership
- Ease of access to additional ownership funds

Limited liability means that investors in the firm's equity securities generally cannot lose more than the amounts that they invest, should the firm perform poorly. This feature can be compared to the unlimited liability of owners of **sole proprietorships** (single owners) and **partnerships** (multiple owners). If a sole proprietorship or partnership cannot meet its obligations to creditors, then creditors may seek satisfaction of their claims from the owner's or partners' personal assets, respectively. As a result, hybrid forms of organization have emerged, such as *limited liability companies (LLCs)* and *limited liability partnerships (LLPs),* which, as their name suggests, include the limited liability feature of corporations. Many public accounting firms are organized as LLPs, such as PricewaterhouseCoopers, LLP and KPMG, LLP. Some relatively well known businesses are also organized as LLCs, such as Orbitz, LLC (the web-based travel service) and BMW of North America, LLC (an importer of BMW products in North America).

Corporations, particularly large ones, are typically owned by a vast number of individuals. This ownership structure spreads the limited risk of ownership over many investors. In the case of a sole proprietorship, the single owner bears all the unlimited risk, whereas in partnerships, the partners share that risk. This difference in the distribution of risks appears to have played an important role in the rise of corporations as the preferred type of business organization.

Transfers of ownership in publicly traded corporations can be easily accomplished through the purchase and sale of investors' equity securities, in other words, the trading of stock. To trade stock, a corporation lists its stock on major stock exchanges, such as the *New York Stock Exchange* or *NASDAQ*. These exchanges attract large numbers of investors, as they can easily and quickly acquire or sell securities as needed to maximize their economic welfare. From the firm's perspective, stock exchanges provide relatively easy access to one type of capital needed to fund its investment and operating needs. In contrast, ownership of sole proprietorships is more difficult to transfer, as it requires finding buyers without benefit of stock exchange services. Transferring ownership of partnerships is also more difficult. If an existing partner leaves or a new partner enters the business, the existing partnership must first be dissolved and a new one then created.

The corporate form of business also allows the firm to increase its equity capital by offering additional shares for sale. In a publicly traded corporation, this means that many individual investors, other then the present owners, might become owners in the firm. The larger set of investors in the public stock markets allows the company access to a considerable amount of resources as it grows. Sole proprietorships, in comparison, have limited access to additional funds as they are constrained by the owner's wealth and ability to borrow. Partnerships also are at a disadvantage, as they usually only raise ownership funds through additional contributions of the partners or by admitting new partners to the business.

The corporate form does possess a potentially significant negative consideration: taxes. Corporations are subject to corporate income taxation, whereas sole-proprietorship and partnership income is taxed only at the individual level. Because individual investors are taxed on the income they receive from corporations (in the form of dividends and capital gains), the net result is that corporate income is taxed twice, once at the corporate level and a second time at the individual level. This tax structure may influence who chooses to invest in corporations and how corporations' securities are priced relative to holdings in other forms of business entities.

> The tax status of an entity has significant valuation implications, as taxes reduce cash flows.

Exhibit 2.2 summarizes some of the pros and cons of the main forms of business organization. Because of their dominance in the market, we focus on the reporting of publicly traded corporations in the remainder of the book. In the next section, we expand an understanding of corporations by discussing the nature of their financial statements.

Exhibit 2.2
Pros and Cons of Forms of
Business Organization

Form of Organization	Pros	Cons
Proprietorship	Income taxed once	Unlimited liability Ownership transfer difficult No sharing of risk Limited access to additional ownership funds
Partnership	Income taxed once Some sharing of risk Some access to additional ownership funds	Unlimited liability Ownership transfer difficult
Corporation	Limited liability Ease of transfer of ownership Relatively easy access to additional ownership funds	Double taxation

FINANCIAL ACCOUNTING REPORTS

As we discussed in Chapter 1, to conduct business, publicly traded corporations raise long-term funds from individuals and institutions through both lending agreements and the issuance of stock. Both lending agreements and stock represent claims on the resources (assets) that the corporation controls. Corporations also obtain short-term funds from other creditors; for example, suppliers often sell inventory to companies on credit. Such credit purchases are, in effect, short-term loans from the suppliers. Exhibit 2.3 shows the *balanced* relationship between the firm's resources on the one side, and claims to those resources on the other.

Financial statements provide information about the firm's resources and claims to resources at periodic points in time, and also about the changes to those resources and claims to resources from the firm's activities between those points in time. The major financial statements include the:

- Statement of Financial Position
- Statement of Earnings

Exhibit 2.3
Resources and Claims against
Resources

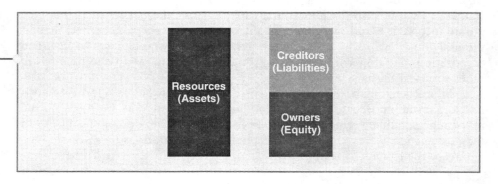

⊙ Statement of Cash Flows
⊙ Statement of Changes in Stockholders' Equity

Below we discuss each statement, as well as provide descriptions of many terms that each statement includes. In this chapter, we simply want to offer you a general sense of what each statement contains. We will provide more detailed explanations of the content in later chapters, so you need not try to fully understand them here.

STATEMENT OF FINANCIAL POSITION

The Statement of Financial Position describes the firm's resources and claims to those resources as seen in Exhibit 2.3. Accounting expressions for resources, creditors, and owners are, respectively, **assets, liabilities,** and **stockholders' equity** (or **common stockholders' equity** or simply **owners' equity**).

ASSETS

In simple terms assets are those resources owned by the company or those that the company has the right to use. From the accountant's point of view, assets are resources that have *probable future value* to the firm and are recognized under GAAP. Assets typically include *cash; accounts receivable* (amounts due from the firm's customers); *inventories* (for use in production or for sale); *plant, property, and equipment* (used to make products or provide services); and various *property rights* (the rights to use an economic resource such as a patent).

Accountants, however, do not consider some economic resources as assets because they fail to meet measurement criteria, such as the general criterion of reliability discussed in Chapter 1. For example, a brand image (e.g., the Coca Cola logo) created through advertising and customer satisfaction cannot be reliably valued and are not, therefore, recognized in the financial statements. Furthermore, the amounts at which resources are reflected as assets often differ from their current economic value. For example, the market or appraisal value of land some years after its acquisition might be greater than its recorded value (sometimes called the *carrying value*), as accounting standards stipulate that land be carried at its historical cost.

LIABILITIES

In simple terms, liabilities represent the amounts owed to others. From the accountant's point of view they represent *probable future sacrifices* of resources. Liabilities may include bank borrowings (*notes payable* or *mortgages payable*), borrowings that are done through publicly traded securities known as bonds (*bonds payable*), amounts due to suppliers (*accounts payable*), and amounts due to others providing goods or services to the company during production, such as utility companies and employees (*utilities payable* and *salaries payable*, respectively). Sometimes the word **accrued** appears with the liability titles (e.g., *accrued warranty liability, accrued expenses*), implying that the amounts have been estimated. Customers may also have some claim on resources if they have prepaid for goods and services that the company must deliver in the future. These types of claims, typically called *deferred revenue, unearned revenues,* or simply *deposits*, reflect items such as prepaid magazine subscriptions.

Similar to assets, accountants also do not consider all economic obligations as liabilities. For example, if a company contracts with another company to purchase goods that will be delivered at a future date at a fixed price, current accounting standards do not require the company to recognize the obligation to pay the supplier when the contract is signed. As neither company has satisfied its part of the contract, neither company recognizes the contract in its accounting records. In accounting jargon, this kind of contract is known as a *mutually unexecuted contract.* Also, some liabilities are so uncertain that they may not meet the criteria for recognition. For instance, potential legal liabilities associated with lawsuits are often excluded from liabilities because it is very uncertain as to whether the company will actually have to pay a settlement.

> As analysts try to predict the future cash flows of the firm, unrecorded liabilities may pose one of the more significant estimation challenges.

STOCKHOLDERS' EQUITY

Unlike creditor and customer claims that a firm settles within some specified time frame, equity claims have no specified time period for payment. Stockholders of a corporation are not assured a specific set of payments. Instead, they usually only receive cash payments when the company declares a *cash dividend* (when the firm generates positive earnings) or when stockholders elect to sell their shares. As a result, stockholders' equity is sometimes referred to as a **residual claim,** because owners can only claim what is left over after all creditor claims have been met. It can also be thought of as the residual claim on assets after deducting liabilities. In other words, owners can claim the difference between what the company owns and what it owes. **Net assets** (also referred to as **net book value**) can be calculated through the accounting equation that we discuss next.

THE ACCOUNTING EQUATION

As mentioned previously, the statement of financial position (often called a **balance sheet**) reports a firm's assets, liabilities, and stockholders' equity at a particular point in time. Further, a characteristic of a balance sheet is that the sum of assets equals the sum of liabilities and stockholders' equity (hence the word "balance"). This characteristic of the balance sheet is commonly referred to as the **accounting equation** (recall that Exhibit 2.3 illustrates this).

> Assets = Liabilities + Stockholders' Equity

It follows from this equation that stockholders' equity equals assets less liabilities. That is:

> Stockholders' Equity = Assets − Liabilities

Stockholders' equity is also called *net assets* or *net book value*. To illustrate a statement of financial position, based on the accounting equation, let's next look at a real company, Ross Stores.

STATEMENT OF FINANCIAL POSITION: ROSS STORES

Exhibit 2.4, Ross' 10K report, describes the company's business and operating goals. Reviewing this information first helps to provide insight into the information included in the financial statements.

Exhibit 2.5 shows Ross' Statement of Financial Position for the year ended February 1, 2003. Note that Ross presents two columns of data, one at the beginning of the year (2/2/2002) and the other at the end of the year (2/1/2003). The SEC requires two years of balance sheet data for annual reports. Further, the SEC requires firms to report the balance sheet data as of the end of their **fiscal** (financial) **year.** The fiscal year often ends on the same date as the calendar year, December 31. However, as with Ross, this need not be the case. Due to the seasonal nature of their business, many retail firms use year-ends other than December 31, for example, Tommy Hilfiger Corp (March 31), Wal-Mart (January 31), American Greetings (February 28), and Starbucks (September 30). Finally, note that the accounting equation is satisfied at both points in time. In fact, the accounting equation needs to be satisfied at all points in time in an accounting system.

Ross presents what is known as a **classified balance sheet.** This type of balance sheet lists assets in order of how quickly they can be converted into cash, sometimes referred to as **liquidity order.** In addition, a classified balance sheet also segregates assets into **current** and **noncurrent** categories. **Current assets** are cash and assets that are expected to be converted into cash or expire within one year or one operating cycle of the business, whichever is longer. For a manufacturing firm, the *operating cycle* is the time between the initial acquisition of raw materials and the collection on the sale of the inventory that is sold. Inventory is a current asset because it will be sold and converted into cash during the firm's current operating cycle, which, for most firms, is less than one year. Note that for certain kinds of inventory (e.g., any long-term construction project such as submarines and aircraft) the operating cycle could be longer than a year. This type of inventory would still meet the definition of a current asset as the inventory is sold within an operating cycle.

Ross Stores, Inc. ("Ross" or "the Company") operates a chain of off-price retail apparel and home accessories stores, which target value-conscious men and women between the ages of 25 and 54 primarily in middle-income households. The decisions of the Company, from merchandising, purchasing, and pricing, to the location of its stores, are aimed at this customer base. The Company offers brand-name and designer merchandise at low everyday prices, generally 20 percent to 60 percent below regular prices of most department and specialty stores. The Company believes it derives a competitive advantage by offering a wide assortment of quality brand-name merchandise within each of its merchandise categories in an attractive easy-to-shop environment.

Exhibit 2.4
Ross Stores Business
(from 10K)

THE REAL WORLD

Ross Stores

Exhibit 2.5
Ross Stores—Statement of
Financial Position
(in thousands)

THE REAL WORLD

Ross Stores

	2/1/2003	2/2/2002
ASSETS		
CURRENT ASSETS		
Cash and cash equivalents (includes $10,000 of restricted cash)	$ 150,649	$ 40,351
Accounts receivable	18,349	20,540
Merchandise inventory	716,518	623,390
Prepaid expenses and other	36,904	30,710
Total Current Assets	922,420	714,991
PROPERTY AND EQUIPMENT		
Land and buildings	54,772	54,432
Fixtures and equipment	412,496	351,288
Leasehold improvements	232,388	209,086
Construction-in-progress	61,720	24,109
	761,376	638,915
Less accumulated depreciation and amortization	358,693	307,365
	402,683	331,550
Other long-term assets	36,242	36,184
Total Assets	$1,361,345	$1,082,725
LIABILITIES AND STOCKHOLDERS' EQUITY		
CURRENT LIABILITIES		
Accounts payable	$ 397,193	$ 314,530
Accrued expenses and other	114,586	92,760
Accrued payroll and benefits	99,115	70,413
Income taxes payable	15,790	11,885
Total Current Liabilities	626,684	489,588
Long-term debt	25,000	—
Deferred income taxes and other long-term liabilities	66,473	48,682
STOCKHOLDERS' EQUITY		
Common stock, par value $.01 per share Authorized 300,000,000 shares Issued and outstanding 77,491,000 and 78,960,000 shares	775	790
Additional paid-in capital	341,041	289,734
Retained earnings	301,372	253,931
	643,188	544,455
Total Liabilities and Stockholders' Equity	$1,361,345	$1,082,725

Consistent with the nature of its business, Ross' assets include cash; accounts receivable, representing amounts due from its customers; merchandise inventories, representing costs of goods waiting to be sold; and property and equipment, representing the long-term investments in property and equipment that are necessary to its merchandising activities. In each case, these assets reflect an expected future benefit. For accounts receivable, it is the cash Ross expects to collect from customers. For merchandise inventories, it is the cash or receivables that Ross expects to arise from sales. For property and equipment, it is the sales that Ross expects to generate from their stores.

As with the asset section, the balance sheet classifies liabilities into a current and noncurrent section. Similar to current assets, **current liabilities** are liabilities that become due, or expected to be settled, within one year. Ross' liabilities are consistent with the nature of its business. They include accounts payable, principally representing amounts due to vendors of merchandise that it sells; accrued payroll, representing amounts owed to employees; accrued expenses, representing amounts owed to others for providing certain services, for example, utilities; and income taxes payable, representing amounts owed to the taxing authorities. Ross' liabilities also include long-term debt, representing amounts borrowed to finance its investment and operating activities.

As noted above, stockholders' equity represents the residual claim after liabilities have been met. **Common stock** and **additional paid-in capital** combined represent the amount contributed by stockholders when they purchased shares from the company. The remaining portion of stockholders' equity, **retained earnings,** represents the accumulated amount of net income less dividends distributed to stockholders since the company formed.

As explained earlier, not all resources that Ross controls may be reported as assets on its balance sheet. GAAP restricts what items can appear on the balance sheet, as well as the values assigned to those items that do appear. For example, Ross' slogan "Dress for Less" may have value for its company recognition. However, difficulties in how to measure the economic benefits of slogans or brand names generally prevent their recognition as assets in an accounting sense. Going back to the example of Polaroid that started this chapter, Polaroid states that patents and trademarks are valued at $1 on its financial statements. This treatment recognizes that these assets have value, but by only recognizing them at $1 there is no material effect on the interpretation of the financial statements. Polaroid therefore indicates to its financial statement readers that these items have value even though the company cannot report them under GAAP.

Recall that the accounting values for assets and liabilities may not reflect their current market values. Because stockholders' equity must equal assets less liabilities, it therefore follows that the book value of stockholders' equity does not necessarily equal its market value. For example, if we divide stockholders' equity from Ross' balance sheet ($643,188) by the number of shares of Ross' common stock outstanding (77,491), we obtain a **book value per share** of $8.35 at February 1, 2003. However, Ross' stock price during the year ended February 1, 2003 ranged from $32.76 to $46.88 a share.

> The amount in the common stock accounts represents a par value assigned to the shares at issuance and has little economic significance. Par value should not be confused with market value of the firm's stock. Market value takes into account the entire equity of stockholders and is not limited to the portion of initial contribution labeled as par value.

> Market values are not used to value owners' equity in the financial statements as it would be circular logic to value stockholders' equity at market prices that, in principle, depend on the information contained in financial reports.

FLOW STATEMENTS—CHANGES IN FINANCIAL POSITION

Changes in the firm's financial position from one point in time to another can be broadly classified into those related to *operating, investing,* and *financing activities.* Three statements describe these changes in the financial position of the firm: the Statement of Earnings, the Statement of Cash Flows, and the Statement

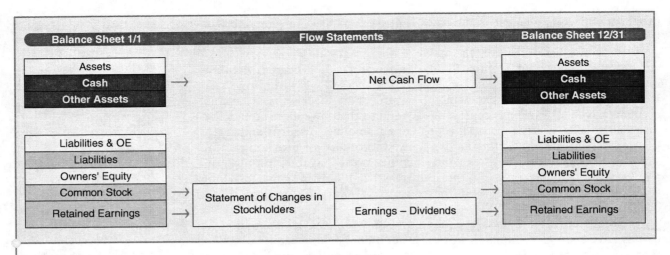

Exhibit 2.6
Financial Statement
Connections

of Changes in Stockholders' Equity. Exhibit 2.6 shows the relationships of the three flow statements to the balance sheet at the beginning and end of the period.

STATEMENT OF EARNINGS

The Statement of Earnings (sometimes called the *Statement of Income,* or *Income Statement*) explains changes in stockholders' equity arising from the firm's operating activities. It reports *revenues* from sales of goods and services to customers and the *expenses* of generating those revenues. Revenues are generally recognized at the point at which the company transfers the risks and benefits of ownership of the goods or services to the buyer. For most product firms, this happens at the date the product is delivered to the customer. Expenses are often classified into costs directly related to the goods sold **(cost of goods sold),** other operating expenses (including selling and administrative costs), financing costs (e.g., interest), and income taxes.

At the time revenues are recognized, the firm records the increase in assets that it has received in exchange for its goods or services. These assets are typically either cash or, if the customer is granted credit, accounts receivable. In some cases, a customer may pay for a product or service in advance of its receipt (e.g., school tuition). When this occurs, the firm cannot recognize the revenue from the sale until the product or service is delivered (as we will discuss in Chapter 4). Therefore, the receipt of cash results in the creation of a liability that represents this deferred revenue (the obligation of the firm to deliver the product or service in the future). Later, when revenue is recognized on the income statement, this liability account is reduced.

When expenses are recognized, they may be associated with decreases in assets (such as the decrease in inventory when cost of goods sold is recognized) or increases in liabilities (such as when salary expense is recognized before salaries are paid to employees).

Net income (loss) (also referred to as *net earnings*), then, is the excess of revenues (expenses) over expenses (revenues):

$$\text{Net Income} = \text{Revenues} - \text{Expenses}$$

Net income (loss) increases (decreases) owners' equity because it is added to the balance in retained earnings. Note that earnings can either be positive (income) or negative (loss).

Accounting recognition of the revenues and expenses that go into the determination of net income are governed by the **accrual concept** of accounting. As explained more fully in Chapter 4, under this concept, revenues are recorded as *earned*, not necessarily when cash is received, and expenses are recorded as *incurred*, not necessarily when cash is paid.

Let's look at the Statement of Earnings for Ross for three fiscal years (Exhibit 2.7). Ross prepares what is known as a single-step income statement. This type of income statement combines all revenues in one section and all expenses except income taxes in a second section. *Sales* are amounts charged to customers for merchandise. *Costs and Expenses* include *costs of goods sold, general and administrative costs,* and *interest expense.* As is the case for most retailers, costs of goods sold include costs associated with buying and distributing merchandise and building occupancy costs. General and administrative costs include salaries, wages, employee benefits, and other expense of managing the firm's activities. Interest expense pertains to the debt that appears on Ross' balance sheet and is therefore considered a nonoperating item. *Earnings before taxes* is then computed (subtracting all expenses from sales). The tax on this income is shown just prior to *Net earnings,* often referred to as the *bottom line.*

Net earnings summarizes the effect of Ross' operating activities on stockholders' equity. It is added to the balance of retained earnings at the end of the previous year in arriving at the balance at February 1, 2003. Because stockholders' equity equals net assets (assets less liabilities), net assets must also

> The accrual concept is very important to fully understand because analysts often use earnings as a starting point to forecast future cash flows of the firm.

For the years ended (in thousands)	2/1/2003	2/2/2002	2/3/2001
SALES	$3,531,349	$2,986,596	$2,709,039
COSTS AND EXPENSES			
Cost of goods sold, including related buying, distribution, and occupancy costs	2,628,412	2,243,384	2,017,923
General, selling, and administrative	572,316	485,455	438,464
Interest expense, net	279	3,168	3,466
	3,201,007	2,732,007	2,459,853
Earnings before taxes	330,342	254,589	249,186
Provision for taxes on earnings	129,164	99,544	97,432
Net earnings	$ 201,178	$ 155,045	$ 151,754

Exhibit 2.7
Ross Stores—Statement of Earnings

THE REAL WORLD

Ross Stores

reflect the results of operations. Intuitively, we can see that sales prices charged to customers not only increase net income (and hence owners' equity) in the form of revenues, but also increase assets by increasing either cash or accounts receivable. Likewise, salaries and wages of employees not only decrease net income (owners' equity) in the form of operating expenses, but either decrease assets by decreasing cash or increase liabilities by increasing accrued payroll. This two-sided effect of revenues or expenses is essential to preserve the relationship in the accounting equation. (This concept is discussed in detail in Chapters 3 and 4 so do not be concerned if it seems difficult to grasp at this point.)

STATEMENT OF CASH FLOWS

The Statement of Cash Flows also describes changes in financial position, specifically the changes in cash. This statement shows how investing, financing, and operating activities affect cash. Investment activities relate to the acquisition or disposal of long-term assets such as property and equipment. Financing activities relate to the issuance and repayment or repurchase of debt and equity. The operating activities section reports the cash inflows and outflows associated with the sales of goods and services to customers.

Under current accounting standards, the operating section of the statement can be presented in one of two forms: a **direct method,** under which the direct cash inflows and outflows are shown, or an **indirect method** (by far the most common), under which net income under the accrual concept is adjusted to its cash flow equivalent. Exhibit 2.8 illustrates the direct method of the Statement of Cash Flows for Rowe Companies (a group of companies that provides home furnishings). In contrast, Exhibit 2.9 shows the indirect method of the Statement of Cash Flows for Ross. Chapter 5 provides a more complete discussion of the differences in these two methods.

Looking at Exhibit 2.9, note how the operating section differs from the one presented in Exhibit 2.8. For the Ross Statement of Cash Flows, the operating section starts with net earnings, which is then adjusted to its cash flow equivalent (net cash provided by operating activities). Further note how the net earnings and the net cash provided by operating activities differ in each year. For instance, in 2003, net income was $201,178 (000s), whereas cash flow from operations was $332,445 (000s).

The investing section contains additions to property and equipment made during the year. Though not in Ross' case, this section may also include amounts invested in temporary investments or costs of acquiring the net assets of another firm. The financing section shows the proceeds and payments on long-term debt, the cash payments of dividends, the proceeds from the issuance of stock for employee stock plans (recall that we mentioned these in Chapter 1 as a common way to compensate certain managers), and repurchases of Ross' own shares.

Now that we have completed a look at three of the major financial statements for Ross, it is useful to revisit the diagram in Exhibit 2.6 that showed the connections among the balance sheet, income statement, and cash flow statement.

The Rowe Companies Annual Report 2003
CONSOLIDATED STATEMENTS OF CASH FLOWS

Year Ended (in thousands)	11/30/2003	12/1/2002	12/2/2001
Increase (Decrease) in Cash			
Cash flows from operating activities:			
Cash received from customers	$300,299	$336,853	$329,558
Cash paid to suppliers and employees	(287,266)	(317,217)	(331,014)
Income taxes received (paid), net	1,352	2,839	585
Interest paid	(5,225)	(4,028)	(2,397)
Interest received	225	347	480
Other receipts—net	942	1,340	1,109
Net cash and cash equivalents provided by (used in) operating activities	10,327	20,134	(1,679)
Cash flows from investing activities:			
Payments received on notes receivable	100	125	125
Increase in cash surrender value	(121)	(150)	(179)
Proceeds from sale of Mitchell Gold	39,573	—	—
Proceeds from sale of property and equipment	—	—	1,056
Capital expenditures	(3,995)	(3,323)	(3,317)
Payments under earn-out and related obligations (Note 2)	(15,759)	—	—
Net cash provided by (used in) investing activities	19,798	(3,348)	(2,315)
Cash flows from financing activities:			
Restricted cash released from (deposited to) collateral for letters of credit	264	(1,938)	—
Net borrowings (repayments) under line of credit	—	(9,368)	5,368
Draws under revolving loans	12,570	3,994	6,865
Proceeds from issuance of long-term debt	—	39,442	—
Repayments under revolving loans	(20,751)	(10,244)	(3,821)
Payments to reduce long-term debt	(18,759)	(47,874)	—
Payments to reduce loans on cash surrender value	(16)	—	—
Proceeds from loans against life insurance policies	—	—	3,014
Proceeds from issuance of common stock	3	38	27
Dividends paid	—	—	(1,379)
Purchase of treasury stock	(2)	(19)	(16)
Net cash provided by (used in) financing activities	(26,691)	(25,969)	10,058
Net increase (decrease) in cash and cash equivalents	3,434	(9,183)	6,064
Cash at beginning of year	274	9,457	3,393
Cash at end of year	$ 3,708	$ 274	$ 9,457

Exhibit 2.9
Ross Stores—Statement of
Cash Flows

THE REAL WORLD

Ross Stores

For the years ended (in thousands)	2/1/2003	2/2/2002	2/3/2001
CASH FLOWS FROM OPERATING ACTIVITIES			
Net earnings	$201,178	$155,045	$151,754
Adjustments to reconcile net earnings to net cash provided by operating activities:			
Depreciation and amortization of property and equipment	53,329	49,896	44,377
Other amortization	12,847	12,725	10,686
Deferred income taxes	17,375	12,633	10,015
Change in assets and liabilities:			
Merchandise inventory	(93,128)	(63,824)	(59,071)
Other current assets net	(4,003)	(16,901)	(980)
Accounts payable	81,958	54,064	5,751
Other current liabilities	54,541	34,384	(26,836)
Other	8,348	4,867	7,653
Net cash provided by operating activities	332,445	242,889	143,349
CASH FLOWS USED IN INVESTING ACTIVITIES			
Additions to property and equipment	(133,166)	(86,002)	(82,114)
Net cash used in investing activities	(133,166)	(86,002)	(82,114)
CASH FLOWS USED IN FINANCING ACTIVITIES			
Borrowings (repayments) under lines of credit	0	(64,000)	64,000
Proceeds from long-term debt	25,000	0	0
Issuance of common stock related to stock plans	50,863	54,581	14,303
Repurchase of common stock	(149,997)	(130,676)	(169,324)
Dividends paid	(14,847)	(13,595)	(12,389)
Net cash used in financing activities	(88,981)	(153,690)	(103,410)
Net increase (decrease) in cash and cash equivalents	110,298	3,197	(42,175)
Cash and cash equivalents:			
Beginning of year	40,351	37,154	79,329
End of year	$150,649	$ 40,351	$ 37,154
SUPPLEMENTAL CASH FLOW DISCLOSURES			
Interest paid	$ 409	$ 3,332	$ 3,352
Income taxes paid	$ 91,875	$ 61,433	$100,359

ARTICULATION OF THE FINANCIAL STATEMENTS

Exhibit 2.10 presents an update of Exhibit 2.6; we have now included the dollar amounts for the key components of these connections. Note how earnings and dividends affect the balance in retained earnings. However, in Ross' case, retained earnings is also affected by the repurchase of shares of its own stock. (We will discuss this type of transaction in Chapter 12.) Ross' Statement of

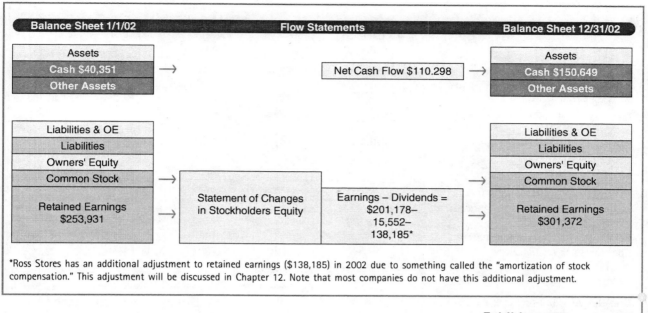

*Ross Stores has an additional adjustment to retained earnings ($138,185) in 2002 due to something called the "amortization of stock compensation." This adjustment will be discussed in Chapter 12. Note that most companies do not have this additional adjustment.

Exhibit 2.10
Financial Statement
Connections—Ross

THE REAL WORLD

Ross Stores

Changes in Stockholders' Equity, discussed next, provides these same direct connections between the beginning and ending balances in the accounts, as well as changes in those accounts.

STATEMENT OF CHANGES IN STOCKHOLDERS' EQUITY

The Statement of Changes in Stockholders' Equity provides details about all of the transactions that affect stockholders' equity, including such items as stock issuance, stock repurchases, net income, and dividends. Exhibit 2.11 shows Ross' Statement of Changes in Stockholders' Equity. Each column represents a particular account within stockholders' equity. The rows represent the balance and the transactions that have occurred over the most recent three years. Recall that retained earnings are increased by net income and decreased by dividends declared to stockholders (except for the adjustment for the repurchase of stock that we have already mentioned).

OTHER STATEMENT DISCLOSURES

A company's annual report to shareholders contains more than the financial statements themselves (see Exhibit 2.12). For example, footnotes describe significant accounting policies employed by the firm (see Exhibit 2.13), as well as elaborate on items that appear in the statements. The report of the firm's auditors attests to the fairness of the financial statements and their conformance

	Common Shares	Stock Amount	Additional Paid-In Capital	Retained Earnings	Total
BALANCE AT JANUARY 29, 2000	88,774	$888	$234,635	$237,908	$473,431
Common stock issued under stock plans, including tax benefit	1,854	18	14,285		14,303
Amortization of stock compensation			9,894		9,894
Common stock repurchased	(10,101)	(101)	(22,690)	(146,533)	(169,324)
Net earnings				151,754	151,754
Dividends declared				(12,511)	(12,511)
BALANCE AT FEBRUARY 3, 2001	80,527	805	236,124	230,618	467,547
Common stock issued under stock plans, including tax benefit	3,378	34	54,547		54,581
Amortization of stock compensation			11,881		11,881
Common stock repurchased	(4,945)	(49)	(12,818)	(117,809)	(130,676)
Net earnings				155,045	155,045
Dividends declared				(13,923)	(13,923)
BALANCE AT FEBRUARY 2, 2002	78,960	790	289,734	253,931	544,455
Common stock issued under stock plans, including tax benefit	2,341	23	50,840		50,863
Amortization of stock compensation			12,241		12,241
Common stock repurchased	(3,810)	(38)	(11,774)	(138,185)	(149,997)
Net earnings				201,178	201,178
Dividends declared				(15,552)	(15,552)
BALANCE AT FEBRUARY 1, 2003	77,491	$775	$341,041	$301,372	$643,188

Exhibit 2.11
Ross Stores—Statement of Changes in Stockholders' Equity (in thousands)

THE REAL WORLD

Ross Stores

with regulatory guidelines. Further, although not formally part of the company's financial statements, management provides its own assessment of the past year's operating results, liquidity, and capital expenditures, as well as financing strategies. Management provides this information through the management's discussion and analysis section of the annual report, commonly known as the *MD&A section.*

Exhibit 2.12
Typical Contents of an Annual Report

Message from Chief Executive Officer
Description of Principal Products or Services
Financial Highlights
Management's Discussion and Analysis
Statement of Financial Position
Statement of Earnings
Statement of Cash Flows
Statement of Changes in Stockholders' Equity
Notes to Financial Statements
Statement of Management's Responsibilities
Auditor's Report
Other Corporate Information

Exhibits 2.13
Ross Stores Footnotes:
Summary of Significant
Accounting Policies

THE REAL WORLD

Ross Stores

Merchandise Inventory. Merchandise inventory is stated at the lower of cost (determined using a weighted average basis) or net realizable value. The Company purchases manufacturer overruns and canceled orders both during and at the end of a season which are referred to as packaway inventory. Packaway inventory is purchased with the intent that it will be stored in the Company's warehouses until a later date, which may even be the beginning of the same selling season in the following year. Packaway inventory accounted for approximately 44 percent and 43 percent of total inventories as of February 1, 2003 and February 2, 2002, respectively.

Cost of Goods Sold. In addition to the product cost of merchandise sold, the Company includes its buying and distribution expenses as well as occupancy costs related to the Company's retail stores, buying, and distribution facilities in its cost of goods sold. Buying expenses include costs to procure merchandise inventories. Distribution expenses include the cost of operating the Company's distribution centers and freight expenses related to transporting merchandise.

Property and Equipment. Property and equipment are stated at cost. Depreciation is calculated using the straight-line method over the estimated useful life of the asset, typically ranging from five to 12 years for equipment and 20 to 40 years for real property. The cost of leasehold improvements is amortized over the useful life of the asset or the applicable lease term, whichever is less. Computer hardware and software costs are included in fixtures and equipment and are amortized over their estimated useful life generally ranging from five to seven years. Reviews for impairment are performed whenever events or circumstances indicate the carrying value of an asset may not be recoverable.

Analysts must understand the accounting choices that firms make in order to interpret their financial statements and to make fair comparisons across firms. The summary of significant accounting policies footnote is very important in conveying this information about the choices the firm has made.

Beyond the annual report, additional financial information is made publicly available through filings with the SEC. These filings include prospectuses accompanying new stock issues, annual 10K reports (such as Exhibit 2.4), and 10Q reports (a 10Q reports contains quarterly financial statement information). These reports typically offer greater detail than the annual report. For example, these filings might include information on competition and risks associated with the firm's principal business, holdings of major stockholders, compensation of top executives, and announcements of various events.

THE INFLUENCE OF FINANCIAL STATEMENTS

Financial statements embody the standards by which other information is often constructed. For example, professional security analysts project revenues and estimate research and development spending. Given that such forecasts and projections pertain to information that will ultimately surface in financial statements (see the report for Archer Daniels in Exhibit 2.14), these reports are likely to reflect the same accounting principles. In other words, the influence of financial reports extends well beyond their contents

Exhibit 2.14
Archer Daniels Midland
Operating Earnings Up

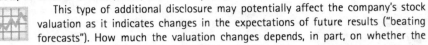

THE REAL WORLD

Archer Daniels

January 19, 2001

DECATUR, Ill. Jan 14 (Reuters)—Archer Daniels Midland Co., the largest U.S. grain producer, said on Friday its fiscal second-quarter operating earnings rose 22 percent, beating forecasts, as sales in ethanol, feed, and cocoa products boosted results.

This type of additional disclosure may potentially affect the company's stock valuation as it indicates changes in the expectations of future results ("beating forecasts"). How much the valuation changes depends, in part, on whether the increase in earnings is sustainable in the future. Although no obvious price reaction resulted on the day after this announcement, the price of ADMs stock rose from around $8 a share to $15 a share between October 2000 and February 2001. This clearly indicates the increased prospects of the company.

as such. There is a confirmation aspect to reports provided by the firm that becomes apparent as you look closely at financial information from other sources.

We opened the chapter relating how Polaroid suffered a drop off in sales, starting in the fourth quarter of 2000. Exhibit 2.15 shows the quarterly sales figures for Polaroid (taken from Polaroid's 10Q reports) over the period from the first quarter of 1998 through the second quarter of 2001. Notice the seasonal pattern of Polaroid's sales. That is, in a given year, Polaroid always realizes its highest sales in the fourth quarter, typically significantly up from the third quarter. However, in 2000, fourth-quarter sales are only slightly higher than those in the third quarter. This departure from the previous trend would be important to investors and analysts as they assessed the value of Polaroid's shares in the fourth quarter of 2001 and beyond. Note that sales then dramatically fell in the first and second quarters of 2001, leading up to Polaroid's declaration of bankruptcy in the third quarter of 2001. Sales are just one of the items that analysts would look at to understand earnings and the market value of Polaroid, but in this case perhaps, the most significant one.

Exhibit 2.15
Polaroid's Sales by Quarter

THE REAL WORLD

Polaroid

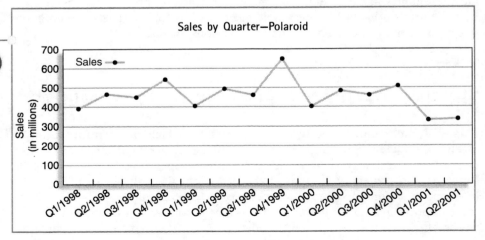

SUMMARY AND TRANSITION

In this chapter, we provided an overview of the corporate form of business and the major financial statements prepared under GAAP as a way to set the stage for examining the construction and use of financial accounting reports in the chapters that follow. As we described, corporations have become the dominant form of business entity due to such features as limited liability and the ease with which ownership can be transferred and capital can be raised.

The main general-purpose financial statements considered include a Statement of Financial Position, which describes the financial position in terms of its assets, liabilities, and stockholders' equity of the firm at a point in time; a Statement of Earnings, which describes the results of the firm's operations in terms of its revenues and expenses from one point in time to another; a Statement of Cash Flows, which describes the firm's investment, financing, and operating activities in terms of their effects on cash; and a Statement of Changes in Stockholders' Equity, which describes transactions affecting contributed capital and retained earnings in further detail.

Our description of these financial statements provides a first glimpse of the typical items comprising the resources that a firm may control (assets) and the claims to those resources held by creditors and owners (liabilities and stockholders' equity, respectively). We identified changes in assets and liabilities arising from the operating activities of the firm as composed of revenues and expenses, leading to the bottom-line number, net income or earnings. Other changes pertained to investment and financing activities. We also reviewed further details of changes in stockholders' equity. In Chapter 3, we describe the mechanics of the accounting system and how to analyze the effects of a particular transaction on these financial statements of the firm. Chapter 4 provides further detail on the measurement and reporting of revenues and expenses. Our coverage of the construction of financial statements then concludes with methods for distinguishing operating, investing, and financing cash flows.

END OF CHAPTER MATERIAL

KEY TERMS

Accounting Equation	Current Assets
Accrual Concept	Current Liabilities
Accrued	Direct Method
Additional Paid-in Capital	Fiscal Year
Assets	Indirect Method
Balance Sheet	Liabilities
Book Value per Share	Limited Liability
Classified Balance Sheet	Liquidity Order
Common Stock	Net Asset
Common Stockholders' Equity	Net Book Value
Cost of Goods Sold	Net income

Noncurrent Assets

Owners' Equity

Partnership

Residual Claim

Retained Earnings

Sole Proprietorship

Statement of Cash Flows

Statement of Changes in Stockholders' Equity

Statement of Earnings

Statement of Financial Position

Stockholders' Equity

ASSIGNMENT MATERIAL

REVIEW QUESTIONS

1. Describe the pros and cons for organizing a business as a corporation rather than a partnership.

2. Describe and illustrate the three major categories of items that appear in a typical statement of financial position.

3. Describe the purpose of the four main financial statements that are contained in all annual reports.

4. What is the meaning of the term net assets?

5. Why might certain economic resources not be considered assets by accountants? Provide an example.

6. What is the accounting equation?

7. What is meant by a classified balance sheet?

8. How do accountants distinguish between current and noncurrent assets and liabilities?

9. Explain the meaning of retained earnings.

10. Why might the book value of a company be different from the market value of the company?

11. What is net income?

12. What are the two methods for reporting cash flow from operations that are allowed under GAAP?

13. What is comprehensive income?

14. How is other comprehensive income reported in the financial statements?

APPLYING YOUR KNOWLEDGE

15. Compare and contrast the statement of earnings and the cash flow statement.

Use the following abbreviations to respond to question 16:

CA—Current Assets

NCA—Noncurrent Assets

CL—Current Liabilities

NCL—Noncurrent Liabilities

CS—Capital Stock

RE—Retained Earnings

NI—Income statement item

CF—Cash flow statement item

16. Classify the following items according to where the item would appear in the financial statements:

   a. Inventory

   b. Taxes Payable

   c. Interest Expense

   d. Dividends

   e. Sales to customers

   f. Manufacturing Equipment

   g. New issuance of common stock

   h. Cash

   i. Bonds Payable (debt due in ten years)

   j. Employee's Wages

Use the following abbreviations to respond to question number 17:

O—Operating Item

F—Financing Item

I—Investing Item

17. Classify each of the following transactions as to whether they are operating, financing, or investing activities:

   a. Cash collected from customers

   b. Repayment of debt

   c. Payment of dividends

   d. Purchase of a truck (by a manufacturing company)

   e. Purchase of a truck (by a truck dealer)

   f. Purchase of shares of stock of another company

   g. Sale of a plant

   h. Utility expenses are incurred

18. Compute the missing balance sheet amounts in each of the following independent situations:

	A	B	C	D
Current Assets	?	$650,000	$230,000	$40,000
Noncurrent Assets	250,000	?	400,000	?
Total Assets	?	1,050,000	?	190,000
Current Liabilities	50,000	500,000	300,000	25,000
Noncurrent Liabilities	?	90,000	?	10,000
Owners' Equity	225,000	?	80,000	?
Total Liabilities and Owners' Equity	350,000	?	?	?

19. Compute the missing amounts in the reconciliation of retained earnings in each of the following independent situations:

	A	B	C	D
Retained Earnings Dec. 31, Year 1	$20,000	$100,000	?	$40,000
Net Income	15,000	?	400,000	22,000
Dividends Declared and Paid	6,000	35,000	250,000	?
Retained Earnings Dec. 31, Year 2	?	115,000	300,000	52,000

20. For each of the following companies, list at least two types of assets and one type of liability that you would expect to find on their balance sheet (try to include at least one item in your list that is unique to that business):

   a. The Washington Post Company—This is a company that is primarily in the newspaper business but also has operations in television stations, cable systems, *Newsweek* magazine, as well as some other smaller operations.

   b. International Paper—This is a company that is primarily in the forest products business, selling both paper and wood products.

   c. SBC—This is a telecommunications company.

   d. Hartford Financial Services Group—This is a multiline insurance company.

   e. Philip Morris Companies, Inc.—This is a company that is primarily in the tobacco business but has also diversified into foods, beer, financial services, and real estate.

   f. Citibank—This is a major commercial bank.

   g. Delta—This is a major airline.

21. For each of the companies listed in question number 20 list at least two line items that you would expect to find on their income statement (try to include at least one item in your list that is unique to that business).

22. For each of the companies listed in question number 20 list at least two line items that you would expect to find on their cash flow statement (try to include at least one item in your list that is unique to that business).

23. Suppose that your best friend wanted to start a new business providing desktop publishing services to customers. Your friend has some savings to start the business but not enough to buy all of the equipment that she thinks she needs. She has asked you for some advice about how to raise additional funds. Give her at least two alternatives and provide the pros and cons for each alternative.

24. Suppose that you and a friend form a partnership in which you both contribute the same amount of cash and you agree to share in profits on a 50–50 basis. Further suppose that you are responsible for running the day-to-day operations of the firm but your friend is a silent partner in the sense that he doesn't work in the business (he has another job). Because you have no other job, the partnership agrees to pay you $1,500 per month. How should the partnership treat this payment, as a distribution of profits or as an expense of doing business? What difference would it make to the distribution to you and your partner?

USING REAL DATA

Base your answer to problems 25–28 on the data from Polaroid provided here.

POLAROID CORP. Balance Sheet	12/31/1999	12/31/2000
Assets		
Current Assets		
Cash and cash equivalents	$ 92,000,000	$ 97,200,000
Receivables, less allowances of $23.9 in 1999 and $23.8 in 2000 (Note 6)	489,700,000	435,400,000
Inventories (Notes 5 and 6)	395,600,000	482,500,000
Prepaid expenses and other assets (Note 4)	130,800,000	103,500,000
Total Current Assets	1,108,100,000	1,118,600,000
Property, Plant, and Equipment:		
Land	14,700,000	6,900,000
Buildings	322,700,000	313,500,000
Machinery and equipment	1,620,100,000	1,597,500,000
Construction in progress	65,500,000	49,600,000
Total property, plant and equipment	2,023,000,000	1,967,500,000
Less accumulated depreciation	1,423,800,000	1,398,300,000
Net Property, Plant, and Equipment	599,200,000	569,200,000
Deferred Tax Assets (Note 4)	243,700,000	279,500,000
Other Assets	89,000,000	75,700,000
Total Assets	$2,040,000,000	$2,043,000,000
Liabilities and Stockholders' Equity		
Current Liabilities		
Short-term debt (Note 6)	$ 259,400,000	$ 363,700,000
Payables and accruals (Note 7)	338,000,000	334,100,000
Compensation and benefits (Notes 10 and 11)	138,100,000	76,700,000
Federal, state and foreign income taxes (Note 4)	14,700,000	18,800,000
Total Current Liabilities	750,200,000	793,300,000
Long-term debt (Note 8)	573,000,000	573,500,000
Accrued postretirement benefits (Note 11)	234,800,000	222,700,000
Other long-term liabilities	111,500,000	78,300,000
Total Liabilities	1,669,500,000	1,667,800,000
Preferred stock, Series A and D, $1 par value, authorized 20,000,000 shares; all shares unissued	—	—
Common stockholders' equity (Note 9)		
Common stock, $1 par value, authorized 150,000,000 shares (75,427,550 shares issued in 1999 and 2000)	75,400,000	75,400,000
Additional paid-in capital	395,200,000	363,100,000
Retained earnings	1,208,800,000	1,219,500,000
Accumulated other comprehensive income	(48,900,000)	(68,900,000)
Less: Treasury stock, at cost (30,811,263 and 29,895,578 shares in 1999 and 2000, respectively)	1,259,700,000	1,213,800,000
Deferred compensation	300,000	100,000
Total common stockholders' equity	370,500,000	375,200,000
Total Liabilities and Common Stockholders' Equity	$2,040,000,000	$2,043,000,000

POLAROID CORP. Income Statement

	12/31/1998	12/31/1999	12/31/2000
Net Sales	$1,845,900,000	$1,978,600,000	$1,855,600,000
Cost of goods sold	1,108,400,000	1,170,500,000	1,055,900,000
Marketing, research, engineering, and administrative expenses (Note 2)	736,500,000	700,500,000	696,400,000
Restructuring charges/(credits) (Note 2)	50,000,000	—	(5,800,000)
Total Costs	1,894,900,000	1,871,000,000	1,746,500,000
Profit/(Loss) from Operations	(49,000,000)	107,600,000	109,100,000
Other income/(expense):			
Interest income	2,900,000	2,700,000	5,500,000
Other	64,800,000	(19,500,000)	28,600,000
Total other income/(expense)	67,700,000	(16,800,000)	34,100,000
Interest expense	57,600,000	77,400,000	85,300,000
Earnings/(Loss) before Income Tax Expense	(38,900,000)	13,400,000	57,900,000
Federal, state and foreign income tax expense (Note 4)	12,100,000	4,700,000	20,200,000
Net Earnings/(Loss)	($51,000,000)	$8,700,000	$37,700,000

POLAROID CORP. Cash Flow

	12/31/1998	12/31/1999	12/31/2000
Cash Flows from Operating Activities			
Net earnings/(loss)	$ (51,000,000)	$ 8,700,000	$ 37,700,000
Depreciation of property, plant, and equipment	90,700,000	105,900,000	113,900,000
Gain on the sale of real estate	(68,200,000)	(11,700,000)	(21,800,000)
Other noncash items	62,200,000	73,800,000	22,900,000
Decrease/(increase) in receivables	79,000,000	(52,700,000)	41,800,000
Decrease/(increase) in inventories	(28,400,000)	88,000,000	(100,600,000)
Decrease in prepaids and other assets	39,000,000	62,400,000	32,900,000
Increase/(decrease) in payables and accruals	25,300,000	(16,500,000)	9,200,000
Decrease in compensation and benefits	(21,000,000)	(72,500,000)	(105,000,000)
Decrease in federal, state, and foreign income taxes payable	(29,900,000)	(54,000,000)	(31,500,000)
Net cash provided/(used) by operating activities	97,700,000	131,400,000	(500,000)
Cash Flows from Investing Activities			
Decrease/(increase) in other assets	(25,400,000)	16,500,000	4,500,000
Additions to property, plant, and equipment	(191,100,000)	(170,500,000)	(129,200,000)

	12/31/1998	12/31/1999	12/31/2000
Proceeds from the sale of property, plant, and equipment	150,500,000	36,600,000	56,600,000
Acquisitions, net of cash acquired	(18,800,000)	–	–
Net cash used by investing activities	(84,800,000)	(117,400,000)	(68,100,000)
Cash Flows from Financing Activities			
Net increase/(decrease) in short-term debt (maturities of 90 days or less)	131,200,000	(86,200,000)	108,200,000
Short-term debt (maturities of more than 90 days)			
Proceeds	73,000,000	41,800,000	–
Payments	(117,200,000)	(24,900,000)	–
Proceeds from issuance of long-term debt	–	268,200,000	–
Repayment of long-term debt	–	(200,000,000)	–
Cash dividends paid	(26,500,000)	(26,600,000)	(27,000,000)
Purchase of treasury stock	(45,500,000)	–	–
Proceeds from issuance of shares in connection with stock incentive plan	6,000,000	300,000	100,000
Net cash provided/(used) by financing activities	21,000,000	(27,400,000)	81,300,000
Effect of exchange rate changes on cash	3,100,000	400,000	(7,500,000)
Net increase/(decrease) in cash and cash equivalents	37,000,000	(13,000,000)	5,200,000
Cash and cash equivalents at beginning of year	68,000,000	105,000,000	92,000,000
Cash and cash equivalents at end of year	$105,000,000	$92,000,000	$ 97,200,000

25. Find the following amounts in the statements of Polaroid:

  a. Net sales in 2000

  b. Marketing, research, engineering, and administrative expenses incurred in 2000

  c. Interest expense in 2000

  d. Income tax expense in 1999

  e. Net income in 1999

  f. Inventories at the end of 2000

  g. Payables and accruals at the beginning of 2000

  h. Retained earnings at the end of 2000

  i. Accumulated other comprehensive income at the end of 2000

  j. Long-term borrowings at the beginning of 2000

  k. Cash produced from operating activities in 2000

    l. Cash payments to acquire property, plant, and equipment in 2000

    m. Dividends paid in 2000

    n. Cash proceeds from new borrowings in 2000

    o. Cash produced or used for investing activities in 2000

    p. Amount of other comprehensive income in 2000

26. What is the trend in net income for the three years presented?

27. What is the trend in cash flow from operations for the three years presented?

28. What is the trend in net sales for the three years presented?

Base your answers to problems 29–35 on the data for Werner Enterprises provided here.

WERNER ENTERPRISES, INC.
CONSOLIDATED BALANCE SHEET
(In thousands, except share amounts)

	2000/12/31	1999/12/31
ASSETS		
Current assets:		
Cash and cash equivalents	$ 25,485	$ 15,368
Accounts receivable, trade, less allowance		
of $3,994 and $3,236, respectively	123,518	127,211
Receivable from unconsolidated affiliate	5,332	—
Other receivables	10,257	11,217
Inventories and supplies	7,329	5,296
Prepaid taxes, licenses, and permits	12,396	12,423
Current deferred income taxes	11,552	8,500
Other	10,908	8,812
Total current assets	206,777	188,827
Property and equipment, at cost		
Land	19,157	14,522
Buildings and improvements	72,631	65,152
Revenue equipment	829,549	800,613
Service equipment and other	100,342	90,322
Total property and equipment	1,021,679	970,609
Less accumulated depreciation	313,881	262,557
Property and equipment, net	707,798	708,052
Notes receivable	4,420	—
Investment in unconsolidated affiliate	5,324	—
Other noncurrent assets	2,888	—
	$ 927,207	$896,879
LIABILITIES AND STOCKHOLDERS' EQUITY		
Current liabilities:		
Accounts payable	$ 30,710	$ 35,686
Short-term debt	—	25,000
Insurance and claims accruals	36,057	32,993
Accrued payroll	12,746	11,846
Income taxes payable	7,157	926
Other current liabilities	14,749	14,755
Total current liabilities	101.419	121.206

	2000/12/31	1999/12/31
Long-term debt	105,000	120,000
Deferred income taxes	152,403	130,600
Insurance, claims, and other long-term accruals	32,301	30,301
Commitments and contingencies		
Stockholders' equity Common stock, $.01 par value, 200,000,000 shares authorized; 48,320,835 shares issued; 47,039,290 and 47,205,236 shares outstanding, respectively	483	483
Paid-in capital	105,844	105,884
Retained earnings	447,943	404,625
Accumulated other comprehensive loss	(34)	—
Treasury stock, at cost; 1,281,545 and 1,115,599 shares, respectively	(18,152)	(16,220)
Total stockholders' equity	536,084	494,772
	$ 927,207	$896,879

WERNER ENTERPRISES, INC.
CONSOLIDATED STATEMENTS OF INCOME
(In thousands, except per share amounts)

	2000/12/31	1999/12/31	1998/12/31
Operating revenues	$1,214,628	$1,052,333	$863,417
Operating expenses:			
Salaries, wages, and benefits	429,825	382,824	325,659
Fuel	137,620	79,029	56,786
Supplies and maintenance	102,784	87,600	72,273
Taxes and licenses	89,126	82,089	67,907
Insurance and claims	34,147	31,728	23,875
Depreciation	109,107	99,955	82,549
Rent and purchased transportation	216,917	185,129	139,026
Communications and utilities	14,454	13,444	10,796
Other	(2,173)	(11,666)	(11,065)
Total operating expenses	1,131,807	950,132	767,806
Operating income	82,821	102,201	95,611
Other expense (income):			
Interest expense	8,169	6,565	4,889
Interest income	(2,650)	(1,407)	(1,724)
Other	(154)	245	114
Total other expense	5,365	5,403	3,279
Income before income taxes	77,456	96,798	92,332
Income taxes	29,433	36,787	35,086
Net income	$ 48,023	$ 60,011	$ 57,246
Average common shares outstanding	47,061	47,406	47,667
Basic earnings per share	$ 1.02	$ 1.27	$ 1.20
Diluted shares outstanding	47,257	47,631	47,910
Diluted earnings per share	$ 1.02	$ 1.26	$ 1.19

WERNER ENTERPRISES, INC.
CONSOLIDATED STATEMENTS OF CASH FLOWS
(In thousands)

	2000/12/31	1999/12/31	1998/12/31
Cash flows from operating activities:			
Net income	$ 48,023	$ 60,011	$ 57,246
Adjustments to reconcile net income to net cash provided by operating activities:			
Depreciation	109,107	99,955	82,549
Deferred income taxes	18,751	22,200	14,700
Gain on disposal of operating equipment	(5,055)	(13,047)	(12,251)
Equity in income of unconsolidated affiliate	(324)	—	—
Tax benefit from exercise of stock options	130	663	389
Other long-term assets	(2,888)	—	—
Insurance, claims, and other long-term accruals	2,000	(500)	1,472
Changes in certain working capital items:			
Accounts receivable, net	3,693	(32,882)	(868)
Prepaid expenses and other current assets	(8,474)	(8,725)	(5,186)
Accounts payable	(4,976)	(12,460)	3,979
Accrued and other current liabilities	10,160	16,762	(4,090)
Net cash provided by operating activities	170,147	131,977	137,940
Cash flows from investing activities:			
Additions to property and equipment	(169,113)	(255,326)	(258,643)
Retirements of property and equipment	60,608	84,297	86,260
Investment in unconsolidated affiliate	(5,000)	—	—
Proceeds from collection of notes receivable	287	—	—
Net cash used in investing activities	(113,218)	(171,029)	(172,383)
Cash flows from financing activities:			
Proceeds from issuance of long-term debt	10,000	30,000	40,000
Repayments of long-term debt	(25,000)	—	—
Proceeds from issuance of short-term debt	—	30,000	20,000
Repayments of short-term debt	(25,000)	(15,000)	(20,000)
Dividends on common stock	(4,710)	(4,740)	(4,201)
Repurchases of common stock	(2,759)	(3,941)	(9,072)
Stock options exercised	657	2,188	1,335
Net cash provided by (used in) financing activities	(46,812)	38,507	28,062
Net increase (decrease) in cash and cash equivalents	10,117	(545)	(6,381)
Cash and cash equivalents, beginning of year	15,368	15,913	22,294
Cash and cash equivalents, end of year	$ 25,485	$ 15,368	$ 15,913
Supplemental disclosures of cash flow information:			
Cash paid during year for:			
Interest	$ 7,876	$ 7,329	$ 4,800
Income taxes	3,916	13,275	26,100
Supplemental disclosures of noncash investing activities:			
Notes receivable from sale of revenue equipment	$ 4,707	$ —	$ —

WERNER ENTERPRISES, INC.
CONSOLIDATED STATEMENTS OF STOCKHOLDERS' EQUITY
(In thousands, except share amounts)

	Common Stock	Paid-in Capital	Retained Earnings	Accumulated Other Comprehensive Loss	Treasury Stock	Total Stockholders' Equity
BALANCE, December 31, 1997	$387	$104,764	$296,533	$ –	($6,566)	$395,118
Purchases of 592,600 shares of common stock	–	–	–	–	(9,072)	(9,072)
Dividends on common stock ($.09 per share)	–	–	(4,428)	–	–	(4,428)
Five-for-four stock split	96	(96)	–	–	–	–
Exercise of stock options, 119,391 shares	–	670	–	–	1,054	1,724
Comprehensive income:						
Net income	–	–	57,426	–	–	57,246
BALANCE, December 31, 1998	483	105,338	349,351	–	(14,584)	440,588
Purchases of 302,600 shares of common stock	–	–	–	–	(3,941)	(3,941)
Dividends on common stock ($.10 per share)	–	–	(4,737)	–	–	(4,737)
Exercise of stock options, 198,526 shares	–	546	–	–	2,305	2,851
Comprehensive income:						
Net income	–	–	60,011	–	–	60,011
BALANCE, December 31, 1999	483	105,884	404,625	–	(16,220)	494,772
Purchases of 225,201 shares of common stock	–	–	–	–	(2,759)	(2,759)
Dividends on common stock ($.10 per share)	–	–	(4,705)	–	–	(4,705)
Exercise of stock options, 59,255 shares	–	(40)	–	–	827	787
Comprehensive income (loss):						
Net income	–	–	48,023	–	–	48,023
Foreign currency translation adjustments	–	–	–	(34)	–	(34)
Total comprehensive income	–	–	48,023	(34)	–	47,989
BALANCE, December 31, 2000	$483	$105,844	$447,943	($34)	($18,152)	$536,084

29. Verify that total assets equal total liabilities and owners' equity for Werner in 2000.

30. Find the following amounts in the statements of Werner:

  a. Revenues in 2000

  b. Salaries, wages, and benefits incurred in 2000

  c. Interest expense in 2000

  d. Income tax expense in 1999

     e. Net income in 1999

     f. Inventories at the end of 2000

     g. Accounts payable at the beginning of 2000

     h. Retained earnings at the end of 2000

     i. Long-term borrowings at the beginning of 2000

     j. Cash produced from operating activities in 2000

     k. Cash payments to acquire property, plant, and equipment in 2000

     l. Dividends paid in 2000

     m. Cash proceeds from new borrowings in 2000

     n. Cash produced or used for investing activities in 2000

31. Does Werner finance the firm mainly from creditors (total liabilities) or from owners (owners' equity) in 2000? Support your answer with appropriate data.

32. List the two largest sources of cash and the two largest uses of cash in 2000. (Consider operations to be a single source or use of cash.)

33. Suggest some reasons why income was $48,023 (000) in 2000, yet cash flow from operations was $170,147 (000).

34. What is the comprehensive net income for Werner in 2000?

35. On December 31, 2000, find the price of Werner's stock (use the library or the web) and compute the total market value of the company's stock that is outstanding based on the number of shares that were outstanding as of that date. Compare this value with the book value of owner's equity on Werner's balance sheet as of that date. If these numbers are different, offer an explanation for this discrepancy.

Base your answers to problems 36–42 on the data for Emulex Corporation provided here.

EMULEX CORP.: Balance Sheet	2001/07/01	2000/07/01
Assets		
Current assets:		
Cash and cash equivalents	$ 36,471,000	$ 23,471,000
Investments	148,204,000	128,234,000
Accounts and other receivables, less allowance for doubtful accounts of 1,298 in 2001 and 844 in 2000	40,239,000	24,332,000
Inventories, net	38,616,000	12,635,000
Prepaid expenses	2,527,000	1,021,000
Deferred income taxes	1,579,000	453,000
Total current assets	267,636,000	190,146,000
Property and equipment, net	18,379,000	6,927,000
Long-term investments	38,805,000	29,293,000
Goodwill and other intangibles, net	590,316,000	0
Deferred income taxes and other assets	2,878,000	3,629,000
Total Assets	$918,014,000	$229,995,000

	2001/07/01	2000/07/01
Liabilities and Stockholders' Equity		
Current liabilities:		
Accounts payable	$ 29,253,000	$ 17,869,000
Accrued liabilities	11,749,000	6,355,000
Income taxes payable and other current liabilities	300,000	320,000
Total current liabilities	41,302,000	24,544,000
Deferred income taxes and other liabilities	26,000	0
	41,328,000	24,544,000
Commitments and contingencies (note 9)		
Stockholders' equity:		
Preferred stock, $0.01 par value; 1,000,000 shares authorized (150,000 shares designated as Series A Junior Participating Preferred Stock); none issued and outstanding	0	0
Common stock, $0.10 par value; 120,000,000 shares authorized; 81,799,322 and 72,466,848 issued and outstanding in 2001 and 2000, respectively	8,180,000	7,247,000
Additional paid-in capital	861,461,000	155,190,000
Deferred compensation	(12,366,000)	0
Retained earnings	19,411,000	43,014,000
Total stockholders' equity	876,686,000	205,451,000
Total liabilities and stockholders' equity	$918,014,000	$229,995,000

EMULEX CORP.: Income Statement

	2001/07/01	2000/07/01	1999/07/01
Net revenues	$245,307,000	$139,772,000	$68,485,000
Cost of sales	120,812,000	73,346,000	40,138,000
Cost of sales—inventory charges related to consolidation	0	0	1,304,000
Total cost of sales	120,812,000	73,346,000	41,442,000
Gross profit	124,495,000	66,426,000	27,043,000
Operating expenses:			
Engineering and development	27,002,000	14,727,000	11,766,000
Selling and marketing	16,734,000	10,077,000	6,953,000
General and administrative	12,111,000	6,923,000	4,279,000
Amortization of goodwill and other intangibles	52,085,000	0	0
In-process research and development	22,280,000	0	0
Consolidation charges, net	0	0	(987,000)
Total operating expenses	130,212,000	31,727,000	22,011,000
Operating income (loss)	(5,717,000)	34,699,000	5,032,000
Nonoperating income	14,301,000	9,131,000	480,000
Income before income taxes	8,584,000	43,830,000	5,512,000
Income tax provision	32,187,000	11,016,000	247,000
Net income (loss)	($23,603,000)	$32,814,000	$5,265,000

EMULEX CORP.: Cash Flow

	2001/07/01	2000/07/01	1999/07/01
Cash flows from operating activities:			
Net income (loss)	($23,603,000)	$32,814,000	$5,265,000
Adjustments to reconcile net income (loss) to net cash provided by operating activities:			
Depreciation and amortization	4,801,000	1,814,000	1,648,000
Gain on sale of strategic investment	(1,884,000)	0	0
Stock-based compensation	1,756,000	0	0
Amortization of goodwill and other intangibles	52,085,000	0	0
In-process research and development	22,280,000	0	0
Loss (gain) on disposal of property, plant, and equipment	400,000	112,000	(750,000)
Deferred income taxes	(536,000)	(5,643,000)	0
Tax benefit from exercise of stock options	32,188,000	16,661,000	0
Impairment of intangibles	0	175,000	125,000
Provision for doubtful accounts	435,000	435,000	86,000
Changes in assets and liabilities:			
Accounts receivable	(15,714,000)	(7,679,000)	(5,033,000)
Inventories	(25,007,000)	(1,552,000)	(1,177,000)
Prepaid expenses and other assets	(111,000)	(701,000)	18,000
Accounts payable	5,882,000	6,474,000	4,486,000
Accrued liabilities	4,006,000	2,064,000	(2,987,000)
Income taxes payable	(37,000)	(32,000)	215,000
Net cash provided by operating activities	56,941,000	44,942,000	1,896,000
Cash flows from investing activities:			
Net proceeds from sale of property, plant, and equipment	0	30,000	2,999,000
Additions to property and equipment	(11,657,000)	(5,703,000)	(1,953,000)
Payment for purchase of Giganet, Inc., net of cash acquired	(15,530,000)	0	0
Purchases of investments	(524,091,000)	(637,892,000)	(115,380,000)
Maturity of investments	491,009,000	595,745,000	0
Proceeds from sale of strategic investment	5,484,000	0	0
Net cash used in investing activities	(54,785,000)	(47,820,000)	(114,334,000)
Cash flows from financing activities:			
Principal payments under capital leases	(12,000)	(18,000)	(76,000)
Net proceeds from issuance of common stock under stock option plans	9,742,000	4,083,000	184,000
Proceeds from note receivable issued in exchange for restricted stock	1,114,000	0	0
Net proceeds from stock offering	0	0	132,838,000
Net cash provided by financing activities	10,844,000	4,065,000	132,946,000
Net increase in cash and cash equivalents	13,000,000	1,187,000	20,508,000
Cash and cash equivalents at beginning of year	23,471,000	22,284,000	1,776,000
Cash and cash equivalents at end of year	$36,471,000	$23,471,000	$22,284,000

	2001/07/01	2000/07/01	1999/07/01
Supplemental disclosures:			
Noncash investing and financing activities			
Fair value of assets acquired	$ 7,832,000		
Fair value of liabilities assumed	8,136,000	$ 0	$ 0
Common stock issued and options			
assumed for acquired business	661,678,000	0	0
Cash paid during the year for:			
Interest	$ 352,000	$ 21,000	$ 60,000
Income taxes	221,000	32,000	53,000

36. What is Emulex's fiscal year-end date?

37. Find the following amounts in the statements of Emulex:

a. Net sales in 2001

b. Cost of sales in 2001

c. Interest expense in 2001

d. Income tax expense in 2001

e. Amortization of goodwill in 2001 and in 2000

f. Net income in 2001

g. Inventories at the end of 2001

h. Goodwill at the end of 2001

i. Additional paid-in capital at the end of 2001

j. Cash from operating activities for 2001

k. Cash from investing activities for 2001

l. Cash from financing activities for 2001

38. Does Emulex finance its business primarily from creditors or from owners? Support your answer with appropriate data.

39. In 2001 Emulex purchased a new business. How did Emulex pay for this acquisition?

40. What is the trend in sales and net income over the last three years, and can you provide an explanation for why there is a loss in 2001?

41. Does Emulex pay dividends on its stock?

42. On July 1, 2001 find the stock price of Emulex's stock (use the library or the web) and compute the total market value of the company's stock that is outstanding, based on the number of shares that were outstanding as of that date. Compare this value with the book value of owner's equity on Emulex's balance sheet as of that date. If these numbers are different, offer an explanation for this discrepancy.

BEYOND THE BOOK

43. For a company of your choosing, answer the following questions:

a. What are the major sections included in your annual report?

b. What are the three most important points made in the letter to the shareholders?

    c. What are the titles to the major financial statements included in the report?

    d. What are the total assets, total liabilities, and total stockholders' equity of the firm? What percent of the company's total assets are financed through liabilities?

    e. What were the net sales in the most recent year? Is this up or down from the prior year (answer in both dollar and percentage amounts)?

    f. What is the net income and earnings per share in the most recent year? Is this up or down from the prior year (answer in both dollar and percentage amounts)?

    g. Are any of the following items reported in the income statement: discontinued operations, extraordinary items, accounting method changes? If so, which ones?

    h. What is the net cash provided (used) by operating, financing, and investing activities for the most recent year?

    i. What is the last day of your company's fiscal year end?

    j. Who are the independent auditors, and what type of opinion did they give the company?

44. Refer to the footnotes that accompany the company you chose in 43.

    a. In the section "Summary of Significant Accounting Policies," what key policies are discussed?

    b. Does your company have long-term debt? If so, what is the interest rate?

    c. If your company has inventory, what do the footnotes tell you about the inventory?

    d. From the footnotes, does it appear that there are any obligations that the company may have that do not appear to be reflected as liabilities on the balance sheet? If so, what are they?

CHAPTER 3

The Accounting Process

LEARNING OBJECTIVES

After reading this chapter you should be able to:

1 Recognize common business transactions and understand their impact on general-purpose financial statements.

2 Understand the dual nature of accounting transactions as reflected in the accounting equation.

3 Explain the basic construction of the Statement of Financial Position, the Statement of Earnings, and the Statement of Cash Flows.

4 Distinguish between economic events that are commonly recognized in accounting as transactions and those that are not.

5 Apply the concept of nominal or temporary accounts to record revenues and expenses, and identify their relationship to the Statement of Earnings and Statement of Financial Position.

6 Describe the accounting cycle and recognize the timing issues inherent in reporting financial results.

On March 2, 2001, investors reacted very favorably to an initial public offering (an Initial Public Offering or IPO is the first time a private company decides to issue shares to the public) from AFC Enterprises, Inc. The company operates and franchises quick-service restaurants, bakeries, and cafés (3618 in the United States and 27 in foreign countries) under the names Popeye's Chicken & Biscuits, Church's Chicken, Cinnabon, Seattle's Best Coffee, and Torrefazione Italia. The company also sells specialty coffees at wholesale and retail under the Seattle Coffee brand name. Sales totaled about $2.4 billion in 2000.

Although originally issued at $17, AFC shares opened at $19.50, climbed as high as $20.75, and ended the day at $20.38 on the Nasdaq Stock Market. The company had originally expected the shares to be offered at between $15 and $17. After the IPO, AFC had 29.5 million shares outstanding. You can see that with almost 30 million shares issued, AFC raised a substantial amount of money to fund its operations.

Investors and analysts use financial statements to guide their predictions and investment decisions. For example, when a company such as AFC Enterprises decides to issue stock to the public, it files information (in a document called a *prospectus*) containing past and projected financial performance. Investors, potential investors, managers, and other stakeholders rely on this financial statement information to help determine the company's value. As a result, these users must understand the process and assumptions underlying the construction of financial statements in order to make sound decisions based (in part) on these statements.

In the following pages, we present the fundamental aspects of the *double-entry accounting system* for constructing financial statements. The mechanical aspects of recording transactions are sometimes referred to as *bookkeeping.* You may well question why you should be concerned with this bookkeeping aspect of accounting, especially in light of today's computerized technology. The answer: You need to understand what the preparers are doing so that you can better interpret the output of their work, the financial statements. Let's start first with the balance sheet accounts, which underlie the financial statements.

BALANCE SHEET ACCOUNTS

Most of the balance sheet accounts are categorized as assets, liabilities, or stockholders' equity. Before examining specific transactions, let's review these in more detail.

ASSETS

The Financial Accounting Standards Board (FASB) Concepts Statement Number 6 (CON 6) defines an asset as follows (FASB, SFAC No. 6, 1985):

> Assets are probable future economic benefits obtained or controlled by a particular entity as a result of past transactions or events.

Probable future economic benefits means that a firm expects either future cash inflows or smaller cash outflows to result from the asset. For example, a prepaid expense, such as the premium on an insurance policy, is considered to be an asset because the coverage that the policy provides benefits future periods. However, as we noted in Chapter 2, some items have economic value but are not recognized as assets. For instance, if a firm faces uncertainty about future realization of cash flows, an item might not be recognized as an asset (e.g., research and development expenditures). Pepsico spends a significant amount of money each year for marketing its products. While this may create value for the business (brand recognition), they expense their advertising costs as they are incurred. Or, an item may be valuable to an entity but not owned or controlled by that entity, such as skilled employees.

Most assets originate as the result of a transaction with a party outside of the firm. A firm generally recognizes assets at the price it paid to acquire the assets. Exhibit 3.1 lists assets commonly found on a balance sheet:

Exhibit 3.1
Common Assets

Cash The amount of money that the firm has, including the amounts in checking and savings accounts.

Marketable Securities Short-term investments, such as stocks and bonds, in the securities of other companies.

Accounts Receivable Amounts owed to the firm that result from credit sales to customers.

Inventory Goods held for resale to customers.

Prepaid Expenses Expenses that have been paid for, but have not been used, such as rent paid in advance and insurance premiums.

Property, Plant, and Equipment (PP&E) Buildings, land, and equipment to be used for business operations over several years.

Intangible Assets Assets that have value, but do not have a physical presence, such as patents, trademarks, and goodwill.

Deferred Tax Assets Amounts of expected future tax savings.

LIABILITIES

In contrast to assets, liabilities are amounts recognized in accounting that result in expected future outflows of cash or delivery of goods or services. Exhibit 3.2 lists some of the more common balance sheet liabilities. Similar to assets, liability recognition also usually involves a transaction with an external party. FASB Con 6 defines liabilities as follows (FASB, SFAC No. 6, 1985):

Liabilities are probable future sacrifices of economic benefits arising from present obligations of a particular entity to transfer assets or provide services to other entities in the future as a result of past transactions or events.

Exhibit 3.2
Common Liabilities

Accounts Payable Amounts owed to suppliers from the purchase of goods on credit.

Notes Payable Amounts owed to a creditor (bank or supplier) that are represented by a formal agreement called a note. Notes payable can be either short-term (due in less than one year) or long-term (due more than one year in the future).

Accrued Liabilities Amounts that are owed to others relating to expenses that the company has incurred, but are not paid in cash as of the balance sheet date, such as interest payable or a warranty liability.

Taxes Payable Amounts currently owed to taxing authorities.

Deferred Taxes Amounts that the company expects to pay to taxing authorities in the future.

Bonds Payable Amounts owed to a creditor that are paid out over longer periods; they generally involve fixed interest payments as well as a large payment at the end of some specified period. Some bonds payable can be traded on exchanges in the same way as stock is traded. Bonds payable are generally long-term in nature, meaning that they are payable in a period more than one year from the date of issuance.

STOCKHOLDERS' EQUITY

Owners' or stockholders' equity is the last main category on the balance sheet. Stockholders' equity consists of two major components: contributed capital and retained earnings. **Contributed capital** reflects the amount of capital that a firm's owners have invested in the business. This amount is typically the sum of the **par** or **stated value** of stock issued, plus the amounts in excess of par, **additional paid-in-capital.** The sum of common stock plus additional paid-in-capital represents the total investment by shareholders at the time the company issued the stock.

Retained earnings is the total amount of earnings (revenues minus expenses) recorded in the accounting system to date, but not yet distributed to shareholders as dividends. Dividends are distributions of earnings to shareholders and are not considered an expense to the company. Remember that retained earnings are not cash. A company may have substantial earnings yet have no cash for at least two reasons. First, accounting rules require that earnings be recognized on an accrual basis. For example, firms sometimes recognize revenues before receiving cash (as in sales on account), and sometimes recognize expenses before paying cash out (as in wages owed to employees). Second, a company may use its cash to invest in noncash assets (e.g., a new computer system or repay debt).

> We would not expect a company to accumulate large amounts of cash, even if the company is very profitable. This is because cash as an asset does not generate high rates of return. Thus, management, seeking to maximize shareholders' wealth, generally keeps only as much cash as it requires to meet its operating needs and to make the repayment of its debt. Additional amounts may be held in anticipation of further investments.

NOMINAL ACCOUNTS

Balance sheet accounts (sometimes called **real** or **permanent accounts**) include a number of assets, liabilities, and stockholders' equity accounts such as those discussed in the previous sections. **Nominal accounts** (or **temporary accounts**) are accounts that a firm uses to determine its earnings. These accounts consist of revenue and expense accounts such as sales, cost of goods sold, wage and salary expenses, and selling and administrative expenses. Ultimately, these accounts affect a permanent account, namely retained earnings. (We'll discuss how this is accomplished later.) However, at this point, it is worth noting that the reason that revenue and expenses are considered to be temporary accounts is that the balances in these accounts are transferred (or *closed*) to retained earnings at the end of each accounting period. By closing revenue and expense accounts each period, the balances in these accounts reflect only the firm's operating performance for one period at a time. The retained earnings account contains cumulative earnings less dividends distributed to stockholders since the firm's inception.

Now that you have a good understanding of the types of accounts, let's see next how firms use them to record transactions.

ACCOUNTING FOR TRANSACTIONS

The starting point in constructing financial statements is the accounting recognition of **transactions,** or economic events. Most, but not all, transactions are triggered by an exchange between the firm and another party. Accounting recognition of these transactions take the form of an **entry,** which indicates the financial effects of that event on accounts that appear on the firm's financial statements.

Recall from Chapter 2 that the accounting equation states that

$$\text{Assets} = \text{Liabilities} + \text{Stockholders' Equity}$$

When firms record transactions in the accounting system, this equality must always be maintained.

To analyze transactions, you can use two approaches. The first approach is based on the accounting equation. Each transaction is analyzed in terms of how it affects assets, liabilities, and stockholders' equity (we'll illustrate this approach later in this chapter). The equation approach is only useful when first learning accounting, so you can more easily see how transactions affect the accounting equation and financial statements. However, this approach quickly becomes unwieldy and inefficient when dealing with a large number of transactions and accounts. As a result, most firms use the second approach, the double-entry accounting system.

DOUBLE-ENTRY ACCOUNTING SYSTEM

The **double-entry accounting system** expresses account balances and changes in account balances using terms called **debits** and **credits.** Although it requires some investment of your time and effort to be able to use debits and credits, having this skill is extremely useful. Once you understand the double-entry accounting system, you can efficiently assess the effects of a variety of types of transactions on a company's financial statements, as well as address valuation and income measurement issues.

The system of using debit and credits serves as the basis of virtually every accounting system worldwide. Further, the Sarbane's Oxley Act requires that top management certify to the fundamental accuracy of their company's financial statements. Such certification requires that management possess a basic understanding of the accounting process, in order to be able to communicate with the preparers of financial statements. Understanding the process of generating financial statements is an essential component of financial literacy.

T-ACCOUNTS

A debit means simply an entry or balance on the left-hand side of an account, and a credit is an entry or balance on the right-hand side of an account. Increases and decreases in specific accounts can be expressed by debit and credit entries following set conventions. The conventions that dictate the rules for debits and credits are structured so that all accounting transactions will maintain the equality of the accounting equation at all times. The basic form of an account can be represented using a so-called **T-account** of the following form (note that we have represented the balance on the debit side of the account but also recognize that the balance could appear on either side of the account):

Account Title	
Balance	
Debit	Credit
Balance	

A T-account shows the beginning and ending balance in an account, as well as the debit and credit entries for transactions affecting the account during a particular period of time. Whether an account is increased or decreased by a debit or credit depends on whether the account represents an asset, liability, or stockholders' equity, in other words, has a debit or a credit balance. As Exhibit 3.3 shows, assets are increased by debit entries and decreased by credit entries. Liabilities and stockholders' equity accounts (capital stock, additional paid in capital, and retained earnings) are increased by credits and decreased by debits.

As shown in Exhibit 3.3, we normally expect asset accounts to carry a debit balance, while liability and stockholders' equity accounts normally carry a credit balance. One way to think about these results is that the accounting equation shows assets on the left side (debit) and liabilities and stockholders' equity on the right (credit). An exception is retained earnings. A profitable company will have a credit balance in this account, but it can have a debit balance if it incurs a cumulative net loss. Finally, remember that to maintain the accounting equation, the sum of all debit account balances must equal the sum of all credit account balances.

JOURNAL ENTRIES

In a double-entry accounting system, firms typically track transactions as they occur in a chronological listing known as a **journal.** Each entry in the journal, known as a **journal entry,** summarizes both sides of a transaction (debit and

Exhibit 3.3
T-Accounts

T-Accounts for Assets, Liabilities, and Stockholders' Equity			
Assets		**Liabilities**	
Beginning balance Debits increase	Credits decrease	Debits decrease	Beginning balance Credits increase
Ending balance			Ending balance
Capital Stock (common stock + paid-in-capital)		**Retained Earnings**	
Debits decrease	Beginning balance Credits increase	Debits decrease	Beginning balance Credits increase
	Ending balance		Ending balance

credit). By convention, in a journal entry, the debit portion of the entry is shown first, followed by the credit portion. (See the sample journal entries that follow.) The credit entry is slightly indented from the debit to make the entry clear. The total debits for a transaction must equal the total credits for that transaction.

| Title of Account Debited | Amount Debited |
| Title of Account Credited | Amount Credited |

For example, the journal entry to record the purchase of $100 of inventory for cash would appear as follows:

| Inventory | 100 | |
| Cash | | 100 |

We will explain this transaction later, but for now just recognize the form of the journal entry.

After recording journal entries, they are then posted to the T-accounts. Posting simply means transferring the information in the journal entry to the appropriate T-accounts. (In this text, we will often simplify this two-step approach by recording the transaction directly to the T-account, bypassing the journal entry step.) The set of T-accounts that a company uses is collectively referred to as the **ledger.**

To illustrate the application of the accounting equation, journal entries, and T-accounts, assume that a company borrows $50,000,000 cash from a bank and signs a promissory note. This note specifies an interest rate and when the amount borrowed must be repaid. Using the accounting equation approach, we view this transaction as shown here (shown in millions of dollars):

Assets = Liabilities + Stockholders' Equity

	Notes	
Cash	Payable	
+50	= +50	

Notice that the asset (Cash) is increased, and the liability (Notes Payable) is also increased. Observe also that we maintain the equality of the accounting equation. The journal entry for this transaction would appear as follows:

| Cash | 50 | |
| Notes Payable | | 50 |

The debit to the Cash account means that cash (an asset) has increased by $50 and the credit to Notes Payable (a liability) means that account is increased as well. Posting this journal entry to the appropriate T-accounts, the transaction would be recorded as:

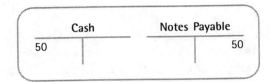

Observe that both the T-account and the journal entry maintain the equality of total debits and total credits. Note also that dollar signs ($) are generally omitted from journal entries and T-accounts. Journal entries are a useful way to represent individual transactions, while T-accounts illustrate the effect of a series of transactions on the accounts that comprise a company's financial statements.

COMPUTERIZED ACCOUNTING

The basic accounting process, still used today, has existed for centuries. Before computers, firms literally recorded accounting entries in paper journals, and then posted the individual components of those entries to paper ledger accounts. You can easily imagine the large amount of paperwork involved in a manual accounting system, even for a modestly sized business. Although today's accounting systems are computerized, they continue follow the same basic process. Transactions still give rise to entries in some form (a journal), from which summaries (ledger) by account can be created, which then serve as a foundation for the construction of financial statements.

Modern accounting systems are structured much differently than in the past and may be simply one part of a company's software system. These sophisticated systems provide a wide variety of management tools. For example, some systems may instantly determine the impact of a revenue or expense transaction on a company's income statement and balance sheet. There are several companies that provide very sophisticated systems, and Oracle is one of those companies. Exhibit 3.4 provides a description of Oracle's business.

Even though computers have eased the paperwork requirements of accounting systems, you still need to know how they work. Let's look at an example that illustrates the accounting process and the preparation of financial statements.

Exhibit 3.4
Oracle Corporation:
Description of Business
(Oracle 10-K, 2003)

THE REAL WORLD

Oracle Corporation

We are the world's largest enterprise software company. We develop, manufacture, market, and distribute computer software that helps our customers manage and grow their businesses and operations. Our offerings include new software licenses, software license updates, and product support and services, which include consulting, advanced product services, and education. We also offer an integrated suite of business applications software and other business software infrastructure, including application server, collaborative software, and development tools.

AN ILLUSTRATION OF TRANSACTION ANALYSIS

Biohealth, Inc., is a hypothetical, wholesale health-products distributor (similar to an actual company in the health supply industry). As is often true for publicly traded companies, Biohealth is denoted by its *ticker symbol,* in this case BHT, used on the stock exchanges where the company's stock trades. BHT distributes (not manufactures) a wide variety of healthcare products and prescription medicines to hospitals, retail chains, and other health-related outlets. It also provides software solutions to a variety of businesses in the healthcare sector for managing their ordering and inventory. BHT was incorporated on December 20, 20X0 and began operations the following January.

The following economic events/transactions occurred in December prior to the start of BHT's operations:

1. BHT issued 250 million shares of common stock with a par value of $1 per share for $6.50 per share.

2. BHT acquired fixtures for $540 million. BHT estimates that the fixtures will be used for nine years.

3. The purchase of fixtures was partially financed with a $400 million note due in five years. The loan carries an interest rate of 7 percent.[1]

These transactions reflect BHT's start-up financing and investing activities. Let's look at them more closely.

ANALYSIS OF FINANCING AND INVESTING ACTIVITIES

Exhibit 3.5 summarizes the impact of these initial three transactions on the accounting equation. Notice how the accounts to the left of the equal (=) sign are added together, as well as the accounts to the right of the equal sign, to

#–Type	Assets		=	Liabilities			
	Cash	Fixtures	=	Notes payable	Common Stock	Paid–in Capital	Retained Earnings
Bal. 12/20/20X0	0	0	=	0	0	0	0
1-Financing	1,625		=		250	1,375	
2-Investing	(540)	540	=				
3-Financing	400		=	400			
Bal. 12/31/20X0	1,485	540	=	400	250	1,375	0

Exhibit 3.5
Impact of BHT's Financing and Investing Activities on the Accounting Equation (in millions of dollars)

[1] A note is a loan accompanied by a written promise to repay the amount owed. Interest on notes is always expressed in terms of an annual rate even if the note is for a period longer or shorter than one year. For example, the total interest on a six-month $1,000 note with an interest rate of 5 percent would be $1,000 \times .05 \times 6/12 = $25.

determine the ending balance. On each line of the exhibit, from individual transactions to ending balances, the accounting equation holds. Negative amounts, as shown in Exhibit 3.5, are enclosed in parentheses.

Issuing Stock (Transaction 1)

The first transaction increases Cash by $1,625 million (250 million shares × $6.50/share), increases Common Stock by $250 million (250 million shares × $1/share), and increases Additional Paid-In Capital by $1,375 million (the difference between cash and par value). We classify this transaction as a financing activity because it relates to how the company funds its operating and investing activities. Note that dollar figures are reported in millions, a common practice in financial statements.

Purchasing Fixtures (Transaction 2)

The second transaction increases assets (Fixtures) by $540 million, and decreases Cash by $540 million. This transaction is an investing activity. Investing activities involve purchase and sale of assets that are used over multiple periods such as property, plant, and equipment. Note that later in the chapter we classify fixtures under property, plant, and equipment (PPE).

Borrowing Funds (Transaction 3)

Although the third transaction relates to the investing activity in Transaction 2, it, by itself, is a financing activity. Here, the company borrows funds to finance its purchase of fixtures. Note that interest is not recognized yet on the loan as it is a charge that the firm incurs with the passage of time. Investing and financing activities often occur simultaneously. For example, America Online (AOL) acquired all of Time-Warner's common stock in January 2000. We classify AOL's stock acquisition of Time Warner as an investing activity because America Online now controls the assets of Time Warner. However, we also classify this as a financing activity, as AOL funded this transaction by issuing additional shares of AOL stock.

Using Journal Entries and T-Accounts to Record Transactions

We show the journal entries and T-accounts for the first three BHT transactions in Exhibits 3.6 and 3.7, respectively. The journal entry for Transaction 1 summarizes

Exhibit 3.6
Journal Entries for BHT's Financing and Investing Transactions (in millions of dollars)

Transaction #1		
Cash	1,625	
Common Stock		250
Additional Paid-in Capital		1,375
Transaction #2		
Fixtures	540	
Cash		540
Transaction #3		
Cash	400	
Notes Payable		400

Exhibit 3.7
T-Accounts for BHT's
Financing and Investing
Transactions (in millions of
dollars)

Cash			Fixtures		
Bal.	0		Bal.	0	
(1)	1,625	540 (2)	(2)	540	
(3)	400		Bal.	540	
Bal.	1,485				

Notes Payable		Common Stock	
	Bal. 0		Bal. 0
	400 (3)		250 (1)
	Bal. 400		Bal. 250

Additional Paid-In Capital	
	Bal. 0
	1,375 (1)
	Bal. 1,375

BHT's issuance of stock by showing an increase in BHT's Cash (debit to Cash) and increases in both Common Stock and Additional Paid-in Capital (credits to those accounts). The journal entry for Transaction 2 reflects an increase in assets (Fixtures) by a debit to Fixtures and a decrease in Cash by a credit to Cash. Finally, the journal entry for Transaction 3 shows an increase in Cash and an increase in Notes Payable by a debit to Cash and a credit to Notes Payable, respectively.

As Exhibit 3.7 shows, each T-account includes the sum of all transactions affecting the account to date. The beginning balances in the accounts are zero as the company just started business at the beginning of this period. Finally, note that the sum of the debit balances equals the sum of the credit balances.

Observe that the three investing and financing transactions had no effect on the retained earnings account because none of them involved the generation of revenues or concurrent expenses. Earlier in the chapter, we mentioned the notion of permanent and nominal accounts. However, no nominal accounts have been affected by transactions thus far.

Now that we've recorded the journal entries and posted them to the ledger (T-accounts), we can use this information to construct the financial statements.

CONSTRUCTING THE FINANCIAL STATEMENTS

Exhibit 3.8 shows BHT's Balance Sheet as of 12/31/20X0, summarizing the financial statement position of the firm. The balance sheet omits the beginning of the period, because the balances are all zero. Further, we don't need to prepare an income statement, as none of the initial three transactions produced revenue or expenses.

Exhibit 3.9 shows BHT's Statement of Cash Flows for the month ended 12/31/20X0. The statement indicates that the firm has not yet produced any cash flows from operating activities. Also, note that the total change in cash equals

Exhibit 3.8
Biohealth, Inc. (BHT) Balance
Sheet (in millions) as of
12/31/20X0

Assets	
Current Assets:	
Cash	$1,485
Property, Plant, and Equipment:	
Fixtures	540
Total Assets	$2,025
Liabilities and Stockholder's Equity	
Liabilities:	
Notes Payable	$ 400
Total Liabilities	400
Stockholders' Equity	
Common Stock	250
Additional Paid in Capital	1,375
Retained Earnings	0
Total Stockholders' Equity	$1,625
Total Liabilities and Stockholders' Equity	$2,025

Exhibit 3.9
Biohealth, Inc. (BHT)
Statement of Cash Flows (in
millions) for the Month
Ending 12/31/20X0

Cash Flow from Investing Activities	
Purchase Fixtures	($540)
Cash Flow from Financing Activities	
Proceeds from Issuance of Common Stock	1,625
Proceeds from Loan	400
Total Cash from Financing Activities	2,025
Net Change in Cash	$1,485
Cash Balance 12/20/20X0	0
Cash Balance 12/31/20X0	$1,485

the cash balance at the end of 12/31/20X0, because the company started with no cash on hand. Finally, the beginning cash balance is as of 12/20/20X0, the date the company formed. Normally, in a month-ending statement, the date would have been 12/1/20X0.

ANALYSIS OF OPERATING ACTIVITIES

Now that we've examined BHT's initial financing and investing activities, let's next look at a series of transactions occurring in BHT's first year of operation, starting on 1/1/20X1. The following events occurred during 20X1 (all figures are in millions of dollars).

4. BHT purchased inventory costing $34,340 on account.

5. BHT sold goods for $35,724 on account.

6. The cost of the inventory sold was $30,420.

7. BHT received $33,260 in customer payments on accounts receivable.

8. BHT paid $29,200 on its accounts payable.

9. BHT paid $4,800 to lease warehouse space for inventory storage for the year and for other miscellaneous selling and administrative costs.

10. Depreciation expense on the fixtures was $60 ($540/9 years).

11. BHT paid interest on the note payable of $28.

12. BHT declared and paid dividends of $150.

Most of these transactions are operating transactions because they relate to BHT's profit-generating activities. Operating transactions can involve revenue and expense accounts (nominal accounts), but they may also involve only asset or liability accounts. For example, Inventory and Accounts Payable accounts are affected when a company buys inventory on credit. While this acquisition of inventory might be viewed as an investing activity, accounting standards classify it as operating because the company holds the inventory for resale in the short term. We classify assets such as Accounts Receivable, Inventory, and Prepaid Expenses as operating assets in part because they are short-term or current in nature, and in part because they relate to the operating cycle of the business. In contrast, we do not regard marketable securities as operating assets.

Recall from Chapter 2 that classification as a current asset generally means that we expect the asset to be converted into cash or consumed within one year or within one operating cycle of the business, whichever is longer. Similarly, obligations such as accounts payable and other short-term payables are considered operating liabilities in part because they will be paid in less than one year (current liabilities) and in part because they relate to operating activities. However, debt may also be classified as current if it is to be repaid within a year. Thus, some but not all changes in various current assets and current liabilities are considered to be operating transactions.

Before examining how we recognize these operating transactions in the accounting system, we need to first discuss revenues and expenses in more detail.

Revenues and Expenses

Revenues reflect the sales value of goods or services sold by an enterprise. *Expenses* are the costs related to generating revenue, such as the cost of inventory sold and employee wages. Recall that net income is the difference between revenues and expenses. The cumulative amount of net income, minus dividends paid to shareholders over all accounting periods to date, appears on the balance sheet in the form of retained earnings. Exhibit 3.10 shows the changes of Retained Earnings in the balance sheet.

While we could immediately proceed to talk about the nominal accounts (revenue and expense accounts) and how to incorporate them into our entries,

Exhibit 3.10
Retained Earnings Flow
through the Balance Sheet

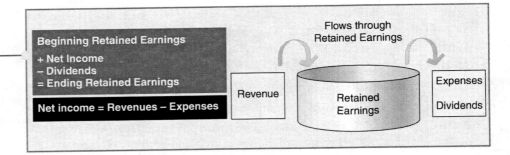

Summary Impact of Operating Activities on the Accounting Equation

Transaction #– explanation	Assets					=	Liabilities		CS	PIC	Retained Earnings
	Cash	AR	Inventory	PPE	(AD)	=	AP	NP	CS	PIC	Revenue – Expenses
Balance 12/31/20X0	1,485			540		=		400	250	1,375	
4. Purchase inventory			34,340			=	34,340				
5. Sales revenue		35,724				=					35,724
6. Cost of sales			(30,420)			=					(30,420)
7. Cash collection	33,260	(33,260)				=					
8. Payment for inventory	(29,200)					=	(29,200)				
9. S&A expenses	(4,800)					=					(4,800)
10. Depreciation expense					(60)	=					(60)
11. Interest expense	(28)					=					(28)
12. Dividend paid	(150)					=					(150)
Balance 12/31/20X1	567	2,464	3,920	540	(60)	=	5,140	400	250	1,375	266

Exhibit 3.11
Impact of BHT's Operating
Transactions on the Balance
Sheet

we take a two-step approach to analyzing operating transactions. In the section that follows, we will focus our attention on the permanent accounts as portrayed in the accounting equation to examine BHT's operating transactions. We will, therefore, portray revenue and expense events in terms of their (ultimate) impact on the Retained Earnings account (a permanent account) on the balance sheet. Accordingly, we treat revenues as direct increases (credits) to retained earnings and expenses as direct decreases (debits) to retained earnings as shown in Exhibit 3.11. It is important that you understand the ultimate effects on the permanent accounts, and it is often easier to focus on this effect first before we look more closely at nominal accounts. Following the accounting equation analysis of the transactions, we will present a more in-depth discussion of the nominal accounts and then illustrate the same transactions using journal entries and T-accounts, including the nominal accounts. If you prefer to consider the balance sheet equation effects and the journal entries simultaneously, then prior to reading about the transactions that follow, skip ahead to the section called "Nominal Accounts Revisited" and read about nominal accounts. You can then simultaneously follow the accounting equation effects in Exhibit 3.11 as well as the journal entry effects in Exhibit 3.15.

Using the Accounting Equation to Analyze Operating Activities

Exhibit 3.11 summarizes the effects of Transactions 4 through 12 using the accounting equation. We use the following abbreviations for the balance sheet accounts: AR, Accounts Receivable; PPE, Property, Plant, and Equipment; AD, Accumulated Depreciation; AP, Accounts Payable; NP, Notes Payable; CS, Common Stock; PIC, Paid-In Capital; and RE, Retained Earnings.

Purchasing Inventory on Account (Transaction 4)

Transaction 4 involves the credit (on account) purchase of inventory for resale. We consider this an operating activity because BHT expects to sell the inventory during the upcoming year for a price that exceeds its cost, generating profit for the company. The purchase is "on account," meaning that BHT pays for the inventory after its purchase. The result is that BHT has a liability, Accounts Payable, for the cost of the inventory purchased. The impact on the accounting equation is as follows:

4. Purchase of inventory on account

		Assets			=	Liabilities		Stockholders' Equity		
Cash	AR	Inventory	PPE	(AD)	=	AP	NP	CS	PIC	RE
		34,340			=	34,340				

Purchasing inventory does not constitute an expense. The inventory holds future value and is owned by the firm. Therefore, it should be recorded as an asset. The cost of purchasing inventory eventually becomes an expense (cost of goods sold) at the time that BHT sells the inventory to a customer, that is, at the point when the firm no longer owns it (see Transactions 5 and 6).

Selling Inventory on Account (Transaction 5)

Transaction 5 involves the sale of inventory on account. "On account," in this context means that BHT did not collect cash at the time of the sale but expects to do so at some future date. The amount owed to BHT, accounts receivable, represents an asset. This new asset for BHT stockholders results in an increase in stockholders' equity. Further, BHT sells its inventory for more than its cost. We refer to the gross sales value of inventory sold as **sales revenue.** At the same time, the stockholders lost an existing asset (inventory). The cost of inventory sold is accounted for separately as an expense called **cost of goods sold** (see Transaction 6, which follows). The difference between the gross sales value of the inventory (sales revenue) and its cost (cost of goods sold) is **gross profit** to BHT. The gross profit amount affects BHT's stockholders' equity in the form of an increase in retained earnings. The impact of the sales revenue itself on the accounting equation is as follows:

5. Recognize sales revenue for sales on account

	Assets				=	Liabilities		Stockholders' Equity		
Cash	AR	Inventory	PPE	(AD)	=	AP	NP	CS	PIC	RE
	35,724				=					35,724

The recognition of revenues can often be a source of confusion and, potentially, manipulation. In some cases companies improperly recognize revenues and the SEC can force them to restate their earnings. Such an example is that of Lucent Technologies, as illustrated in Exhibit 3.12.

Recognizing Cost of Goods Sold (Transaction 6)

As previously mentioned, cost of goods sold is an expense related to generating the revenues recorded in Transaction 5. By accounting convention, a firm reports this expense in the same period as the related revenue. In this way, cost of goods sold is matched with the related revenue. An asset (inventory) was given up, so stockholders' equity also decreases. Specifically, this transaction decreases retained earnings. The impact on the accounting equation is shown as follows:

6. Recognize cost of goods sold

	Assets				=	Liabilities		Stockholders' Equity		
Cash	AR	Inventory	PPE	(AD)	=	AP	NP	CS	PIC	RE
		(30,420)			=					(30,420)

Exhibit 3.12

THE REAL WORLD

Lucent Technologies

In February 2001, Lucent Technologies, Inc. announced its cooperation with the SEC in a probe of the company's accounting practices. On November 21, 2000, Lucent had indicated that $125 million in improperly booked sales could reduce its results for the fourth quarter ended September 30, 2000. The announcement resulted in a 16 percent drop in the company's stock value. After an internal review, Lucent announced on December 21, 2000, that it was reducing previously reported fourth-quarter revenues by $679 million to $8.7 billion.

The fact that firms generally recognize revenues at the time of sale, rather than at the time of collection, could have important implications for the valuation of companies. Some companies may erroneously or fraudulently recognize sales by an accounting entry even when no legitimate sale has taken place. To minimize this type of opportunistic behavior, a firm's financial records are subject to examination by external auditors, internal control systems, and oversight by external members of a firm's board of directors. Further, legal sanctions apply to those firms that are found to have engaged in such behavior. However, as the Lucent example illustrates, none of these mechanisms are perfect.

Observe that neither the revenue or expense recognition for these transactions affected cash, due to accrual accounting. As we explain fully in Chapter 4, under this concept, a firm recognizes revenues when they have been earned. In this case, revenue recognition occurs when the inventory is delivered to the buyer and the firm can reasonably expect to collect cash in the future, not necessarily when BHT receives the cash. Similarly, a firm recognizes expenses not when it pays out cash, but when the cost (expenditure) can be matched to revenues (implying there is no future benefit to be received). Thus, a firm records inventory as assets upon purchase, and then records the cost of inventory sold as an expense when revenue is earned.

While some firms can calculate the cost of goods sold at the time of sale, many firms determine the cost of goods sold at the end of the period through the following calculation:

Cost of Goods Sold Calculation:

Cost of Goods Sold = Cost of Beginning Inventory + Purchases − Cost of Ending Inventory

Collecting Receivables (Transaction 7)

Transaction 7 indicates the collection of cash for sales on account. This transaction involves an exchange of one type of an asset (accounts receivable) for another (cash), and therefore has no effect on retained earnings. BHT already recognized the revenue from the sale when the sale took place.

7. Recognize collection of cash from past sales

	Assets				=	Liabilities		Stockholders' Equity		
Cash	AR	Inventory	PPE	(AD)	=	AP	NP	CS	PIC	RE
33,260	(33,260)				=					

Paying Accounts Payable (Transaction 8)

Transaction 8 records the payment for the inventory and other items that BHT purchased on account during the year.

8. Record payments on account

	Assets				=	Liabilities		Stockholders' Equity		
Cash	AR	Inventory	PPE	(AD)	=	AP	NP	CS	PIC	RE
(29,200)					=	(29,200)				

Paying Selling and Administrative Costs (Transaction 9)

Transaction 9 involves the payment of cash for rent and other selling and administrative expenses that BHT incurred during the year. Because these cash expenditures do not result in assets with future value, these costs immediately become expenses. These expenses affect the accounting equation as follows:

9. Payment of cash for rent and selling and administrative expenses

		Assets			=	Liabilities		Stockholders' Equity		
Cash	AR	Inventory	PPE	(AD)	=	AP	NP	CS	PIC	RE
(4,800)					=					(4,800)

Depreciating Fixtures (Transaction 10)

When a firm purchases plant and equipment, it records these items as assets because they provide future benefits to the firm. Plant and equipment contribute to the production of products or services that can be sold in later periods. This productive capacity of plant and equipment, however, diminishes over time. As a result, for accounting purposes, the costs incurred in acquiring the plant and equipment should be expensed over the life of the plant and equipment. Specifically, accounting standards require that the costs incurred should be allocated to expense over the *useful life* of the asset using a rational and systematic method. We call these methods **depreciation methods,** and the expense that results **depreciation expense.** GAAP allows several depreciation methods, which we'll discuss in more detail in Chapter 9. These methods require several estimates. Exhibit 3.13 illustrates the disclosure made by Hasbro, Inc. regarding the use of estimates.

For example, the *straight-line depreciation* method assumes an equal amount of the cost of the asset is to be used up each year of its useful life. The method also factors in the possibility that the asset has some remaining estimated value

Exhibit 3.13
Hasbro, Inc. and Subsidiaries

THE REAL WORLD

Hasbro, Inc.

Notes to Consolidated Financial Statements

(1) Summary of Significant Accounting Policies

Preparation of Financial Statements

The preparation of financial statements in conformity with generally accepted accounting principles requires management to make estimates and assumptions that affect the amounts reported in the financial statements and notes thereto. Actual results could differ from those estimates.

Within GAAP, managers must make some significant estimates, such as the useful life and salvage value of a firm's property, plant, and equipment. Hasbro's disclosure reminds its financial statement readers of the estimates that management makes and the impact of these estimates on those statements.

at the end of its useful life, referred to as *salvage value*. A firm using this method therefore calculates depreciation expense dividing the original cost, less the salvage value, by the number of years of useful life. If BHT uses the straight-line method, with fixtures having a useful life of 9 years and a zero salvage value, its depreciation expense for the fixtures is [(Original Cost − Salvage)/Useful Life = ($540 − 0)/9 years = $60 million/year].

A firm records depreciation by an entry to Depreciation Expense (for the moment, retained earnings) and an entry to an account called Accumulated Depreciation. Accumulated Depreciation is a contra-asset account. **Contra-asset accounts** have credit balances and are an offset to a related asset account. In this case, the original cost of the fixtures is shown in the PP&E account. The entry shows Accumulated Depreciation as a direct reduction of this account. BHT reports the contra-asset on the balance sheet as a subtraction from the related asset account. The impact of recording depreciation on the accounting equation is shown as follows:

> The use of the accumulated depreciation account is helpful for analysis because it allows the financial statement user to observe the original cost of an asset from the asset account and then, using the information in the accumulated depreciation account, infer such information as the age of plant and equipment and how long before they may need to be replaced.

10. Recognition of depreciation expense

		Assets			=	Liabilities		Stockholders' Equity		
Cash	AR	Inventory	PPE	(AD)	=	AP	NP	CS	PIC	RE
				(60)	=					(60)

We show the Accumulated Depreciation account as a negative amount. On the balance sheet, after the first year's depreciation is recorded, the asset and related accumulated depreciation accounts for fixtures would appear on the balance sheet as follows:

Fixtures	$540
Less	
Accumulated depreciation	(60)
Net fixtures	$480

At the end of the second year, the accumulated depreciation account would show that two years of depreciation had been recognized, and fixtures and related accumulated depreciation on the balance sheet would appear as:

Fixtures	$540
Less	
Accumulated depreciation	(120)
Net Fixtures	$420

By keeping the accumulated depreciation separate from the original cost of the fixtures, the financial statement reader can estimate both how close assets are to being fully depreciated and the years remaining in the asset's estimated useful life. This information may be helpful predict when a firm will need to replace or upgrade equipment. For example, suppose a company discloses that its depreciation expense is $60 million, the asset is being depreciated using the straight-line method over nine years, and its accumulated depreciation is $300. We can then estimate that the asset's remaining useful life is 4 years (9 − (300/60) = 4). If a company does not list accumulated depreciation on the balance sheet, but instead shows property, plant, and equipment net of accumulated depreciation, a breakdown between the asset and related accumulated depreciation accounts is often provided in the firm's footnotes to the financial statements.

Paying Interest (Transaction 11)

When a firm borrows funds, it must pay for the use of the funds in the form of interest payments. In this case, we assume that the loan has simple interest at a rate of 7 percent per annum and is paid in cash. Thus, the interest on the loan is $28 million ($400 × .07) and affects the accounting equation as follows:

11. Payment of interest expense

					=	Liabilities		Stockholders' Equity		
Cash	AR	Inventory	PPE	(AD)	=	AP	NP	CS	PIC	RE
(28)					=					(28)

While we treat interest as an operating activity, others argue that interest expense should be considered a financing activity because it relates to borrowing funds. In fact, we employ this view in Chapter 14 when we consider valuing a firm. However, the FASB states that interest should be classified as an operating activity for cash flow purposes.

Dividends (Transaction 12)

Dividends return a certain amount of the profits to owners in the form of cash. A company's Board of Directors frequently declares dividends on a quarterly basis. However, a firm usually does not pay dividends at the date they are declared. Instead, a firm often pays them within the month following declaration. To deal with this delay, a firm creates a new liability, Dividends Payable. Dividends are not an expense of doing business and are not reported on the income statement. However, they do directly reduce retained earnings, as the owners are withdrawing a part of their profits from the firm. We will discuss dividends in more detail later in the text. Here, however, for simplicity, we assume that BHT pays dividends immediately in cash.

12. Declaration of dividends

					Assets		=	Liabilities			Stockholders' Equity	
Cash	AR	Inventory	PPE	(AD)		=	AP	NP	CS	PIC	RE	
(150)						=					(150)	

Now that we've examined how BHT's operating transactions affected the accounting equation, we're ready to look at the respective journal entries and T-accounting. However, before we can do that we need to provide more detail of the accounts used to record the firm's profit-measurement activities. In other words, we need to discuss nominal accounts.

Nominal Accounts Revisited

Recall that stockholders' equity consists of contributed capital and retained earnings. To record changes in retained earnings that result from a firm's operating activities, a firm uses *nominal accounts*, separate revenue and expense accounts, whose balances are transferred to retained earnings at the end of the accounting period. As mentioned earlier, the idea is to measure operating performance one period at a time, as retained earnings reflects *cumulative* revenues and expenses over all accounting periods. By using these nominal accounts, a firm can better analyze the inflows and outflows pertaining to the operating activities of the company for the accounting period just completed.

A firm uses separate accounts for each category of revenue and expense. A firm can then more easily determine the amounts to be included in the various line items on its income statement. Consistent with the usual effects of revenues increasing retained earnings and expenses decreasing retained earnings, revenues are increased by credits, while expenses are increased by debits. Accordingly, revenue accounts will normally have a credit balance, and expense accounts will normally have a debit balance. T-accounts for revenues and expenses are shown below:

T-Accounts for Revenues and Expenses

Revenues		Expenses	
Debits Decrease	Credits Increase	Debits Increase	Credits Decrease

Exhibit 3.14 summarizes the normal balance in each type of account and indicates how the account is affected by debit (left) and credit (right) entries.

With this improved understanding of nominal accounts, we're ready to resume analyzing BHT's operating transactions, now by using journal entries and T-accounts.

Exhibit 3.14
Normal Account Balances and
Debit and Credit Effects on
Accounts

Account Type	Normal Balance	Debit Entries	Credit Entries
Asset	Debit	Increase	Decrease
Liability	Credit	Decrease	Increase
Common Stock	Credit	Decrease	Increase
Paid-in-Capital	Credit	Decrease	Increase
Retained Earnings	Credit	Decrease	Increase
Revenue	Credit	Decrease	Increase
Expense	Debit	Increase	Decrease

Using Journal Entries and T-Accounts to Record Transactions

We show the journal entries and T-accounts for Transactions 4 through 12 in Exhibits 3.15 and 3.16, respectively. Note in Exhibit 3.16 that the beginning balances at the start of 20X1 carry forward from the end of the previous year (20X0). Further, note that the retained earnings account does not include entries other than the dividends declared at this point. This is because the nominal accounts, revenue and expense, have not yet been closed. These accounts will be closed and their balances moved to retained earnings after preparing the income statement. (We'll provide more details on the closing process in the next section.)

Exhibit 3.15
Journal Entries for Operating
Transactions

Transaction #4		
Inventory	34,340	
Accounts Payable		34,340
Transaction #5		
Accounts Receivable	35,724	
Sales		35,724
Transaction #6		
Cost of Sales	30,420	
Inventory		30,420
Transaction #7		
Cash	33,260	
Accounts Receivable		33,260
Transaction #8		
Accounts Payable	29,200	
Cash		29,200
Transaction #9		
S&A Expenses	4,800	
Cash		4,800
Transaction #10		
Depreciation Expense	60	
Accumulated Depreciation		60
Transaction #11		
Interest Expense	28	
Cash		28
Transaction #12		
Retained Earnings	150	
Cash		150

Exhibit 3.16
Added Operating Transactions
to BHT's T-Accounts

Cash	
Bal. 1,485	
	29,200 (8)
(7) 33,260	4,800 (9)
	28 (11)
	150 (12)
Bal. 567	

Account Receivable	
Bal. 0	
(5) 35,724	
	33,260 (7)
Bal. 2,464	

Inventory	
Bal. 0	
(4) 34,340	30,420 (6)
Bal. 3,920	

Fixtures	
Bal. 540	

Accumulated Depreciation Fixtures	
	Bal. 0
	60 (10)
	Bal. 60

Note Payable	
	Bal. 400

Account Payable	
	Bal. 0
(8) 29,200	34,340 (4)
	Bal. 5,140

Capital Stock	
	Bal. 250

Paid-in Capital	
	Bal. 1,375

Retained Earnings	
	Bal. 0
(12) 150	

Sales Revenue	
	Bal. 0
	35,724 (5)
	Bal.35,724

Cost of Sales	
Bal. 0	
(6) 30,420	
Bal. 30,420	

S&A Expense	
Bal. 0	
(9) 4,800	
Bal. 4,800	

Depreciation Expense	
Bal. 0	
(10) 60	
Bal. 60	

Interest Expense	
Bal. 0	
(11) 28	
Bal. 28	

Note: Beginning account balances include the financing and investing activities prior to the start of 20X1.

CONSTRUCTING THE FINANCIAL STATEMENTS

Exhibit 3.17 shows a balance sheet for 12/31/20X1 compared to 12/31/20X0. Although total assets have dramatically increased, cash has decreased. Note also that the ending balance in retained earnings is determined using the closing entries discussed in the next section. An income statement and statement of cash flows follow in Exhibits 3.18 and 3.19, respectively. BHT provides an income statement only for the year ending 12/31/20X1, as the firm did not begin operations during 20X0. BHT provides cash flow statements for 20X0 and 20X1 for comparative purposes. As briefly discussed in Chapter 2, BHT, like most firms, prepares the cash flow statement using the *indirect approach* (we'll cover this in more depth in Chapter 5). That is, BHT determines its cash from operations

Exhibit 3.17
Balance Sheet for Biohealth,
Inc. (BHT)

	As of 12/31/20X1	As of 12/31/20X0
Assets		
Current Assets:		
Cash	$ 567	$1,485
Accounts Receivable	2,464	0
Inventory	3,920	0
Total Current Assets	6,951	1,485
Property, Plant, and Equipment (Fixtures)	540	540
Less: Accumulated Depreciation	(60)	0
Net Property Plant and Equipment	480	540
Total Assets	$7,431	$2,025
Liabilities and Stockholders' Equity		
Liabilities:		
Current Liabilities:		
Accounts Payable	$5,140	$ 0
Long-Term Debt:		
Notes Payable	400	400
Total Liabilities	5,540	400
Stockholders' Equity		
Common Stock	250	250
Additional Paid-In Capital	1,375	1,375
Retained Earnings	266	0
Total Stockholders' Equity	1,891	1,625
Total Liabilities and Stockholders' Equity	$7,431	$2,025

Exhibit 3.18
Income Statement for
Biohealth, Inc. (BHT)

	Year Ending 12/31/20X1
Sales Revenue	$35,724
Less: Cost of Goods Sold	(30,420)
Gross Profit	5,304
Selling and Administrative Expenses	(4,800)
Depreciation Expense	(60)
Interest Expense	(28)
Net Income	$ 416
Earnings per Share[2]	$ 1.66

[2]Earnings per share is the amount of earnings per share of common stock outstanding. There are some specific requirements regarding how this is computed that will be discussed later. However, in this case it is simply net income/shares of common stock outstanding, or $416,000,000/250,000,000.

	Year Ending 12/31/20X1	Year Ending 12/31/20X0
Cash from Operations:		
Net Income	$416	$ 0
Add: Noncash Expenses		
Depreciation	60	0
Less: Changes in Current Assets and Current Liabilities:		
Increase in Accounts Receivable	(2,464)	0
Increase in Inventory	(3,920)	0
Increase in Accounts Payable	5,140	0
Total Cash from Operations	(768)	0
Cash from Investing		
Purchase Fixtures	0	(540)
Total Cash from Investing	0	(540)
Cash from Financing		
Borrow on Long-Term Note	0	400
Dividend Payments	(150)	
Issue Stock	0	1,625
Total Cash from Financing	(150)	2,025
Total Change in Cash	($918)	$1,485

Exhibit 3.19
Statement of Cash Flows for the Years Ending 20X1 and 20X0 Biohealth, Inc. (BHT)

starting with net income and then adjusting for noncash operating transactions. Note that the activities in 20X0 were limited to financing and investing activities, as no BHT operations occurred during this start-up period.

The cash flow statement for 20X1 illustrates why cash decreased even though the company earned a profit. Although dividends somewhat reduced cash during the period, operations proved to be the primary driver of the decline in cash, as it had a negative cash flow of $768. This decrease was caused primarily by the increase in accounts receivable and inventory. Increasing inventory requires cash to buy or make the inventory, and the increase in accounts receivable reflects uncollected revenues, resulting in less cash. Offsetting this was the positive effect of the increase in accounts payable during the period. When a company buys things on credit (thereby increasing accounts payable), it conserves cash. Finally, depreciation also produced a minor effect. Depreciation expense is added back to net income. Although it is an expense and it decreases net income, it does not use cash.

CLOSING ENTRIES

After preparing the income statement, the balances in the temporary revenue and expense accounts must be transferred to the retained earnings account (a permanent account). This will reset the balance in each temporary account to zero, to start the next accounting period. For example, the accounting period for BHT was from 1/1/20X1 through 12/31/20X1. The entries that accomplish the transfer of balances from the revenue and expense accounts to retained earnings are called **closing entries.** We'll distinguish closing entries in this text by lettering the entries rather than numbering them.

Sometimes companies use a single temporary account, the **income summary account,** to accumulate balances from all the income statement accounts. Firms often find it useful to summarize the net of the revenues and expenses during the closing process to calculate taxes. Firms use the income summary account only during the closing process; it carries a zero balance at all other times. The balances from all the individual revenue and expense accounts are closed to this summary account. The balance in the income summary account is then closed to retained earnings. Exhibit 3.20 shows the journal entries and T-accounts to close the revenue and expense accounts for BHT. After making these closing entries, the balances in the revenues, expenses, and income summary accounts return to zero.

Exhibit 3.20
Closing Entries for BHT Revenue and Expense Accounts Period Ended 12/31/20X1

Journal Entries

Account Titles	Debit	Credit
a. Sales Revenue	35,724	
Income Summary		35,724
b. Income Summary	35,308	
Cost of Sales		30,420
S&A Expenses		4,800
Depreciation Expense		60
Interest Expense		28
c. Income Summary	416	
Retained Earnings		416

Closing Entries T-Accounts

Sales Revenue	
	Bal. 35,724
(a) 35, 724	
	Bal. 0

Cost of Sales	
Bal. 30,420	
	30,420 (b)
Bal. 0	

S&A Expenses	
Bal. 4,800	
	4,800 (b)
Bal. 0	

Depreciation Expense	
Bal. 60	
	60 (b)
Bal. 0	

Interest Expense	
Bal. 28	
	(28) (b)
Bal. 0	

Retained Earnings	
	Bal. 0
(12) 150	416 (c)
	Bal. 266

Income Summary	
	Bal. 0
(b) 35,308	35,724 (a)
(c) 416	
	Bal. 0

Finally, just prior to making closing entries, a firm typically makes **adjusting entries.** Adjusting entries improve the accuracy of firm's financial statements, by enabling it to meet the accrual concept. For example, BHT's recording of depreciation is one type of adjusting entry. Other adjusting entries include the recognition of interest expense that has not been paid and wages that have been incurred but not paid. We'll discuss adjusting entries again in Chapter 4 and Appendix A covers adjusting entries in more detail.

THE ACCOUNTING CYCLE

The accounting cycle refers to the series of steps in the accounting process, which a firm repeats each time it prepares financial statements. While accounting systems may differ from very simple systems in a sole proprietorship, to multibillion-dollar systems in large companies, the process remains essentially the same:

1. *Identify transactions.* As we indicated earlier, some economic events are not recognized in accounting as transactions. For example, if Dell signed a contract with another company to furnish a large number of computers to the company over a period of time, this would be an event of economic consequence to Dell, but it would not be recorded as an accounting transaction.

2. *Journalize transactions.* A journal entry provides a summary of a particular event's impact on assets, liabilities, and stockholders' equity.

3. *Post journal entries to ledger accounts.* In this book, we use T-accounts to represent ledgers. In real accounting systems, ledger accounts can take many forms, but the key to thinking about the ledger is to realize that it carries forward all of the transactions that affect a particular account. In the case of permanent accounts as seen on the balance sheet (assets, liabilities, and various stockholders' equity accounts), the balances carry-forward over accounting periods. For example, the balance in accounts receivable at the end of 20X0 is the same as the balance at the beginning of 20X1. In contrast, the nominal or temporary accounts (revenues and expenses) will start each accounting period with a zero balance.

4. *Prepare period-end adjusting entries and then post them to ledger accounts.* An example would be recording depreciation.

5. *Prepare the income statement.*

6. *Close nominal accounts to retained earnings.*

7. *Prepare the balance sheet and cash flow statement.*

One final issue with regard to the accounting cycle is the frequency with which financial statements should be prepared. On one hand, a firm should prepare financial statements as often as necessary to provide timely information to management, stockholders, creditors, and others with an interest in the firm. On the other hand, a firm must balance the benefits of having up-to-date information with the cost of preparing the statements. In some businesses, management may need up-to-date information, in which case daily reports may be necessary. This is becoming more common as the cost of compiling timely information continues to decrease. In other businesses, a monthly statement may be sufficient.

Regardless of what time period a firm selects, firms will follow the same procedures as outlined in this chapter.

Companies whose stock is traded on a public exchange and who fall under the authority of the SEC are required to file financial statements quarterly, as well as on an annual basis. The frequency with which a firm prepares its financial statements is sometimes expressed in terms of how often the firm closes its books. If it closes its books monthly, the accounting cycle for the firm is one month, and the nominal (temporary) accounts are reset on a monthly basis. However, although a company may close its books more frequently than at year-end, annual financial statements require that revenues and expenses be accumulated over the entire year. Thus, firms do interim closings only for purposes of preparing interim statements.

ANALYZING FINANCIAL STATEMENTS

Understanding the accounting cycle will help you to use the information in the financial statements more effectively. To illustrate, as an investor or potential investor, you can obtain financial statements, but not information about the individual transactions that gave rise to those statements. However, by understanding the accounting process, you may be able to deduce some of the major transactions by analyzing the financial statements.

Say you looked at Exhibits 3.17, 3.18, and 3.19 without knowing BHT's transactions. By understanding the accounting process, you would be able to observe the following:

- Cash has declined for the year despite the fact that BHT reported a profit.
- The balance sheet shows an increase in Accounts Receivable, suggesting that cash collection from sales was less than the revenue recognized.
- The balance sheet shows an increase in Inventory, indicating that the company is purchasing more inventory than it is selling.
- Accounts Payable increased during the year, suggesting that the company is purchasing more inventory than it is paying to suppliers.

As BHT formed in 20X0, we would not be surprised by these findings, as they are typical of a new business. However, in an established company, significant changes in balance sheet accounts may signal information about the company's future cash flows. For example, if a company records large amounts of sales on account, and accounts receivable increases more rapidly than the sales, the company may not be collecting its accounts receivable on a timely basis or it may have relaxed its credit policies. This may signal future cash flow problems (defaults by customers). Similarly, increasing inventory coupled with decreasing (or less rapidly) increasing sales may signal that a company is having difficulty selling its inventory. In Chapter 6, we continue to consider how to assess past performance based on the information contained in financial statements, as well as to predict future performance.

As you progress through this text, you will appreciate more fully the power of the information conveyed about a company in its financial statements and the value to you of understanding the concepts underlying financial statement construction. Of particular importance is predicting transactions' impact on each of the major financial statements. For example, as a manager, you might consider generating additional sales by providing a more liberal credit policy (e.g., allowing customers with weaker credit to purchase goods on account). With a good knowledge of accounting, you could anticipate the effects of such a change in credit policies on the financial statements. In this particular case, you would likely see increased sales on the income statement, coupled with increased accounts receivable because weaker credit customers might pay more slowly or not at all. You might also see cash flows decline even if sales increased. This could occur due to a combination of two factors, slower sales collections and a need to purchase and pay for more inventory to sell to customers who have not yet paid. Thus, this business decision would impact all of the major financial statements.

SUMMARY AND TRANSITION

This chapter provided an overview of the accounting process used to generate financial statements. Understanding the framework of accounting allows you to readily determine the impact of economic events on the financial statements. This knowledge will allow you as a manager or investor to make sound decisions using information generated from the accounting process.

The accounting process contains two basic concepts: duality and the nominal (temporary) account. The concept of duality portrays accounting events in terms of the dual effects on the resources of the firm (its assets), the claims of creditors (its liabilities), and the owners' wealth (stockholders' equity). The duality concept is apparent in the accounting equation and the requirements that debits equal credits in the accounting representation of each transaction. Nominal accounts are used to describe changes in stockholders' equity that result from operating activities, principally revenues and expenses.

Understanding the accounting process is necessary to understanding the information conveyed in the financial statements that are the final product of that process. However, apart from the accounting process itself, there are many accounting choices and judgments that affect the implementation of that process and, thereby, shape the content of those statements. Chief among these are the recognition criteria which determine when an economic event should get recognized in the accounting system (such as the timing of recognizing revenues and expenses) and the valuation principles that determine the values of the assets and liabilities of the firm that meet the recognition criteria. These choices and judgments are addressed in the chapters that follow.

END OF CHAPTER MATERIAL

KEY TERMS

Additional Paid-In Capital
Adjusting Entries
Closing Entries

Contra-Asset Account
Contributed Capital
Cost of Goods Sold

Credits

Debits

Depreciation Expense

Depreciation Methods

Double-Entry Accounting System

Entry

Journal

Journal Entry

Ledger

Nominal Accounts

Par Value

Permanent Accounts

Retained Earnings

Sales Revenue

Stated Value

Summary Account

T-Account

Temporary Accounts

Transactions

ASSIGNMENT MATERIAL

REVIEW QUESTIONS

1. Explain what double-entry accounting means and provide an example.
2. Define an asset, according to GAAP.
3. Define a liability, according to GAAP.
4. Describe what owners' equity represents.
5. Discuss how retained earnings changes over time.
6. What is a permanent account?
7. What is a nominal or temporary account?
8. What is the proper form for a journal entry?
9. What is a ledger?
10. What is depreciation?
11. How is straight-line depreciation calculated?
12. What is a contra-asset account and how is it used in the context of depreciation?
13. "Expense accounts have debit balances, and debit entries increase these accounts." Reconcile this statement with the normal effects of entries on owners' equity accounts and the resulting balances.
14. Describe the closing process.
15. Discuss why one firm might close their books monthly and another might close them weekly.

APPLYING YOUR KNOWLEDGE

15. Explain why you agree or disagree with the following statement: "Retained earnings are like money in the bank; you can always use them to pay your bills if you get into trouble."
16. Respond to each of the following statements with a true or false answer:
    a. Debits increase liability accounts.
    b. Revenues are credit entries to owners' equity.

c. Cash receipts from customers are debited to accounts receivable.

d. Dividends declared decrease cash at the date of declaration.

e. Dividends are an expense of doing business and should appear on the income statement.

f. Selling goods on account results in a credit to accounts receivable.

g. Making a payment on an account payable results in a debit to accounts payable.

17. For each of the transactions below, indicate which accounts are affected and whether they increase or decrease.

   a. Issue common stock for cash.

   b. Buy equipment from a supplier on credit (short term).

   c. Buy inventory from a supplier partly with cash and partly on account.

   d. Sell a unit of inventory to a customer on account.

   e. Receive a payment from a customer on his or her account.

   f. Borrow money from the bank.

   g. Declare a dividend (to be paid later).

   h. Pay a dividend (that was previously declared).

18. For each of the following transactions, indicate how income and cash flow are affected (increase, decrease, no effect) and by how much:

   a. Issue common stock for $1,000.

   b. Sell, on account, a unit of inventory for $150 that cost $115. The unit is already in inventory.

   c. Purchase equipment for $500 in cash.

   d. Depreciate plant and equipment by $300.

   e. Purchase a unit of inventory, on account, for $100.

   f. Make a payment on accounts payable for $200.

   g. Receive a payment from a customer for $75 on his or her account.

   h. Declare a dividend for $400.

   i. Pay a dividend for $400.

19. Show how each of the following transactions affects the balance sheet equation:

   a. Borrow $1,500 from the bank.

   b. Buy land for $20,000 in cash.

   c. Issue common stock for $5,000. The par value of the stock is $1,500.

   d. Buy inventory costing $3,000 on account.

   e. Sell inventory costing $2,500 to customers, on account, for $3,500.

   f. Make a payment of $250 to the electric company for power used during the current period.

   g. Declare a dividend of $350.

   h. Depreciate equipment by $500.

20. Show how each of the following transactions affects the balance sheet equation:

   a. Issue common stock for $10,000. The stock has no par value attached to it.

b. Receive a payment from a customer on his or her account in the amount of $325.

c. Make a payment to the bank of $850. Of this amount, $750 represents interest and the rest is a repayment of principal.

d. Return a unit of inventory costing $200 that was damaged in shipment. You have already paid for the unit and have requested a refund from the supplier.

e. Dividends of $175 that were previously declared are paid.

f. Purchase equipment costing $1,800. You pay $600 in cash and give the supplier a note for the balance of the purchase price.

g. Sales on account of $15,000 are reported for the period.

h. A count of physical inventory at the end of the period indicates an ending balance of $575. The beginning balance was $485, and the purchases for the period were $11,500. Record the cost of goods sold.

21. For each of the following transactions, indicate how each immediately affects the balance sheet equation and what other effects there will be in the future as a result of the transaction:

a. Purchase equipment.

b. Borrow money from the bank.

c. Purchase inventory on account.

d. Sell inventory on account to customers.

e. Buy a patent for a new production process.

22. Indicate the effects of the following transactions on the balance sheet equation developed in the chapter. Assume that the fiscal year end of the firm is December 31.

a. Borrow $2,500 from the bank on 1/1/X1.

b. Pay interest on the bank loan on 12/31/X1. The interest rate is 10 percent.

c. Buy equipment on 1/1/X1 for $2,000. The equipment has an estimated useful life of five years and an estimated salvage value at the end of five years of $500.

d. Record the depreciation for the equipment as of 12/31/X1, assuming the firm uses the straight-line method.

e. Sales for the period totaled $5,500, of which $3,500 were on account. The cost of the products sold was $3,600.

f. Collections from customers on account totaled $2,800.

g. Purchases of inventory on account during 20X1 totaled $2,700.

h. Payments to suppliers totaled $2,900 during 20X1.

i. Dividends were declared and paid in the amount of $100.

23. Indicate the effects of the following transactions on the balance sheet equation developed in the chapter. Assume that the fiscal year end of the firm is December 31.

a. Issue common stock for $25,000, with a par value of $8,000.

b. Sales recorded for the period totaled $60,000, of which $25,000 were cash sales.

c. Cash collections on customer accounts totaled $37,000.

d. Sign a contract to purchase a piece of equipment that costs $1,200, and put a downpayment of $100 on the purchase.

e. Dividends of $1,300 are declared.

f. Dividends of $1,150 that had previously been declared are paid.

g. Depreciation of $3,300 was taken on the property, plant, and equipment.

h. Purchase $31,350 of inventory on account.

i. Inventory costing $35,795 was sold.

24. Indicate whether each of the following accounts normally has a debit or a credit balance:

a. Accounts Receivable

b. Accounts Payable

c. Sales Revenue

d. Dividends Declared

e. Dividends Payable

f. Depreciation Expense

g. Common Stock (par value)

h. Cost of Goods Sold

i. Loan Payable

25. For each of the following accounts indicate whether the account would normally have a debit or a credit balance:

a. Cash

b. Accounts Payable

c. Common Stock

d. Sales Revenues

e. Inventory

f. Cost of Goods Sold

g. Paid-In Capital

h. Retained Earnings

i. Accumulated Depreciation

26. For each of the following transactions construct a journal entry:

a. Inventory costing $1,500 is purchased on account.

b. Inventory costing $1,200 is sold on account for $1,800.

c. Accounts receivable of $800 are collected.

d. The firm borrows $10,000 from the bank.

e. The firm issues common stock for $2,500 and $1,500 is considered par value.

f. New equipment costing $3,500 is purchased with cash.

27. The T. George Company started business on 1/1/X2. Listed below are the transactions that occurred during 20X2.

Required:

a. Construct the journal entries to record the transactions of the T. George Company for 20X2.

b. Post the journal entries to the appropriate T-accounts.

c. Prepare a balance sheet and income statement for 20X2.

d. Prepare the closing entries for 20X2.

Transactions:

1. On 1/1/X2, the company issued 10,000 shares of common stock for $175,000. The par value of the stock is $10 per share.

2. On 1/1/X2, the company borrowed $125,000 from the bank.

3. On 1/2/X2, the company purchased (for cash) land and a building costing $200,000. The building was recently appraised at $140,000.

4. Inventory costing $100,000 was purchased on account.

5. An investment was made in Calhoun Company stock in the amount of $75,000.

6. Sales to customers totaled $190,000 in 20X2. Of these, $30,000 were cash sales.

7. Collections on accounts receivable totaled $135,000.

8. Payments to suppliers totaled $92,000 in 20X2.

9. Salaries paid to employees totaled $44,000. There were no unpaid salaries at year end.

10. A count of inventories at year end revealed $10,000 worth of inventory.

11. The building was estimated to have a useful life of 20 years and a salvage value of $20,000. The company uses straight-line depreciation.

12. The interest on the bank loan is recognized each month and is paid on the first day of the succeeding month; that is, January's interest is recognized in January and paid on February 1. The interest rate is 12 percent.

13. The investment in Calhoun Company paid dividends of $5,000 in 20X2. All of it had been received by year end.

14. Dividends of $15,000 were declared on 12/15/X2 and were scheduled to be paid on 1/10/X3.

28. The Hughes Tool Company started business on 10/1/X3. Its fiscal year runs through September 30 of the following year. Following are the transactions that occurred during fiscal year 19X4 (the year starting 10/1/X3 and ending 9/30/X4).

Required:

a. Construct the journal entries to record the transactions of the The Hughes Tool Company for fiscal year 20X4.

b. Post the journal entries to the appropriate T-accounts.

c. Prepare a balance sheet and income statement for fiscal year 20X4.

d. Prepare the closing entries for fiscal year 20X4.

Transactions:

1. On 10/1/X3, J. Hughes contributed $100,000 to start the business. Hughes is the sole proprietor of the business.

2. On 10/2/X3, Hughes borrowed $300,000 from a venture capitalist (a lender who specializes in start-up companies). The interest rate on

the loan is 11 percent. Interest is paid twice a year on March 31 and September 30.

3. On 10/3/X3, Hughes rented a building. The rental agreement was a two-year contract that called for quarterly rental payments of $20,000, payable in advance on January 1, April 1, July 1, and October 1. The first payment was made on 10/3/X3 and covers the period from October 1 to December 31.

4. On 10/3/X3, Hughes purchased equipment costing $250,000. The equipment had an estimated useful life of seven years and a salvage value of $40,000.

5. On 10/3/X3, Hughes purchased initial inventory with a cash payment of $100,000.

6. Sales during the year totaled $800,000, of which $720,000 were credit sales.

7. Collections from customers on account totaled $640,000.

8. Additional purchases of inventory during the year totaled $550,000, all on account.

9. Payments to suppliers totaled $495,000.

10. Inventory on hand at year end amounted to $115,000.

11. J. Hughes withdrew a total of $40,000 for personal expenses during the year.

12. Interest on the loan from the venture capitalist was paid at year-end, as well as $20,000 of the principal.

13. Other selling and administrative expenses totaled $90,000 for the year. Of these, $20,000 were unpaid as of year end.

29. The A.J. Smith Company started business on 1/1/X4. The company's fiscal year ends on December 31. Following are the transactions that occurred during 20X4.

Required:

a. Construct the journal entries to record the transactions of the The A.J. Smith Company for fiscal year 20X4.

b. Post the journal entries to the appropriate T-accounts.

c. Prepare a balance sheet and income statement for fiscal year 20X4.

d. Prepare the closing entries for fiscal year 20X4.

Transactions:

1. On 1/1/X4, the company issued 25,000 shares of common stock at $15 per share. The par value of each share of common stock is $10.

2. On 1/1/X4, the company purchased land and buildings from another company in exchange for $50,000 in cash and 25,000 shares of common stock. The land's value is approximately one-fifth of the total value of the transaction.

3. Equipment worth $100,000 was purchased on 7/1/X4, in exchange for $50,000 in cash and a one-year, 10 percent note, principal amount $50,000. The note pays semiannual interest, and interest was unpaid on 12/31/X4.

4. The equipment is depreciated using the straight-line method, with an estimated useful life of 10 years and an estimated salvage value of $0.

5. The buildings purchased in transaction 2 are depreciated using the straight-line method, with an estimated useful life of 30 years and an estimated salvage value of $40,000.

6. During the year, inventory costing $200,000 was purchased, all on account.

7. Sales during the year were $215,000, of which credit sales were $175,000.

8. Inventory costing $160,000 was sold during the year.

9. Payments to suppliers totaled $175,000.

10. At the end of the year, accounts receivable had a positive balance of $10,000.

11. On March 31, 20X4, the company rented out a portion of its building to Fantek Corporation. Fantek is required to make quarterly payments of $5,000 each. The payments are due on April 1, July 1, October 1, and January 1 of each year, with the first payment on 4/1/X4. All scheduled payments were made during 20X4.

12. Selling and distribution expenses amounted to $30,000, all paid in cash.

13. During the year, inventory worth $10,000 was destroyed by fire. The inventory was not insured.

14. The company calculates taxes at a rate of 30 percent. During the year, $3,000 was paid to the taxing authority.

15. Dividends of $4,000 were declared during the year, and $1,000 remained unpaid at year end.

30. The accounting system closing process takes some amount of time at the end of the accounting period in order to check for errors, make adjusting entries, and prepare the financial statements. In recent years there has been a real push to speed up this process for most firms. Discuss the incentives that companies might have to implement in order to make this a faster process.

31. During the year-end audit process, the auditing firm may find errors and omissions in the recording of transactions and will then ask management to make an adjusting entry to correct for these errors. In light of the purpose of the audit opinion, discuss plausible arguments that management might give to convince the auditor to waive making these suggested adjustments.

32. Suppose that a company has a bonus plan in which managers can earn a bonus if they meet certain net income targets. If the management team has discretion as to which depreciation method they might use, with the straight-line reporting the least amount of depreciation in the early years of the life of the asset, discuss the incentives that management would have in choosing a depreciation method. Also discuss how owners might protect themselves from any self-serving behavior on the part of management.

33. Discuss how creditors might protect their interests (relative to owners) when they negotiate their lending agreement with the firm.

USING REAL DATA

34. Base your answers to the following questions on the financial statements of Russ Berrie.

RUSS BERRIE & Co., Inc.:
Income Statement

	12/31/2001	12/31/2000	12/31/1999
Net sales	$294,291,000	$300,801,000	$287,011,000
Cost of sales	132,611,000	132,908,000	123,216,000
Gross profit	161,680,000	167,893,000	163,795,000
Selling, general and administrative expense	112,570,000	106,991,000	108,023,000
Information system write-off	0	0	10,392,000
Investment and other income net	(8,560,000)	(10,202,000)	(8,587,000)
Income before taxes	57,670,000	71,104,000	53,967,000
Provision for income taxes	17,496,000	23,163,000	17,531,000
Net income	$ 40,174,000	$ 47,941,000	$ 36,436,000

RUSS BERRIE & Co., Inc.:
Balance Sheet

	12/31/2001	12/31/2000
Assets		
Current assets		
Cash and cash equivalents	$148,872,000	$ 77,794,000
Marketable securities	94,181,000	141,032,000
Accounts receivable, trade, less allowance of $3,454 in 2001 and $3,460 in 2000	63,481,000	58,673,000
Inventories, net	37,374,000	47,430,000
Prepaid expenses and other current assets	4,550,000	5,508,000
Deferred income taxes	6,705,000	6,003,000
Total current assets	355,163,000	336,440,000
Property, plant, and equipment, net	24,623,000	26,745,000
Inventories—long-term, net	2,284,000	0
Other assets	4,574,000	3,824,000
Total assets	$386,644,000	$367,009,000
Liabilities and Shareholders' Equity		
Current liabilities		
Accounts payable	5,376,000	4,913,000
Accrued expenses	20,003,000	20,313,000
Accrued income taxes	6,848,000	7,192,000
Total current liabilities	32,227,000	32,418,000

	12/31/2001	12/31/2000
Commitments and contingencies		
Shareholders' equity		
Common stock: $0.10 stated value; authorized 50,000,000 shares; issued 2001, 25,682,364 shares; 2000, 25,413,626 shares	2,587,000	2,541,000
Additional paid-in-capital	73,794,000	63,103,000
Retained earnings	392,272,000	381,479,000
Accumulated other comprehensive loss	(4,165,000)	(4,310,000)
Unearned compensation	(75,000)	(149,000)
Treasury stock, at cost (5,632,014 shares at December 31, 2001 and 5,557,514 shares at December 31, 2000)	(109,996,000)	(108,073,000)
Total shareholders equity	354,417,000	334,591,000
Total liabilities and shareholders' equity	$386,644,000	$367,009,000

RUSS BERRIE & Co., Inc.:
Cash Flow

	12/31/2001	12/31/2000	12/31/1999
Cash flows from operating activities:			
Net income	$ 40,174,000	$47,941,000	$36,436,000
Adjustments to reconcile net income to net cash provided by operating activities:			
Depreciation and amortization	4,021,000	3,998,000	5,008,000
Information system write-off	0	0	10,392,000
Provision for accounts receivable reserves	1,828,000	2,298,000	2,534,000
Income from contingency reserve reversal	0	(2,544,000)	0
Other	415,000	390,000	(456,000)
Changes in assets and liabilities:			
Accounts receivable	(6,636,000)	414,000	(9,058,000)
Inventories, net	7,772,000	(3,123,000)	894,000
Prepaid expenses and other current assets	958,000	3,995,000	(197,000)
Other assets	(166,000)	78,000	(1,460,000)
Accounts payable	463,000	(1,315,000)	1,979,000
Accrued expenses	(310,000)	(631,000)	421,000
Accrued income taxes	(344,000)	1,086,000	(1,099,000)
Total adjustments	8,001,000	4,646,000	8,958,000
Net cash provided by operating activities	48,175,000	52,587,000	45,394,000
Cash flows from investing activities:			
Purchase of marketable securities	(97,335,000)	(48,959,000)	(46,365,000)
Proceeds from sale of marketable securities	144,331,000	45,567,000	60,017,000

	12/31/2001	12/31/2000	12/31/1999
Proceeds from sale of property, plant, and equipment	89,000	79,000	116,000
Capital expenditures	(2,405,000)	(4,087,000)	(8,435,000)
Net cash provided by (used in) investing activities	44,680,000	(7,400,000)	5,333,000
Cash flows from financing activities:			
Proceeds from issuance of common stock	10,737,000	2,155,000	2,416,000
Dividends paid to shareholders	(29,381,000)	(17,764,000)	(16,861,000)
Purchase of treasury stock	(1,923,000)	(15,619,000)	(44,292,000)
Net cash (used in) financing activities	(20,567,000)	(31,228,000)	(58,737,000)
Effect of exchange rate changes on cash and cash equivalents	(1,210,000)	(1,073,000)	(146,000)
Net increase (decrease) in cash and cash equivalents	71,078,000	12,886,000	(8,156,000)
Cash and cash equivalents at beginning of year	77,794,000	64,908,000	73,064,000
Cash and cash equivalents at end of year	$148,872,000	$77,794,000	$64,908,000
Cash paid during the year for:			
Interest	$ 196,000	$ 127,000	$ 118,000
Income taxes	17,841,000	22,077,000	18,630,000

a. Determine the amount of dividends declared during fiscal 2001.

b. Determine the amount of dividends paid during fiscal 2001.

c. Assuming that all sales were on account, determine the amount of cash collected from customers.

d. Assuming that the only transactions that flow through the accounts payable to suppliers and others are purchases of inventory and assuming that all additions to inventory were purchases of inventory, determine the cash payments to suppliers.

e. The other comprehensive income account reflects the translation of Russ Berrie's foreign subsidiaries. What has been the experience with these subsidiaries over time—have they resulted in net gains or net losses from translation?

f. In 1999, the company wrote off the cost of some of its information systems. How significant was this write-off (express your answer as a percent of income before the write-off)? How might an analyst factor this loss into his or her evaluation of the company's stock?

g. How does the company finance its business (use data to support your answer)?

h. How healthy is the company from a cash flow perspective?

35. Use the data from the financial statements of the GAP to answer the following questions:

a. Determine the amount of dividends declared during the year ended 2/2/2002.

b. Determine the amount of dividends paid during the year ended 2/2/2002.

c. The GAP reports the ratio of each expense line item relative to net sales on its income statement. Use these data to discuss how profitable GAP has been over the last three years in selling its products.

d. What has been the trend in revenues and earnings over the last three years (use data to support your answer)?

e. How does the company finance its business (use data to support your answer)?

f. How healthy is the company from a cash flow perspective?

g. If you were an analyst, how might you react to the trends you see in income, debt, and cash flows over the years presented?

GAP, Inc. Income Statement
($ in thousands except share and per share amounts)

	52 Weeks Ended Feb. 2, 2002	% to Sales	53 Weeks Ended Feb. 3, 2001	% to Sales	52 Weeks Ended Jan. 29, 2000	% to Sales
Net sales	$13,847,873	100.00%	$13,673,460	100.00%	$11,635,398	100.00%
Costs and expenses						
Cost of goods sold and occupancy expenses	9,704,389	70.1	8,599,442	62.9	6,775,262	58.2
Operating expenses	3,805,968	27.5	3,629,257	26.5	3,043,432	26.2
Interest expense	109,190	0.8	74,891	0.5	44,966	0.4
Interest income	(13,315)	(0.1)	(12,015)	(0.0)	(13,211)	(0.1)
Earnings before income taxes	241,641	1.7	1,381,885	10.1	1,784,949	15.3
Income taxes	249,405	1.8	504,388	3.7	657,884	5.6
Net earnings (loss)	($7,764)	(0.1%)	$877,497	6.4%	$1,127,065	9.7%

GAP, Inc. Balance Sheet

	Feb. 2, 2002	Feb. 3, 2001
Assets		
Current assets:		
Cash and equivalents	$1,035,749,000	$408,794,000
Merchandise inventory	1,677,116,000	1,904,153,000
Other current assets	331,685,000	335,103,000
Total current assets:	3,044,550,000	2,648,050,000
Property and equipment		
Leasehold improvements	2,127,966,000	1,899,820,000

	Feb. 2, 2002	Feb. 3, 2001
Furniture and equipment	3,327,819,000	2,826,863,000
Land and buildings	917,055,000	558,832,000
Construction-in-progress	246,691,000	615,722,000
	6,619,531,000	5,901,237,000
Accumulated depreciation and amortization	(2,458,241,000)	(1,893,552,000)
Property and equipment, net	4,161,290,000	4,007,685,000
Lease rights and other assets	385,486,000	357,173,000
Total assets	$7,591,326,000	$7,012,908,000
Liabilities and shareholders' equity:		
Current liabilities		
Notes payable	$ 41,889,000	$ 779,904,000
Current maturities of long-term debt	0	250,000,000
Accounts payable	1,105,117,000	1,067,207,000
Accrued expenses and other current liabilities	909,227,000	702,033,000
Total current liabilities	2,056,233,000	2,799,144,000
Long-term liabilities:		
Long-term debt	1,961,397,000	780,246,000
Deferred lease credits and other liabilities	564,115,000	505,279,000
Total long-term liabilities	2,525,512,000	1,285,525,000
Shareholders' equity:		
Common stock $.05 par value		
Authorized 2,300,000,000 shares; issued 948,597,949 and 939,222,871 shares; outstanding 865,726,890 and 853,996,984 shares	47,430,000	46,961,000
Additional paid-in capital	461,408,000	294,967,000
Retained earnings	4,890,375,000	4,974,773,000
Accumulated other comprehensive losses	(61,824,000)	(20,173,000)
Deferred compensation	(7,245,000)	(12,162,000)
Treasury stock, at cost	(2,320,563,000)	(2,356,127,000)
Total shareholders' equity	3,009,581,000	2,928,239,000
Total liabilities and shareholders' equity	$7,591,326,000	$7,012,908,000

GAP, Inc. Cash Flow

Cash Flows from Operating Activities	52 Weeks Ended Feb. 2, 2002	53 Weeks Ended Feb. 3, 2001	52 Weeks Ended Jan. 29, 2000
Net earnings (loss)	($7,764,000)	$877,497,000	$1,127,065,000
Adjustments to reconcile net earnings (loss) to net cash provided by operating activities:			
Depreciation and amortization	810,486,000	590,365,000	436,184,000
Tax benefit from exercise of stock options and vesting of restricted stock	58,444,000	130,882,000	211,891,000
Deferred income taxes	(28,512,000)	(38,872,000)	2,444,000

	52 Weeks Ended Feb. 2, 2002	53 Weeks Ended Feb. 3, 2001	52 Weeks Ended Jan. 29, 2000
Change in operating assets and liabilities:			
Merchandise inventory	213,067,000	(454,595,000)	(404,211,000)
Prepaid expenses and other	(13,303,000)	(61,096,000)	(55,519,000)
Accounts payable	42,205,000	249,545,000	118,121,000
Accrued expenses	220,826,000	(56,541,000)	(5,822,000)
Deferred lease credits and other long-term liabilities	22,390,000	54,020,000	47,775,000
Net cash provided by operating activities	1,317,839,000	1,291,205,000	1,477,928,000
Cash flows from investing activities:			
Net purchase of property and equipment	(940,078,000)	(1,858,662,000)	(1,238,722,000)
Acquisition of lease rights and other assets	(10,549,000)	(16,252,000)	(39,839,000)
Net cash used for investing activities	(950,627,000)	(1,874,914,000)	(1,278,561,000)
Cash flows from financing activities:			
Net increase (decrease) in notes payable	(734,927,000)	621,420,000	84,778,000
Proceeds from issuance of long-term debt	1,194,265,000	250,000,000	311,839,000
Payments of long-term debt	(250,000,000)	0	0
Issuance of common stock	139,105,000	152,105,000	114,142,000
Net purchase of treasury stock	(785,000)	(392,558,000)	(745,056,000)
Cash dividends paid	(76,373,000)	(75,488,000)	(75,795,000)
Net cash provided by (used for) financing activities	271,285,000	555,479,000	(310,092,000)
Effect of exchange rate fluctuations on cash	(11,542,000)	(13,328,000)	(4,176,000)
Net increase (decrease) in cash and equivalents	$ 626,955,000	($41,558,000)	($114,901,000)
Cash and equivalents at beginning of year	408,794,000	450,352,000	565,253,000
Cash and equivalents at end of year	$1,035,749,000	$408,794,000	$ 450,352,000

36. Use the financial statements of Hasbro to answer the following questions:

a. Determine the amount of dividends declared during fiscal year 2001.

b. Determine the amount of dividends paid during fiscal year 2001.

c. Assuming that all sales were on account, determine the amount of cash collected from customers.

d. Assuming that the only transactions that flow through the accounts payable to suppliers and others are purchases of inventory, and assuming that all additions to inventory were purchases of inventory, determine the cash payments to suppliers.

e. What has been the trend in revenues and earnings over the last three years (use data to support your answer)?

f. How does the company finance its business (use data to support your answer)?

g. How healthy is the company from a cash flow perspective?

h. If you were an analyst, how might you react to the trends you see in income, debt, and cash flows over the years presented?

HASBRO, Inc. Income Statement

	12/30/2001	12/30/2000	12/30/1999
Net revenues	$2,856,339,000	$3,787,215,000	$4,232,263,000
Cost of sales	1,223,483,000	1,673,973,000	1,698,242,000
Gross profit	1,632,856,000	2,113,242,000	2,534,021,000
Expenses			
Amortization	121,652,000	157,763,000	173,533,000
Royalties, research and development	335,358,000	635,366,000	711,790,000
Advertising	290,829,000	452,978,000	456,978,000
Selling, distribution, and administration	675,482,000	863,496,000	799,919,000
Restructuring	(1,795,000)	63,951,000	64,232,000
Loss on sale of business units	0	43,965,000	0
Total expenses	1,421,526,000	2,217,519,000	2,206,452,000
Operating profit (loss)	211,330,000	(104,277,000)	327,569,000
Nonoperating (income) expense			
Interest expense	103,688,000	114,421,000	69,340,000
Other (income) expense, net	11,443,000	7,288,000	(15,616,000)
Total nonoperating expense	115,131,000	121,709,000	53,724,000
Earnings (loss) before income taxes and cumulative effect of accounting change	96,199,000	(225,986,000)	273,845,000
Income taxes	35,401,000	(81,355,000)	84,892,000
Net earnings (loss) before cumulative effect of accounting change	60,798,000	(144,631,000)	188,953,000
Cumulative effect of accounting change, net of tax	(1,066,000)	0	0
Net earnings (loss)	$ 59,732,000	($144,631,000)	$ 188,953,000

HASBRO, Inc. Balance Sheet

	12/30/2001	12/30/2000
Assets:		
Current assets		
Cash and cash equivalents	$ 233,095,000	$ 127,115,000
Accounts receivable, less allowance for doubtful accounts of $49,300 in 2001 and $55,000 in 2000	572,499,000	685,975,000
Inventories	217,479,000	335,493,000
Prepaid expenses and other current assets	345,545,000	431,630,000
Total current assets	1,368,618,000	1,580,213,000
Property, plant, and equipment, net	235,360,000	296,729,000
Other assets		
Goodwill, less accumulated amortization of $269,496 in 2001 and $225,770 in 2000	761,575,000	803,189,000
Other intangibles, less accumulated amortization of $398,183 in 2001 and $347,149 in 2000	805,027,000	902,893,000

	12/30/2001	12/30/2000
Other	198,399,000	245,435,000
Total other assets	1,765,001,000	1,951,517,000
Total assets	$3,368,979,000	$3,828,459,000
Liabilities and shareholders' equity:		
Current liabilities		
Short-term borrowings	$ 34,024,000	$ 226,292,000
Current installments of long-term debt	2,304,000	1,793,000
Accounts payable	123,109,000	191,749,000
Accrued liabilities	599,154,000	819,978,000
Total current liabilities	758,591,000	1,239,812,000
Long-term debt	1,165,649,000	1,167,838,000
Deferred liabilities	91,875,000	93,403,000
Total liabilities	2,016,115,000	2,501,053,000
Shareholders' equity		
Preference stock of $2.50 par value. Authorized 5,000,000 shares; none issued	0	0
Common stock of $.50 par value. Authorized 600,000,000 shares; issued 209,694,630 shares in 2001 and 2000	104,847,000	104,847,000
Additional paid-in capital	457,544,000	464,084,000
Deferred compensation	(2,996,000)	(6,889,000)
Retained earnings	1,622,402,000	1,583,394,000
Accumulated other comprehensive earnings	(68,398,000)	(44,718,000)
Treasury stock, at cost, 36,736,156 shares in 2001 and 37,253,164 shares in 2000	(760,535,000)	(773,312,000)
Total shareholders' equity	1,352,864,000	1,327,406,000
Total liabilities and shareholders' equity	$3,368,979,000	$3,828,459,000

HASBRO, Inc. Cash Flow

	12/30/2001	12/30/2000	12/30/1999
Cash flows from operating activities:			
Net earnings (loss)	$59,732,000	($144,631,000)	$188,953,000
Adjustments to reconcile net earnings (loss) to net cash provided by operating activities:			
Depreciation and amortization of plant and equipment	104,247,000	106,458,000	103,791,000
Other amortization	121,652,000	157,763,000	173,533,000
Deferred income taxes	38,697,000	(67,690,000)	(38,675,000)
Compensation earned under restricted stock program	2,532,000	2,754,000	0
Loss on sale of business units	0	43,965,000	0
Change in operating assets and liabilities (other than cash and cash equivalents):			
Decrease (increase) in accounts receivable	99,474,000	395,682,000	(11,248,000)
Decrease (increase) in inventories	109,002,000	69,657,000	(44,212,000)

	12/30/2001	12/30/2000	12/30/1999
Decrease (increase) in prepaid expenses and other current assets	45,936,000	(84,006,000)	(26,527,000)
(Decrease) increase in accounts payable and accrued liabilities	(194,525,000)	(292,313,000)	193,626,000
Other, including long-term advances	(14,272,000)	(25,083,000)	(147,729,000)
Net cash provided by operating activities	372,475,000	162,556,000	391,512,000
Cash flows from investing activities:			
Additions to property, plant, and equipment	(50,045,000)	(125,055,000)	(107,468,000)
Investments and acquisitions, net of cash acquired	0	(138,518,000)	(352,417,000)
Other	(7,734,000)	82,863,000	30,793,000
Net cash utilized by investing activities	(57,779,000)	(180,710,000)	(429,092,000)
Cash flows from financing activities:			
Proceeds from borrowings with original maturities of more than three months	250,000,000	912,979,000	460,333,000
Repayments of borrowings with original maturities of more than three months	(250,127,000)	(291,779,000)	(308,128,000)
Net (repayments) proceeds of other short-term borrowings	(190,216,000)	(341,522,000)	226,103,000
Purchase of common stock	0	(367,548,000)	(237,532,000)
Stock option and warrant transactions	8,391,000	2,523,000	50,358,000
Dividends paid	(20,709,000)	(42,494,000)	(45,526,000)
Net cash (utilized) provided by financing activities	(202,661,000)	(127,841,000)	145,608,000
Effect of exchange rate changes on cash	(6,055,000)	(7,049,000)	(5,617,000)
Increase (decrease) in cash and cash equivalents	105,980,000	(153,044,000)	102,411,000
Cash and cash equivalents at beginning of year	127,115,000	280,159,000	177,748,000
Cash and cash equivalents at end of year	$233,095,000	$127,115,000	$280,159,000
Supplemental information			
Interest paid	$103,437,000	$ 91,180,000	$ 64,861,000
Income taxes paid (received)	($34,813,000)	$ 95,975,000	$108,342,000

BEYOND THE BOOK

37. Find the 10-K, proxy statement, and annual report of a typical company in the manufacturing business. Answer the following questions:

a. From either the 10-K or annual report, discuss how important inventory is in relationship to other assets on the firm's balance sheet. Also address how important property, plant, and equipment is to the firm.

b. How does the company finance its business?

c. Compare the information provided in the 10-K and annual report and discuss at least five things that are in the 10-K that are not in the annual report. If you were a stockholder, would you want to know these things and why?

    d. From the proxy statement, what were the major issues (at least four) that were discussed at the annual meeting?

    e. What is the total compensation paid to the five highest-paid employees? Who was the highest paid? What percent of sales was the total paid? Does this seem reasonable and why?

    f. How many directors does the company have? How old are they and what percent of the board is female? How much do the directors get paid to attend meetings?

38. For the company you selected in problem 31, find at least three articles that discuss the nature of the markets for this company and the forecast of what the future may be for this sector of the economy. Write a one-page summary of your findings.

Income Measurement and Reporting

After reading this chapter you should be able to:

❶ Understand and apply the accrual basis of accounting and the related recognition and matching concepts.

❷ Explain the operating cycle and its relation to accrual accounting.

❸ Discuss revenue recognition methods and the reasons why revenue is recognized at different times for different economic events.

❹ Identify links between accrual accounting and firm valuation.

❺ Construct accrual entries for both revenue and expense transactions.

❻ Explain how the income statement format reflects the concept of separating transitory items from operating earnings.

In late May 2001, ConAgra Foods announced that accounting and conduct matters at its United Agri Products Company (UAP) subsidiary would result in the restatement of its financial results. Certain accounting adjustments would also result in a restatement for fiscal 1998. The restatement reduced revenues and earnings for fiscal years 1998, 1999, and 2000, and increased revenues and earnings in fiscal year 2001. ConAgra restated its earnings due to accounting irregularities in its UAP subsidiary that related, in part, to its revenue recognition practices. In the days leading up to the announcement, ConAgra's stock price fell by approximately 6 percent. Clearly, as ConAgra's press release illustrates, investors and analysts pay close attention to the earnings reported by publicly traded companies.

To further your understanding of the earnings reported by companies, we examine the concepts of accrual-basis accounting in this chapter. Specifically, we examine the recognition criteria for revenues and expenses, and related implications for the recognition of assets and liabilities. We compare and contrast this accrual-basis recognition of revenues and expenses with the timing of the actual cash flows that result from these transactions.

You need to understand accrual accounting and how it differs from a cash basis for at least two reasons. First, investors and analysts often use forecasts of earnings to estimate future cash flows, which, in turn, affects their assessments of a firm's value. Second, owners often use earnings and stock prices (which may depend on earnings) to measure management performance. Accrual accounting, however, allows managers sufficient latitude to influence the performance measures upon which they are evaluated and paid. As a result, owners must understand this latitude in setting management compensation arrangements, and investors and analysts must do so in assessing firm value.

Let's begin with a discussion of the general concepts of accrual-based accounting.

ACCRUAL ACCOUNTING

In **accrual-basis accounting,** a firm recognizes revenues and expenses in the period in which they occur, rather than in the period in which the cash flows related to the revenues and expenses are realized. In contrast, **cash-basis accounting** recognizes revenues and expenses in the period in which the firm realizes the cash flow. For example, under the accrual basis, a firm that sells goods to customers on credit recognizes the sales revenue at the point of physical transfer of the goods. Under the cash basis, however, the firm waits to recognize the sale until it collects the cash. As the diagram in Exhibit 4.1 illustrates, this difference in timing of revenue recognition can have a significant impact on the period in which the revenues are reported if the date of delivery of the goods falls in a different accounting period than the collection of cash. Because the cash might be collected in an accounting period later than the period in which the goods were delivered, it is clear that the choice of when to recognize revenue may have a significant impact on the statement of earnings.

Firms use accrual-basis accounting because it provides information about future cash flows that is not available under the cash method. In our sales example, investors want to know the firm's sales, even if the cash has not been collected, in order to better predict the future cash flows upon which the value of the firm depends. Similarly, a company's expected future payments are also relevant information. However, accrual accounting, while more informative than the cash basis, also involves considerable judgment. As a result, accounting standard setters developed criteria to assure that firms use similar assumptions in

Exhibit 4.1
Revenue Recognition Timing

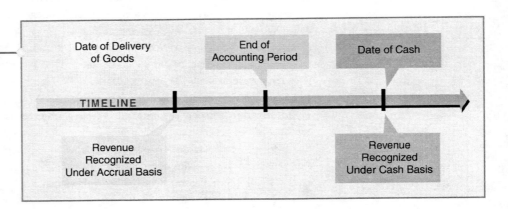

their judgments. In that way, the resulting revenue and expense numbers will be as consistent as possible with the qualitative characteristics of accounting information discussed in Chapter 1, such as neutrality, reliability, and verifiability.

The FASB's criteria are intended to guide all recognition decisions. These criteria detail what items should be recognized in the financial statements and when the items should be recognized. The following criteria apply to all financial statement components, including revenues, expenses, assets, liabilities, and stockholders' equity accounts:

Definition: The item meets the definition of an element of financial statements.

Measurability: The item has a relevant attribute measurable with sufficient reliability.

Relevance: The information about the item is capable of making a difference in user decisions.

Reliability: The information about the item is representationally faithful, verifiable, and neutral.

The above criteria include the concept of an attribute. *Attributes* are characteristics of financial statement items that we might choose to measure. For instance, inventory possesses several attributes. One of them is the cost the company incurs to either make or buy the inventory. A second attribute is the current selling price of the inventory. Whatever attribute we choose to measure, however, the recognition criteria require it to be "relevant." Often, accounting regulators must determine which attribute is the most relevant and reliable to report in the financial statements. We continue to address this issue as we progress through the text.

Recall in Chapter 3 that we defined assets, liabilities, and owners' equity. Later in this chapter we define revenues and expenses. All these definitions are based on the concepts of accrual accounting. Double-entry accounting links the recognition of revenues, expenses, assets, and liabilities. Let's look more closely at how revenue and expense recognition reflects these accrual-accounting concepts.

REVENUE RECOGNITION

Revenue recognition refers to the point in time at which revenue should be reported on the statement of earnings, a crucial element of accrual accounting. Typically, firms implement accrual accounting by first determining the revenues to be recognized and then matching the costs incurred in generating that revenue to determine expenses. It follows that the timing of revenue and expense recognition determines the earnings that are reported. Given that the information conveyed by earnings is a factor in estimating the value of the firm, revenue recognition is particularly important to analysts, investors, managers, and others with an interest in those estimates.

It is reasonable to imagine that these individuals desire earnings to be reported as early as possible in order to gain access to information upon which they can improve their estimates. However, this desire is likely to be tempered by an understanding that revenue recognized in advance of collecting the cash from customers implies some uncertainty that could be avoided if revenue recognition can be delayed until those collections are made. In other words, there is a trade-off between early access to information and the level of uncertainty contained in the revenue and related expenses reported on the statement of earnings. For example, an extreme view would argue that when a firm purchases inventory, it immediately adds value to the company because the goods can be sold later for a profit. Therefore, the firm should recognize the revenue (profit) upon inventory purchases, assuming that future sales will occur. The difficulty with this argument, of course, is the considerable uncertainty about both the timing and the amount of revenue that may be realized from future sales. For example, a company might purchase or manufacture inventory and be unable to sell it because of changing demand or excess supply.

Consider the electronic game industry in 2001. Three competitors, Microsoft, Sony, and Nintendo, sought industry dominance with the XBox, Playstation 2, and the Game-Cube, respectively. Manufacturers of these products needed to determine how many units to manufacture, set prices for the product, make arrangements with distributors (such as Toys Я Us, Wal-Mart, and Target), and ship the product in sufficient numbers to satisfy customers. Furthermore, the companies needed to consider the costs of product warranties and returns of unsold products. Finally, the three firms assumed that third-party software manufacturers would be able to offer a sufficient quality and variety of games on the different platforms to satisfy consumer demand. All of these factors worked to create substantial uncertainty about the profits from a particular product line. Thus, it would be difficult for any of these companies to argue that sales should have been recognized at the time they manufactured the products.

Because of the tension between the desire to recognize the value added by investment and production activities as early as possible, and the uncertainties involved in accurately portraying these results, accounting standard setters developed **revenue recognition criteria.** These criteria establish the requirements that must be met in order to recognize revenue on a company's books.

REVENUE RECOGNITION CRITERIA

GAAP requires that revenues be recognized at the earliest point in the firm's operating cycle, at which it meets the following criteria:

- Revenue is realized or realizable
- Revenue is earned by the enterprise

Realized or **realizable** means that an exchange of goods or services has taken place, the seller has either received cash or the right to receive cash, and collection is reasonably assured. **Earned** means that the goods or services have been delivered, and related obligations are substantially complete. In applying the earned criteria, a firm must apply judgment in determining whether the risks and rewards of ownership of the product have effectively been transferred to the buyer. That is, has there been substantial performance by both the seller and the buyer such that the earnings process is essentially complete? For instance, Werner Enterprises, a major trucking company, recognizes "operating revenues and related direct costs when the shipment is delivered." Because Werner is

At the time of this writing, the FASB is considering an approach for revenue recognition that is more closely linked to changes in assets and liabilities than the notions of realization and completion of the earnings process. Concerns with the present criteria for revenue realization are that they are sometimes in conflict with concepts of assets and liabilities, imprecisely defined, and difficult to consistently apply when the revenue generating process involves multiple steps.

Exhibit 4.2

THE REAL WORLD
Target Corporation

Target Corporation—Revenues

Revenue from retail sales is recognized at the time of sale. Leased department sales, net of related cost of sales, are included within sales and were $33 million in 2000, $31 million in 1999, and $29 million in 1998. Net credit revenues represent revenue from receivable-backed securities, which is comprised of finance charges and late fees on internal credit sales, net of the effect of publicly held receivable-backed securities. Internal credit sales were $5.5 billion, $5 billion, and $4.5 billion in 2000, 1999, and 1998, respectively.

responsible for transporting the goods of the customer, management judges that the earning process is only complete when the goods are ultimately delivered.

The revenue recognition criteria can be met at different points in a firm's operating cycle depending on the nature of the business. In the following sections, we illustrate some common points of revenue recognition used by various industries.

At Point of Delivery

A fairly common point of revenue recognition for manufacturing and retail firms is at the point when they deliver a product or service to a customer. As we noted previously, Werner, Inc. reports its revenue when the shipment is delivered. This is the point at which the customer accepts the risks and rewards of ownership of the asset, and at which point Werner ceases its obligation to the customer (the revenue has been earned). Further, the customer is now obligated to pay Werner for the delivery (the revenue is realizable).

Target's revenue recognition policy as shown in Exhibit 4.2 is more complex than that of Werner. Target derives its revenues not only from product sales but also from interest on credit sales to customers. However, for its product sales, the method of revenue recognition is at the time of delivery (which is also the time of sale). Target's 2000 income statement (shown later in Exhibit 4.11) reports sales of $36,362 million and net credit revenues of $541 million.

As Service Is Provided or Cost Incurred

For a firm that sells subscriptions, cash may be received in advance. The firm recognizes the revenue as it incurs costs in the fulfillment of those subscriptions. For example, Reader's Digest sells magazine subscriptions to individuals and newstands. In a footnote to its 2003 annual report, the company describes its revenue recognition methods as reported in Exhibit 4.3. As the footnote describes, Reader's Digest has three primary sources of revenue. It uses a

Exhibit 4.3

THE REAL WORLD
Readers Digest

Footnote on Revenue Recognition

Sales of our magazine subscriptions, less estimated cancellations, are deferred and recognized as revenues proportionately over the subscription period. Revenues from sales of magazines through the newsstand are recognized at the issue date, net of an allowance for returns. Advertising revenues are recorded as revenues at the time the advertisements are published, net of discounts and advertising agency commissions.

different recognition method for each type of revenue. The company recognizes subscriptions over the subscription period, newsstand sales at the issue date, and advertising revenues upon advertisement publication. The collection of cash does not determine the timing of revenue recognition. In the case of subscriptions, the revenue is earned as the goods are furnished to the purchaser. In the case of newsstand sales, the shipments are determined on a standing order (based on past sales), and newsstands pay only for the magazines that they sell. Thus, recognizing revenues at the issue date means that accurate estimation of the number of magazines to issue and of returns is critical to accurate revenue recognition. Finally, advertising revenues are recognized when the magazine is published (which constitutes providing the service to those purchasing advertisements).

Based on Contractual Agreements

Firms sometimes retain a substantial financial interest in the product or service, even after the initial sale. For example, Krispy Kreme, a typical franchiser, provides a significant amount of service related to establishing the business between the time of signing the agreement and the opening of the business. The company typically provides financing to the purchaser, allowing franchise fees to be paid in installments. Krispy Kreme defers revenues from the initial franchise fee until the opening of the new store is complete (i.e., the revenue has been earned).

Retail land sales also pose unique accounting problems. Retail land sales involve the sale of undeveloped land. Sales contracts may offer buyers below-market interest rates and attractive financing terms, with the land serving as collateral for the sale (sometimes called a *collateralized sale*). Because of uncertainties regarding the future costs of developing the land as well as the collectibility of the receivable (particularly when there are low down payments), accounting regulators established criteria to determine the conditions under which revenue from a retail land sale could be recognized at the signing of a sales contract. For example, footnotes to Amrep Corporation's annual report (reported in Exhibit 4.4) illustrate a typical disclosure in the case of retail land sales.

At Time of Production

When both the value and the assurance of sale can be estimated at the time of production, such as in certain agricultural and mining operations, a firm recognizes revenue at that point. Often, the company has a supply contract with

Exhibit 4.4

THE REAL WORLD

Amrep Corporation

Revenue Recognition Footnote

Land sales are recognized when the parties are bound by the terms of the contract, all consideration (including adequate cash) has been exchanged, and title and other attributes of ownership have been conveyed to the buyer by means of a closing. Profit is recorded either in its entirety or on the installment method depending on, among other things, the ability to estimate the collectibility of the unpaid sales price. In the event the buyer defaults on the obligation, the property is taken back and recorded in inventory at the unpaid receivable balance, net of any deferred profit, but not in excess of fair market value less estimated cost to sell.

a buyer that establishes the price of the commodity to be delivered and a time schedule for its delivery. For example, Kinross Gold Corporation (Kinross Annual Report 2000) notes that "Gold and Silver in inventory, in transit and at refineries, are recorded at net realizable value and included in accounts receivable with the exception of Kubaka bullion. The estimated net realizable value of Kubaka bullion is included in inventory until it is sold."

As Cash Is Collected

In most cases, revenue recognition criteria are met prior to collection. Firms can reasonably estimate collections at the time of sale, and the revenue is thus realizable. However, for some circumstances, collection of the receivable is sufficiently in doubt that revenue cannot be recognized at the time of sale. Recognition prior to collection would therefore not reflect the underlying economic reality. In these cases firms can use two methods to recognize revenue and related expenses as cash is collected: the installment method and the cost recovery method.

With the **installment method,** a firm recognizes gross profits in proportion to cash payments received. With the **cost recovery method,** a firm defers gross profit recognition until enough cash is collected to recover the costs. For example, assume that Wilson Land Company sells a home site for $100,000 that cost Wilson $60,000. The purchaser agrees to pay Wilson for the land in three payments of $40,000, $30,000, and $30,000. Exhibit 4.5 shows the amount of gross profit recognized each year under the installment method and the cost recovery method.

Either method results in the same total gross profit over three years. How, then, to determine the appropriate method of revenue recognition in a particular case? Firms generally use the cost recovery method only when considerable uncertainty exists about ultimate collection of the total sales price (so no profit is recognized until the costs have been covered). The decision, then, becomes whether to recognize a real estate sale under the installment method or at the time of sale. As a rule, retail land sales should only be recognized at the time of sale if both collection is assured and the seller has no remaining obligations to the buyer.

During Construction

In the long-term construction industry, major projects can take years to complete. Thus the operating cycle in this industry is very long, requiring special income recognition methods: the completed contract method and the percentage completion method. Under the **completed contract method,** a firm waits to recognize revenues and expenses until the project is complete. Under the **percentage**

Exhibit 4.5
Installment Method versus Cost Recovery Method

Profit % = ($100,000 − 60,000)/$100,000 = 40%

Year	Installment method gross profit	Cost recovery method gross profit
1	40% × $40,000 = $16,000	$0 ($40,000 cost recovered)
2	40% × $30,000 = $12,000	$10,000 ($20,000 cost recovered)
3	40% × $30,000 = $12,000	$30,000
Total	$40,000	$40,000

Exhibit 4.6
Revenue Recognition Using
Percentage of Completion
Method (dollars in billions)

Year	Degree of Completion	Revenue Recognized	Expenses Recognized	Gross Profit Recognized
1	$8/$15 = 53.33%	.533 × $20 = $10.67	$8	$2.67
2	$4/$15 = 26.67%	.267 × $20 = $5.33	$4	$1.33
3	$3/$15 = 20.00%	.20 × $20 = $4.00	$3	$1.00
Total	100.00%	$20.00	$15	$5.00

of completion method, a firm recognizes revenues and expenses in proportion to the degree of completion of the project. Degree of completion is typically measured by the cost incurred to date relative to the total estimated cost. For example, assume that Horning Construction agrees to build a casino. The purchaser agrees to pay $20 billion to Horning for the project. Horning expects to spend three years building the casino and estimates the following costs: Year 1, $8 billion; Year 2, $4 billion; Year 3, $3 billion. Exhibit 4.6 shows the amount of revenue and expenses recognized each year under percentage of completion.

Under the completed contract method, Horning Construction would recognize all of the revenue and expense at the end of year 3, at contract completion. Typically, though, firms use the completed contract method for short construction periods. However, to use the percentage completion method, firms must be able to accurately estimate costs to obtain reliable profit forecasts. As a result, if there is a high degree of cost uncertainty, the completed contract method may be used even for long-term contracts.

Although the percentage of completion and completed contract methods are the more common, firms sometimes use other methods of accounting for long-term construction contracts, such as the installment and cost recovery methods described earlier. Firms will likely use the installment method when the uncertainty pertains largely to assurance of collection (buyer's performance) rather than the reliability of future cost estimates (seller's performance). The cost recovery method is especially conservative and appropriate in cases where considerable uncertainty exists about collection and future costs.

Now that we have reviewed several aspects of revenue recognition, let's turn to the related issue of expense recognition.

EXPENSE RECOGNITION

The **matching concept** requires that firms recognize both the revenue and the costs required to produce the revenue (expenses) at the same time. The implications of this are two-fold. First, it means that firms must defer some costs on the balance sheet until they can be matched with sales. In some cases, though, direct matching with sales is not practical. In these cases, firms often expense the deferred costs based on the passage of time. Second, firms will not incur some costs at the time of the sale (e.g., warranty costs). Firms will thus need to estimate these costs, and accrue an expense to give proper matching with the revenue reported.

Perhaps the best example of direct matching is when a retail or wholesale company recognizes revenue at the time of delivery. Here, a related expense, **cost of goods sold,** which represents the cost of inventory that the company had on its balance sheet as an asset prior to the sale, must also be recognized. Target provides an example of such a company. Its cost of goods sold can be seen in Exhibit 4.11 (later in the chapter).

Matching is applied differently depending on the type of cost. Some costs, such as costs of goods sold, can be matched directly with sales. However, other costs, such as executive salaries, insurance, and depreciation of various assets used in the business, can be more difficult to directly link to revenue. In this case, firms usually either charge the costs to income as incurred (e.g., salaries and various administrative costs) or allocate the costs systematically over time periods (e.g., depreciation, interest, insurance). Werner, Inc. (the trucking company mentioned earlier) provides a service to its customers, so it has no cost of goods sold. However, if you review the income statement for Werner, you would see sales-related expenses such as salaries, fuel costs, and depreciation on its trucks, which are related to the delivery service it provides to its customers.

With expense recognition, GAAP guidelines focus on whether or not a cost should be treated as an asset (a **deferred expense**) or as an expense. For example, Prepaid Legal Services pays its sales force an advance of up to three years' worth of commissions on new customer sales. In the years prior to 2001, Prepaid treated these prepayments as deferred expenses (assets) and then expensed these deferred expenses over time to match them with revenues from the provided legal services. However, in 2001 the SEC concluded that Prepaid's accounting methods were not in accordance with GAAP arguing that the future revenue from these sales was highly uncertain. Effective in its third quarter 10-Q filing with the SEC as shown in Exhibit 4.7, Prepaid changed its accounting

---

In the November 14, 2001, 10-Q filing of Prepaid Legal Services, the following disclosure was made:

As previously reported, in January 2001 and May 2001, the staff of the Division of Corporation Finance of the Securities and Exchange Commission (SEC) reviewed the Company's 1999 and 2000 Forms 10-K, respectively. On May 11, 2001, the Company received a letter from the staff of the Division of Corporation Finance advising that, after reviewing the Company's Forms 10-K, it was the position of the Division that the Company's accounting for commission advance receivables was not in accordance with GAAP. The Company subsequently appealed this decision to the Chief Accountant of the SEC. On July 25, 2001, the Company announced that the Chief Accountant concurred with the prior staff opinion of the Division of Corporation Finance. The Company subsequently announced that it would not pursue any further appeals and that it would amend its previously filed SEC reports to restate the Company's financial statements to reflect the SEC's position that the Company's advance commission payments should be expensed when paid. As previously discussed, the change in accounting treatment reduced total assets from $247 million at December 31, 2000 to $93 million, reduced total liabilities from $100 million to $48 million (due to the elimination of deferred taxes related to the receivables) and therefore reduced stockholders' equity from $147 million to $45 million. The elimination of the receivables reduced 2000 net income from $43.6 million, or $1.92 per diluted share, to $20.5 million, or $.90 per diluted share. The Company expects to amend its 2000 Annual Report on Form 10-K in the near future to reflect the change in accounting for commission of advance receivables and restate all periods included in the 2000 Form 10-K. The financial statements and the explanation thereof contained in this Form 10-Q reflect the change in the accounting treatment for advance payments made to associates.

Exhibit 4.7

THE REAL WORLD
Prepaid Legal Services

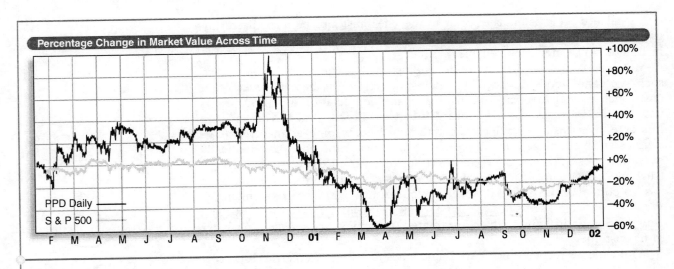

Percentage Change in Market Value Across Time

PPD Daily ———
S & P 500 ———

Exhibit 4.8
Prepaid Legal Services Inc.

THE REAL WORLD

methods to conform with the SEC ruling. The company now expenses the commissions in the period in which they were paid.

The concern over Prepaid's accounting methods stemmed back to December 2000, when a research report questioned the firm's economic viability. The graph in Exhibit 4.8 demonstrates the changes in value that took place between the issuance of this report and the change of policy in late 2001.

Now that we've discussed accrual-accounting concepts, let's next look at how firms put into practice these revenue and expense recognition criteria.

RECORDING ACCRUAL ENTRIES

In this section, we use four common types of economic events to illustrate how accrual accounting is applied and how the cash flow timing differs for each event. Exhibit 4.9 summarizes these revenue and expense events, and provides a simple example of each. Let's look more closely at each of these transactions.

REVENUES THAT ARE RECEIVED IN CASH BEFORE THEY ARE EARNED

In this situation the firm must record the cash received as an asset. However, as the firm cannot yet treat the transaction as earned revenue, it must postpone the recognition of revenue. The firm will, therefore, record a liability, **deferred revenue** (or *unearned revenue* or *customer deposits*), that represents an obligation to provide goods or services to the customer in the future. This obligation clearly meets the definition of a liability in that it most definitely represents a future sacrifice of resources to the firm. Recall our earlier illustration of Reader's Digest and its revenue recognition of subscriptions.

To illustrate the entries to be made for this type of transaction, let's return to our BHT example from Chapter 3. Suppose that BHT receives $20 million

Exhibit 4.9
Common Accrual Accounting
Events

Revenue Events	Example
Cash that is received in advance before the revenues are recognized as having been earned	Magazine subscriptions are usually paid in advance and earned when the publisher delivers the magazines.
Revenues that are recognized as having been earned before the revenues are received in cash	Sales on account, interest revenue on notes is earned with the passage of time and paid at regular intervals.

Expense Events	Example
Expenses that are paid in advance before they are recognized as having been incurred	Insurance is generally paid in advance to cover a future period. The expense is incurred with the passage of time as dictated by the policy.
Expenses that are recognized as having been incurred before they are paid in cash	Salary expense is incurred when the employees work, even though they may be paid later, such as once every two weeks.

in cash from customers for goods to be delivered in the future. BHT would make the following journal entry at the time cash is received:

Cash	20	
Deferred Revenue		20

→ Assets
→ liabilities

Later, when BHT earns the revenues (likely at delivery), the firm would make the following entry:

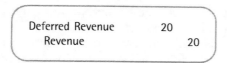

Deferred Revenue	20	
Revenue		20

REVENUES THAT ARE EARNED BEFORE THEY ARE RECEIVED IN CASH

For most firms, revenue recognition criteria are most often met before the firms collect the cash. Here, the firm records revenues on its income statement and also an asset (accounts receivable). Accounts receivable meets the definition of an asset as the firm has probable future value in the right to receive cash from the customer at some point in the future. Recall in Chapter 3 that we showed you this type of transaction for BHT, as follows:

Accounts Receivable	35,724	
Sales		35,724

As another example, consider interest accrued on a note receivable. A firm earns revenue (interest) on the note with the passage of time, periodically receiving cash. If the cash hasn't yet been received, the firm would record interest revenue and an asset (typically called interest receivable). To illustrate, suppose that BHT allows a customer to pay its bill over a longer period than normal by issuing a note receivable for the amount of the sale (say $100). Further, suppose that this note specifies that the customer pays 5 percent interest. At the end of the first year, the customer would owe an additional $5 for the interest ($100 × 5%). BHT records this earned revenue (assuming it hadn't been paid yet) as follows:

Interest Receivable	5	
Interest Revenue		5

When BHT collects the interest, it makes the following entry:

Cash	5	
Interest Receivable		5

EXPENSES THAT ARE PAID IN CASH BEFORE THEY ARE INCURRED

Cash payment often precedes the incurrence of an expense, such as with prepaid insurance. Insurance companies usually require payment of insurance policy premiums in advance of the coverage. If the firm has just paid its premium, then it should record the reduction in cash and the creation of an asset, typically called prepaid insurance. Prepaid insurance meets the definition of an asset: the insurance provides probable future value in terms of coverage (protection from risk) over the remaining period of the policy. The firm will then convert the prepaid insurance into an expense with the passage of time. For example, if BHT pays $150 for an insurance policy covering its plant, property, and equipment for the following year, it records the following entry at the date of payment:

Prepaid Insurance	150	
Cash		150

As time passes, the insurance is consumed as coverage expires. If six months have passed and half of the coverage, or $75 worth of the amount prepaid, has been consumed, BHT would make the following entry:

Insurance Expense	75	
Prepaid Insurance		75

EXPENSES THAT ARE INCURRED BEFORE THEY ARE PAID IN CASH

Salary expense is often incurred prior to it being paid, as most firms issue checks to employees after services have been received. If employees have worked for the firm, but haven't been paid, the firm should record an expense and a liability (salaries payable) indicating its obligation to pay the employees at a later date. To illustrate, if BHT employees earned $25 during the last week of December but will not be paid until the end of the first week in January, BHT would make the following entry on December 31:

Salaries Expense	25	
Salaries Payable		25

→ *assets*
→ *liabilities.*

When BHT pays the employees, it would make the following entry:

Salaries payable	25	
Cash		25

The flexibility within GAAP as it relates to accrual entries might allow management to understate discretionary or estimated expenses or overstate estimated revenues in order to meet analysts' forecasts or internal performance targets. Considerable attention has been given to the implications of management's discretion within GAAP on earnings forecasts, estimates of firm value, and management compensation.

Note that the initial entry in each of the previous four examples results in the creation of an asset or liability. These accrual-based assets and liabilities would not exist under the cash basis. In fact, most assets and liabilities that exist on a GAAP-prepared balance sheet, except cash, arise as a consequence of accrual-based accounting. These include receivables (revenue recognized before cash is received), inventories, prepaid expenses, property and equipment, intangible assets (cash paid before expense is recognized), payables and accrued liabilities (expense recognized before cash is paid), and deferred revenues (cash received before revenue is recognized).

Almost all of the transactions we have just discussed involve the use of an adjusting entry. Recall from our discussion in Chapter 3 that adjusting entries are made at the end of the period for transactions that do not involve an exchange with an external party. For example, when BHT recorded its deferred revenue, this entry was triggered by the receipt of cash. However, the later recognition of deferred revenue on the income statement was not accompanied by an exchange event and therefore was recorded via an adjusting entry. Similarly, the recording of prepaid insurance was triggered by the cash payment of the premium, while the recognition of insurance expense was recorded via an adjusting entry by the accountant after it was determined how much of the insurance coverage had expired. For a more detailed discussion of various adjusting entries refer to Appendix A.

VALUATION IMPLICATIONS OF INCOME RECOGNITION

Reported net income plays an important role in determining a company's value. Simply put, net income from an accrual-accounting is informative about future cash flows to the business that, in turn, implies future potential cash flows to investors. The stream of future cash flows to investors determines the value of a company (as we describe more fully in Chapter 14). A company must generate positive cash flows for investors either in the form of dividends or an increased stock price in order to remain a viable business.

Both revenue and expense recognition involve assumptions and estimation. Accounting standards seek to provide relevant and timely information about a company to assist in forecasting its future while at the same time assuring the reliability of the information in the face of estimation and uncertainty. The criteria for revenue and expense recognition seek to balance these desired attributes in providing guidelines for the determination of earnings. Nevertheless, the link between current income and future cash flows remains uncertain. To improve our understanding of the imprecise relation between current earnings and future cash flows, let's look at the income statement more closely.

INCOME STATEMENT FORMAT

Financial statements should provide information that helps current and potential investors, creditors, and other users to assess the amount, timing, and uncertainty of prospective net cash flows to the firm. The income statement reports on a company's financial performance and provides information about future expected cash flows.

GAAP does not specify the format of the income statement in detail. As a result, the degree to which specific line items are combined into the aggregate line items that appear on the statement (sometimes referred as the degree of aggregation), as well as the labels used for the aggregate items, vary widely across firms. Because this can make statement interpretation challenging for the novice financial statement user, let's take a closer look at the line items.

LINE ITEM DEFINITIONS

When looking at the income statement, you should first determine which items relate to the core operations of the business, or are *persistent*, and which are *transitory*, or unrelated to the company's core operations. Investors value persistent profits more highly than transitory ones as they are more likely to continue in the future. For example, a business might report a loss from a lawsuit that involves a substantial cash outlay. However, this one-time cost has different implications for the value of the firm than a loss caused by operations (e.g., when product's costs exceed its sales). Thus, proper classification of items as continuing/recurring or noncontinuing/nonrecurring provides investors and financial statement users with more accurate forecasts of future cash flow.

To this end, the FASB provides direction in its definition (FASB Concepts No. 6, "Elements of Financial Statements") of revenues and expenses (FASB, SFAC No. 6, 1985):

- *Revenues:* "inflows or other enhancements of assets of an entity or settlements of its liabilities (or a combination of both) from delivering or producing goods, rendering services, or other activities that constitute the entity's ongoing major or central operations."

- *Expenses:* "outflows or other using up of assets or incurrences of liabilities (or a combination of both) from delivering or producing goods, rendering services, or carrying out other activities that constitute the entity's ongoing major or central operations."

- *Gains:* "increases in equity (net assets) from peripheral or incidental transactions of an entity and other events and circumstances affecting the entity except those that result from revenues or investments by owners."
- *Losses:* "decreases in equity (net assets) from peripheral or incidental transactions of an entity and from all other transactions and other events and circumstances affecting the entity except those that result from expenses or distributions to owners."

INCOME STATEMENT LABELS

The degree of aggregation and labeling of income statement items varies widely across companies. For example, some companies will explicitly list items such as gross profit, income from continuing operations, and other subcategories, while others simply list all revenues and subtract all costs. Income statements that provide greater detail and breakdown of costs by category are referred to as **multiple step.** Those that simply list revenue and expenses in two broad categories are called **single step.** Because valuing companies requires the ability to estimate future cash flows to owners, financial disclosures that help users to discern which revenues and costs are related to core continuing activities are most useful to financial statement users.

In general, multiple-step income statements include the following categories:

- Gross Profit
- Income from Continuing Operations
- Nonrecurring Items
- Extraordinary Items
- Accounting Changes and Errors

Let's look at each of the categories in more detail.

Income from Continuing Operations

Income from continuing operations is the difference between a company's operating revenues and its operating expenses. It does not include revenues from nonoperating sources nor from operations that a company discontinues. For example, Exhibit 4.10 shows the income statement for Albertson's, Inc., a large national grocery store chain. Note the line "Operating Profit," which reflects income from continuing operations. However, while Albertson's expects most of the operating items to continue from period to period, the company also lists several items that might not be considered recurring: "Merger-Related and Exit Costs," "Litigation Settlement," and "Impairment Store Closures." Albertson's separately discloses these one-time or limited-term items to allow analysts to adjust these charges out of the operating profits before trying to use the historical data to forecast future operating profits.

Exhibit 4.11 shows an income statement for Target for 2000 including comparative results for 1999 and 1998. Note that a complete income statement also includes earnings per share information (described later in the chapter). Target

Exhibit 4.10
Albertson Corporation
Consolidated Statement of
Earnings (millions except per
share data)

THE REAL WORLD

Albertson Corporation

one-time/limited
time expenses.

In millions except per share data	52 weeks 02/01/2001	52 weeks 02/01/2000	52 weeks 01/28/1999
Sales	$36,762	$37,478	$35,872
Cost of sales	26,336	27,164	26,156
Gross profit	10,426	10,314	9,716
Selling, general, and administrative expenses	8,740	8,641	7,846
Merger-related and exit costs	24	396	195
Litigation settlement		37	
Impairment-store closures			24
Operating profit	1,662	1,240	1,651
Other (expense) income:			
Interest, net	(385)	(353)	(337)
Other, net	(3)	12	24
Earnings before taxes and extraordinary items	1,274	899	1,338
Income taxes	509	472	537
Earnings before extraordinary items	765	427	801
Extraordinary loss on extinguishment of debt, net of tax benefit of $7		(23)	
Net earnings	$ 765	$ 404	$ 801

Exhibit 4.11
Target Corporation
Consolidated Results of
Operations (millions except
per share data)

THE REAL WORLD

Target Corporation

	2000	1999	1998
Sales	$36,362	$33,212	$30,203
Net credit revenues	541	490	459
Total revenues	36,903	33,702	30,662
Cost of sales	25,295	23,029	21,085
Selling, general, and administrative expenses	8,190	7,490	6,843
Depreciation and amortization	940	854	780
Interest expense	425	393	398
Earnings before income taxes and extraordinary charges	2,053	1,936	1,556
Provision for income taxes	789	751	594
Net earnings before extraordinary charges	1,264	1,185	962
Extraordinary charges from purchase and redemption of debt, net of tax	—	41	27
Net earnings	$ 1,264	$ 1,144	$ 935
Earnings before extraordinary charges	$ 1.40	$ 1.32	$ 1.07
Extraordinary charges	—	(.04)	(.03)
Basic earnings per share	$ 1.40	$ 1.28	$ 1.04
Earnings before extraordinary charges	$ 1.38	$ 1.27	$ 1.02
Extraordinary charges	0	(.04)	(.03)
Diluted earnings per share	$ 1.38	1.23	.99

reports cost of sales; selling, general, and administrative expenses; depreciation; and amortization and interest expense. These reflect typical categories for a retail or wholesale company that sells products. However, Target's income statement does not explicitly show operating earnings. Thus Target's income statement readers must determine from the account titles, placement on the financial statement, and the disclosures provided in Target's footnotes which items represent Target's operating income.

Note that Target shows "Net Credit Revenues" in its total revenue section. This is interest income that represents income from Target's financing operations. Financing is one of Target's core operations, so analysts would probably classify this as a part of operating revenues. If, however, firms report interest income primarily from investment activities, the revenue would be classified as nonoperating or other revenue.

Nonrecurring Items

In addition to separating operating from nonoperating items, investors also want to identify recurring versus nonrecurring items. Unusual or infrequent revenues and/or expenses should be highlighted to signal financial statement users that the items do not have the same kind of information about future cash flows as do normal recurring ones. Some firms simply label unusual items as such. In other cases, accounting standard setters provide specific guidelines for how to report such items.

GAAP requires three items to be shown after the computation of tax expense: **discontinued operations, extraordinary items,** and the **cumulative effect of changes in accounting principles.** Because these items appear below both operating and nonoperating items and after the computation of tax expense, they are often referred to as "below the line" items. Because they are shown after the tax computation, firms show these items on a net of tax basis. For example, Target reported an extraordinary charge of $41 million in 1999. This $41 million represents the net amount after subtracting the tax effect.

they do not generate tax. So appear below the line

Discontinued Operations

Results from discontinued operations represent amounts related to a line of business, such as a product, that a company decides to discontinue. The income statement items related to discontinued operations include (1) any gain or loss from operations of the discontinued business after the decision is made to discontinue and prior to actual termination of operations, and (2) any gain or loss on disposal of the business. In December, 2002, H.J. Heinz decided to spin off its pet snacks, U.S. tuna, U.S. retail private label soup and private label gravy, College Inn broths, and its U.S. infant feeding businesses. The income statement for Heinz in Exhibit 4.12 reflects the discontinued operations.

Extraordinary Items

Extraordinary items are both unusual in nature and infrequent in occurrence. These gains and losses are not expected to recur, and hence are segregated from operations. Because management may have an incentive to classify all bad news as extraordinary, the FASB developed guidelines that specify when a firm may classify an item as extraordinary. For example, the "unusual" nature criteria guidelines specify that the item must be unusual within the existing context of

> Note that analysts often consider certain items as nonrecurring beyond those specified for GAAP purposes when they are valuing the firm. For instance, if a firm recorded a restructuring charge during the period, it wouldn't earmark this item as extraordinary but it is nonrecurring. If an item is less than likely to recur, then an analyst would put less weight on this item when determining value.

Exhibit 4.12
H.J. HEINZ Co. Income
Statement

THE REAL WORLD

H.J. Heinz

52 Weeks Ended (in 000s):	Apr-30-03	May-1-02	May-2-01
Sales	$8,236,836	$7,614,036	$6,987,698
Cost of products sold	5,304,362	4,858,087	4,407,267
Gross profit	2,932,474	2,755,949	2,580,431
Selling, general, and administrative expenses	1,758,658	1,456,077	1,591,472
Operating income	1,173,816	1,299,872	988,959
Interest income	31,083	26,197	22,597
Interest expense	223,532	230,611	262,488
Other expense/(income), net	112,636	44,938	(5,358)
Income from continuing operations before income taxes and cumulative effect of change in accounting principle	868,731	1,050,520	754,426
Provision for income taxes	313,372	375,339	190,495
Income from continuing operations before cumulative effect of change in accounting principle	555,359	675,181	563,931
Income/(loss) from discontinued operations, net of tax	88,738	158,708	(70,638)
Income before cumulative effect of change in accounting principle	644,097	833,889	493,293
Cumulative effect of change in accounting principle	(77,812)	–	(15,281)
Net income	$ 566,285	$ 833,889	$ 478,012

The issues surrounding extraordinary items highlight the difficulties involved in determining operating earnings or income from continuing operations. Management has an incentive to classify losses as extraordinary and to suggest that the losses will not persist into the future, and to move nonoperating and one-time gain items to revenues to make them appear as if they will recur. Accounting and auditing standards are intended to minimize these opportunities.

the business. Tornado damage in Oklahoma City, Oklahoma, would likely not be considered extraordinary because these storms frequently occur in Oklahoma. The possibility of tornado damage would therefore be considered a normal business risk of locating in Oklahoma. However, tornado damage in New Hampshire might meet these criteria.

GAAP also occasionally specifies extraordinary-item treatment for transactions that would not normally meet the criteria. For example, from 1975 through 2001, when companies retired debt early and incurred a book gain or loss, they reported these items as extraordinary. These gains and losses had no future cash flow implications. However, early retirements of debt have become so common that the FASB recently concluded that gains and losses on debt retirements should no longer be classified as extraordinary.

The FASB concluded that events related to the terrorist attack on the World Trade Center on September 11, 2001 were not extraordinary. The event would clearly be classified as unusual and infrequent, but the FASB was not convinced that the costs associated with this event were easily measurable. Further, the FASB was concerned that managers of poorly performing firms (particularly in the airline industry) would be tempted to classify all of their operating losses as extraordinary. Firms can still give significant footnote disclosure to explain any event that they believe significantly impacted their operations during the fiscal year. The obvious difficultly for analysts is to sort out which of the firm's results are expected to continue and which were related to this one-time event.

Accounting Changes and Errors

Accounting changes and errors comprise a third category of item that can result in separate disclosure. Accounting changes can occur from a change in accounting principle or from a change in estimate. Changes in accounting estimates do not require any restatements and may not even be disclosed. However, voluntary changes in accounting principle require firms to provide an adjustment for the effects of the change in prior years. In the year of the change, there will be a catch-up adjustment, known as the *cumulative effect* of the accounting principle change. Firms report this catch-up adjustment in a matter similar to that used for disposal of a segment of a business and extraordinary items. Accounting errors in prior period do require the restatement of prior periods through an adjustment to the beginning balance of the retained earnings account. These are called **prior period adjustments.**

PRO-FORMA EARNINGS

Recently, the SEC increased its focus on companies' misuse of accounting to mislead investors. One area of concern has been the presentation of pro forma earnings that represent a company in a more favorable light than actual earnings. **Pro forma earnings,** also called "as if" earnings, are earnings restated to reflect certain assumptions different from those in the actual earnings statement. For example, Waste Management, Inc. reported net income of $30 million for the third quarter of 2001. However, in its press release announcing its third quarter earnings, Waste Management reported pro forma earnings of $225 million. Items that the company eliminated from the pro forma earnings included consulting fees and truck painting.

In the November 2001 press release, Waste Management, Inc. announced financial results for its third quarter ended September 30, 2001. Revenues for the quarter were $2.90 billion as compared to $3.12 billion in the one-year-ago period. Included in the third quarter revenues was $203 million from operations which have since been sold. Net income reported for the quarter was $30 million, or $.05 per diluted share, for the third quarter 2000. On a pro forma basis, after adjusting for unusual costs and certain other items, including a charge related to the agreement to settle the class action lawsuit, third quarter 2001 net income was $225 million, or $.36 per diluted share as compared with $208 million or $33 per diluted share, in the one-year-ago period. Note that this disclosure offers significant information about which items are nonrecurring (e.g., sold operations and the lawsuit settlement). Also note that the company failed to include these items in its pro-forma disclosure.

EARNINGS PER SHARE

GAAP requires firms to disclose **earnings per share** in the income statement. (See the disclosure of Target in Exhibit 4.11.) There are two components of earnings per share, basic earnings per share and fully-diluted earnings per share. **Basic**

earnings per share is simply net income divided by the weighted average number of shares of common stock outstanding for a company. Hence, it measures the per share earnings accruing to shareholders. A company reports **fully-diluted earnings per share** when it has stock options and other instruments that are convertible into shares of common stock that could potentially reduce the common shareholder's proportionate share of earnings if the instruments were converted. For example, when a company provides an executive stock option plan, more shares outstanding will occur if and when the executives exercise their options. This will reduce the proportionate equity in earnings of current shareholders. The fully-diluted earnings per share figure provides an estimate of this type of dilution. It calculates how low earnings per share might become if everything is converted. We'll provide a more detailed discussion of earnings per share and its computation in Chapter 12.

> Analysts often focus on per share earnings when forecasting earnings and, as we discussed, the ability to meet earnings forecasts can significantly affect a company's share price.

COMPREHENSIVE INCOME

FASB Concepts Statement 6 (FASB, SFAC No. 6, 1985) defines **comprehensive income** as the change in equity of a firm due to transactions and other events and circumstances from nonowner sources. It includes all changes in equity except those resulting from investments by owners and distributions to owners. At first glance, this appears to be a definition of earnings. The difference is that accounting standards allow for some items that affect owners' equity to bypass the income statement and be recorded directly in stockholders' equity.

Primarily, these transactions relate to holding gains and losses on certain investments in equity securities and the balance sheet effects of foreign currency translations. Foreign currency translation gains and losses occur when a company has a subsidiary in another country whose accounting records are maintained in a currency other than the U.S. dollar. When the results of this subsidiary are combined to produce the consolidated financial statements of the company, they must be translated from the currency in which they are kept to U.S. dollars by applying various exchange rates. This translation produces gains and losses in dollar terms that must be accounted for and reported. In many circumstances, these gains and losses bypass the income statement and end up in comprehensive income. Accounting standards require that comprehensive income be reported separately from earnings, usually disclosed in the Statement of Shareholders' Equity.

SUMMARY AND TRANSITION

Understanding the basis for recognition of revenues and expenses, as well as how those are presented, is critical to analyzing and using financial statements for decision making. The income statement provides useful information about future cash flows, but that information must also be both timely and reliable. In some cases, the trade-offs for more timely information may reduce the certainty of the information presented. As we saw in this chapter, a firm might wait and recognize revenues on long-term construction contracts until it receives cash. However, months or even years may lapse between the time construction begins and the contract price is fully collected. This lag reduces the usefulness of the information. Financial accounting standards are not intended to eliminate uncertainty, but they are intended to balance the conflict between the goals of providing relevant and timely information with information that is reliable and accurate.

At a conceptual level, accrual accounting seeks to recognize revenues as earned, rather than as the cash is received, and expenses as incurred, rather than as the cash is paid. To implement this concept, those who set the standards have devised criteria for revenue and related expense recognition that identify where in the operating cycle recognition is appropriate.

The usefulness of earnings in valuing the firm is enhanced by separating continuing/recurring operating items from more transitory noncontinuing/nonrecurring ones, such as profits or losses from discontinued operations, restructuring charges, and extraordinary items. The effects of accounting changes should also be identified to improve estimates of future earnings numbers.

END OF CHAPTER MATERIAL

KEY TERMS

Accrual-Basis Accounting	Deferred Revenue
Cash-Basis Accounting	Multiple-Step Income Statement
Revenue Recognition	Single-Step Income Statement
Revenue Recognition Criteria	Income from Continuing Operations
Realized/Realizable	Discontinued Operations
Earned	Extraordinary Items
Installment Method	Cumulative Effect of Changes in Accounting Principles
Cost Recovery Method	Prior Period Adjustment
Completed Contract Method	Pro Forma Earnings
Percentage Completion Method	Earnings per Share
Matching Concept	Basic Earnings per Share
Cost of Goods Sold	Fully-Diluted Earnings per Share
Deferred Expense	Comprehensive Income

ASSIGNMENT MATERIAL

REVIEW QUESTIONS

1. What advantages and disadvantages do you see in using the cash basis of accounting rather than the accrual basis?
2. Respond to each of the following statements with a true or false answer:
   a. Dividends declared decrease cash immediately.
   b. The cash basis recognizes expenses when they are incurred.
   c. There is no such thing as a prepaid rent account on the cash basis.

    d. Dividends are an expense of doing business and should appear on the income statement.

    e. On the accrual basis, interest should only be recognized when it is paid.

3. Explain how a prepaid expense (such as rent) gets handled under accrual basis accounting.

4. Explain how an accrued expense (such as interest) gets handled under accrual basis accounting.

5. Suppose that a firm's accounting policy was to recognize warranty expense only when warranty service was provided. Discuss whether this meets the matching concept under accrual basis accounting and other ways that this transaction might be handled.

6. Diagram a typical operating cycle of a manufacturing firm and briefly explain what assets and liabilities are likely to be created as a result of this operating cycle.

7. List the two major revenue recognition criteria that exist under GAAP.

8. Describe the concept of revenue being "earned" and contrast it with the concept of revenue being "realized."

9. Explain the difference between the percentage completion method and the completed contracts method.

10. Explain the difference between the installment method and the cost recovery method.

11. Explain the meaning of the matching concept.

APPLYING YOUR KNOWLEDGE

12. Brickstone Construction Company signs a contract to build a building in four years for $40,000,000. The expected costs for each year are:

Year 1:	$ 9,750,000
Year 2:	12,025,000
Year 3:	6,500,000
Year 4:	4,225,000
Total	$32,500,000

The building is completed in year 4. Compute for each year, the total revenue, expenses, and profit under:

a. The Percentage of Completion Method

b. The Completed Contract Method

13. Sandra Carlson sold her house, which cost her $210,000, to Bob Fletcher for $300,000. Bob agreed to pay $60,000 per year for a period of five years. Compute the revenue, expense, and profit for each of the five years (ignoring interest):

a. The Installment Method

b. The Cost-Recovery Method

14. Imperial Corporation purchases a factory from Superior Manufacturing Company for $1,500,000. The cost of the factory on Superior's book is $975,000. The terms of agreement are that yearly installment payments of $705,000, $505,000, $455,000, and $255,000 will be made over the next four years. Each of these payments includes an interest payment of $105,000 per year. Compute the revenue, expense, and profit for each of the four years accruing to Superior Manufacturing Company as per:

   a. The Installment Method

   b. The Cost Recovery Method

15. Cruise Shipping, Inc. agreed to rebuild the *Santa Marice;* an old cargo ship owned by the Oceanic Shipping Company. Both parties signed the contract on November 28, Year 1, for $120 million which is to be paid as follows:

   $12 million at the signing of the contract
   $24 million on December 30, Year 2
   $36 million on June 1, Year 3
   $48 million at completion, on August 15 Year 4.

   The following cost were incurred by Cruise Shipping, Inc. (in millions):

Year 1:	$19.2
Year 2:	38.4
Year 3:	24.0
Year 4:	14.4
Total	$96.0

   a. Compute the revenue, expense, and profit for each of the four years (ignoring interest) for Cruise Shipping, Inc. as per:

      1. The Installment Method

      2. The Cost-Recovery Method

      3. The Percentage of Completion Method

      4. The Completed Contract Method

   b. Which method do you think should be employed by Cruise Shipping, Inc. to show the company's performance under the contract? Why?

16. Computronics Corporation received a contract on March 3, Year 1 for setting up a central communication and pricing center for a small university. The contract price was $1,000,000 which is to be paid as follows:

   $150,000   at the signing of the contract
   $ 60,000   on July 1, Year 1
   $ 30,000   on December 31, Year 1
   $ 80,000   on March 25, Year 2
   $100,000   on August 25, Year 2
   $180,000   on December 31, Year 2
   $400,000   on June 30, Year 3

The system was completed on June 30, Year 3.
Estimated and actual costs were:

$150,000   for the six months ending June 30, Year 1
$225,000   for the six months ending December 31, Year 1
$262,500   for the six months ending June 30, Year 2
$75,000   for the six months ending December 31, Year 2
$37,500   for the six months ending June 30, Year 3

Total $750,000

a. Compute the revenue, expense, and profit for each of the six months as per:

   1. The Percentage of Completion Method

   2. The Completed Contract Method

   3. The Installment Method

   4. The Cost-Recovery Method

b. Which method should be used by Computronics Corporation? Why?

17. Forte Builders, a construction company, recognizes revenue from its long-term contracts using the percentage completion method. On March 29, 20X3, the company signed a contract to construct a building for $500,000. The company estimated that it would take four years to complete the contract and would cost the company an estimated $325,000. The expected costs in each of the four years are as follows:

Year	Cost
20X3	$113,750
20X4	97,500
20X5	81,250
20X6	32,500
Total	$325,000

On December 31, 20X4, the date Forte closes its books, the company revised its estimates for the cost in 20X5 and 20X6. It estimated that the contract would cost $200,000 in 20X5 and $100,000 in 20X6 to complete the contract. Compute the revenue, expense, and profit/loss for each of the four years.

18. Samson Industries purchased furniture and appliances from the Metal and Wood Company for $75,000 under the following payment plan which called for semiannual payments over two years:

Payment	Amount
1	$33,600
2	16,800
3	22,400
4	11,200
Total	$84,000

Each payment contains interest (assume that the proportionate share of interest in each payment is the same as the proportion of that payment to the total payments). Assuming that the cost of the furniture and appliances is $60,000, compute the revenue, expense, and profit that Metal and Wood Company would report for each of the installment payments under:

a. The Installment Method

b. The Cost-Recovery Method

19. On June 21, 20X1, Tristar Electric Company signed a contract with Denton Power, Incorporated to construct a small hydroelectric generating plant. The contract price was $10,000,000, and it was estimated that the project would cost Tristar $7,850,000 to complete over a three-year period. On June 21, 20X1, Denton paid Tristar $1,000,000 as a default-deposit. In the event that Denton backed out of the contract, Tristar could keep this deposit. Otherwise the default-deposit would apply as the final payment on the contract (assume for accounting purposes that this is treated as a deposit until completion of the contract). The other contractual payments are as follows:

Date	Amount
10/15/X1	$3,150,000
4/15/X2	1,350,000
12/15/X2	1,800,000
3/15/X3	1,755,000
8/10/X3	945,000
Total	$9,000,000

Estimated costs of construction were as follows:

Year	Amount
1	$3,532,500
2	2,747,500
3	1,570,000

The contract was completed on January 10, 20X4. Tristar closes its books on December 31 each year. Compute the revenue, expense, and profit to be recognized in each year using:

a. The Installment Method

b. The Cost-Recovery Method

c. The Percentage Completion Method

d. The Completed Contracts Method

20. Financial analysts frequently refer to the quality of a firm's earnings. Discuss how the quality of two firms' earnings might differ depending on the revenue recognition method that the two firms use.

21. Suppose that a firm is currently private but is thinking of going public (i.e., issuing shares in a publicly traded market). Discuss the incentives that the

firm might have to misstate its income statement via its revenue recognition policies.

22. Suppose that you are the sales manager of a firm with an incentive plan that provides a bonus based on meeting a certain sales target. Explain how meeting your sales target is influenced by the revenue recognition principles of the firm.

23. Suppose that you are a sales manager of a U.S.-based firm that sells products in Israel, which has traditionally had a high inflation rate. This means that the exchange rate of shekels per dollar typically increases dramatically from year to year. If your compensation is a function of sales as measured in dollars, what risks do you face in meeting your targets and how might you mitigate the risks that you face in meeting those targets?

24. Explain the incentives that a firm has in choosing its revenue recognition method for both financial reporting and tax purposes.

25. In the toy industry it is common to allow customers to return unsold toys within a certain specified period of time. Suppose that a toy manufacturer's year end is December 31 and that the majority of its products are shipped to customers during the last quarter of the year in anticipation of the Christmas holiday. Is it appropriate for the company to recognize revenue upon shipment of the product? Support your answer citing references to revenue recognition criteria.

26. Suppose that an importer in Seattle buys goods from a supplier in Hong Kong. The goods are shipped by cargo vessel. For goods that are in transit at year end, what recognition should the Seattle importer make of these goods in its financial statements? Support your answer based on revenue recognition criteria.

27. Suppose that a company recognizes revenues at the time that title passes to its inventory and that it ships its inventory FOB (free on board) shipping point (i.e., title passes at the shipping point). Suppose at year end that it has loaded a shipment of goods on a truck that is parked on the grounds of the company based on a firm purchase order from a customer. How should the firm treat this inventory in its financial statements at year end?

28. Firms often sell their accounts receivable to raise cash to support their operations. Suppose that a firm sells its accounts receivable with recourse. Recourse means that the buyer can return the account receivable to the selling company if it cannot collect on the receivable. How should this transaction be treated in the financial statements of the selling company?

29. Suppose that ESPN (the sports channel) sells $10,000,000 in advertising slots to be aired during the games that it broadcasts during the NCAA basketball tournament. Suppose further that these slots are contracted for during the month of September with a downpayment of $2,000,000. The ads will be aired in March. If the fiscal year end of ESPN is December 31, how should ESPN recognize this revenue in its financial statements?

30. Suppose that The GAP (a clothing retailer) sells gift certificates for merchandise. During the Christmas holiday period, suppose that it issues $500,000 in gifts certificates. If the firm's fiscal year end is December 31, how should it recognize the issuance of these gift certificates in its financial statements at year end?

31. Suppose that the XYZ Software company produces an inventory tracking software that it sells to manufacturing companies. Further suppose that the software sells for $100,000 each and it requires the company to provide customization to the buyers' operations, which can take several months. If the fiscal year end is September 30 and the company sells ten units of the product in August, how should it recognize these "sales" in the financial statements at year end?

32. Suppose that you are the auditor of ABC Manufacturing Company and during your audit of the firm's inventory you observe a significant amount of inventory that appears to be extremely old. How would you recommend that the firm deal with this inventory and how will it affect the revenues and expenses recognized during the period? Explain the incentives that the management of the firm might have for keeping the inventory in its warehouse.

33. Assume that a company is discontinuing a line of products due to lack of profitability. It is not sure whether this discontinuance meets the criteria for separate recognition as a discontinued line of business. The alternatives are to incorporate the losses from this line within normal operations or report them as a separate line item called "discontinued operations." As a stock analyst, discuss how the alternatives might affect your analysis of the company's stock.

USING REAL DATA

34. Zale Corporation sells fine jewelry and giftware in a chain of stores nationwide. The following footnotes appeared in the 2001 annual report along with the income statement below:

Revenue Recognition

The Company recognizes revenue in accordance with the Securities and Exchange Commissions Staff Accounting Bulletin No. 101, Revenue Recognition in Financial Statements (SAB 101). Revenue related to merchandise sales is recognized at the time of the sale, reduced by a provision for returns. The provision for sales returns is based on historical evidence of the Company s return rate. Repair revenues are recognized when the service is complete and the merchandise is delivered to the customers. Net Sales include amortized extended service agreements (ESA) which are amortized over the two-year service agreement period. ESA revenue and related expenses were previously netted in selling, general, and administrative expenses. Prior periods sales and cost of sales have been restated to reflect ESA revenue. The amortized ESA revenues were $25.0 million, $20.8 million, and $16.8 million for the years ended July 31, 2001, 2000, and 1999, respectively, and related ESA costs were $12.5 million, $10.8 million, and $9.5 million for the years ended July 31, 2001, 2000, and 1999, respectively.

Advertising Expenses are charged against operations when incurred and are a component of selling, general, and administrative expenses in the consolidated income statements. Amounts charged against operations were $78.5 million, $66.4 million, and $49.0 million for the years ended July 31, 2001, 2000, and 1999, respectively, net of amounts contributed by vendors to the Company. The amounts of prepaid advertising at July 31, 2001 and 2000, are $6.0 million and $6.4 million, respectively, and are classified as components of other assets in the Consolidated Balance Sheet.

Unusual Charges—Executives

Effective September 6, 2000, Robert J. DiNicola retired as Chairman of the Board but remained as a nonemployee member of the Board. In connection with his severance arrangement, the Company agreed to pay certain benefits of approximately $1.9 million consisting principally of an amount equivalent to one year of salary and bonus and other severance-related benefits including the accelerated vesting of certain options held by Mr. DiNicola.

Additionally, the Board approved the provision to Mr. DiNicola by the Company of a full recourse, $2.2 million interest-bearing loan at 8.74 percent for the sole purpose of purchasing 125,000 stock options prior to their expiration. The Company also extended the exercise period on an additional 500,000 stock options set to expire on September 6, 2002 to the earlier of the original ten-year term (to expire July 9, 2007), the maximum term pursuant to the Company's stock option plan, or two years after Mr. DiNicola leaves the Board of Directors. Based on the intrinsic value of these stock options on the modification date, no compensation charge was recorded by the Company.

Effective February 12, 2001, Beryl B. Raff resigned as Chairman of the Board and Chief Executive Officer. In connection with her resignation, the Company agreed to pay certain benefits of approximately $2.5 million consisting principally of an amount equivalent to three years of salary and other severance-related benefits including accelerated vesting of certain options and restricted stock.

Robert J. DiNicola was reappointed as Chairman of the Board and Chief Executive Officer, effective February 21, 2001, under a three-year contract with terms substantially consistent with his previous contract when he held the same position. In August 2001, the Company entered into a five-year employment agreement with Mr. DiNicola effective upon Mr. DiNicola's reelection as Chairman of the Board and Chief Executive Officer, replacing the earlier employment agreement. In April 2001, the Company extended a $2.1 million, three-year interest bearing loan at 7.25 percent to Mr. DiNicola for the purpose of purchasing a home. In August 2001, the loan was modified and extended with the entire principal amount to be repaid in August 2006.

Nonrecurring Charge

Upon the return of Robert J. DiNicola as Chairman and Chief Executive Officer on February 21, 2001, the Company performed an in-depth review to determine the inventory that was not of a quality consistent with the strategic direction of the Company's brands. As a result of that review, the Company recorded a nonrecurring charge in Cost of Sales of $25.2 million to adjust the valuation of such inventory and provide for markdowns to liquidate or sell-through the inventory.

ZALE CORP.: Income Statement	07/31/2001	07/31/2000	07/31/1999
Net sales	$2,068,242,000	$1,814,362,000	$1,445,634,000
Cost of sales	1,034,970,000	930,826,000	746,663,000
Nonrecurring charge	25,236,000	0	0
Gross margin	1,008,036,000	883,536,000	698,971,000
Selling, general, and administrative Expenses	804,780,000	630,687,000	509,570,000
Depreciation and amortization expense	58,290,000	42,431,000	29,478,000
Unusual item—executive transactions	4,713,000	0	0
Operating earnings	140,253,000	210,418,000	159,923,000
Interest expense, net	6,857,000	32,178,000	30,488,000
Earnings before income taxes	133,396,000	178,240,000	129,435,000
Income taxes	51,348,000	66,726,000	48,503,000
Net earnings	$ 82,048,000	$ 111,514,000	$ 80,932,000

a. Provide support for Zale's revenue recognition policy for its extended service agreements.

b. From an analyst's point of view, discuss why the change in reporting ESA's as part of revenue rather than as an offset to expenses would be important.

c. From an analyst's point of view, discuss why the disclosure of advertising costs by year might be important.

d. From an analyst's point of view, discuss how you might use the disclosures concerning the unusual and nonrecurring charges to assist you in predicting the stock price for Zale.

35. Lands' End, Incorporated is a direct merchant of clothing and other cloth products that are sold primarily through catalog mailings. The cost of catalog production and mailing is fairly substantial for a company such as Lands' End. Discuss how the costs associated with catalog production and mailing should be treated for accounting purposes. Frame your answer in terms of the revenue recognition criteria and the matching concept discussed in this chapter.

36. Many consumer electronics retailers have offered extended warranty contracts to their customers. These contracts typically provide warranty coverage beyond the manufacturer's warranty period, usually anywhere between 12 and 60 months from the date of purchase. The cost of these contracts is generally collected at the time of the purchase of the product. The following is the revenue recognition Disclosure for Best Buy, Inc.:

Revenue Recognition

We recognize revenues from the sale of merchandise at the time the merchandise is sold. We recognize service revenues at the time the service is provided, the sales price is fixed or determinable, and collectibility is reasonably assured.

We sell extended service contracts, called Performance Service Plans, on behalf of an unrelated third party. In jurisdictions where we are not deemed to be the obligor on the contract at the time of sale, commissions are recognized in revenues at the time of sale. In jurisdictions where we are deemed to be the obligor on the contract at the time of sale, commissions are recognized in revenues ratably over the term of the service contract.

Discuss why Best Buy's revenue recognition policy, with regard to commissions on Performance Service Plans, is different in different jurisdictions. Base your defense on the nature of the transaction and the revenue recognition criteria found in GAAP. In jurisdictions in which they are the obligor, what might happen to them should the third party not be able to live up to this agreement?

37. In the early 1990s a new business emerged to help individuals deal with the financial burdens of terminal illnesses, such as AIDS. If a terminally ill person has a life insurance policy, an investor group of companies could buy the insurance policy from the individual for a lump sum settlement amount. The seller could then use the proceeds to pay their bills. The buyer agrees to continue to make the premium payments until the individual dies and then collects the proceeds of the insurance policy upon death. These types of agreements are called viatical settlements. Depending on the estimated life span of the individual and the creditworthiness of the insurance company, the buyer might offer somewhere between 25 to 80 percent of the face value of the policy.

a. If you were an investor, how would you decide how much to pay for a given viatical agreement?

b. Having agreed on a price, how would you recognize revenue from this agreement (assume for the purposes of this question that there is more than one year from the inception of the agreement to the death of the seller) over the life of the contract?

c. Given your revenue recognition method outlined in part b, how would you treat the payment of premiums over the life of the contract?

d. Discuss any ethical dilemmas that the buyers of viatical agreements might face in the conduct of their business.

BEYOND THE BOOK

38. Using an electronic database, search for a company that has changed its revenue recognition methods during the last three years. Answer the following questions:

a. Describe the method that was used before the change as well as the new method.

b. Does the company give a reason for the change? If so, describe the change; if not, speculate on why the change occurred.

c. How significant an effect did the change have on the firm's financial statements? As an investor, how would you view this change?

d. Did the auditor agree with the change? Do you agree and why?

Prepare a short two- to three-page paper to respond to these questions.

Financial Statements: Measuring Cash Flow

After reading this chapter you should be able to:

1 Understand and interpret the information about operating, investing, and financing activities found in the cash flow statement.

2 Explain the relationship between the cash flow statement and changes in balance sheet accounts.

3 Construct a cash flow statement using the indirect method.

4 Define free cash flows and explain how they can be determined from the Statement of Cash Flows.

Moody's Investor Service announced it was reviewing the debt rating for Georgia-Pacific (GP), citing concerns with Georgia-Pacific's weakening cash flow. Mark Gray, an analyst with Moody's said, "We looked at the company's position and we were concerned about the scope of the asset sales to Willamette and the weakening cash flow over the near term that would limit their debt reduction ability."

The announcement of Moody's review of Georgia-Pacific's debt rating highlights the importance of strong cash flows to a company's value. A downgrade in debt raises the cost of borrowing for Georgia-Pacific as well as lowers equity values. In this chapter we discuss the content and meaning of the information contained in the statement of cash flows.

Broadly speaking, the statement of cash flows reflects the operating, investing, and financing activities of the firm described in Chapter 1. As such, the statement of cash flows provides different information than the income statement that focuses on changes in stockholders' equity arising from operations. The cash flow statement explains changes in cash in terms of changes in noncash accounts appearing on successive balance sheets. These changes are not limited to those involving operations, but include those involving investing and financing.

Further, with respect to operating activities, the cash flow statement offers a different perspective than reflected on the income statement. As we discussed in Chapter 4, firms determine net income on an accrual basis by the application of revenue and expense recognition criteria. Recall that under the accrual basis of accounting, revenue may be earned and expenses incurred before or after the cash flows to which they relate. Net income, therefore, reflects the revenues earned and the expenses incurred by the firm as a result of its operating activities during the period, *not* the operating cash inflows and outflows. Operating cash flows may precede or follow the recognition of revenues or expenses on the income statement. Timing issues thus separate the recognition of income from the actual cash flows of the firm.

For example, if a firm's sales grow rapidly but a significant lag exists between the cash outflows to make the company's product and the inflows from the sales collections, the firm may experience a severe liquidity crisis. In other words, a firm may possess insufficient available cash to make the required payments for items such as salaries and accounts payable. This liquidity crisis may then spark the need to obtain additional financing to pay bills and to support the company's growth. If analysts focused on only the income statement, they would miss the liquidity crisis. Further, as the income statement does not report on the investing and financing activities of the firm, analysts would not see any attempts made by the firm to address the liquidity crisis (e.g., through additional financing or a slowdown in investing). The cash flow statement not only makes any liquidity crisis transparent, it also indicates how a firm addresses the crises. Because it contains such crucial data, let's take a closer look at the information a typical cash flow statement provides.

CASH FLOW STATEMENT COMPONENTS

SFAS 95 (FASB, SFAS No. 95, 1987) requires that all companies issue a cash flow statement and provides guidelines regarding its format. The Statement of Cash Flows provides information about changes in cash flows from all sources: operating, investing, and financing activities of an entity.

CASH FLOW FROM OPERATING ACTIVITIES

Cash flow from operations includes cash inflows from sales of goods and services to customers, and cash outflows from expenses related to the sales of goods and services to customers, such as cost of goods sold and selling and administrative expenses. In fact, cash from operations can be viewed as a measure of cash-basis

TECH DATA CORP.: Cash Flow

	01/31/2002	01/31/2001	01/31/2000
Cash flows from operating activities:			
Cash received from customers	$17,511,511,000	$20,114,486,000	$16,788,960,000
Cash paid to suppliers and employees	(16,406,265,000)	(20,047,551,000)	(16,684,316,000)
Interest paid	(55,871,000)	(94,823,000)	(69,554,000)
Income taxes paid	(72,745,000)	(62,048,000)	(34,176,000)
Net cash provided by (used in) operating activities	976,630,000	(89,936,000)	914,000
Cash flows from investing activities:			
Acquisition of businesses, net of cash acquired	(183,000)	(19,198,000)	(42,898,000)
Expenditures for property and equipment	(28,466,000)	(38,079,000)	(59,038,000)
Software development costs	(20,719,000)	(22,705,000)	(18,381,000)
Net cash used in investing activities	(49,368,000)	(79,982,000)	(120,317,000)
Cash flows from financing activities:			
Proceeds from the issuance of common stock, net of related tax benefit	36,432,000	35,539,000	19,663,000
Net (repayments) borrowings on revolving credit loans	(1,118,167,000)	248,712,000	99,447,000
Proceeds from issuance of long-term debt, net of expense	284,200,000	0	0
Principal payments on long-term debt	(634,000)	(557,000)	(162,000)
Net cash (used in) provided by financing activities	(798,169,000)	283,694,000	118,948,000
Effect of change in year end of certain subsidiaries (Note 3)	0	0	23,626,000
Effect of exchange rate changes on cash	(10,091,000)	(6,637,000)	0
Net increase in cash and cash equivalents	119,002,000	107,139,000	23,171,000
Cash and cash equivalents at beginning of year	138,925,000	31,786,000	8,615,000
Cash and cash equivalents at end of year	$ 257,927,000	$ 138,925,000	$ 31,786,000

Exhibit 5.1
Direct Method Cash Flow Statement

THE REAL WORLD

Tech Data Corp.

earnings because it measures the cash inflows from sales in the period of collection and the cash outflows for expenses in the period of payment.

There are two approaches to presenting cash flow from operations, the **direct method** and the **indirect method.** Under the direct method, a firm first reports cash received from revenue-producing activities, and then subtracts its cash payments for expenses. Exhibit 5.1 illustrates this type of statement (see the shaded operating section). Notice that the company shown (Tech Data, a distributor of hardware and software products) combined its operating cash outflows to employees and suppliers into a single line item.

In contrast, the indirect method starts with net income and shows the adjustments necessary to arrive at cash flows from operations. Exhibit 5.2 shows this method in the statements of Tofutti Brands, Inc. (a producer of soy-based products).

FASB 95 allows the use of either method, as both methods produce identical results of cash from operations. However, most firms use the indirect approach. As a result, FASB 95 requires firms that report under the direct

Exhibit 5.2
Indirect Method Cash Flow
Statement

THE REAL WORLD

Tofutti Brands

TOFUTTI BRANDS, Inc.: Cash Flow	12/29/2001	12/29/2000	12/30/1999
Cash flows from operating activities:			
Net income	$ 1,150,000	$ 956,000	$ 850,000
Adjustments to reconcile net income to net cash flows from operating activities:			
Provision for bad debts	40,000	60,000	60,000
Accrued interest on investments	0	(34,000)	(3,000)
Deferred taxes	(119,000)	(176,000)	332,000
Change in assets and liabilities:			
Accounts receivable	(625,000)	(105,000)	64,000
Inventories	92,000	(342,000)	17,000
Prepaid expenses	(1,000)	(1,000)	5,000
Accounts payable and accrued expenses	9,000	17,000	(51,000)
Accrued compensation	0	175,000	115,000
Income taxes payable	(144,000)	209,000	103,000
Net cash flows from operating activities	402,000	759,000	1,492,000
Cash flows from investing activities:			
Proceeds from redemption of investments	269,000	0	(250,000)
Other assets	(144,000)	(22,000)	(22,000)
Net cash flows from investing activities	125,000	(22,000)	(272,000)
Cash flows from financing activities:			
Notes payable	(8,000)	(22,000)	(18,000)
Issuance of common stock	35,000	50,000	84,000
Purchase of treasury stock	(436,000)	(247,000)	0
Net cash flows from financing activities	(409,000)	(219,000)	66,000
Net change in cash and equivalents	118,000	518,000	1,286,000
Cash and equivalents, at beginning of period	2,211,000	1,693,000	407,000
Cash and equivalents, at end of period	$ 2,329,000	$2,211,000	$1,693,000
Supplemental cash flow information:			
Interest paid		$ 2,000	$ 5,000
Income taxes paid	$ 750,000	$ 579,000	$ 151,000

method to also disclose the operating section data prepared under the indirect method (see Exhibit 5.3). Compare the net cash from operations in both Exhibits 5.1 and 5.3, and note how the amounts are identical. However, you can see that the indirect method disclosure (Exhibit 5.3) provides more information about investments in current operating assets net of operating liabilities than the direct method (Exhibit 5.1).

TECH DATA CORP.: Cash Flow	01/31/2002	01/31/2001	01/31/2000
Reconciliation of net income to net cash provided by (used in) operating activities:			
Net income	$ 110,777,000	$177,983,000	$127,501,000
Adjustments to reconcile net income to net cash provided by (used in) operating activities:			
Depreciation and amortization	63,488,000	63,922,000	57,842,000
Provision for losses on accounts receivable	40,764,000	41,447,000	40,877,000
Special charges (Note 13)	27,000,000	0	0
Deferred income taxes	(11,848,000)	(1,789,000)	1,306,000
Changes in assets and liabilities:			
Decrease (increase) in accounts receivable	314,000,000	(313,197,000)	(202,790,000)
Decrease (increase) in inventories	702,219,000	(146,093,000)	(220,585,000)
(Increase) in prepaid and other assets	(6,248,000)	(11,603,000)	(25,430,000)
(Decrease) increase in accounts payable	(264,722,000)	11,863,000	136,748,000
Increase in accrued expenses	1,200,000	87,531,000	85,445,000
Total adjustments	865,853,000	(267,919,000)	(126,587,000)
Net cash provided by (used in) operating activities	$976,630,000	($89,936,000)	$ 914,000

CASH FLOW FROM INVESTING ACTIVITIES

Investing activities involve the cash flow effect of transactions related to a company's long-term assets and investments. Examples include cash paid or received to purchase or sell property, plant, and equipment; investments in securities of other companies; and acquisitions of other companies. The investing activities section provides information about how a company uses its cash to generate future earnings. Investments represent opportunities for future earnings growth. For a growth company, we would normally expect cash from investing activities to be a net outflow, although this depends on the company's growth strategy.

For example, in Tech Data's cash flow statement (Exhibit 5.1), you see significant annual investments in property and equipment, and software development. Contrast this with Tofutti's cash flow statement (Exhibit 5.2), which includes little activity in the investing section. The company primarily leases its facilities (the cash flows from leasing would appear in the operating section) and therefore does not have significant investments in plant and equipment.

The investment section of the cash flow statement is where you would also see investments in other companies including acquisitions. You can see this kind of activity in Tech Data's statements. Note that in most acquisitions the investment cash flow occurs on the date of acquisition. Subsequent to the date of acquisition, the cash flows from operating the newly acquired company will start to appear in the operating section. At the date of acquisition, the firm reports new assets and liabilities from the acquisition (e.g., receivables, inventory, PP&E, accounts payable) that would appear in the firm's balance sheet as of the acquisition date. If a firm acquired a new company mid-year, then the net change in certain asset accounts (such as inventories) would include the changes due to operations and the changes due to the acquisition.

CASH FLOW FROM FINANCING ACTIVITIES

This section of the cash flow statement provides information about transactions with owners and creditors. Financing activities include issuance and repayment of debt such as loans, bank advances, and bonds payable, as well as issuances and repurchases of stock and payments of dividends.

Tofutti (Exhibit 5.2) shows relatively minor outflows of cash to repay notes payable. The remaining transactions relate to issuance of stock and repurchase of shares that are held in its treasury account. Tech Data's statements (Exhibit 5.1) show significantly more activity related to long-term debt.

Now that you can identify the components of the cash flow statement, how do you use its information? One of the best ways is by understanding the mechanics of preparing a cash flow statement. Going through the preparation process can shed light on how a firm generates and uses cash. Additionally, reconciling a firm's cash flow statement to its balance sheet and income statement can be a useful tool for financial statement analysis.

PREPARATION OF THE STATEMENT OF CASH FLOWS

In this section, we'll show how to prepare a cash flow statement (indirect method) using Biohealth, Inc. (BHT), the fictitious wholesale company we discussed in previous chapters. Exhibit 5.4 shows the balance sheets for BHT at 12/31/20X2 and 12/31/20X1. Exhibit 5.5 shows the income statement for BHT for the year ending 12/31/20X2.

We use a T-account worksheet to determine the net effects of the transactions for BHT for 20X2 on the cash account, as shown in Exhibit 5.6. Note that we use this worksheet only to assist in the construction of the cash flow statement. Do not confuse this worksheet with the firm's accounting system that contains the actual entries made to the system. In fact, you can also use a simple spreadsheet instead of a T-account worksheet.

The first step is to place the beginning and ending balances of all of the accounts from the balance sheet in the T-accounts, as shown in Exhibit 5.6. Then, we analyze the changes in the various accounts on the balance sheet and classify them into operating, investing, and financing activities. In order to do this, we rely on information from the income statement as well as any additional information provided about the company's operating, financing, and investing transactions. For example, the following additional information applies to the transactions of BHT for the year ending 12/31/20X2:

Exhibit 5.4
BHT Balance Sheet

Biohealth, Inc. (BHT)
Balance Sheet ($ in millions)

	As of 12/31/20X2	As of 12/31/20X1
Assets		
Current assets:		
Cash	$ 1,510	$ 567
Accounts receivable	3,650	2,464
Inventory	4,400	3,920
Prepaid expenses	360	0
Total current assets	9,920	7,101
Property, plant, and equipment (PPE)	950	540
Less: accumulated depreciation	(210)	(60)
Net property plant and equipment	740	480
	$10,660	$7,581
Liabilities and Stockholders' Equity		
Liabilities:		
Current liabilities:		
Accounts payable	$ 6,671	$5,140
Long-term debt:		
Notes payable	950	400
Total liabilities	7,621	5,540
Stockholders' equity		
Common stock	300	250
Additional paid-in capital	1,950	1,375
Retained earnings	789	266
Total stockholders' equity	3,039	2,041
	$10,660	$7,581

Exhibit 5.5
BHT Income Statement

Biohealth, Inc. (BHT)
Income Statement

	Year ending 12/31/20X2
Revenues	$43,850
Less: Cost of goods sold	(37,272)
Gross profit	6,578
Selling and administrative expenses	5,320
Depreciation expense	150
Interest expense	85
Net income	$1,023

Exhibit 5.6
BHT Cash Flow T-Account
Worksheet

BHT Cash Flow T-Account Worksheet Set Up

	Cash		Accumulated Depreciation—PPE	
Bal.	567		60	Bal.
Operating:				
Investing:			210	Bal.
			Accounts payable	
Financing:			5,140	Bal.
Bal.	1,510		6,671	Bal.
	Accounts receivable		Notes payable	
Bal.	2,464		400	Bal.
			950	Bal.
Bal.	3,650			
	Inventory		Common Stock	
Bal.	3,920		250	Bal.
Bal.	4,400		300	Bal.
	Prepaid Expenses		Additional Paid-in capital	
Bal.	0		1,375	Bal.
Bal.	360		1,950	Bal.
	PPE		Retained Earnings	
Bal.	540		266	Bal.
Bal.	950		789	Bal.

1. All inventory is purchased on credit from suppliers.
2. All sales to customers are for credit.
3. Borrowed $550 million during 20X2.
4. Issued 50 million shares of $1 par stock at $12.50 per share during 20X2.
5. Declared and paid $500 million in dividends to shareholders during 20X2.

Items 1 and 2 simply summarize common assumptions and need not correspond to the transactions that actually occurred. Items 3 through 5 provide information that you would find in the Statement of Stockholders' Equity and Notes to the Financial Statements.

We are now ready to create the worksheet entries for the cash flow statement. The basic approach is to examine each balance sheet account (other than cash) that changed and then assess its effect on cash. Next, we create a worksheet entry to show this effect on cash along with the corresponding change in the balance sheet account. Once we analyze all of the balance sheet accounts and complete the worksheet entries, we should have the basis of our cash flow statement. Let's start now with determining the worksheet entries for the operating section and then proceed through the investing and financing sections.

WORKSHEET ENTRIES FOR CASH FROM OPERATIONS

The starting point typically begins with analyzing the change in retained earnings. In the indirect approach, we record net income in the Cash account of the worksheet (as well as in the Retained Earnings account, to ensure that debits equal credits) as if it increased cash. We know, however, that not all revenues increase cash and not all expenses use cash. Therefore, subsequent entries will make adjustments to correct for the noncash components of earnings.

We obtain net income from the income statement in Exhibit 5.5, giving us the first entry:

| (1) | Cash | 1,023 | |
| | Retained Earnings | | 1,023 |

We now need to correct our "mistake" of reporting net income as if it were all cash. We start with adjustments to correct the revenue portion of net income.

Adjusting Net Income

Changes in current assets and liabilities in the operating section serve to correct line items in the net income number to their cash flow equivalent. For revenues, these adjustments serve to undo the effects of recognizing revenues when earned rather than as the cash is received, and for expenses the effects of recognizing them when incurred rather than when paid. We can thus view increases in current operating assets as requiring cash (and decreases providing cash) and increases in current operating liabilities as providing cash (and decreases requiring cash). Exhibit 5.7 summarizes the effects of these changes. With this understanding of adjustments, let's return now to our BHT example.

Exhibit 5.7
Adjustments to Net Income
Using the Indirect Method

Positive adjustments to income to determine cash from operations result from:

Decreases in current operating assets (A/R, inventory, prepaid assets, etc.)
Increases in current operating liabilities (A/P, Salaries Payable, etc.)*

Negative adjustments to income to determine cash from operations result from:

Increases in current operating assets other than cash
Decreases in current operating liabilities

*Notes Payable and the Current Portion of Long-Term Debt are typically not considered to be a part of operating liabilities even though they are generally classified as current liabilities. Also, there are instances where operating liabilities are classified as noncurrent and changes in those liabilities are included in the operating section of the cash flow statement.

Revenue Adjustments to Net Income

Because sales revenue is recorded on an accrual basis, not when cash is collected, we need to adjust income for the difference between sales revenue recognized and cash collected on accounts receivable (AR). This difference can be found in the change in the accounts receivable balance. In the case of BHT, accounts receivable increased, meaning that cash collections on account were less than the amount of sales recognized. Recall that we assume that all sales are on account. Therefore, we calculate cash collections on accounts receivable as follows:

$$
\begin{aligned}
\text{Cash Collections} &= \text{Beginning AR} + \text{Sales} - \text{Ending AR} \\
&= \text{Sales} - (\text{Ending AR} - \text{Beginning AR}) \\
&= \text{Sales} - \text{Change in AR}
\end{aligned}
$$

For BHT, cash collections for 20X1 are therefore:

$$
\begin{aligned}
\text{Cash Collections} &= \$2,464 + \$43,850 - \$3,650 \\
\text{Cash Collections} &= \$43,850 - (\$3,650 - \$2,464) \\
&= \$43,850 - \$1,186 = \$42,664
\end{aligned}
$$

> Management could possibly report fraudulent earnings by reporting nonexistent sales and accounts receivable. Note however that the increase in sales that result from this behavior would be offset by the increase in receivables in the determination of operating cash flows; i.e., operating cash flows are unaffected by accruals per se. It would be far more difficult to implement fraud that affected cash flows.

Because cash collections are less than sales, when we reported net income in the cash account, we overstated the effect of sales on cash. As a result, we need to adjust by reducing cash for the increase in accounts receivable. A simpler alternative to the previous calculation would be to identify the change in the accounts receivable account. With a net debit to the accounts receivable account, by default, we would need to credit the Cash account for this difference, thereby reducing the amount reported in net income in the Cash account from Transaction 1. The entry to record this is:

(2)	Accounts receivable	1,186	
	Cash		1,186

This negative adjustment to cash matches the increase in the current operating asset, accounts receivable.

Cost of Goods Sold Adjustment to Net Income

After revenues, cost of goods sold is typically the first expense that appears on the income statement. Understanding the cash flow impact of the cost of inventory sales requires considering two separate timing relationships: (1) the relationship between the purchase of inventory (INV) and its recognition as a cost when sold, and (2) the relationship between the purchase of inventory and the payment for that inventory.

Recall from Chapter 3 the cost of goods sold equation:

$$
\begin{aligned}
\text{Cost of Goods Sold} &= \text{Beginning Inventory} + \text{Purchases} - \text{Ending INV} \\
&= \text{Purchases} - (\text{Ending INV} - \text{Beginning INV}) \\
&= \text{Purchases} - \text{Change in INV}
\end{aligned}
$$

Because we assume that all inventory is purchased on accounts payable (AP), we therefore calculate cash paid for purchases as:

$$
\begin{aligned}
\text{Payments} &= \text{Beginning AP} + \text{Purchases} - \text{Ending AP} \\
&= \text{Purchases} - (\text{Ending AP} - \text{Beginning AP}) \\
&= \text{Purchases} - \text{Change in AP}
\end{aligned}
$$

The difference between the expense (cost of goods sold) on the income statement and the cash paid to suppliers can be explained by the change in accounts payable less the change in inventory:

$$
\begin{aligned}
&\text{Cost of Goods Sold} - \text{Payments} \\
&= (\text{Purchases} - \text{Change in INV}) - (\text{Purchases} - \text{Change in AP}) \\
&= \text{Purchases} - \text{Purchases} - \text{Change in INV} + \text{Change in AP} \\
&= \text{Change in AP} - \text{Change in INV}
\end{aligned}
$$

The cost of goods sold for BHT was $37,272 during the current year. We can apply the above equations to calculate the purchases for the period as $37,752 (= CGS + Ending INV − Beginning INV = 37,272 + 4,400 − 3,920). Then we can use the purchases to calculate the payments for the period as $36,222 (= Purchases + Beginning AP − Ending AP = 37,752 + 5,140 − 6,671). The difference between the cost of goods sold reported in income and the payments is therefore $1,051 ($37,272 − 36,222). Notice that this amount equals the difference between the change in AP (1,531) and the change in INV (480).

Again, we can avoid calculations by recording an entry that explains the change in the balance of both inventory and accounts payable with the corresponding entry to the operating section of the cash account, as follows:

(3)	Inventory	480	
	Cash		480

The change in accounts payable is:

| (4) | Cash | 1,531 | |
| | Acct. Payable | | 1,531 |

Depreciation Adjustment to Net Income

Depreciation is a noncash expense that a firm recognizes for financial reporting. It represents the allocation of the cost of plant and equipment over its useful life. Because depreciation expense is noncash, the amount of expense is added back to earnings to arrive at cash from operations. Sometimes depreciation is mistakenly thought of as a source of cash. This is incorrect in that depreciation does not generate cash for a business. Rather, it is an expense that does not require the use of cash (beyond the amount previously reported as an investment activity on earlier cash flow statements).

For many companies, depreciation is a large expense. Hence, cash from operations may be considerably larger than net income. However, because BHT is a wholesaling company and it leases its warehouses, it does not have proportionately as much depreciation as companies with large amounts of plant and equipment (e.g., in Exhibit 5.3 you can see a fairly substantial adjustment for depreciation for Tech Data Corp.). The entry to add back the depreciation expense to net income is:

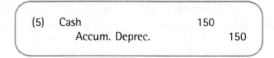

| (5) | Cash | 150 | |
| | Accum. Deprec. | | 150 |

Prepaid Expense Adjustment to Net Income

BHT also had an increase in its prepaid expenses account. While we could calculate the differences between expenses related to this prepayment and the actual cash flows as we did with inventory, we can again avoid this. Instead, we simply determine how the balance in this operating asset account changes and record the appropriate entry, as follows:

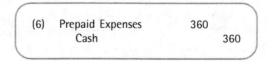

| (6) | Prepaid Expenses | 360 | |
| | Cash | | 360 |

This completes the adjustments for the operating activities for BHT, as there are no other operating asset or liability accounts to consider. Other companies might also have accrued expenses, such as salaries payable, that would require adjustment. Further, GAAP requires firms to recognize all interest and tax cash flows in the operating section, so we might also have to adjust for changes in accounts such interest payable, taxes payable, and deferred taxes.

WORKSHEET ENTRIES FOR CASH FROM INVESTING

Only one investing activity occurred for BHT for the year ending 20X2: the acquisition of property, plant, and equipment. The entry is:

(7)	Property, Plant, and Equipment	410	
	Cash		410

Analyzing the cash from investing, however, may be more complex for a company that acquires or disposes of multiple groups of assets during a period. When a company disposes of a long-term asset such as property, plant, and equipment, it may report a gain or loss in the income statement from that transaction. Notice that the cash inflow from this sale should appear in the investing section. However, the gain or loss will appear in net income (and therefore will have been included in the cash account as part of net income in Transaction 1). Should this occur, we would need to remove the gain or loss from the operating section as the cash flows associated with these transactions should appear in the investing section. To remove a gain, we would credit the cash account; to remove a loss, we would debit the cash account.

WORKSHEET ENTRIES FOR CASH FROM FINANCING

BHT had several financing transactions during 20X2, including payment of dividends of $500 million. Recall that dividends are a distribution to shareholders, and as such are not an expense to the company. Hence, dividends are considered a financing transaction. When the board of directors declares dividends, an entry is made debiting retained earnings and crediting dividends payable. Later, when the dividend is actually paid to stockholders, dividends payable is debited and cash is credited. Because there is no dividends payable account, we know that all declared dividends have also been paid. Thus, the aggregate entry to record this in the worksheet is:

(8)	Retained earnings	500	
	Cash		500

BHT also issued a note payable. This is also a financing activity that increases the amount of cash available to BHT to fund its operations. The entry is:

(9)	Cash	550	
	Note payable		550

		Cash				Accumulated Depreciation—PPE	
Bal.		567				60	**Bal.**
Operating:						150	**(5)**
Net Income	(1)	1,023	1,186	(2)	AR Increase		
Increase in AP	(4)	1,531	480	(3)	Inventory Increase		
Depreciation	(5)	150	360	(6)	Increase in	210	**Bal.**
Expense					Prepaid Expenses		
Investing:							
			410	(7)	Purchase PPE		

					Accounts Payable	
Financing:					5,140	**Bal.**
Issue note payable	(9)	550			1,531	**(4)**
Issue common stock	(10)	625	500	(8) Pay Dividends		
					6,671	**Bal.**
Bal.		1,510				

		Accounts Receivable			Notes Payable	
Bal.		2,464			400	**Bal.**
	(2)	1,186			550	**(9)**
					950	**Bal.**
Bal.		3,650				

		Inventory			Common Stock	
Bal.		3,920			250	**Bal.**
	(3)	480			50	**(10)**
Bal.		4,400			300	**Bal.**

		Prepaid Expenses			Additional Paid-In Capital	
Bal.		0			1,375	**Bal.**
	(6)	360			575	**(10)**
Bal.		360			1,950	**Bal.**

		PPE			Retained Earnings	
Bal.		540			266	**Bal.**
	(7)	410		(8) 500	1,023	**(1)**
Bal.		950			789	**Bal.**

Exhibit 5.8
T-Account Worksheet
Entries for BHT

	Year ending 12/31/20X2	Year ending 12/31/20X1
Cash from operations:		
Net income	$1,023	$416
Add: noncash expenses		
Depreciation	150	60
Changes in current assets and liabilities		
Increase in accounts receivable	(1,186)	(2,464)
Increase in inventory	(480)	(3,920)
Increase in prepaid expenses	(360)	
Increase in accounts payable	1,531	5,140
Total cash from operations	678	(768)
Cash from investing		
Purchase fixtures (PPE)	(410)	(0)
Total cash from investing	(410)	(0)
Cash from financing		
Issuance of long-term note	550	0
Issuance of common stock	625	
Dividends	(500)	(150)
Total cash from financing	675	(150)
Total change in cash	943	(918)
Cash balance 1/1/20X2	567	1,485
Cash balance 12/31/20X2	$1,510	$567

Exhibit 5.9
Statement of Cash Flows for the Years Ending 20X2 and 20X1 Biohealth, Inc (BHT)

The final financing transaction affecting cash is the issuance of common stock. We record this as follows:

(10)	Cash	625	
	Common Stock		50
	Additional Paid-In Capital		575

At this point, we have analyzed all of the changes in the balance sheet accounts other than cash and, therefore, also explained all of the changes in cash. Exhibit 5.8 shows our completed worksheet entries. We can now construct the cash flow statement from the information contained within the Cash account in Exhibit 5.8. Exhibit 5.9 shows our completed cash flow statement for 2002, along with the cash flow statement from the prior year (which we presented in Chapter 3).

SUMMARY OF CASH FLOW STATEMENT
PREPARATION—INDIRECT METHOD

To summarize, the preparation of the cash flow statement involves the following steps:

Cash from operations:
  Net income
  Add:
          Depreciation and amortization
          Losses on sales of noncurrent assets and liabilities
          Decreases in current operating assets other than cash
          Increases in operating liabilities

  Deduct:
          Gains on sales of noncurrent assets and liabilities
          Increases in current operating assets other than cash
          Decreases in current operating liabilities

Cash from investing:
  Add:
          Proceeds from sales of noncurrent assets and nonoperating current assets
          Proceeds from sales of other companies

  Deduct:
          Purchases of noncurrent assets and nonoperating current assets
          Acquisitions of other companies

Cash from financing:
  Add:
          Issuance of debt (borrowings)
          Issuance of stock

  Deduct:
          Debt repayments
          Dividends
          Stock repurchases

ARTICULATION OF THE CASH FLOW STATEMENT

As we said earlier, reconciling a firm's cash flow statement to its balance sheet and income statement can be a useful analytical tool. In simple cases, such as for Tofutti, the adjustments for changes in the various assets and liabilities that appear on the cash flow statement **articulate** with (are the same as) the corresponding changes in the balance sheet of the company. Exhibit 5.10 shows the balance sheet of Tofutti and includes a column that shows the net changes in the assets and liabilities of the firm. The operating items are highlighted. To demonstrate the articulation, look at the net change in inventories, accounts payable, and accrued expenses, and compare these changes with the net adjustments on the cash flow statement in Exhibit 5.2. Note that both the decrease in inventory and the increase in accounts payable result in a positive adjustment to net income consistent with the information in Exhibit 5.10.

The one account that does not appear to articulate is accounts receivable, where you will observe a change on the balance sheet of $585,000 and a change

TOFUTTI BRANDS, Inc.:
Balance Sheet

	12/29/2001	12/29/2000	Net Change
Assets			
Current assets:			
Cash and equivalents	$2,329,000	$2,211,000	$ 118,000
Short-term investments	0	269,000	(269,000)
Accounts receivable, net of allowance for doubtful accounts of $325,000 and $270,000, respectively	1,461,000	876,000	585,000
Inventories	816,000	908,000	(92,000)
Prepaid expenses	10,000	9,000	1,000
Deferred income taxes	478,000	359,000	119,000
Total current assets	5,094,000	4,632,000	462,000
Other assets:			
Other assets	325,000	181,000	144,000
	$5,419,000	$4,813,000	$606,000
Liabilities and stockholders' equity			
Current liabilities:			
Notes payable	$ 0	$ 8,000	($8,000)
Accounts payable and accrued expenses	155,000	146,000	9,000
Accrued compensation	375,000	375,000	0
Income taxes payable	187,000	331,000	(144,000)
Total current liabilities	717,000	860,000	(143,000)
Commitments and contingencies			
Stockholders' equity:			
Preferred stock—par value $.01 per share; authorized 100,000 shares, none issued	0	0	0
Common stock—par value $.01 per share; authorized 15,000,000 shares, issued and outstanding 6,091,267 shares at December 29, 2001 and 6,354,567 shares at December 30, 2000	61,000	64,000	(3,000)
Less: Treasury stock, at cost (18,100 shares and 122,400 shares at December 29, 2001 and December 30, 2000, respectively)	(38,000)	(247,000)	209,000
Additional paid-in capital	3,156,000	3,763,000	(607,000)
Accumulated earnings	1,523,000	373,000	1,150,000
Total stockholders' equity	4,702,000	3,953,000	749,000
Total liabilities and stockholders' equity	$5,419,000	$4,813,000	$606,000

of ($625,000) on the cash flow statement. However, the adjustment for the provision for bad debts in the cash flow statement also affects the accounts receivable account, because accounts receivable is reported net of the effects of bad debts on the balance sheet. Therefore, if you net the $40,000 adjustment for bad debts on the cash flow statement with the change in accounts receivable of ($625,000), you get the same change in net accounts receivable of $585,000

Although not all countries require preparation of a cash flow statement, cash flows are increasingly important in international markets. Many companies voluntarily disclose cash flow statements. International accounting standards (IAS Number 7) state that the cash flow statement is a basic financial statement that explains the change in cash and cash equivalents during a period. In some countries, a funds flow statement is presented. The funds statement is similar to the cash flow statement, but it reconciles changes in total working capital rather than cash.

reported on the balance sheet. We will revisit the issue of accounting for bad-debts in Chapter 7. The cash statement will not always articulate with the balance sheet primarily due to acquisitions and foreign currency translation, both of which are beyond the scope of this book.

SUPPLEMENTAL DISCLOSURES TO THE CASH FLOW STATEMENT

Companies often report supplemental disclosures on the cash flow statement. For example, GAAP requires firms to report all interest cash flows in the operating section. However, because users might want to view these amounts as financing cash flows, GAAP requires that firms disclose the dollar amount of interest cash flows that exist in the operating section. Many firms (like Tofutti) do this by providing supplemental cash flow information at the bottom of the statement, as shown in Exhibit 5.2. Other firms provide this information in a footnote to the financial statements. GAAP also requires all tax cash flows to be reported in the operating section, even though you could argue that they apply to all three sections. As a result, GAAP requires supplemental disclosure of the tax cash flows (again, see Exhibit 5.2).

In addition, a firm may engage in transactions that do not directly affect cash. However, if a transaction is considered a significant noncash activity, GAAP requires the firm to disclose this type of transaction as supplemental information. For example, Polaroid disclosed that, in 2000, it recorded noncash items of $22.9 million in cash flow from operating activities that consisted primarily of $12.0 million for the issuance of shares relating to their Retirement Savings Plan.

INTERPRETING THE CASH FLOW STATEMENT

The cash flow statement provides both insights into the effectiveness with which a company manages its cash flows, as well as signals of the underlying quality of its earnings flows. Management of cash flows is an important activity in a business. If a company's operating cash inflows are insufficient to meet operating cash outflow demands, a company may be forced to engage in additional borrowing or issuance of stock, or sale of long-term assets to meet cash needs. If the firm cannot raise sufficient cash from these sources, it may be forced into bankruptcy. For example, Kmart Corporation filed Chapter 11 bankruptcy following a slow holiday season in 2001. One source of the company's problem was the inability to pay suppliers on a timely basis due to the declining sales.

In the case of Tofutti (Exhibit 5.2), you can see that net income increased each year over the most recent three-year period of time. However, you also can observe that cash from operating activities has declined over this same period. To understand why, look to the adjustments to net income. Observe that in 2000 the three largest negative adjustments were for inventories, deferred taxes, and accounts receivable.

Although we discuss deferred taxes in greater depth later in Chapter 10, the simple explanation for now is that federal tax laws often allow or require different accounting methods to be used in calculating taxable income than those methods used to report under GAAP. In the case of depreciation, for example, the tax code provides a benefit to businesses in the form of allowing for more rapid depreciation write-offs for tax purposes than firms use for financial reporting. As a result, tax payments are deferred because taxable income (i.e., income reported for tax purposes) is usually less than income before taxes reported for financial accounting purposes. Hence, tax payments are less than the tax expense reported on net income. The difference between the actual tax liability and the tax expense reported for financial reporting is reported as an account called "deferred taxes." Notice for Tofutti that the adjustment for deferred taxes goes in different directions in different years. Negative adjustments mean that there were net, noncash, income-improving effects during the year as a result of deferred taxes, and vice versa for positive adjustments.

While taxes are a difficult item to fully explain at this point, we can provide interpretation for the other two items. The negative adjustments for both the inventory and accounts receivable balance mean that they are increasing over the year. One explanation might be an increase in the firm's sales. Looking at the income statement for Tofutti (Exhibit 5.11), sales did significantly increase in 2000 over 1999. In fact, Tofutti's sales showed a growth of approximately

TOFUTTI BRANDS, Inc.: Income Statement	12/29/2001	12/29/2000	12/30/1999
Net sales	$16,254,000	$13,343,000	$11,912,000
Cost of sales	10,550,000	8,192,000	7,349,000
Gross profit	5,704,000	5,151,000	4,563,000
Operating expenses:			
Selling	1,896,000	1,724,000	1,521,000
Marketing	391,000	277,000	199,000
Research and development	483,000	397,000	376,000
General and administrative	1,381,000	1,288,000	1,043,000
	4,151,000	3,686,000	3,139,000
Operating income	1,553,000	1,465,000	1,424,000
Other income	268,000	103,000	12,000
Income before income tax	1,821,000	1,568,000	1,436,000
Income taxes	671,000	612,000	(586,000)
Net income	$1,150,000	$956,000	$850,000

Exhibit 5.11
Income Statement

THE REAL WORLD

Tofutti Brands, Inc.

12 percent. However, the net change in inventories of $342,000 (see the cash flow statement, Exhibit 5.2) to bring the balance in inventories to $908,000 (see the balance sheet, Exhibit 5.10) seems to be approximately a 60 percent increase in inventories. This seems out of line with the growth in sales. You would want to, therefore, seek a better explanation for what happened to inventories during 2000. Tofutti explains in its 10-K that part of this increase in inventory was the result of introducing new products (as well as an increase in sales).

In 2001 the largest single adjustment ($625,000) is in accounts receivable, while inventories actually show a decline. Again, looking at the income statement, you can see that sales grew substantially in 2001. This provides some explanation for the growth in accounts receivable, but the growth in accounts receivable is much higher (67 percent) than the annual sales growth (22 percent). If you read Tofutti's annual report, you will see that management indicates that sales increased significantly in the last quarter of the year that led to the high level of accounts receivable at year end. This is obviously good news in terms of future prospects as sales are going up significantly.

However, notice that in the current period this immense growth is starting to put a strain on cash from operations. This is not unusual for a rapid-growth company, but is something that the company must take into consideration in its planning to make sure that it does not end up in a cash crisis. Because Tofutti has a significant balance in its cash account (which has also been increasing over this period of time), it seems to be in no immediate danger of a cash crisis.

Interestingly, Tofutti reported a smaller amount of bad debt expense in 2001 than in 2000 despite a considerable increase in accounts receivable. Bad debt expense reported in 2001 was $40,000 compared to $60,000 in 2000 and 1999. In Tofutti's statement, the provision for bad debts (sometimes called bad debt expense) is a deduction in arriving at net income, for the company's estimate of the sales made during the period that it does not expect to collect (customers who never pay their bill). As such it is a noncash expense.

Further, as the balance sheet shows, although Tofutti's allowance for uncollectible accounts increased about 20 percent from 2000 to 2001, it did not increase proportionately to the increase in accounts receivable. This is a potential concern because a relationship usually exists between sales, accounts receivable, and the amount of estimated bad debt expense recognized (we discuss this in more depth in Chapter 7). If Tofutti underestimated its bad debt expense during 2001, the reported net accounts receivable may be too high, leading to overstated assets and earnings for Tofutti. The fact that a significant portion of Tofutti's increased earnings has not been collected may be a red flag, signaling to investors that future cash flows may not be as strong as the income statement alone suggests.

In summary, cash from operations can provide important information about a company's current and future prospects. GAAP guidelines for revenue and expense recognition are intended to result in earnings that, in part, reflect expected future cash flows, but both revenue and expense recognition rules, even if appropriately applied, involve significant estimation. Furthermore, managers may manage earnings to meet targeted earnings numbers or analyst's forecasts. As a result, careful study of cash from operations, together with the other financial statement information, may provide clues about a company's performance not evident from either statement alone. A company with increasing receivables, inventory, and payables may show positive earnings. However, if the company fails to generate cash and pay its creditors, the company may have financial distress regardless of the earnings reported.

VALUATION IMPLICATIONS OF THE CASH FLOW STATEMENT

Cash flows can have significant implications for the valuation of firms, and firms like Procter & Gamble often refer to cash flow in their announcements of performance as shown in Exhibit 5.12.

The cash flow statement provides information not directly available from either the income statement or the balance sheet. In order for a company to retain and grow in value, it must not only earn a profit, it must also generate cash that can be used to invest in growing the business or paying dividends to shareholders. The cash flow statement provides insights not only into the sources of a company's cash, but how it uses that cash. Analysts look at both sources of information to help determine the company's ultimate profit potential.

Many companies even report performance in terms of cash flows as well as earnings. Cemex reported the following information about its 2001 fourth-quarter results (the term EBITDA stands for Earnings Before Interest, Taxes, Depreciation, and Amortization): "Cash earnings increased 11% to US$446 million, compared to US$400.5 million in the fourth quarter of 2000; lower interest expense enabled cash earnings to outpace EBITDA growth." Note that the "cash earnings" referred to in the Cemex disclosure is close to the cash from operations a firm would report on its cash flow statement except that it is before taxes and there are no adjustments for the changes in the working capital accounts (i.e., accounts receivable, inventories, accounts payable).

Analysts' estimates of the market value of firm typically rely on projections of free cash flows to equity holders as the principal input. **Free cash flows** to equity holders are the cash flows from operating activities, less cash flows used for investing activities, plus cash flows from debt financing activities, and less the increase in cash needed to sustain operations. Equivalently, if the entire increase in cash is required by operations, then free cash flows to equity holders

---

Exhibit 5.12

THE REAL WORLD
Procter & Gamble

CINCINNATI, January 31, 2002—The Procter & Gamble Company today reported that it exceeded consensus expectations for second quarter results. P&G delivered on the high end of its financial guidance for the October–December quarter, behind record quarter unit volume. For the quarter ended December 31, 2001, unit volume grew five percent versus the prior year led by double-digit growth in the health and beauty care businesses. Excluding acquisitions and divestitures, unit volume increased four percent. Net sales were $10.40 billion, up two percent versus one year ago. "We are seeing clear improvements in our results, and we're pleased to have met our commitments once again," said P&G President and Chief Executive A. G. Lafley. "We're continuing our unyielding focus on delivering better consumer value on our brands, building core categories, reducing the company's cost structure, and improving our cash flow."

are cash distributions to stockholders (dividends and stock repurchases), net of cash proceeds from stock issues. The concept is that these are cash flows that would be available to stockholders each period to provide a return to them.

To illustrate the calculation of free cash flows, consider the calculation of the free cash flows for our BHT example (refer back to Exhibit 5.11 for the line items on the cash flow statement):

Cash from operations:	$678
Cash from investing:	(410)
Cash from borrowing:	550
Change in cash:	(943)
Total free cash flows to equity:	($125)

Observe that the total free cash flows to equity (stockholders) can also be determined by subtracting proceeds from the issuance of stock from dividends ($500 − $625 = −$125). Note that we are assuming the entire change in cash ($943) is needed to support operations.

SUMMARY AND TRANSITION

In order to help determine firm value, earnings must provide a signal of future cash flows. This means that earnings should be indicative of the firm's ability to generate future cash flows. This does not imply a one-to-one correlation between the pattern of operating cash flows and earnings, but it does suggest that revenues should reflect cash inflows in a systematic manner and that expenses should likewise reflect operating cash outflows. One way to think about earnings is as a smoothing of cash flows. The cash flow statement makes the association between earnings and operating cash flows more apparent than it might be otherwise.

Cash flows from investing activities are also important. In order to grow, companies must generally invest in long-term assets. The cash flow statement provides information about asset replacements as well as investments in new assets. The difference between operating cash flows and investing cash flows is a measure of the extent to which the company is able to finance its growth internally.

Cash flows from financing activities show amounts raised externally from creditors and stockholders, net of repayments and dividends. Careful analysis of this section provides indications of the company's debt commitments and dependency of stockholders in obtaining the cash necessary to sustain operating and investing activities.

We will return to an analysis of the information contained in the cash flow statement in the next chapter. As is probably evident from reading this chapter, full understanding of the cash flow statement can be daunting. While the cash flow statement can be complex, an investment in understanding its information is worth the time for anyone with a serious interest in interpreting and using financial statements. The cash flow statement can be a useful tool to help filter the information provided in the balance sheet and income statement in order to get a more complete view of a company's past and future expected performance.

END OF CHAPTER MATERIAL

KEY TERMS

Articulate
Direct Method

Free Cash Flows
Indirect Method

ASSIGNMENT MATERIAL

REVIEW QUESTIONS

1. Discuss why it is important for firms to prepare a cash flow statement in addition to an income statement.

2. Discuss how a firm's receivables, inventory, and payables policies affect cash flow relative to the income produced in a given period.

3. What is meant by a lead/lag relationship in terms of the cash flow statement?

4. For a firm with a cash flow problem, list at least three potential reasons for the problem, and suggest a possible solution for each of these reasons.

5. Describe the three major categories of cash flows that are required to be disclosed by SFAS 95.

6. Discuss the difference between the direct and indirect (reconciliation) methods for constructing the operation section of the cash flow statement.

7. Depreciation is a source of cash. Explain your reasons for agreeing or disagreeing with this statement.

APPLYING YOUR KNOWLEDGE

8. In what section of the cash flow statement (operating, investing, or financing) would each of the following items appear?
   a. Purchase of net plant, property, and equipment
   b. Proceeds from a bank loan
   c. Collections from customers
   d. Dividends to stockholders
   e. Proceeds from the sale of marketable securities (stocks and bonds)
   f. Retirements of debt
   g. Change in accounts receivable
   h. Net income
   i. Gain/loss from the sale of plant, property, and equipment
   j. Cash proceeds from the sale of plant, property, and equipment

9. Explain why a high sales growth rate can create significant cash flow problems for a company.

10. Explain the timing of the cash flows related to the purchase, use, and ultimately the sale of property, plant, and equipment.

11. Discuss the classification of interest cash flows in the statement of cash flows under SFAS No. 95 and discuss why you believe this is either appropriate or not.

12. For each of the transactions listed below,

   a. Indicate the effect on balance sheet categories in the following format:

Trans. #	Cash	Other Current Assets	Noncurrent Assets	Current Liabilities	Noncurrent Liabilities	Owners' Equity

   b. State, for the transactions affecting cash, whether they relate to an operating, investing, or financing activity.

   Transactions:

   1. Credit purchases, $10,000
   2. Cash paid to suppliers, $8,000
   3. Credit sales, $25,000
   4. Cost of goods sold, $15,000
   5. Cash payments received on accounts receivable, $18,000
   6. Salaries accrued, $1,500
   7. Salaries paid (previously accrued), $1,000
   8. Machine purchased for $800 in cash
   9. Depreciation expense, $200
   10. Borrowed (long-term) $5,000 to purchase plant
   11. Interest of $50 is accrued and paid on the amount borrowed for the purchase of the plant
   12. Debentures worth $1,000 are issued
   13. Equipment having book value of $700 is sold for $700 cash
   14. Dividends declared, $350
   15. Dividends paid, $200
   16. Insurance premium for the next year paid, $175
   17. 1000 shares of stock issued at $1 per share
   18. Rent received for building, $250
   19. Income taxes accrued and paid, $325

13. For each of the transactions listed below,

   a. Indicate the effect on balance sheet categories in the following format:

Trans. #	Cash	Other Current Assets	Noncurrent Assets	Current Liabilities	Noncurrent Liabilities	Owners' Equity

   b. State, for the transactions affecting cash, whether they relate to an operating, investing, or financing activity.

   Transactions:

   1. 5,000 shares of common stock are issued at $10 per share.
   2. Plant, property, and equipment worth $120,000 is purchased for $50,000 in cash and the balance in common stock.

3. Rent payments of $5,000 are received in advance.

4. Sales contracts for $100,000 are signed and a $25,000 deposit is received in cash.

5. Merchandise inventory worth $85,000 is purchased on account.

6. Goods worth $15,000 were found defective and returned to suppliers. These goods had been purchased on account.

7. Sales were $175,000 of which $100,000 was on account.

8. Cash is paid to suppliers in the amount of $60,000.

9. Equipment recorded at $10,000 was destroyed by fire.

10. The company purchased 500 shares of X Company stock at $5 per share for short-term investment purposes.

11. The company purchased 2,000 shares of Z Company at $8 per share in an effort to buy a controlling interest in the company (a supplier).

12. Interest expense for the year amounted to $2,500 and was paid in cash.

13. The sales contract in question 4 was cancelled. $10,000 of the deposit was returned and the rest was forfeited.

14. A bank loan for $75,000 was taken out and is due in five years.

15. Equipment with a cost of $50,000 was sold for $60,000. The $60,000 was in the form of a note.

16. During the year, warranty services costing $3,500 were provided to customers. A provision for warranty services was provided in a separate transaction.

17. Depreciation for the year totaled $20,000.

18. Dividends of $10,000 were declared and $5,000 remained unpaid at year end.

19. Patents on a new manufacturing process were purchased for $5,000.

20. Research and development expenses amounted to $15,000 and were charged to expense as incurred.

14. Compute the cash flow from operations in each of the following cases:

	I	II	III
Sales Revenues	$25,000	$35,000	$65,000
Depreciation Expense	3,000	5,000	20,000
Cost of Goods Sold	15,000	38,000	41,000
Other Expenses	1,500	700	1,200
Dividends Paid	3,000	–	1,000
Increase (Decrease) in:			
Inventories	5,000	(10,000)	15,000
Accounts Receivable	3,500	1,000	(2,000)
Prepayments	(500)	(1,000)	1,800
Salaries Payable	(10,000)	5,000	(15,000)
Interest Payable	(5,000)	(500)	5,000
Other Current Liabilities	8,000	(10,000)	800

15. Compute the cash flow from operations in each of the following cases:

	I	II	III
Sales Revenues	$175,000	$200,000	$225,000
Cost of Goods Sold	100,000	185,000	195,000
Depreciation	20,000	15,000	10,000
Interest Expense	5,000	25,000	15,000
Dividends Paid	8,000	–	5,000
Profit (Loss) on Sale of PP&E	–	(10,000)	25,000
Increase (Decrease) in:			
Common Stock	10,000	5,000	–
Bonds Payable	20,000	(30,000)	(15,000)
Interest Payable	(25,000)	(5,000)	10,000
Accounts Payable	(25,000)	10,000	15,000
Accounts Receivable	50,000	(40,000)	35,000
Inventories	(10,000)	(15,000)	25,000
PP&E	100,000	(50,000)	–

16. Financial statement data for Dennison Corporation for 20X8 is as follows:

Dennison Corporation
Comparative Balance Sheets

	12/31/X7	12/31/X8
Assets		
Cash	$25,500	$4,400
Accounts Receivable	59,000	35,000
Inventories	30,000	50,000
Total Current Assets	114,500	89,400
Property, Plant, and Equipment	165,000	180,000
Accumulated Depreciation	(61,900)	(80,400)
Total Noncurrent Assets	103,100	99,600
Total Assets	$217,600	$189,000
Liabilities and Owners' Equity		
Accounts Payable	$38,600	$28,500
Salaries Payable	24,000	12,000
Total Current Liabilities	62,600	40,500
Bank Loan	50,000	40,000
Total Liabilities	112,600	80,500
Common Stock	100,000	100,000
Retained Earnings	5,000	8,500
Total Liabilities and Owners' Equity	$217,600	$189,000

Income Statement		
Sales		$185,500
Expenses:		
Cost of Goods Sold	87,500	
Salaries Expense	48,000	
Depreciation Expense	23,500	
Interest Expense	8,000	
Loss on Sale of PP&E	5,000	
Total Expenses		172,000
Net Income		$13,500

Additional Information:

1. Equipment originally costing $35,000 was sold for $25,000.

2. Dividends declared and paid during the year were $10,000.

Required:

Prepare a statement of cash flows for Dennison Corporation for the year ended 12/31/X8, supported by a T-account worksheet. Use the indirect approach to prepare the operating section.

17. Financial statement data for Matrix, Incorporated is as follows:

Matrix, Incorporated
Balance Sheets

	12/31/X3
Assets	
Cash	15,500
Accounts Receivable	10,000
Trade Notes Receivable	5,000
Inventories	20,500
Total Current Assets	51,000
Property, Plant, and Equipment	160,000
Accumulated Depreciation	(35,500)
Total Noncurrent Assets	124,500
Total Assets	$175,500
Liabilities and Owners' Equity	
Accounts Payable	5,000
Salaries Payable	18,000
Total Current Liabilities	23,000
Bonds Payable	50,000
Total Liabilities	73,000
Common Stock	100,000
Retained Earnings	2,500
Total Liabilities and Owners' Equity	$175,500

Matrix, Incorporated
Trial Balance for the Year
Ended 12/31/X4

	Debits	Credits
Cash	$2,900	
Accounts Receivable	12,500	
Prepaid Rent	6,000	
Inventories	18,900	
Cost of Goods Sold	275,500	
Depreciation Expense	10,000	
Rent Expense	12,000	
Interest Expense	15,000	
Salaries Expense	24,000	
Property, Plant, and Equipment	160,000	
Accumulated Depreciation		$ 45,500
Accounts Payable		13,800

	Debits	Credits
Interest Payable		9,000
Salaries Payable		6,000
Bonds Payable		10,000
Common Stock		100,000
Retained Earnings		2,500
Sales		350,000
Totals	$536,800	$536,800

Required:

a. Prepare an income statement and a reconciliation of retained earnings for the year ended 12/31/X4.

b. Prepare a balance sheet for the year ended 12/31/X4.

c. Prepare a statement of cash flows for the year ended 12/31/X4 supported by a T-account worksheet. Use the indirect approach to prepare the operating section.

18. The financial statement data for Crescent Manufacturing Company is as follows:

Crescent Manufacturing Company Comparative Balance Sheets	12/31/X0	12/31/X1
Assets		
Cash	17,800	12,800
Marketable Securities	125,000	25,000
Accounts Receivable	38,600	69,600
Prepaid Insurance	6,000	—
Inventories	43,300	93,300
Total Current Assets	230,700	200,700
Property, Plant, and Equipment	225,000	300,000
Accumulated Depreciation	(36,300)	(86,300)
Total Noncurrent Assets	188,700	213,700
Total Assets	$419,400	$414,400
Liabilities and Owners' Equity		
Accounts Payable	12,600	15,000
Interest Payable	8,000	5,600
Dividends Payable	20,000	30,000
Total Current Liabilities	40,600	50,600
Mortgage Payable	100,000	75,000
Bonds Payable	75,000	75,000
Total Liabilities	215,600	200,600
Common Stock	250,000	250,000
Treasury Stock	(50,000)	(60,000)
Retained Earnings	3,800	23,800
Total Owners' Equity	203,800	213,800
Total Liabilities and Owners' Equity	$419,400	$414,400

	12/31/X0	12/31/X1
Income Statement		
Sales	$508,000	
Interest Revenue	12,500	
Gain on Sale of Marketable Securities	25,000	
Total Revenues		$545,500
Expenses:		
Cost of Goods Sold	330,000	
Depreciation Expense	50,000	
Insurance Expense	12,000	
Interest Expense	43,500	
Salaries Expense	60,000	
Total Expenses		495,500
Net Income		$ 50,000

Additional Information:

1. 10,000 shares of Sigma Company, which were purchased at a cost of $10 per share, were sold at a price of $12.50 per share.

2. Dividends declared during the year amounted to $30,000 and remained unpaid at year end.

Required:

Prepare a statement of cash flows for Crescent Manufacturing Company for the year ended 12/31/X1 supported by a T-account worksheet. Use the indirect method to prepare the operation section.

19. The Balance Sheet for Simco Corporation as of the beginning and the end of the 20X1 appears below. During the year, no dividends were declared or paid, there was no sale of PP&E and no debt repaid. Net Income for the period was $35,000 and included $25,000 in depreciation expenses. Prepare a statement of cash flows for Simco Corporation for the current year and also prepare a T-account worksheet supporting the cash flow statement. Use the cash reconciliation approach.

SIMCO CORPORATION
Balance Sheet

	12/31/X0	12/31/X1
Assets		
Current Assets		
Cash	$ 10,000	$ 8,000
Accounts Receivable	86,000	100,000
Inventories	102,000	112,000
Total Current Assets	198,000	220,000
Property, Plant, and Equipment	485,000	600,000
Less: Accumulated Depreciation	125,000	150,000
Total PP&E	360,000	450,000
Total Assets	$558,000	$670,000

	12/31/X0	12/31/X1
Liabilities and Owners' Equity		
Current Liabilities		
Accounts Payable	$ 78,000	$ 95,000
Wages Payable	30,000	40,000
Total Current Liabilities	108,000	135,000
Long-Term Debt		
Bonds Payable	100,000	125,000
Total Liabilities	208,000	260,000
Owners' Equity		
Common Stock	150,000	175,000
Retained Earnings	200,000	235,000
Total Liabilities and Owners' Equity	$558,000	$670,000

20. Comparative Balance Sheets of Marvel Cosmetics Company for 20X2 are as follows:

MARVEL COSMETICS COMPANY
Comparative Balance Sheet

	12/31/X1	12/31/X2
Assets		
Current Assets		
Cash	$ 188,000	$ 200,000
Accounts Receivable	133,000	120,000
Trade Notes Receivable	61,000	70,000
Inventory	326,000	439,000
Total Current Assets	708,000	829,000
Noncurrent Assets		
Land	500,000	525,000
Machinery	238,000	483,000
Accumulated Depreciation	(97,500)	(143,000)
Total Noncurrent Assets	640,500	865,000
Total Assets	$1,348,500	$1,694,000
Liabilities and Owners' Equity		
Current Liabilities		
Accounts Payable	$ 158,000	$ 145,000
Interest Payable	10,000	17,500
Total Current Liabilities	168,000	162,500
Noncurrent Liabilities		
Debentures	200,000	350,000
Total Liabilities	368,000	512,500
Owners' Equity		
Common Stock	550,000	650,000
Retained Earnings	430,500	531,500
Total Owners' Equity	980,500	1,180,500
Total Liabilities and Owners' Equity	$1,348,500	$1,694,000

Additional Information:

a. Net Income is $151,000 and includes depreciation expenses of $105,500.

b. Dividends declared and paid during the year were $50,000.

c. A machine costing $80,000 was sold at its book value of $20,000.

d. There was no Repayment of long-term debt.

Prepare a Statement of Cash Flows for Marvel Cosmetics Company for the year ended 12/31/X2, supported by a T-account worksheet.

21. The financial statement data for Pharmex Pharmaceutical Company for 20X5 is as follows:

PHARMEX PHARMACEUTICAL COMPANY	12/31/X4	12/31/X5
Comparative Data		
Debits		
Cash	80,000	50,000
Accounts Receivable	185,000	235,000
Inventories	296,000	325,000
Machinery	545,000	555,000
Total	1,106,000	1,165,000
Credits		
Accumulated Depreciation	122,500	172,500
Accounts Payable	97,500	82,500
Bonds Payable	150,000	175,000
Common Stock	350,000	400,000
Retained Earnings	386,000	335,000
Total	1,106,000	1,165,000
Income Statement Data		
Sales		1,052,000
Gain on Sale of PP&E		15,000
Cost of Goods Sold		878,000
Depreciation Expense		75,000
Interest Expenses		60,000
Rent Expense		85,000

Additional Information:

Acquisition cost of new machinery is $135,000. Old machinery having an original cost of $125,000 was sold at a gain of $15,000. Dividends of $20,000 were declared and paid.

a. Prepare an income statement including a reconciliation of retained earnings for the year ended 12/31/X5.

b. Prepare a statement of cash flows for Pharmex Pharmaceuticals Company for the year ended 12/31/X5 supported by a T-account work sheet.

22. From the perspective of a bank loan officer, discuss why the cash flow statement may or may not be more important in your analysis of a company that is applying for a loan.

23. From the perspective of a stock analyst, discuss why the cash flow statement may or may not be more important in your analysis of a company for which you must make a recommendation.

USING REAL DATA

24. Use the data in the cash flow statement for Amazon.Com, Inc. to answer the questions that follow.

Amazon.com, Inc. Consolidated Statements of Cash Flows (in thousands) Years Ended December 31,	2001	2000	1999
Cash and cash equivalents, beginning of period	$822,435	$ 133,309	$ 71,583
Net loss	(567,277)	(1,411,273)	(719,968)
Adjustments to reconcile net loss to net cash used in operating activities:			
Depreciation of fixed assets and other amortization	84,709	84,460	36,806
Stock-based compensation	4,637	24,797	30,618
Equity in losses of equity-method investees, net	30,327	304,596	76,769
Amortization of goodwill and other intangibles	181,033	321,772	214,694
Noncash restructuring-related and other	73,293	200,311	8,072
Loss (gain) on sale of marketable securities, net	(1,335)	(280)	8,688
Other losses (gains), net	2,141	142,639	—
Noncash interest expense and other	26,629	24,766	29,171
Cumulative effect of change in accounting principle	10,523	—	—
Changes in operating assets and liabilities:			
Inventories	30,628	46,083	(172,069)
Prepaid expenses and other current assets	20,732	(8,585)	(54,927)
Accounts payable	(44,438)	22,357	330,166
Accrued expenses and other current liabilities	50,031	93,967	95,839
Unearned revenue	114,738	97,818	6,225
Amortization of previously unearned revenue	(135,808)	(108,211)	(5,837)
Interest payable	(345)	34,341	24,878
Net cash used in operating activities	(119,782)	(130,442)	(90,875)
Investing Activities:			
Sales and maturities of marketable securities	370,377	545,724	2,064,101
Purchases of marketable securities	(567,152)	(184,455)	(2,359,398)
Purchases of fixed assets, including internal use software and web-site development	(50,321)	(134,758)	(287,055)

	2001	2000	1999
Investments in equity-method investees and other investments	(6,198)	(62,533)	(369,607)
Net cash provided by (used in) investing activities	(253,294)	163,978	(951,959)
Financing Activities:			
Proceeds from exercise of stock options and other	16,625	44,697	64,469
Proceeds from issuance of common stock, net of issuance costs	99,831	—	—
Proceeds from long-term debt and other	10,000	681,499	1,263,639
Repayment of long-term debt and other	(19,575)	(16,927)	(188,886)
Financing costs	—	(16,122)	(35,151)
Net cash provided by financing activities	106,881	693,147	1,104,071
Effect of exchange-rate changes on cash and cash equivalents	(15,958)	(37,557)	489
Net increase (decrease) in cash and cash equivalents	(282,153)	689,126	61,726
Cash and cash Equivalents, end of period	$540,282	$ 822,435	$ 133,309
Supplemental cash flow information:			
Fixed assets acquired under capital leases	$ 4,597	$ 4,459	$ 25,850
Fixed assets acquired under financing agreements	1,000	4,844	5,608
Equity securities received for commerical agreements	331	106,848	54,402
Stock issued in connection with business acquisitions and minority investments	5,000	32,130	774,409
Cash paid for interest	112,184	67,252	30,526

a. Why is net cash provided by operating activities less negative than net income for the three years presented?

b. What specific items contributed most to the greater net loss in 2000 than in the other two years?

c. How were investment activities in 1999 financed?

d. What trend do you observe for debt and related cash paid for interest over the three years presented?

e. What general concerns do you have about the future operating activities of the company based on your review of the cash flow statement for the three years presented?

25. Use the data in the cash flow statement for Barnes Group, Inc. to answer the questions that follow.

BARNES GROUP, Inc.: Cash Flow	12/31/2001	12/31/2000	12/31/1999
Operating activities:			
Net income	$19,121,000	$35,665,000	$28,612,000
Adjustments to reconcile net income to net cash provided by operating activities:			
Depreciation and amortization	37,045,000	35,871,000	30,602,000
Loss (gain) on disposition of property, plant, and equipment	2,093,000	(1,960,000)	(857,000)
Changes in assets and liabilities:			
Accounts receivable	11,378,000	1,087,000	(1,731,000)
Inventories	(3,629,000)	(7,631,000)	1,980,000
Accounts payable	13,634,000	(5,415,000)	17,356,000
Accrued liabilities	(5,552,000)	1,026,000	(9,524,000)
Deferred income taxes	6,510,000	5,863,000	3,655,000
Other	(13,700,000)	(12,649,000)	(7,296,000)
Net cash provided by operating activities	66,900,000	51,857,000	62,797,000
Investing activities:			
Proceeds from disposition of property, plant, and equipment	1,093,000	2,744,000	1,929,000
Capital expenditures	(22,365,000)	(26,575,000)	(27,222,000)
Business acquisitions, net of cash acquired	(1,036,000)	(104,935,000)	(92,239,000)
Redemption of short-term investments	—	—	2,566,000
Other	(4,286,000)	(5,776,000)	(2,019,000)
Net cash used by investing activities	(26,594,000)	(134,542,000)	(116,985,000)
Financing activities:			
Net (decrease) increase in notes payable	(1,583,000)	(5,201,000)	5,249,000
Payments on long-term debt	(28,000,000)	(60,000,000)	(70,000,000)
Proceeds from the issuance of long-term debt	22,765,000	150,000,000	159,000,000
Proceeds from the issuance of common stock	2,845,000	3,920,000	1,486,000
Common stock repurchases	(8,798,000)	(9,197,000)	(22,351,000)
Dividends paid	(14,806,000)	(14,677,000)	(14,564,000)
Proceeds from the sale of debt swap	13,766,000	—	—
Net cash (used) provided by financing activities	(13,811,000)	64,845,000	58,820,000
Effect of exchange rate changes on cash flows	(930,000)	(2,489,000)	(1,206,000)
Increase (decrease) in cash and cash equivalents	25,565,000	(20,329,000)	3,426,000
Cash and cash equivalents at beginning of year	23,303,000	43,632,000	40,206,000
Cash and cash equivalents at end of year	$48,868,000	$23,303,000	$43,632,000

a. What changes in assets and liabilities contributed most to the increase in net cash provided by operating activities in 2001 over that in 2000?

b. How were business acquisitions financed in 1999 and 2000?

c. What changes in financing activities do you observe in 2001 by comparison to the two previous years?

d. What is your general assessment of the company's ability to finance its investing activities from operating cash flows beyond 2001?

26. Use the data in the cash flow statement for GAP, Inc. to answer the questions that follow.

GAP, Inc.: Cash Flow	52 Weeks Ended Feb. 2, 2002	53 Weeks Ended Feb. 3, 2001	52 Weeks Ended Jan. 29, 2000
Cash flows from operating activities:			
Net earnings (loss)	$ (7,764,000)	$877,497,000	$1,127,065,000
Adjustments to reconcile net earnings (loss) to net cash provided by operating activities:			
Depreciation and amortization	810,486,000	590,365,000	436,184,000
Tax benefit from exercise of stock options and vesting of restricted stock	58,444,000	130,882,000	211,891,000
Deferred income taxes	(28,512,000)	(38,872,000)	2,444,000
Change in operating assets and liabilities:			
Merchandise inventory	213,067,000	(454,595,000)	(404,211,000)
Prepaid expenses and other	(13,303,000)	(61,096,000)	(55,519,000)
Accounts payable	42,205,000	249,545,000	118,121,000
Accrued expenses	220,826,000	(56,541,000)	(5,822,000)
Deferred lease credits and other long-term liabilities	22,390,000	54,020,000	47,775,000
Net cash provided by operating activities	1,317,839,000	1,291,205,000	1,477,928,000
Cash flows from investing activities:			
Net purchase of property and equipment	(940,078,000)	(1,858,662,000)	(1,238,722,000)
Acquisition of lease rights and other assets	(10,549,000)	(16,252,000)	(39,839,000)
Net cash used for investing activities	(950,627,000)	(1,874,914,000)	(1,278,561,000)
Cash Flows from financing activities:			
Net increase (decrease) in notes payable	(734,927,000)	621,420,000	84,778,000
Proceeds from issuance of long-term debt	1,194,265,000	250,000,000	311,839,000
Payments of long-term debt	(250,000,000)	—	—
Issuance of common stock	139,105,000	152,105,000	114,142,000
Net purchase of treasury stock	(785,000)	(392,558,000)	(745,056,000)
Cash dividends paid	(76,373,000)	(75,488,000)	(75,795,000)
Net cash provided by (used for) financing activities	271,285,000	555,479,000	(310,092,000)
Effect of exchange rate fluctuations on cash	(11,542,000)	(13,328,000)	(4,176,000)
Net increase (decrease) in cash and equivalents	626,955,000	(41,558,000)	(114,901,000)
Cash and equivalents at beginning of year	408,794,000	450,352,000	565,253,000
Cash and equivalents at end of year	$1,035,749,000	$408,794,000	$ 450,352,000

a. What trend do you observe in net income for the three years presented?

b. Why does net cash provided by operating activities not display the same trend as noted in your answer to a.?

c. What other information from the cash flow statements can be used to explain the substantial increase in depreciation and amortization from 2001 to 2002?

d. How would you describe the events pertaining to debt that occurred in 2002?

27. Use the data in the cash flow statement for Polaroid Corporation to answer the questions that follow.

POLAROID CORP.: Cash Flow	12/31/1998	12/31/1999	12/31/2000
Cash flows from operating activities:			
Net earnings/(loss)	$ (51,000,000)	$ 8,700,000	$37,700,000
Depreciation of property, plant, and equipment	90,700,000	105,900,000	113,900,000
Gain on the sale of real estate	(68,200,000)	(11,700,000)	(21,800,000)
Other noncash items	62,200,000	73,800,000	22,900,000
Decrease/(increase) in receivables	79,000,000	(52,700,000)	41,800,000
Decrease/(increase) in inventories	(28,400,000)	88,000,000	(100,600,000)
Decrease in prepaids and other assets	39,000,000	62,400,000	32,900,000
Increase/(decrease) in payables and accruals	25,300,000	(16,500,000)	9,200,000
Decrease in compensation and benefits	(21,000,000)	(72,500,000)	(105,000,000)
Decrease in federal, state, and foreign income taxes payable	(29,900,000)	(54,000,000)	(31,500,000)
Net cash provided/(used) by operating activities	97,700,000	131,400,000	(500,000)
Cash flows from investing activities:			
Decrease/(increase) in other assets	(25,400,000)	16,500,000	4,500,000
Additions to property, plant, and equipment	(191,100,000)	(170,500,000)	(129,200,000)
Proceeds from the sale of property, plant, and equipment	150,500,000	36,600,000	56,600,000
Acquisitions, net of cash acquired	(18,800,000)	—	—
Net cash used by investing activities	(84,800,000)	(117,400,000)	(68,100,000)
Cash flows from financing activities:			
Net increase/(decrease) in short-term debt (maturities 90 days or less)	131,200,000	(86,200,000)	108,200,000
Short-term debt (maturities of more than 90 days)			
Proceeds	73,000,000	41,800,000	—
Payments	(117,200,000)	(24,900,000)	—
Proceeds from issuance of long-term debt	—	268,200,000	—
Repayment of long-term debt	—	(200,000,000)	—
Cash dividends paid	(26,500,000)	(26,600,000)	(27,000,000)
Purchase of treasury stock	(45,500,000)	—	—
Proceeds from issuance of shares in connection with stock incentive plan	6,000,000	300,000	100,000
Net cash provided/(used) by financing activities	21,000,000	(27,400,000)	81,300,000
Effect of exchange rate changes on cash	3,100,000	400,000	(7,500,000)
Net increase/(decrease) in cash and cash equivalents	37,000,000	(13,000,000)	5,200,000
Cash and cash equivalents at beginning of year	68,000,000	105,000,000	92,000,000
Cash and cash equivalents at end of year	$105,000,000	$92,000,000	$97,200,000

a. Why is the upward trend in net earnings/(loss) not reflected in net cash provided/(used) by operating activities for the three years presented?

b. How were net additions to property, plant, and equipment in 2000 principally financed?

c. What would be a reasonable estimate of the change in property, plant, and equipment during 2000?

d. What indications are there that the company will need to seek external financing in 2001?

28. Use the data in the cash flow statement for Tech Data Corporation to answer the questions that follow.

TECH DATA CORP.: Cash Flow	01/31/2002	01/31/2001	01/31/2000
Cash flows from operating activities:			
Cash received from customers	$17,511,511,000	$20,114,486,000	$16,788,960,000
Cash paid to suppliers and employees	(16,406,265,000)	(20,047,551,000)	(16,684,316,000)
Interest paid	(55,871,000)	(94,823,000)	(69,554,000)
Income taxes paid	(72,745,000)	(62,048,000)	(34,176,000)
Net cash provided by (used in) operating activities	976,630,000	(89,936,000)	914,000
Cash flows from investing activities:			
Acquisition of businesses, net of cash acquired	(183,000)	(19,198,000)	(42,898,000)
Expenditures for property and equipment	(28,466,000)	(38,079,000)	(59,038,000)
Software development costs	(20,719,000)	(22,705,000)	(18,381,000)
Net cash used in investing activities	(49,368,000)	(79,982,000)	(120,317,000)
Cash flows from financing activities:			
Proceeds from the issuance of common stock, net of related tax benefit	36,432,000	35,539,000	19,663,000
Net (repayments) borrowings on revolving credit loans	(1,118,167,000)	248,712,000	99,447,000
Proceeds from issuance of long-term debt, net of expense	284,200,000	–	–
Principal payments on long-term debt	(634,000)	(557,000)	(162,000)
Net cash (used in) provided by financing activities	(798,169,000)	283,694,000	118,948,000
Effect of change in year end of certain subsidiaries (Note 3)	–	–	23,626,000
Effect of exchange rate changes on cash	(10,091,000)	(6,637,000)	–
Net increase in cash and cash equivalents	119,002,000	107,139,000	23,171,000
Cash and cash equivalents at beginning of year	138,925,000	31,786,000	8,615,000
Cash and cash equivalents at end of year	$ 257,927,000	$ 138,925,000	$ 31,786,000

TECH DATA CORP.: Cash Flow	01/31/2002	01/31/2001	01/31/2000
Reconciliation of net income to net cash provided by (used in) operating activities:			
Net income	$ 110,777,000	$177,983,000	$127,501,000
Adjustments to reconcile net income to net cash provided by (used in) operating activities:			
Depreciation and amortization	63,488,000	63,922,000	57,842,000
Provision for losses on accounts receivable	40,764,000	41,447,000	40,877,000

	01/31/2002	01/31/2001	01/31/2000
Special charges (Note 13)	27,000,000	—	—
Deferred income taxes	(11,848,000)	(1,789,000)	1,306,000
Changes in assets and liabilities:			
Decrease (increase) in accounts receivable	314,000,000	(313,197,000)	(202,790,000)
Decrease (increase) in inventories	702,219,000	(146,093,000)	(220,585,000)
(Increase) in prepaid and other assets	(6,248,000)	(11,603,000)	(25,430,000)
(Decrease) increase in accounts payable	(264,722,000)	11,863,000	136,748,000
Increase in accrued expenses	1,200,000	87,531,000	85,445,000
Total adjustments	865,853,000	(267,919,000)	(126,587,000)
Net cash provided by (used in) operating activities	$976,630,000	$ (89,936,000)	$ 914,000

a. How does the format of the cash flow statements for this company differ from the format used by most companies?

b. What changes do you note in the reconciliation of net income to net cash provided by (used in) operating activities that most explain the dramatic increase in net cash provided by those activities?

c. How did the company finance its investing activities in 2000 and 2001?

d. Where were the funds obtained to repay borrowings on revolving credit loans in 2002?

e. What evidence is there that the company has reversed its growth during 2002 from what it was during the previous two years?

BEYOND THE BOOK

29. For a company of your own choosing, answer the following questions related to its cash flow statement:

a. What is the trend in net income for the three years presented?

b. What is the trend in cash from operations for the three years presented?

c. In the most recent year, explain why the cash from operations differs from net income.

d. What other cash needs did the firm have in the most recent time period outside of operations?

e. Where did the company get the cash to cover the needs identified in part (d)?

f. What concerns do you have about the financial health of the company from your analysis of the cash flow statement?

6

Financial Statement Analysis

After studying this chapter students should be able to:

1. Understand how to adjust financial statements to give effect to differences in accounting methods.

2. Be able to calculate and interpret common financial ratios.

3. Evaluate a firm's short-term and long-term debt repayment abilities and its profitability.

4. Have a basic understanding of methods of forecasting future revenues or earnings.

5. Understand the concept of present value and its application to valuing free cash flows and residual earnings.

In late 2001 Starbucks Corp. announced that it had beat analysts' expectations and reported a first quarter profit (for the quarter ended September 30, 2001) of 25 cents a share. The analysts' previous estimate was 23 cents a share. In the same announcement Starbucks also reported record revenues of $667 million, up 26 percent from $529 million in the same period a year ago. Earnings were $49 million, up 41% over the same period a year ago of $34.7 million. Starbucks also indicated that it had raised its own projections of the year's fiscal earnings by a penny per share.

Despite the very sizeable increase in revenues and earnings over the previous year for Starbucks, note that analysts' forecasts nearly matched Starbucks' reported amounts and thus we would expect very little adjustment to Starbucks' market value as a result of this disclosure. The prominence of revenues in this earnings release is consistent with analysts viewing changes in revenues as a measure of growth and, hence, as a key factor in forecasting future performance.

In virtually all cases, financial statement users are concerned with predicting future outcomes of a firm. However, these forecasts usually begin with an assessment of the firm's *past performance*. In this chapter, we'll show you how financial statement analysis provides this link from evaluating past performance to forecasting future expectations.

OVERVIEW OF FINANCIAL STATEMENT ANALYSIS

Financial statement analysis refers to a set of procedures for transforming past data from a firm's published financial statements into information useful for future decisions. Many different types of decisions are based on financial statement analysis, such as whether to extend credit, buy or sell securities, or reward managers for their performance.

Financial statement analysis typically involves making **inter-temporal** (across time) and **cross-sectional** (across firms) comparisons. Inter-temporal comparisons help to identify trends in past data as well as reveal areas of concern that may warrant special attention. Cross-sectional comparisons (of a firm with its main rivals) indicate relative performance that may have a bearing on future market share. One complication in making both types of comparisons using raw financial statement data is the effect of changes or differences in firm size. For instance, if we were analyzing the pizza business and wanted to compare Domino's, Sbarro, and Bertucci's, they are very different in size with revenues of $1,275 million, $360 million, and $162 million, respectively. Analysts commonly adjust for such differences by using financial ratios in making these comparisons.

Another complication is that accounting policies may vary across time or across firms. When this occurs, analysts may need to adjust for these variations by restating financial statements in order to place them on a common basis. Such restatements answer the question of what the firm's financial statements would look like "as if" they had been prepared under the same set of accounting policies.

Once analysts transform the data into ratios and understand the trends that may be present, they next assess future prospects by constructing **operating forecasts,** for example, the forecast of net income from operations. A formal approach to forecasting extrapolates past operating data through statistical models that take advantage of inter-temporal relationships present in that data (these models are often called *time-series models*). Less formal approaches rely more on analysts' subjective judgments of future trends. Regardless of the approach used, operating forecasts should factor in the outlook for the industry and the economy as a whole, the company's business plan, and the nature of competition.

	02/01/2003	02/01/2002	02/01/2001
Net sales	$1,380,966,000	$1,299,573,000	$1,232,776,000
Cost of sales	633,473,000	651,808,000	622,036,000
Gross margin	747,493,000	647,765,000	610,740,000
Selling, general, and administrative expenses	612,479,000	576,584,000	501,460,000
Amortization of goodwill	–	11,040,000	11,040,000
Operating income	135,014,000	60,141,000	98,240,000
Interest income	3,279,000	1,390,000	2,473,000
Interest expense	6,886,000	6,869,000	7,315,000
Income before income taxes	131,407,000	54,662,000	93,398,000
Income tax provision	51,249,000	25,557,000	41,035,000
Net income	$ 80,158,000	$ 29,105,000	$ 52,363,000

Exhibit 6.1
Consolidated Statements of Income

THE REAL WORLD

AnnTaylor Stores
Corporation

We're now ready to take a closer look at financial statement analysis. We'll use the data from AnnTaylor Stores Corporation (see Exhibits 6.1 and 6.2) to illustrate the process of financial statement analysis. Our first step is to review the financial statements to determine if they need to be restated.

CREATING COMPARABLE DATA FOR FINANCIAL STATEMENT ANALYSIS

Analysts must often consider how a firm's financial statements would appear if it used a different accounting method. For example, analysts may seek to undo the effects of overly aggressive income recognition ("as if" restatements), assess the effects of an impending change in accounting policy, or compare the performance of firms that employ different accounting methods. These adjustments can be quite complex in some situations. A full understanding of restatements requires a level of understanding of accounting that is beyond the scope of this book. However, a basic knowledge of accounting is sufficient to understand the idea of restatements and how to make basic restatements. Here we provide examples of some common restatements. Let's review how analysts create comparable data for each of these situations.

"AS IF" RESTATEMENTS

A useful technique in restating revenues, expenses, or income is to determine first how balances of related accounts appearing on comparative balance sheets would be affected; then, adjust the item in question by the change in the difference between the beginning and ending balances. For example, suppose a company recognized revenue for sales of goods or services at the time of delivery, despite considerable uncertainty about future collections from customers. Analysts determine the effect on the company's revenues, if it

Exhibit 6.2
Consolidated Balance Sheets

THE REAL WORLD

AnnTaylor Stores Corporation

	02/01/2003	02/01/2002
Current assets:		
Cash and cash equivalents	$ 212,821,000	$ 30,037,000
Accounts receivable, net	10,367,000	65,598,000
Merchandise inventories	185,484,000	180,117,000
Prepaid expenses and other current assets	46,599,000	50,314,000
Total current assets	455,271,000	326,066,000
Property and equipment, net	247,115,000	250,735,000
Goodwill, net	286,579,000	286,579,000
Deferred financing costs, net	4,170,000	5,044,000
Other assets	17,691,000	14,742,000
Total assets	$1,010,826,000	$883,166,000
Liabilities and stockholders' equity:		
Current liabilities		
Accounts payable	$ 57,058,000	$ 52,011,000
Accrued salaries and bonus	27,567,000	12,121,000
Accrued tenancy	10,808,000	10,151,000
Gift certificates and merchandise credits redeemable	25,637,000	21,828,000
Accrued expenses	30,125,000	37,907,000
Current portion of long-term debt		1,250,000
Total current liabilities	151,195,000	135,268,000
Long-term debt, net	121,652,000	118,280,000
Deferred lease costs and other liabilities	23,561,000	17,489,000
Stockholders' equity common stock, $.0068 par value; 120,000,000 shares authorized; 48,932,860 and 48,275,957 shares issued, respectively	332,000	328,000
Additional paid-in capital	500,061,000	484,582,000
Retained earnings	296,113,000	218,600,000
Deferred compensation on restricted stock	(3,968,000)	(9,296,000)
	792,538,000	694,214,000
Treasury stock, 4,050,972 and 4,210,232 shares, respectively, at cost	(78,120,000)	(82,085,000)
Total stockholders' equity	714,418,000	612,129,000
Total liabilities and stockholders' equity	$1,010,826,000	$883,166,000

adopted the less-aggressive procedure of delaying recognition until cash was received, as follows:

$$\text{Revenue (as if recognized at time of collection)} =$$
$$\text{Revenue (as Reported)} + \text{Decrease} (-\text{Increase}) \text{ in Accounts Receivable}$$

Consider the data from AnnTaylor. From Exhibit 6.1 we find reported revenues of $1,381.0 (all numbers in millions, rounded to the nearest hundred thousand). From Exhibit 6.2, we compute a decrease in accounts receivable of $55.2 ($10.4 − $65.6). Thus, if AnnTaylor recognized revenue as it collected cash from customers, revenues would equal $1,436.2 ($1,381.0 + $55.2).

Inventories provide another illustration. Different firms often value inventories under different methods, such as the "first-in, first-out" (FIFO) and "last-in, first-out" (LIFO) methods. For instance, Ford Motor Company uses LIFO, whereas Dell Computer uses FIFO. As discussed in more detail in Chapter 8, LIFO usually results in higher costs of goods sold and lower inventory levels on the balance sheet than FIFO. However, GAAP requires firms that apply the LIFO method to include a disclosure explaining the net difference in inventory values as a result of applying these two methods. Firms often report this difference, known as the LIFO reserve, in a footnote. Using these data, you can calculate what the cost of goods sold would have been under FIFO using the following calculation:

Cost of goods sold (as if FIFO had been used) =
Cost of goods sold (as reported, LIFO) + Decrease (−Increase) in LIFO Reserve

One last illustration of the adjustment process relates to a company's accounting treatment of warranty expenses. Most companies, for example Ford Motor Company, recognize warranty costs (on an estimated basis) as expenses at the time of sale rather than when paid. Suppose, however, that an analyst wants to determine a company's warranty settlement cost. In this case, we adjust the expense under the former treatment to determine the amount of claims settled as follows:

Warranty Expense (as if recorded when settled) =
Warranty Expense (as reported) + Decrease (−Increase) in Warranties Payable

THINKING GLOBALLY

International Accounting Issues

Because countries employ different accounting standards, analysts frequently need to make adjustments before conducting a cross-sectional analysis across countries. For example, Canadian companies selectively capitalize (record as assets) research and development (R&D) costs at the time these costs are incurred, while U.S. companies are required by GAAP to write off (record as expenses) those costs immediately.

If research and development (R&D) costs were initially recorded as an asset (as they might be under Canadian standards) and subsequently amortized as an expense, then one could calculate what R&D expense would be reported under the U.S. policy (which requires immediate recognition as an expense when the expenditures are made) as shown below:

R&D Expense (U.S.) = R&D Amortization Expense (Canadian)
+ Increase (−Decrease) in Unamortized R&D Costs (Canadian)

> Note that adjustments made to the income statement might also affect the calculation of income taxes, and therefore all as-if adjustments should also include adjustments for the tax effects.

Note that all of these adjustments focus on the income statement. In each case, however, to maintain the accounting equation, an impact also occurs on the balance sheet through an adjustment of an asset or a liability account. Further, because these adjustments affect net income, a change also occurs in retained earnings. For example, if a company begins accruing an expense that it previously recognized only when paid, then the balance in accrued liabilities increases, expenses on the income statement also increase, and the balance in retained earnings decreases by the reduction in net income.

Finally, note that some changes in the timing of revenue and expense recognition materially affect only the balance sheet. For example, as mentioned, Canadian companies are allowed to capitalize (record as an asset) some research and development (R&D) costs and then later amortize the costs to income. Suppose that a particular Canadian company capitalized costs in an amount equal to its amortization expense in the year you are analyzing. If you were to adjust the statements to conform to U.S. GAAP (where the firm must expense all R&D as incurred), the adjusted expense would be the same as the original expense and therefore there would be no effect of this adjustment on the income statement. However, the balance sheets would still differ as both assets and retained earnings would be lower if no R&D costs had ever been capitalized. In other words, balance sheet restatements reflect the cumulative effects (the effects of applying the new method in all prior years) of differences in accounting methods, whereas income statement restatements reflect only the current year effect.

MANDATED ACCOUNTING CHANGES

Accounting rule changes by the FASB and the SEC frequently occur. Accordingly, analysts need to be aware of the consequences of these changes on the financial statements. However, analysts are assisted with this task as follows:

- The FASB and the SEC typically specify how firms must handle these mandated changes within the financial statements.
- Firms usually document these changes in the footnotes of the financial statements in the period in which the change is made.
- The FASB and the SEC often require that firms also restate past financial statements to give effect to the mandated change in question.
- In some cases, these changes require that the cumulative effects on income of applying the new rules be shown as a separate line item in the income statement for the year in which the change is made.
- Auditors call attention to accounting rule changes in their report to stockholders.

Hence, a question seldom arises as to whether a change has occurred.

The greater challenge for analysts in dealing with mandated accounting changes is to evaluate the economic consequences of the change. For example, suppose a firm previously issued debt containing a covenant (a contractual restriction) that requires net worth (stockholders' equity) determined under GAAP to stay above a specified level. Now suppose that the FASB changes a rule governing revenue recognition, with the result of reducing the firm's net income to the point where it violates the covenant. To avoid this, the firm might have to cut its dividend. This might cause the value of the company's stock to fall due to an increase in risk, because of the reduction of cash flows (dividends) to shareholders.

Another consequence of a change to a more conservative method of revenue recognition might be to alter the incentives (often earnings-based bonuses) to managers provided by compensation contracts. For example, consider an executive who receives a bonus if reported income exceeds a certain level. If the accounting change makes it highly unlikely that this level will be reached in the year of change, no matter how much effort the executive applies, he or she may decide to postpone initiatives until the following year when it is more likely that he or she would receive the bonus. This reduced effort may negatively affect firm value.

DISCRETIONARY ACCOUNTING CHANGES

Within the GAAP framework, managers have considerable discretion in their choices of accounting treatments. Further, evidence suggests that managers make use of their discretion in responding to incentives and furthering the interests of shareholders (when their incentives are aligned). Beyond the consideration of the comparability of the data that result when the change occurs, the bigger issues for analysts are the motivation of the firm's management and the potential for significant economic consequences.

For example, consider firms in an industry that seeks trade relief. These firms must show they have been injured by the anticompetitive practices of foreign rivals. Managers in these companies would have an incentive to make accounting decisions that lower their reported income, in order to demonstrate such injury. Evidence (Lenway and Rayburn, *Contemporary Accounting Research*, 1992) does indicate that in the mid-1980s, U.S. semiconductor producers generally had higher negative accruals coincident with petitions alleging dumping by Japanese producers.

Accounting treatments may also influence real investment and financing decisions. For example, firms generally do not recognize changes in the market value of debt (sometimes referred to as unrealized holding gains and losses) that result when interest rates in the economy change. However, a company seeking to increase or decrease its reported income for reasons mentioned above might decide to retire its debt early, causing the recognition of the gain or loss.

Finally, note that accounting decisions might serve as signaling devices, whereby a firm may be able to persuade investors that it has more favorable future cash flow prospects. For example, as we will see in Chapter 8, if a firm uses the LIFO method of valuing inventories for tax purposes, it must also use this same method for reporting to its shareholders (in periods of rising prices, LIFO results in lower reported net income and therefore lower tax payments). Theorists suggest that firms choosing to forego the tax benefits of LIFO by using FIFO for reporting purposes (and hence for tax purposes) may be signaling that they have stronger cash flow prospects than comparable firms that use LIFO.

Once analysts complete reviewing a firm's financial statements, and restating as necessary, calculating ratios can lead to more meaningful information. In the next section, we'll see how to use ratios to analyze a firm's past performance, which is the next step in financial statement analysis.

Firms using LIFO could mimic the firms with stronger cash flow prospects by also choosing FIFO. However, they may find the loss of tax benefits to outweigh the benefits of not having investors learn that they have weaker cash flow prospects.

USING FINANCIAL RATIOS TO ASSESS PAST PERFORMANCE

To assess a firm's past performance from periodic financial statements, analysts must first adjust the contents for inter-temporal changes or cross-sectional variations in firm size. For example, it does not mean much when assessing operating efficiency to compare income either over time for a firm that is changing in size or between small and large firms. Analysts remove effects of scale (size) by employing financial ratios. Financial ratios are often broadly organized into those that assess profitability and those that assess debt-repayment ability.

ASSESSING PROFITABILITY

From an investor's perspective, **rate of return on equity (ROE)** presents a comprehensive accounting measure of a firm's performance. For a company with only common stock outstanding (we consider other types of stock in Chapter 12), we determine ROE as follows:

$$\text{ROE} = \frac{\text{Net Income}}{\text{Average Stockholders' Equity}}$$

Because a firm earns net income over a period of time, the denominator of this ratio also reflects the level of stockholders' investment over this same period of time. Hence, it makes sense to calculate the average amount invested during the period in the denominator. Most analysts compute the average as simply the sum of the beginning and ending balances of stockholders' equity, divided by two. The implicit assumption in this computation is that the change in balances remained uniform over the period. If the change in balances varied over the period, analysts might then use more sophisticated averaging techniques.

ROE is an accounting measure of the profitability of the firm's past investments. We can compare this measure to the expected rate of return investors require in order to buy the firm's stock, called the cost of equity. Investors measure returns on the firm's stock from market data such as dividends and changes in market prices. The expected rate of return on the firm's stock depends on the risks that equity holders cannot eliminate through holding a well-diversified portfolio (in other words, a portfolio of a wide variety of stocks); something that we discuss further in Chapter 14. An ROE greater than the cost of equity suggests that the firm has been successful in finding projects to invest in whose returns exceed investors' expectations. However, a firm's ability to consistently find projects that result in an ROE in excess of its cost of equity is likely to be limited by competitors attracted to the same projects. Accordingly, in the long run we would anticipate that ROE would converge toward the cost of equity and that the ROE of firms in the same industry would converge to the industry average.

ROE can be decomposed into both a measure of the efficiency with which a firm uses its assets to generate income and of the capital structure of the firm.

$$\text{ROE} = \frac{\text{Net Income}}{\text{Average Assets}} \times \frac{\text{Average Assets}}{\text{Average Stockholders' Equity}}$$

The first component is commonly referred to as **rate of return on assets (ROA)**, and the second component is commonly referred to as **financial leverage.** Thus, a shorthand expression for ROE is:

$$ROE = ROA \times Leverage$$

ROA can be further decomposed into profit margin and asset turnover:

$$ROA = \frac{Net\ Income}{Sales} \times \frac{Sales}{Average\ Assets}$$

or:

$$ROA = Profit\ Margin \times Total\ Asset\ Turnover$$

→ high profit margin

This decomposition allows us to distinguish between operating strategies that emphasize profit per dollar of sales (profit margin) versus sales per dollar of *→ high sales record.* investment in assets (total asset turnover).

For AnnTaylor, we calculate ROE and ROA as follows:

$$ROE = \frac{80.2}{(714.4 + 612.1)/2} = 12.1\%$$

$$ROA = \frac{80.2}{1,381} \times \frac{1,381}{(1,010.8 + 883.2)/2} = 8.5\%$$

$$ROA = 5.8\% \times 1.46 = 8.5\%$$

ROA, as a measure of return on investment on assets, is complicated by employing a numerator (net income) that includes the return to debtholders in the form of interest expense. An alternative measure, more focused on the efficiency of assets employed in the firm's operating activities, is the **rate of return on capital (ROC)**. Here, the numerator of ROC uses operating income. Operating income can be obtained by adding back interest expense, net of taxes, to net income. Because this ratio is an after-tax ratio, we must adjust for taxes related to interest expense. In the denominator, debt and stockholders' equity replace total assets, to represent the net assets contributed by the firm's capital suppliers (total assets less operating liabilities, i.e., liabilities other than debt).

$$ROC = \frac{Net\ Income + Interest\ Expense \times (1 - tax\ rate)}{Average\ Debt + Average\ Stockholders'\ Equity}$$
↙ eliminate operating liabilities

We calculate ROC for AnnTaylor as follows:

$$ROC = \frac{80.2 + 6.9 \times (1 - 51.2/131.4)}{((121.7 + 23.6 + 1.3 + 118.3 + 17.5)/2 + (714.4 + 612.1)/2)} = 10.3\%$$

We obtain the tax rate by comparing the tax expense reported by AnnTaylor ($51.2) with the income before tax ($131.4), resulting in a tax rate of 39 percent (51.2/131.4). We determine the total debt by adding together the long-term debt and the deferred lease cost and other liabilities on the balance sheet (including the current portion of long-term debt from the current liability section). We can then compare the above measure to the composite market return required by the suppliers of both debt and equity capital, commonly referred to as the company's **weighted average cost of capital (WACC).** However, this calculation is beyond the scope of this book. We will provide more discussion on estimating the cost of equity capital in Chapter 14.

Shareholders of a firm leverage their investment by borrowing additional funds from debtholders to invest in additional assets. **Trading on equity** refers to the use of leverage to generate a higher ROE for shareholders. Because ROC provides a measure of the return to investments in assets (before distributions to any capital suppliers), shareholders can generate higher returns to themselves (ROE) as long as ROC on assets financed through debt exceeds the after-tax interest rate charged by debtholders, in other words, the cost of debt capital. Whether stockholders will benefit from trading on equity in the long run depends on the trade-off between the added risk of their position and the added expected return. Note that AnnTaylor generated a ROE of 12.1 percent, versus a ROA of 8.5 percent and a ROC of 10.3 percent. This indicates that they have used leverage to their shareholders' advantage, as ROE is greater than either ROA or ROC.

Recall from the decomposition of ROA that we calculate profit margin by dividing net income by sales. To further explore factors that influence profit margin, we can prepare a common size income statement. A **common size income statement** expresses each component of net income as a percent of sales. Exhibit 6.3 presents common size income statements for AnnTaylor.

The advantage of a common size statement is that it allows analysts to identify factors responsible for changes in profit margin. For example, rising product costs that are not passed on to customers might be reflected in higher cost of sales, as a percent of sales, and lower gross profit margins. Similarly, holding unit costs constant, a change in pricing policy might be evident from a comparison of gross profit margins. Administrative and marketing efficiencies may

Exhibit 6.3
Common Size Income Statement

THE REAL WORLD

AnnTaylor Stores Corporation

	02/01/2003	02/01/2002	02/01/2001
Net sales	100.0%	100.0%	100.0%
Cost of sales	45.9%	50.2%	50.5%
Gross margin	54.1%	49.8%	49.5%
Selling, general, and administrative expenses	44.4%	44.4%	40.7%
Amortization of goodwill	0.0%	0.8%	0.9%
Operating income	9.8%	4.6%	8.0%
Interest income	0.2%	0.1%	0.2%
Interest expense	0.5%	0.5%	0.6%
Income before income taxes	9.5%	4.2%	7.6%
Income tax provision	3.7%	2.0%	3.3%
Net income	5.8%	2.2%	4.2%

also become more apparent when the direct effects of growth in sales are removed.

In Exhibit 6.3, Net Income (as a percent of sales in 2003) is 5.8 percent, the same amount we calculated in the Profit Margin Ratio component of ROA. Net Income in 2003 presents a significant improvement as indicated by the increase in profit margin to 5.8 percent from the 2.2 percent in 2002. Reviewing the common size income statement, we identify this change as a direct result of a significant improvement in the cost of sales relative to sales revenues (50.5 percent to 45.9 percent), as well as a decline in the amortization of goodwill (which disappeared in 2003).

As another example of how to interpret the common size income statement, in Exhibit 6.4 find the common size income statement for Amazon.com for the years 2000 through 2002. Note that Amazon was able to maintain its gross profit percentage at approximately 25 percent over the three years. However, it cut its total operating expenses from 55 percent of sales to 24 percent of sales over

Amazon.com, Inc. Common Size Income Statement	12/31/2002	12/31/2001	12/31/2000
Net sales	100%	100%	100%
Cost of sales	75%	74%	76%
Gross profit	25%	26%	24%
Operating expenses:	0%	0%	0%
Fulfillment	10%	12%	15%
Marketing	3%	4%	7%
Technology and content	5%	8%	10%
General and administrative	2%	3%	4%
Stock-based compensation	2%	0%	1%
Amortization of goodwill and other intangibles	0%	6%	12%
Restructuring-related and other	1%	6%	7%
Total operating expenses	24%	39%	55%
Loss from operations	2%	−13%	−31%
Interest income	1%	1%	1%
Interest expense	−4%	−4%	−5%
Other income (expense), net	0%	0%	0%
Other gains (losses), net	−2%	0%	−5%
Net interest expense and other	−5%	−4%	−9%
Loss before equity in losses of equity method investees	−4%	−17%	−40%
Equity in losses of equity-method investees, net	0%	−1%	−11%
Loss before change in accounting principle	−4%	−18%	−51%
Cumulative effect of change in accounting principle	0%	0%	0%
Net loss	−4%	−18%	−51%

Exhibit 6.4
Amazon.com, Inc. Common Size Income Statement

THE REAL WORLD

Amazon.Com, Inc.

this same period. Note further that this resulted in the conversion of an operating loss of 31 percent from operations in 2000 to a gain of 2 percent from operations in 2002. While Amazon has still shown a net loss, this analysis implies that it has demonstrated significant progress in trying to achieve profitability from its operations.

ASSESSING TURNOVER RATIOS

Total asset turnover, as depicted in the decomposition of ROA, equals sales divided by total assets. The concept of a turnover is that we invest in assets to sell goods and services. We then expect that our investment in assets will be converted (or turned over) into sales. For AnnTaylor this ratio is 1.46, indicating that the investment in total assets is converted or turned over into sales 1.46 times a year. This ratio reflects significant averaging, as property and equipment turns over much less than 1.46 times a year and merchandise inventories turn over much more frequently. As a result, analysts seeking a better understanding of the company's performance in managing its operating assets may find it useful to consider more specific asset turnover ratios, including accounts receivable and inventory turnovers.

We calculate accounts receivable turnover and inventory turnover as follows:

$$\text{Receivables Turnover} = \frac{\text{Sales}}{\text{Average Receivables}}$$

$$\text{Inventory Turnover} = \frac{\text{Cost of Goods Sold}}{\text{Average Inventories}}$$

This type of ratio provides a measure of how many times a firm converts a particular asset into a sale (inventory turnover) or how much a firm needs a particular type of asset to support a given level of sales (accounts receivable turnover). In effect, asset turnover ratios reflect the ability of the company to efficiently use its assets to generate sales.

Often, we convert turnover ratios into an alternative form to represent the number of days that a firm, in a sense, holds an asset, as follows:

$$\text{Days Receivables} = \frac{\text{Average Receivables}}{\text{Average Sales per day}}$$

or:

$$\text{Days Receivables} = \frac{365}{\text{Receivables Turnover}}$$

$$\text{Days Inventory} = \frac{\text{Average Inventories}}{\text{Average Cost of Goods Sold per day}}$$

or:

$$\text{Days Inventory} = \frac{365}{\text{Inventory Turnover}}$$

Decreases in receivables and inventory turnover ratios, or increases in days receivables and inventory, may indicate collection and sales problems, respectively.

Similarly, accounts payable turnover reflects the efficiency with which a firm manages its credit from its suppliers, or alternatively, how much credit the firm needs in support of its sales efforts. We calculate this ratio as follows:

$$\text{Payables Turnover} = \frac{\text{Cost of Goods Sold}}{\text{Average (Accounts) Payable}}$$

$$\text{Days Payables} = \frac{\text{Average (Accounts) Payable}}{\text{Average Cost of Goods Sold per day}}$$

or:

$$\text{Days Payables} = \frac{365}{\text{Payables Turnover}}$$

Other turnover ratios consider various asset groupings such as:

$$\text{Working Capital Turnover} = \frac{\text{Sales}}{\text{Average Current Assets} - \text{Average Current Liabilities}}$$

$$\text{Capital Assets Turnover} = \frac{\text{Sales}}{\text{Average Plant, Property, and Equipment}}$$

Here again, lower turnover ratios may indicate deterioration in operating efficiency. We calculate the applicable turnover ratios for AnnTaylor as follows:

$$\text{Receivables Turnover} = \frac{1,381}{(10.4 + 65.6)/2} = 36.3$$

$$\text{Days Receivables} = \frac{365}{36.3} = 10$$

$$\text{Inventory Turnover} = \frac{633.5}{(185.5 + 180.1)/2} = 3.4$$

$$\text{Days Inventory} = \frac{365}{3.4} = 107.3$$

$$\text{Payables Turnover} = \frac{633.5}{(57.1 + 52.0)/2} = 11.6$$

$$\text{Days Payables} = \frac{365}{11.6} = 31.4$$

$$\text{Working Capital Turnover} = \frac{1,381}{(455.3 + 326.1)/2 - (151.2 + 135.3)/2} = 5.6$$

$$\text{Capital Assets Turnover} = \frac{1,381}{(247.1 + 250.7)/2} = 5.5$$

Looking at these ratios, we can make several observations about AnnTaylor. The days in receivables seems to be relatively small. However, recognize that many of AnnTaylor's sales are for cash. Therefore, by including total sales in the numerator of the turnover ratio we have overstated the sales that result in receivables. This results in an understatement of the days to collect from credit sales. Further recognize that AnnTaylor's credit sales are typically via a nonproprietary credit card and those are immediately converted into cash. Inventory turns over more than three times a year. For a clothing retailer such as AnnTaylor, this makes sense as its product line changes from one season to the next. It also appears that AnnTaylor receives approximately 30 days of credit from their suppliers as the days of payables is slightly over 30 days.

In addition to turnover ratios, we can prepare a common size balance sheet to assess the investments being made in asset categories as well as the amounts and forms of financing. A **common size balance sheet** expresses each line item as a percent of total assets. Exhibit 6.5 presents common size balance sheets for AnnTaylor.

Exhibit 6.5
Common Size Balance Sheet

THE REAL WORLD

AnnTaylor Stores Corporation

	02/01/2003	02/01/2002
Current assets		
Cash and cash equivalents	21.1%	3.4%
Accounts receivable, net	1.0%	7.4%
Merchandise inventories	18.3%	20.4%
Prepaid expenses and other current assets	4.6%	5.7%
Total current assets	45.0%	36.9%
Property and equipment, net	24.4%	28.4%
Goodwill, net	28.4%	32.4%
Deferred financing costs, net	0.4%	0.6%
Other assets	1.8%	1.7%
Total assets	100.0%	100.0%
Liabilities and stockholders' equity:		
Current liabilities		
Accounts payable	5.6%	5.9%
Accrued salaries and bonus	2.7%	1.4%
Accrued tenancy	1.1%	1.1%
Gift certificates and merchandise credits redeemable	2.5%	2.5%
Accrued expenses	3.0%	4.3%
Current portion of long-term debt	0.0%	0.1%
Total current liabilities	15.0%	15.3%
Long-term debt, net	12.0%	13.4%
Deferred lease costs and other liabilities	2.3%	2.0%
Stockholders' equity common stock, $.0068 par value; 120,000,000 shares authorized; 48,932,860 and 48,275,957 shares issued, respectively	0.0%	0.0%
Additional paid-in capital	49.5%	54.9%
Retained earnings	29.3%	24.8%
Deferred compensation on restricted stock	−0.4%	−1.1%
	78.4%	78.6%
Treasury stock, 4,050,972 and 4,210,232 shares, respectively, at cost	−7.7%	−9.3%
Total stockholders' equity	70.7%	69.3%
Total liabilities and stockholders' equity	100.0%	100.0%

In looking at this common size balance sheet, a couple of questions arise. For example, why have accounts receivable and inventory declined? If production costs have declined as shown on the income statement, perhaps the carrying value of inventory has also declined. This, however, does not explain the change in accounts receivable. As sales have actually increased during the year, we would have to investigate further to understand this change. By reading the details of the 10-K report for AnnTaylor, we discover that the firm sold the receivables associated with its proprietary credit card in fiscal year 2003 (we will refer to the fiscal year as the year in which the fiscal year ended, e.g., AnnTaylor ended fiscal year 2003 on February 1, 2003). This resulted in the much lower level of receivables at the end of 2003.

In terms of its financing, the common size balance sheet indicates that AnnTaylor finances its assets with approximately 12 percent long-term debt and 70 percent equity (relative to total assets). This leads us to the next section in which we focus on the ability of the company to pay its long-term debt.

> Analysts are often led to search other sources of information to answer the questions that are raised by financial statement analysis such as the changes in accounts receivable for AnnTaylor.

ASSESSING DEBT REPAYMENT ABILITY

Analysts assessing a company's debt-paying ability often separate short-term and long-term debt-paying ability. While this distinction may be somewhat arbitrary, a qualitative difference exists in how we measure the ability of a firm to repay debt that either matures before cash flows are generated by future operations or concurrently with those flows.

SHORT-TERM DEBT

Measures of the firm's ability to meet current obligations from existing assets include:

$$\text{Current Ratio} = \frac{\text{Current Assets}}{\text{Current Liabilities}}$$

$$\text{Quick Ratio} = \frac{\text{Cash, Marketable Securities, and Receivables}}{\text{Current Liabilities}}$$

$$\text{Cash Ratio} = \frac{\text{Cash and Cash Equivalent Investments}}{\text{Current Liabilities}}$$

→ Current − Inventory − other /

These ratios primarily differ by the ease and speed with which assets included in the numerator can be converted to cash. Inventories are the furthest removed, as sales of inventory often give rise to receivables before producing cash. Receivables are closer to being converted to cash but are less easily converted than marketable securities. Low ratios may suggest future problems in repaying short-term liabilities as they become due.

The following ratios reflect AnnTaylor's short-term debt-repayment ability:

$$\text{Current Ratio} = \frac{455.3}{151.2} = 3$$

$$\text{Quick Ratio} = \frac{212.8 + 10.4}{151.2} = 1.5$$

$$\text{Cash Ratio} = \frac{212.8}{151.2} = 1.4$$

Due to the significant changes in cash and receivables that we noted earlier, these ratios may differ somewhat in the current year. In fact, when we compute them for the prior year, the ratios are 2.4, 0.7, and 0.2, respectively.

LONG-TERM DEBT

In the long term, a firm's ability to meet obligations is closely related to its ability to generate cash flows from operations. Interest coverage ratios consider the ability of the firm either to earn sufficient income or produce sufficient cash to make interest payments on the long-term debt.

$$\text{Interest Coverage} = \frac{\text{Income before Interest and Tax Expenses}}{\text{Interest Expense}}$$

The interest coverage ratio is based on net income, a long-run predictor of cash from operations but is not a cash flow measure itself. Some analysts also compute the cash equivalent ratio as follows:

$$\text{Interest Coverage} = \frac{\text{Cash from Operations before Interest and Tax Payments}}{\text{Interest Payments}}$$

Why do we compute income or cash before taxes? Recall that a firm meets its interest requirements before taxes are assessed. Low interest coverage ratios imply a greater risk of being unable to service debt as a consequence of fluctuations in operating results.

A different perspective on repayment ability focuses on debt capacity as measured by balance sheet leverage ratios:

$$\text{Debt Equity Ratio} = \frac{\text{Short-term Debt} + \text{Long-term Debt}}{\text{Stockholders' Equity}}$$

The debt-equity ratio predominantly measures the financial risk when assessing the risk/expected return trade-off relevant to investors. The more debt a company has, the more interest payments the company will be obligated to pay before common stock investors can earn a return on their investment.

The following ratios reflect AnnTaylor's long-term debt repayment ability and financial risk:

$$\text{Interest Coverage} = \frac{151.4 + 6.9}{6.9} = 20$$

$$\text{Debt Equity Ratio} = \frac{121.6}{714.4} = .2$$

We calculate the cash flow measure of interest coverage from information contained in the cash flow statement (not included here). In the statement, we see that cash from operations equaled $155.5 in 2003. In the supplemental disclosure to the statement, we find interest payments of $1.3 and tax payments of $40.1 (all figures in millions). We therefore calculate the cash measure as 151.5 (($155.5 + 1.3 + 40.1)/1.3). This amount is primarily due to a large portion of the company's interest expense being noncash expenses.

We have reviewed many financial ratios and how to compute them. Exhibit 6.6 provides a summary listing. Next, let's review how we can use this information

Exhibit 6.6
Summary Table of Ratios

$$\text{ROE} = \frac{\text{Net Income}}{\text{Average Stockholders' Equity}}$$

$$\text{ROA} = \frac{\text{Net Income}}{\text{Sales}} \times \frac{\text{Sales}}{\text{Average Assets}}$$

$$\text{ROC} = \frac{\text{Net Income} + \text{Interest Expense} \times (1 - \text{tax rate})}{\text{Average Debt} + \text{Average Stockholders' Equity}}$$

$$\text{Receivables Turnover} = \frac{\text{Sales}}{\text{Average Receivables}}$$

$$\text{Days Receivables} = \frac{365}{\text{Receivables Turnover}}$$

$$\text{Inventory Turnover} = \frac{\text{Cost of Goods Sold}}{\text{Average Inventories}}$$

$$\text{Days Inventory} = \frac{365}{\text{Inventory Turnover}}$$

$$\text{Payables Turnover} = \frac{\text{Cost of Goods Sold}}{\text{Average (Accounts) Payable}}$$

$$\text{Days Payables} = \frac{365}{\text{Payables Turnover}}$$

$$\text{Working Capital Turnover} = \frac{\text{Sales}}{\text{Average Current Assets} - \text{Average Current Liabilities}}$$

$$\text{Capital Assets Turnover} = \frac{\text{Sales}}{\text{Average Plant, Property, and Equipment}}$$

$$\text{Current Ratio} = \frac{\text{Current Assets}}{\text{Current Liabilities}}$$

$$\text{Quick Ratio} = \frac{\text{Cash, Marketable Securities, and Receivables}}{\text{Current Liabilities}}$$

$$\text{Cash Ratio} = \frac{\text{Cash and Cash Equivalent Investments}}{\text{Current Liabilities}}$$

$$\text{Interest Coverage} = \frac{\text{Income Before Interest and Tax Expenses}}{\text{Interest Expense}}$$

$$\text{Debt/Equity Ratio} = \frac{\text{Short-term Debt} + \text{Long-term Debt}}{\text{Stockholders' Equity}}$$

to get a better understanding of a firm's past performance as well as make more accurate forecasts of the future.

USING FINANCIAL RATIOS TO ASSESS COMPARATIVE PERFORMANCE

Ratios can be used to assess comparative performance. To do so, the analyst typically would look for trends in the data both across time (*inter-temporal* comparisons) and across firms (*cross-sectional* comparisons).

INTER-TEMPORAL COMPARISONS

We use inter-temporal comparisons of financial ratios to help reveal changes in performance as well as identify causes for those changes. For example, AnnTaylor's ROE increased from 4.9 percent (29.1/(612.1 + 574)/2) in fiscal year 2002 to 12.1 percent in 2003. From the common-size income statements (Exhibit 6.3), we find that the major cause of this improvement results from the change in profit margins (from 2.2 percent to 5.8 percent). Further investigation points to a reduction in cost of sales as a percent of sales (from 50.2 percent to 45.9 percent). In turn, from management's discussion and analysis (not included here but available in the 10-K report), we note that the higher percent cost of sales in 2001 is a consequence of an inventory write-down (inventory values written down resulting in a loss) in that year.

Another significant change pertains to AnnTaylor's short-term debt-paying ability. The current ratio, quick ratio, and cash ratio all increased significantly during fiscal year 2003. Most of the change in these ratios relates to an increase in cash, as reflected in the cash ratio that went from 0.2 at the end of fiscal year 2002 to 1.4 at the end of fiscal year 2003. Offsetting some of the increase in the current and quick ratios due to cash is the decline in the accounts receivable. Again, management's discussion and analysis provide an explanation: the company sold its proprietary credit card receivables during fiscal year 2003. Further, we observe that the company's receivables turnover increased from 21 (1,299.6/(65.6 + 58)/2) to 36.3 during that year.

CROSS-SECTIONAL COMPARISONS

Another dimension in the use of financial ratios to evaluate performance lies in cross-sectional comparisons with other companies, especially those in the same industry. In order to illustrate, we calculated similar ratios from the Talbots' financial statements (Exhibits 6.7 and 6.8). Talbots, like AnnTaylor, is also a women's clothing retailer specializing in classic styles.

Exhibit 6.9 provides a comparison of the ratios for AnnTaylor and Talbots. Looking first at profitability:

	AnnTaylor	Talbots
ROE	12.1%	21.3%
ROA	8.5%	14.2%
ROC	10.3%	18.0%

Exhibit 6.7
Statement of Net Income

THE REAL WORLD

Talbots

	02/01/2003	02/01/2002	02/01/2001
Net sales	$1,595,325,000	$1,612,513,000	$1,594,996,000
Costs and expenses:			
Cost of sales, buying, and occupancy	963,501,000	967,163,000	936,009,000
Selling, general, and administrative	435,757,000	435,334,000	467,324,000
Operating income:	196,067,000	210,016,000	191,663,000
Interest			
Interest expense	3,262,000	6,102,000	7,706,000
Interest income	409,000	927,000	3,364,000
Interest expense, net	2,853,000	5,175,000	4,342,000
Income before taxes	193,214,000	204,841,000	187,321,000
Income taxes	72,455,000	77,840,000	72,119,000
Net Income	$120,759,000	$127,001,000	$115,202,000

	02/01/2003	02/01/2002	02/01/2001
Net sales	100.0%	100.0%	100.0%
Costs and expenses:			
Cost of sales, buying, and occupancy	60.4%	60.0%	58.7%
Selling, general, and administrative	27.3%	27.0%	29.3%
Operating income:	12.3%	13.0%	12.0%
Interest			
Interest expense	0.2%	0.4%	0.5%
Interest income	0.0%	0.1%	0.2%
Interest expense, net	0.2%	0.3%	0.3%
Income before taxes	12.1%	12.7%	11.7%
Income taxes	4.5%	4.8%	4.5%
Net Income	7.6%	7.9%	7.2%

Talbots surpasses AnnTaylor on all the above measures of profitability. We can trace a major cause of this higher performance to selling, general, and administrative expenses from a common size income statement (shown in Exhibit 6.7). These expenses are only 27.3 percent for Talbots as compared to 44.3 percent for AnnTaylor. Total asset turnover provides another contributing factor to the difference in these rates of return (1.9 for Talbots versus 1.5 for AnnTaylor). AnnTaylor does a better job of collecting on its receivables but is less efficient with regard to its inventory turnover.

From a debt-repayment point of view, Talbots also has an advantage in the long-run in that its interest coverage ratio is 60. However, it does have a slightly higher debt-to-equity ratio at 0.28 and its current, quick, and cash ratios are all less favorable than AnnTaylor's at 2.95, 1.4, and 0.17, respectively.

Exhibit 6.8
Balance Sheet

THE REAL WORLD

Talbots

	02/01/2003	02/01/2002
Current assets:		
Cash and cash equivalents	$ 25,566,000	$ 18,306,000
Customer accounts receivable, net	181,189,000	172,183,000
Merchandise inventories	175,289,000	183,803,000
Deferred catalog costs	5,877,000	8,341,000
Due from affiliates	8,793,000	9,618,000
Deferred income taxes	10,255,000	8,222,000
Prepaid and other current assets	28,929,000	29,089,000
Total current assets	435,898,000	429,562,000
Property and equipment, net	315,227,000	277,576,000
Goodwill, net	35,513,000	35,513,000
Trademarks, net	75,884,000	75,884,000
Deferred income taxes	0	3,595,000
Other assets	9,403,000	8,934,000
Total Assets	$871,925,000	$831,064,000
Current liabilities:		
Accounts payable	$ 48,365,000	$ 49,645,000
Accrued income taxes	11,590,000	1,019,000
Accrued liabilities	87,986,000	79,628,000
Total current liabilities	147,941,000	130,292,000
Long-term debt	100,000,000	100,000,000
Deferred rent under lease commitments	20,688,000	19,542,000
Deferred income taxes	2,921,000	0
Other liabilities	32,699,000	13,354,000
Commitments		
Stockholders equity:		
Common stock, $0.01 par value; 200,000,000 authorized; 75,270,013 shares and 74,935,856 share issued, respectively, and 57,505,802 shares and 60,382,406 shares outstanding, respectively	753,000	749,000
Additional paid-in capital	389,402,000	378,955,000
Retained earnings	572,741,000	472,594,000
Accumulated other comprehensive income (loss)	(15,437,000)	(5,508,000)
Restricted stock awards	(78,000)	(697,000)
Treasury stock, at cost:17,764,211 shares and 14,553,450 shares, respectively	(379,705,000)	(278,217,000)
Total stockholders' equity	567,676,000	567,876,000
Total liabilities and stockholders' equity	$871,925,000	$831,064,000

While the assessment of past performance is useful, analysts are primarily concerned with forecasting the future. To that end, analysts often use their analysis of past performance to assist them in the forecasting of the future results of the firm. We now turn to a discussion of forecasting.

Ratio	Ann Taylor	Talbots
ROE	12.1%	21.3%
ROA	8.5%	14.2%
Profit Margin	5.8%	7.6%
Total Asset Turnover	1.46	1.90
ROC	10.3%	18.0%
Receivables Turnover	36.3	9.0
Days of Receivables	10.0	40.4
Inventory Turnover	3.4	5.4
Days of Inventory	107.3	68.0
Accounts Payable Turnover	11.6	19.7
Days of Accounts Payable	31.4	18.6
Working Capital Turnover	5.6	5.4
Capital Asset Turnover	5.5	5.4
Current Ratio	3	2.95
Quick Ratio	1.5	1.4
Cash Ratio	1.4	0.17
Interest Coverage	20	60
Debt/Equity	0.2	0.28

Exhibit 6.9
Ratio Comparison of Ann Taylor and Talbots

THE REAL WORLD

Ann Taylor and Talbots

FORECASTING

The financial analyst's principal stock-in-trade lies in forming estimates of firm values based on forecasts of future earnings or cash flows. In developing forecasts, analysts may use their understanding of markets for the firm's products or services to model supply and demand, formal statistical methods to exploit past observations in characterizing time series behavior, experience and judgment to determine future trends, or some combination of these approaches. The value of a forecast ultimately is derived from improved decision making based on the estimates that the forecast produces.

Forecasting future operating performance usually begins with predicting sales. There are many ways in which to approach this task. An economist might form a set of equations that models industry supply and demand (called *structural* equations as they describe the structure of market supply and demand conditions faced by the firm). Economists may then use estimates of these equations to predict the future price of a firm's output, which, when combined with projected production, would lead to a forecast of sales. The data required by such a model might include wages of workers and income of consumers, implying the need to forecast these factors.

An alternative modeling approach looks for a functional relationship between sales and time. By examining past observations of sales, analysts may detect a systematic relationship between sales and the passage of time that can be reasonably portrayed by a mathematical equation. For example, sales might be growing at a fixed rate such as 2 percent a year or it might be growing at a certain percentage of another variable, such as population growth.

Evidence indicates that the market may react differentially to whether a firm meets or fails to meet analysts' forecasts, although the evidence is mixed as to the direction. See Skinner and Sloan, *Review of Accounting Studies* (2002) and Payne and Thomas, *The Accounting Review* (2003).

Less-formal approaches to forecasts rely on analysts' intuition and judgment. The simplest approach would be to predict that next period's sales would equal this period's sales. Another approach might be to portray future sales as a weighted average of current sales and the previous forecast. Last, but not least, rather than rely on economic or mathematical models or simply intuition, we can instead build a statistical model of time series behavior from an analysis of past observations based only on the data. In other words, an analyst might statistically examine the properties of the data themselves to specify a forecasting model. Let's look at this approach in more detail.

TIME SERIES ANALYSIS

Time series analysis basically estimates a model of the process generating the variable of interest (in our case, sales) from past observations. Typically, the initial step in identifying such a model is to estimate the *statistical correlations* (how one variable behaves relative to another) between lagged observations. For example, current sales might be correlated with sales of the previous period, sales of two periods ago, sales of three periods ago, and so on. These correlations allow analysts to determine a tentative model. For example, some firms display seasonal variations in quarterly sales such that, say, fourth quarter sales are more highly correlated with fourth quarter sales of the previous year than with third quarter sales of the current year (e.g., holiday-season sales for toy manufacturers). Accordingly, a suitable forecasting model of quarterly sales would likely take that correlation information into account.

Once we formulate a model, we then check how well the estimated model captures the time series behavior of the data. This might involve a measure of *forecast errors* (deviations between actual sales and sales predicted by the model). If necessary, we repeat the process until the measure used to check the model indicates that it fits the data sufficiently well.

However, analysts want to forecast earnings, so providing a sales forecast using time series analysis is only half the battle. Analysts must also forecast expenses for the firm, usually by relating them to sales. For example, analysts might employ common-size ratios under the assumption that expenses would remain a constant percentage of sales. Some expenses may also depend on planned investments in working capital and long-term assets, such as plant, property, and equipment. Thus, a comprehensive approach toward forecasting earnings or cash flows often involves projecting a full set of financial statements including successive balance sheets. These forecasted financial statements are called the **pro forma statements.**

PRO FORMA STATEMENTS

Firms sometimes prepare pro forma statements to depict the consequences of a future financing event. For example, an initial public offering (IPO) of stock for sale to the public requires the preparation of a *prospectus* (a document filed with the SEC) containing financial statements that reflect the disposition of the anticipated proceeds from the sale of stock and the pro forma changes to assets, liabilities, and stockholders' equity that would result.

Exhibit 6.10
Intel Corporation

THE REAL WORLD

Intel Corporation

Pro forma information is required by SFAS No. 123 as if the company had accounted for its employee stock options (including shares issued under the Stock Participation Plan, collectively called "options") granted subsequent to December 31, 1994 under the fair value method of that statement.

For purposes of pro forma disclosures, the estimated fair value of the options is amortized to expense over the options' vesting periods. The company's pro forma information follows:

(In millions-except per share amounts)	2001	2000	1999
Net income	$254	$9,699	$6,860

To judge the significance of these adjustments, note that the reported net income for Intel was $1,291, $10,535, and $7,314 (in millions) for the years 2001, 2000, and 1999, respectively. Therefore, the effect of this adjustment was less than 10 percent of net income in 1999 and 2000 but was an 80 percent decline in income in 2001. This could have a significant influence on an analyst's forecast of the future income on the company.

Firms also use pro forma statements to depict the consequences of an alternative accounting treatment when more than one method is allowed. For example, accounting rules for employee stock options (considered in Chapter 12) allow firms to either recognize compensation expense associated with those options or not recognize compensation expense but disclose pro forma net income as if the compensation expense had been recorded. Exhibit 6.10 illustrates the disclosure for Intel.

Although our principal perspective in developing forecasts of operating data is at the firm level, analysts must also characterize the future prospects of the industry and economy at large. Business cycles and industry trends often factor prominently in forming predictions regarding the outlook for firms susceptible to the influence of those factors. In such cases, we might begin to build a forecast for the firm by first developing or obtaining forecasts at an industry- or economy-wide level. An integrated approach might involve joint analyses of firm, industry, and economy data with the objective of improving estimates at the firm level.

A risk to forecasting models that focus only on time series data is that analysts might be ignoring changes in competitive strategy and changes in organizational structure. For example, how would analysts handle a firm's merger with another company? This event might fundamentally alter the basic statistical properties of a the firm's sales or earnings. In this case, analysts can capture this change with a more encompassing model. Or, analysts might modify pre-merger operating data as if both firms had always been a single entity (an example of employing pro forma statements) and then apply one of the forecasting approaches described above.

TIME VALUE OF MONEY

Analysts utilize forecasts of future results to help them value the stock of a company today. Before we explain more fully how analysts incorporate their forecasts of future results to arrive at these value estimates, it is important to talk about the concepts of the time value of money, specifically the *present value* of money.

A standard question in an effort to convey the concept of time value of money is to ask whether you would prefer to receive a dollar today or a dollar tomorrow. Most people will respond by saying that they would prefer to receive the dollar today. When asked why, many observe that if they had the dollar today then they would be at least as well off as if they waited until tomorrow because they could always choose to hold the dollar rather than spend it. Moreover, they would have the option not to hold the dollar and spend it if they so chose, which implies more value. It often occurs to at least some that if they had the dollar today, then they could immediately deposit it in their bank and, given that their bank pays interest on a daily basis, they would have more than a dollar tomorrow. In other words, there is a time value to money.

There are many familiar examples of the time value of money. TV ads for automobiles often present prospective buyers with a low interest rate on funds borrowed to pay for a car or a lump sum reduction in the purchase price if they pay in cash. Bank statements may show interest earned on funds held on deposit, copies of information returns filed by insurance companies and brokerage houses also report interest earned, while similar filings by mortgage companies report interest paid. It is hard to escape some exposure to the notion of interest and a time value to money.

In virtually all of the situations where time value of money is relevant, the problem is to somehow compare a dollar amount today, known as **present value,** with an amount in the future, known as **future value.** The calculations that we often employ to compare values at different points in time are referred to as **time value of money** calculations and they all involve the time value of money being expressed as an **interest rate** or **discount rate.** Next we consider the process of converting a present value into a future value and vice versa.

FUTURE VALUE

A useful way to approach the concept of the present value of a future value (sometimes referred to as a **future sum**) is to turn the issue around and ask what an investment of cash today would yield in terms of cash in the future if, in the interim, that investment earned interest. Suppose that one could invest $1,000 in a bank savings account that pays interest at a rate of 5 percent for one year. At the end of the year, the account would contain $1,050, the initial investment of $1,000 plus interest of $50 ($1,000 × 0.05). Now, suppose that the $1,050 was left in the savings account for a second year and the interest was allowed to also earn interest (called **compounding of interest**). At the end of that year the account would contain $1,102.50 ($1,050 + $1,050 × 0.05 or $1,000 × (1 + 0.05)^2). Note that the $50 of interest earned in the first year then earned $2.50 of interest in the second year, reflecting the compounding of interest. Mathematically, the future value of C dollars at the end of two years at an interest rate of r, compounded annually, can be expressed as follows (where **FV** is referred to as a **future value factor**):

$$\text{Future Value}(2) = C + rC + r(C + rC) = C + 2rC + r^2C = C(1 + r)^2 = C \times FV_{2r}$$

Generalizing in the above to n years at rate r, we obtain

$$FV_{n,r} = (1 + r)^n$$
$$\text{Future Value}(n) = C \times FV_{n,r}$$

Note that many books, this one included, contain a table of such future value factors arranged by the number of periods (n) and the interest rate per period (r). Such tables are often referred to as **future value of \$1** tables. Functions that calculate these factors are also incorporated into handheld financial calculators and spreadsheet programs such as Microsoft Excel™.

PRESENT VALUE

The concept of present value reverses the exercise by posing the question: what is an amount to be received in the future worth now? Intuitively, one would expect present value to be less than the future amount because, if we had the cash now, then it could be invested, earn interest, and be worth more in the future.

In the numerical example above, the present value of \$1,050 to be received in one year given an interest rate (discount rate) of 5 percent and annual compounding would be \$1,050 ÷ 1.05 or \$1,000. Similarly, the present value of \$1,102.50 to be received two years hence would be \$1,102.50 ÷ $(1.05)^2$, or \$1,000 again. It should be fairly clear that mathematically, the present value of C dollars to be received in two years at a discount rate of r, compounded annually, can be expressed as follows (where **PV** is the **present value factor**):

$$\text{Present Value}(2) = \frac{C}{(1 + r)(1 + r)} = \frac{C}{(1 + r)^2} = C \times PV_{2,r}$$

Again, generalizing to n years, results in:

$$PV_{n,r} = \frac{1}{(1 + r)^n}$$
$$\text{Present Value}(n) = C \times PV_{n,r}$$

ADJUSTING FOR UNCERTAINTY

In applying time value of money concepts to an investor's decisions, the interest rate (discount rate) that the investor would use should reflect their own personal time preference for money. Typically this rate will be a function of the other opportunities available to the investor for return on investment and some adjustment for the risk or uncertainty associated with the investment opportunity. The issue of risk is that if one waits until tomorrow to receive the dollar, then something may happen between today and tomorrow such that tomorrow's dollar (or some portions of the dollar) might not materialize. All else held constant, the interest rate required by an investor when there is uncertainty about the outcome of the investment might be higher than the interest rate on a sure thing, depending on the risk preferences of the investor. If the investor is risk averse, then the discount rate employed by that investor would likely be higher to compensate for bearing the risk. By risk averse we mean that the individual strictly prefers a sure thing to a gamble for which the expected payoff is the same as the payoff on the sure thing. For example, risk averse individuals often buy insurance. They prefer to pay a certain premium to an insurance company for coverage of a possible loss when the expected loss is less than the premium.

MODELS FOR VALUING EQUITY

One application of both forecasting and the time value of money is to estimate the value of the equity of a firm. The two basic approaches used by analysts for estimating the value of equity are the **discounted cash flow (DCF)** and **residual income (RI)** models. Both approaches begin with forecasts of operating results. In the DCF approach, forecasting techniques are used to estimate future free cash flows to equity (discussed in Chapter 5); in the RI approach, a quantity known as *future abnormal earnings* is estimated rather than cash flows.

DCF APPROACH

Under the DCF approach, operating income is transformed into cash from operations by adding back noncash expenses including depreciation and amortization of operating assets, and subtracting changes in operating working capital. This is the same format used in the cash flow statement to produce cash from operations under GAAP. Cash from operations is then reduced by cash used in investment activities and increased by net borrowings (or reduced by net repayments of borrowings) to arrive at an amount known as **free cash flow** to equity holders (i.e., stockholders). Free cash flows must then be forecasted over the future life of the firm. Typically, DCF analysis also establishes a **time horizon** for the analysis, and the firm's value at the end of that time period (known as the **terminal value**) is estimated. This terminal value is then discounted along with the estimates of free cash flow, using the present value techniques described earlier, to obtain the estimate of the value for the firm's stock. The discount rate employed reflects the rate of return investors require in order to buy the firm's stock. This rate is sometimes called the firm's equity **cost of capital.**

To illustrate, let FCF_1, FCF_2, and FCF_n denote free cash flows received at the end of future periods 1, 2, and so forth, up to the end of the life of the firm in period n. The terminal period is n, and let TV_n be the estimated terminal value. We can calculate the present value of the firm and the estimated value of stockholders' equity as follows:

$$\text{Value of Stockholders' Equity} = \frac{FCF_1}{(1 + r)} + \frac{FCF_2}{(1 + r)^2} + \cdots\cdots + \frac{FCF_n}{(1 + r)^n} + \frac{TV_n}{(1 + r)^n}$$

Exhibit 6.11 provides condensed financial data for a hypothetical firm in the form of pro forma financial statements over an assumed remaining firm life (investment horizon) of four years. The initial balance sheet at time 0 reflects

Balance Sheet Period	0	1	2	3	4
Equipment, Net	1,000	750	500	250	0
Total Assets	1,000	750	500	250	0
Common Stock	1,000	1,000	1,000	1,000	0
Retained Earnings	0	−250	−500	−750	0
Total Liability and Owners' Equity	1,000	750	500	250	0

Income Statement Period	1	2	3	4
Revenue	500	500	500	500
Depreciation	−250	−250	−250	−250
Net Income	250	250	250	250

Cash Flow Statement Period	1	2	3	4
Net Income	250	250	250	250
Depreciation	250	250	250	250
Operating Cash Flow	500	500	500	500
Dividends	−500	−500	−500	−500
Change in Cash	0	0	0	0

Exhibit 6.11
Pro forma Financial Statements Hypothetical Firm

equipment of $1,000 purchased from the proceeds of a common stock issue for that amount. The equipment will last four years, at which point it becomes valueless. To keep the calculation simple we will assume that the terminal value is zero at that point in time. Revenues are forecasted to be $500 per year. The only expense is depreciation, which we assume is $250 per year. All available cash each year is distributed in the form of a dividend to common stockholders. The cost of equity is assumed to be 10 percent.

In this example, free cash flows are equivalent to cash from operations on the cash flow statement as there are no investment or debt cash flows. Because free cash flow is the same in all four years, the present value of those cash flows, our estimate of equity value, can be calculated as follows:

$$
\begin{aligned}
\text{Value of Stockholders' Equity} \\
= 500 \times \left(\frac{1}{1+.10} + \left(\frac{1}{1+.10}\right)^2 + \left(\frac{1}{1+.10}\right)^3 + \left(\frac{1}{1+.10}\right)^4 \right) \\
= 500 \times \left(\frac{1-(1+.10)^{-4}}{.10} \right) = 1,585
\end{aligned}
$$

where the last term contained in parentheses is a shorthand way of expressing the present value factor for a series of constant amounts received each year. This stream of cash flows (the four $500 payments) is called an **annuity,** and the factor in the last equation would be called a *present value of an annuity factor.* A more detailed description of present value and annuities, along with related tables of present value factors, is provided in Appendix B.

Observe that the value of stockholders' equity derived from the free cash flows of $1,585 is also the present value of the stream of future dividends. Thus, a value of stockholders' equity of $1,585 makes sense when one looks at firm value from an investor's perspective. The interpretation would be that if you purchased the stock in this company for $1,585 and received the four dividends of $500 each, you would have received a return of 10 percent on your investment, due to the fact that we used a discount rate of 10 percent to present value the cash flows.

RI APPROACH

Under the RI approach, a quantity known as **abnormal earnings** is calculated. Abnormal earnings are simply those earnings that are above or below the earnings currently expected by investors, given their investment in the firm and their required (expected) rate of return. Abnormal earnings are calculated by deducting a charge for the use of capital provided by stockholders from net income. This **capital charge** is determined by multiplying the book value of stockholders' equity at the start of the year by cost of equity capital (rate). The present value of abnormal earnings projected over the life of the firm is then added to the initial book value of stockholders' equity to arrive at an estimate of the value of stockholders' equity. To put this in simple terms, if the firm issued stock for $1,000 and invested the proceeds in operating assets and stockholders expected to earn 10 percent on their investment, then they would expect $100 in earnings every period. If earnings were above or below $100 then they would be viewed as abnormal earnings.

Let AE_1, AE_2 and AE_K denote abnormal earnings for future periods $1, 2, k$, and so on over the remaining life of the firm. The value of stockholders' equity is then:

$$\text{Value of Stockholder's Equity} = \text{Book Value of Stockholder's Equity} + \frac{AE_1}{(1 + r)} + \frac{AE_2}{(1 + r)^2} + \text{................} + \frac{AE_k}{(1 + r)^k} + \text{................}$$

Using the data from Exhibit 6.11, the cost of capital charge is calculated by multiplying stockholders' equity at the beginning of each period by the cost of capital (10 percent). Abnormal earnings are then calculated as the reported net income minus the capital charge:

Year 1: $150 = $250 − (10% × $1,000)

Year 2: $175 = $250 − (10% × $750)

Year 3: $200 = $250 − (10% × $500)

Year 4: $225 = $250 − (10% × $250)

The book value of stockholders' equity is the $1,000 of common stock at the start of the forecast horizon. Accordingly, the value of stockholders' equity can be determined from accounting numbers as follows:

$$\text{Value of Stockholders' Equity} = 1,000 + 150 \times \left(\frac{1}{1.10}\right) + 175 \times \left(\frac{1}{1.10}\right)^2$$
$$+ 200 \times \left(\frac{1}{1.10}\right)^3 + 225 \times \left(\frac{1}{1.10}\right)^4 = 1,585$$

Not surprisingly, the value of stockholders' equity is the same under both a DCF and an RI approach. It should also not be surprising that this asset is worth more than the $1,000 paid to acquire it given that the investor is expecting a 10 percent return. If you just consider the first year, the asset would be expected to return only $100 in income, yet it returns $250 or $150 more than expected. This is true in each of the four years of the asset's life, as shown in the calculation of abnormal earnings. Therefore, the $1,000 asset is worth more ($1,585) than its cost.

SUMMARY AND TRANSITION

Financial statement analysis encompasses many dimensions. Because companies often employ different methods of accounting, it may be necessary to transform financial statements to reflect common accounting practices when making cross-sectional comparisons. Fortunately, accounting reports often contain sufficient information, either in the statements themselves or in accompanying footnotes and supporting schedules, to make these transformations.

A further problem in working from data contained in financial statements for purposes of both time series and cross-sectional comparisons is adjusting for differences in size. To remedy this problem, analysts construct financial ratios that place accounting numbers on a common scale. Besides controlling for differences in size, financial ratios are useful in assessing operating performance. Two broad classes of financial ratios for use in this respect are ratios that measure profitability and ratios that measure debt-repayment ability.

One of the more common ratios for assessing profitability from the stockholders' perspective is rate of return on equity (ROE), determined by dividing net income by stockholders' equity. ROE can be usefully broken down into rate of return on assets (ROA) and leverage, as measured by the ratio of total assets-to-debt. In turn, ROA can be broken down into profit margin and asset turnover, measures of the company's efficiency in converting sales into profits and assets into sales, respectively. The company's ability to generate a higher return on stockholders' equity through the use of financial leverage can be determined by comparing ROE to the rate of return on capital (ROC), where capital is defined as debt plus stockholders' equity, and interest, net of taxes, is added to net income in the numerator of this ratio.

Indicators of a company's short-term debt repayment ability include liquidity ratios, such as the current ratio (current assets divided by current liabilities), quick ratio (current assets other than inventories and prepaid expenses divided by current liabilities), and cash ratio (cash divided by current liabilities). Common ratios for assessing long-term debt-repayment ability include interest coverage (income before interest expense and taxes divided by interest expense) and debt to total debt and equity.

Financial analysts are principally concerned with predicting future performance. This typically begins with a forecast of sales. Sales forecasts might be based on economic models of supply and demand facing the firm, mathematical models that relate sales to time, models based on subjective judgment, and statistical models that extrapolate past sales behavior. Projections of future operating expenses often involve common-size ratios and an assumption that costs will remain proportional to sales. Industry- and economy-wide data may also be useful in forming predictions concerning how the company will fare. The company's strategies in meeting its competition may be relevant as well.

Analysts may then use the forecasted data to provide an estimate of the market value of equity using time value of money techniques. Two basic models are used in this process: the discounted cash flow model and the residual income model.

At this point in the book, we have provided an overview of the basics of financial reporting and financial statement analysis. In the next several chapters, we will return to the balance sheet and focus on more detailed accounting issues related to each of the major types of assets, liabilities, and owners' equity accounts.

END OF CHAPTER MATERIAL

KEY TERMS

Abnormal Earnings	Interest Rate
Annuity	Inter-temporal
Capital Asset Turnover	Inventory Turnover
Capital Charge	Operating Forecasts
Cash Ratio	Present Value
Common Size Balance Sheet	Present Value Factor
Common Size Income Statement	Pro Forma Statements
Compounding of Interest	Profit Margin
Cost of Capital	Quick Ratio
Cross-sectional	Receivables Turnover
Current Ratio	Residual Income Model (RI)
Debt/Equity Ratio	Return on Assets (ROA)
Discount Rate	Return on Capital (ROC)
Discounted Cash Flow Model (DCF)	Return on Equity (ROE)
Financial Leverage	Terminal Value
Financial Statement Analysis	Time Horizon
Free Cash Flow	Time Value of Money
Future Sum	Total Asset Turnover
Future Value	Trading on Equity
Future Value Factor	Weighted Average Cost of Capital (WACC)
Interest Coverage	Working Capital Turnover

ASSIGNMENT MATERIAL

REVIEW QUESTIONS

1. Compare and contrast inter-temporal and cross-sectional analysis.
2. For each of the following ratios, reproduce the formula for their calculation:
   a. ROA
   b. ROC
   c. ROE
   d. Receivable Turnover
   e. Inventory Turnover
   f. Payables Turnover
   g. Current
   h. Quick
   i. Debt/Equity
   j. Interest Coverage
3. Describe leverage and explain how it is evidenced in the ROA, ROC, and ROE ratios.
4. Explain, using the profit margin and total asset turnover ratios, how two companies in the same industry can earn the same ROA, yet may have very different operating strategies.
5. What is the advantage of preparing common-size statements in financial statement analysis?
6. Explain why the current ratio is subject to manipulation as a measure of liquidity.
7. Explain how as-if restatements might be used in financial statement analysis.
8. Explain how mandated and discretionary accounting method changes can affect financial statement analysis.
9. What is the purpose of adjusting for scale?
10. Describe the discounted cash flow approach to estimating the value of stockholders' equity.
11. Describe how free cash flow would be calculated.
12. Describe the residual income approach to estimating the value of stockholders' equity.

APPLYING YOUR KNOWLEDGE

13. Discuss the implications that different country accounting standards have for the statement analysis of foreign competitor companies.
14. Suppose that you are analyzing two competitor companies, one a U.S. company and the other a company in the United Kingdom, whose statements are expressed in pounds. Discuss whether it is necessary to convert the statements of the UK company into U.S. dollars before computing ratios.

15. Auditors typically conduct a preliminary review of a firm's financial statements using analytical procedures, which include ratio analysis. As an auditor, why would ratio analysis be useful in auditing the financial statements?

16. Contracts with lenders, such as bonds, typically place restrictions on the financial statement ratios. Two commonly used ratios are the current ratio and the debt/equity ratio. Explain why these might appear as restrictions; in other words, do they protect the lender?

17. Management compensation plans typically specify performance criteria in terms of financial statement ratios. For instance, a plan might specify that management must achieve a certain level of return on investment (e.g., ROA). If management were trying to maximize their compensation, how could they manipulate the ROA ratio to achieve this maximization?

18. The financial data for Nova Electronics Company and Pulsar Electricals for the current year is as follows:

	Annual Sales	Accounts Receivable Jan 1	Accounts Receivable Dec 31
Nova Electronics	3,893,567	1,103,879	1,140,251
Pulsar Electricals	1,382,683	357,934	243,212

   a. Compute the Accounts Receivable Turnover for each company.

   b. Compute the average number of days required by each company to collect the receivables.

   c. Which company is more efficient in terms of handling its accounts receivable policy?

19. Information regarding the activities of Polymer Plastics Corporation is as follows:

	Year 1	Year 2	Year 3	Year 4	Year 5
Cost of Goods Sold	363,827	411,125	493,350	579,686	608,670
Average Inventory	60,537	76,560	107,338	156,672	202,895

   a. Do a time series analysis for the inventory turnover for each year and also compute the average number of days that inventories are held for the respective years.

   b. Is Polymer Plastics Corporation efficiently managing its inventories?

20. The following financial information relates to Delocro Mechanical, Inc. (amounts in thousands):

	Year 1	Year 2	Year 3	Year 4
Sales	2,000	2,200	2,420	2,662
Average Total Assets	1,111	1,222	1,344	1,479
Average Owners' Equity	620	682	750	825
Net Income	200	230	264	304
Interest Expense	50	55	61	67
Tax Rate	40%	40%	40%	30%

For each year calculate:

a. Return on Owners' Equity (ROE)

b. ROI

   i. Profit Margin Ratio

   ii. Total Asset Turnover

c. Comment on the profitability of Delocro Mechanical, Inc.

21. Empire Company's balance sheet is as follows:

Total Assets	$500,000	Liabilities	$100,000
		Owner's Equity	400,000
	$500,000		$500,000

The interest rate on the liabilities is 10 percent, and the income tax rate is 30 percent.

a. If the ROE is equal to the ROI, compute the Net Income.

b. Compute the ROE, taking the Net Income determined in part a.

c. Compute the income before interest and taxes for the net income derived in part a.

d. Assume that total assets remain the same (i.e., at $500,000) and that loans increase to $300,000, while Owners' Equity decreases to $200,000. The interest rate is now 8 percent, and the income tax rate remains at 30 percent. What is the ROE if you require the same ROA as calculated in part b?

e. Compare the ROE in both situations and comment.

22. Spectrum Associates' financial data is as follows (amounts in thousands):

	Year 1	Year 2	Year 3	Year 4
Current Assets				
Accounts Receivable	$ 700	$ 800	$ 600	$ 650
Cash	200	100	200	150
Other Current Assets	100	100	250	100
Inventories	500	1,000	1,450	2,100
	$1,500	$2,000	$2,500	$3,000
Current Liabilities				
Accounts Payable	$ 600	$ 700	$ 825	$ 800
Accrued Salaries	300	400	495	400
Other Current Liabilities	100	150	165	300
	$1,000	$1,250	$1,475	$1,500

a. Compute the current and quick ratios for years 1 through 4.

b. Comment on the short-term liquidity position of Spectrum Associates.

23. Artscan Enterprises' financial data is as follows:

	Year 1	Year 2	Year 3
Income before Interest and Taxes	$ 400	$ 600	$ 800
Interest	70	100	135
Current Liabilities	375	475	750
Noncurrent Liabilities	625	1,125	1,600
Owners' Equity	$1,000	$1,500	$2,000

  a. Compute the Debt/Equity and Times Interest Earned Ratio.

  b. Comment on the long-term liquidity position of Artscan Enterprises.

24. State the immediate effect (increase, decrease, no effect) of the following transactions on:

  a. Current Ratio

  b. Quick Ratio

  c. Working Capital

  d. ROE

  e. Debt/Equity Ratio

  Transaction:

    1. Inventory worth $25,000 is purchased on credit.

    2. Inventory worth $125,000 is sold on account for $158,000.

    3. Payments of $65,000 are made to suppliers.

    4. A machine costing $120,000 is purchased. $30,000 is paid in cash, and the balance will be paid in equal installments for the next three years.

    5. Shares of common stock worth $100,000 are issued.

    6. Equipment costing $80,000 with accumulated depreciation of $50,000 is sold for $40,000 in cash.

    7. Goods worth $35,000 were destroyed by fire. Salvage value of some of the partly burnt goods was $3,000, which is received in cash. The goods were not insured.

25. Calculate the present value of $10,000 to be received ten years from now at 12 percent assuming that interest is compounded:

  a. annually

  b. quarterly

  c. monthly

26. Calculate the present value of an annuity of $100 each year for the next ten years at 12 percent assuming that interest is compounded once a year.

27. Suppose that the free cash flows for a firm are estimated to be $500 per year in each of the next ten years and that the terminal value at the end of the ten years is expected to be $2,000. If your desired rate of return given the risk of this investment was 15 percent, using the DCF approach, what would be the maximum price you would be willing to pay for the entire firm?

28. Suppose that the abnormal earnings of the firm are estimated to be $200 a year for each of the next ten years and that it has a current book value of

$1,500. Using the residual income approach, what would be the maximum amount you would pay for the entire firm if your desired rate of return given the risk of this investment were 12 percent?

USING REAL DATA

29. Use the data from the financial statements of Dell and Gateway to answer the following questions.

DELL COMPUTER CORP. Balance Sheet	01/31/2003	01/31/2002
Current assets:		
Cash and cash equivalents	$ 4,232,000,000	$ 3,641,000,000
Short-term investments	406,000,000	273,000,000
Accounts receivable, net	2,586,000,000	2,269,000,000
Inventories	306,000,000	278,000,000
Other	1,394,000,000	1,416,000,000
Total current assets	8,924,000,000	7,877,000,000
Property, plant, and equipment, net	913,000,000	826,000,000
Investments	5,267,000,000	4,373,000,000
Other noncurrent assets	366,000,000	459,000,000
Total assets	$15,470,000,000	$13,535,000,000
Liabilities and stockholders' equity		
Current liabilities:		
Accounts payable	$ 5,989,000,000	$ 5,075,000,000
Accrued and other	2,944,000,000	2,444,000,000
Total current liabilities	8,933,000,000	7,519,000,000
Long-term debt	506,000,000	520,000,000
Other	1,158,000,000	802,000,000
Commitments and contingent liabilities (Note 6)		
Total liabilities	10,597,000,000	8,841,000,000
Stockholders equity:		
Preferred stock and capital in excess of $.01 par value; shares issued and outstanding: none	—	—
Common stock and capital in excess of $.01 par value; shares authorized: 7,000; shares issued: 2,681 and 2,654, respectively	6,018,000,000	5,605,000,000
Treasury stock, at cost; 102 and 52 shares, respectively	(4,539,000,000)	(2,249,000,000)
Retained earnings	3,486,000,000	1,364,000,000
Other comprehensive income (loss)	(33,000,000)	38,000,000
Other	(59,000,000)	(64,000,000)
Total stockholders' equity	4,873,000,000	4,694,000,000
Total liabilities and stockholders' equity	$15,470,000,000	$13,535,000,000

DELL COMPUTER CORP. Income Statement

	01/31/2003	01/31/2002	01/31/2001
Net revenue	$35,404,000,000	$31,168,000,000	$31,888,000,000
Cost of revenue	29,055,000,000	25,661,000,000	25,445,000,000
Gross margin	6,349,000,000	5,507,000,000	6,443,000,000
Operating expenses:			
Selling, general, and administrative	3,050,000,000	2,784,000,000	3,193,000,000
Research, development, and engineering	455,000,000	452,000,000	482,000,000
Special charges	–	482,000,000	105,000,000
Total operating expenses	3,505,000,000	3,718,000,000	3,780,000,000
Operating income	2,844,000,000	1,789,000,000	2,663,000,000
Investment and other income (loss), net	183,000,000	(58,000,000)	531,000,000
Income before income taxes and cumulative effect of change in accounting principle	3,027,000,000	1,731,000,000	3,194,000,000
Provision for income taxes	905,000,000	485,000,000	958,000,000
Income before cumulative effect of change in accounting principle	2,122,000,000	1,246,000,000	2,236,000,000
Cumulative effect of change in accounting principle, net	–	–	59,000,000
Net income	$ 2,122,000,000	$ 1,246,000,000	$ 2,177,000,000

DELL COMPUTER CORP. Cash Flow Statement

	01/31/2003	01/31/2002	01/312/001
Cash flows from operating activities:			
Net income	$2,122,000,000	$1,246,000,000	$2,177,000,000
Adjustments to reconcile net income to net cash provided by operating activities:			
Depreciation and amortization	211,000,000	239,000,000	240,000,000
Tax benefits of employee stock plans	260,000,000	487,000,000	929,000,000
Special charges	–	742,000,000	105,000,000
(Gains)/losses on investments	(67,000,000)	17,000,000	(307,000,000)
Other, primarily effects of exchange rate changes on monetary assets and liabilities denominated in foreign currencies	(410,000,000)	178,000,000	135,000,000
Changes in:			
Operating working capital	1,210,000,000	826,000,000	642,000,000
Noncurrent assets and liabilities	212,000,000	62,000,000	274,000,000
Net cash provided by operating activities	3,538,000,000	3,797,000,000	4,195,000,000
Cash flows from investing activities:			
Investments:			
Purchases	(8,736,000,000)	(5,382,000,000)	(2,606,000,000)
Maturities and sales	7,660,000,000	3,425,000,000	2,331,000,000
Capital expenditures	(305,000,000)	(303,000,000)	(482,000,000)
Net cash used in investing activities	(1,381,000,000)	(2,260,000,000)	(757,000,000)

	01/31/2003	01/31/2002	01/312/001
Cash flows from financing activities:			
Purchase of common stock	(2,290,000,000)	(3,000,000,000)	(2,700,000,000)
Issuance of common stock under employee plans	265,000,000	298,000,000	395,000,000
Net cash used in financing activities	(2,025,000,000)	(2,702,000,000)	(2,305,000,000)
Effect of exchange rate changes on cash	459,000,000	(104,000,000)	(32,000,000)
Net increase (decrease) in cash	591,000,000	(1,269,000,000)	1,101,000,000
Cash and cash equivalents at beginning of period	3,641,000,000	4,910,000,000	3,809,000,000
Cash and cash equivalents at end of period	$4,232,000,000	$3,641,000,000	$4,910,000,000

GATEWAY, INC. Balance Sheet

	12/31/2003	12/31/2002
ASSETS		
Current assets:		
Cash and cash equivalents	$ 349,101,000	$ 465,603,000
Marketable securities	739,936,000	601,118,000
Accounts receivable, net	210,151,000	197,817,000
Inventory	114,136,000	88,761,000
Other, net	250,153,000	602,073,000
Total current assets	1,663,477,000	1,955,372,000
Property, plant, and equipment, net	330,913,000	481,011,000
Intangibles, net	13,983,000	23,292,000
Other assets, net	20,065,000	49,732,000
	$2,028,438,000	$2,509,407,000
Liabilities and equity		
Current liabilities:		
Accounts payable	$ 415,971,000	$ 278,609,000
Accrued liabilities	277,455,000	364,741,000
Accrued royalties	48,488,000	56,684,000
Other current liabilities	257,090,000	240,315,000
Total current liabilities	999,004,000	940,349,000
Other long-term liabilities	109,696,000	127,118,000
Total liabilities	1,108,700,000	1,067,467,000
Commitments and contingencies (Note 5)		
Series C redeemable convertible preferred stock, $.01 par value, $200,000 liquidation value, 50 shares authorized, issued and outstanding in 2003 and 2002	197,720,000	195,422,000
Stockholders' equity:		
Series A convertible preferred stock, $.01 par value, $200,000 liquidation value, 50 shares authorized, issued and outstanding in 2003 and 2002	200,000,000	200,000,000
Preferred stock, $.01 par value, 4,900 shares authorized; none issued and outstanding	—	—
Class A common stock, nonvoting, $.01 par value, 1,000 shares authorized; none issued and outstanding	—	—

	12/31/2003	12/31/2002
Common stock, $.01 par value, 1,000,000 shares authorized; 324,392 shares and 324,072 shares issued and outstanding in 2003 and 2002, respectively	3,244,000	3,240,000
Additional paid-in capital	734,550,000	732,760,000
Retained earnings (Accumulated deficit)	(218,571,000)	307,379,000
Accumulated other comprehensive income	2,795,000	3,139,000
Total stockholders' equity	722,018,000	1,246,518,000
	$2,028,438,000	$2,509,407,000

GATEWAY, INC. Income Statement

	12/31/2003	12/31/2002	12/31/2001
Net sales	$3,402,364,000	$4,171,325,000	$ 5,937,896,000
Cost of goods sold	2,938,800,000	3,605,120,000	5,099,704,000
Gross profit	463,564,000	566,205,000	838,192,000
Selling, general, and administrative expenses	974,139,000	1,077,447,000	2,022,122,000
Operating loss	(510,575,000)	(511,242,000)	(1,183,930,000)
Other income (loss), net	19,328,000	35,496,000	(94,964,000)
Loss before income taxes and cumulative effect of change in accounting principle	(491,247,000)	(475,746,000)	(1,278,894,000)
Provision (benefit) for income taxes	23,565,000	(178,028,000)	(271,683,000)
Loss before cumulative effect of change in accounting principle	(514,812,000)	(297,718,000)	(1,007,211,000)
Cumulative effect of change in accounting principle, net of tax	—	—	(23,851,000)
Net loss	(514,812,000)	(297,718,000)	(1,031,062,000)
Preferred stock dividends and accretion	(11,138,000)	(11,323,000)	—
Net loss attributable to common stockholders	$ (525,950,000)	$ (309,041,000)	$(1,031,062,000)

GATEWAY, INC. Cash Flow

	12/31/2003	12/31/2002	12/31/2001
Cash flows from operating activities:			
Net loss	$(514,812,000)	$(297,718,000)	$(1,031,062,000)
Adjustments to reconcile net loss to net cash provided by (used in) operating activities:			
Depreciation and amortization	163,973,000	159,458,000	199,976,000
Provision for uncollectible accounts receivable	11,297,000	11,139,000	23,151,000
Deferred income taxes	6,000,000	257,172,000	(27,282,000)
Loss on investments	808,000	30,272,000	186,745,000
Write-down of long-lived assets	66,397,000	52,975,000	418,304,000
Gain on settlement of acquisition liability	—	(13,782,000)	—
Loss on sale of property	6,052,000	—	—
Cumulative effect of change in accounting principle	—	—	23,851,000
Gain on extinguishment of debt	—	—	(6,890,000)
Other, net	1,941,000	(1,929,000)	(1,707,000)
Changes in operating assets and liabilities:			
Accounts receivable	(23,633,000)	11,020,000	301,630,000

	12/31/2003	12/31/2002	12/31/2001
Inventory	(25,375,000)	31,505,000	194,799,000
Other assets	306,258,000	(76,975,000)	21,729,000
Accounts payable	137,716,000	(59,856,000)	(442,312,000)
Accrued liabilities	(95,117,000)	(103,868,000)	(87,714,000)
Accrued royalties	(8,196,000)	(79,014,000)	(2,747,000)
Other liabilities	39,382,000	54,924,000	(40,810,000)
Net cash provided by (used in) operating activities	72,691,000	(24,677,000)	(270,339,000)
Cash flows from investing activities:			
Capital expenditures	(72,978,000)	(78,497,000)	(199,493,000)
Proceeds from sale of investment	–	11,100,000	–
Purchases of available-for-sale securities	(530,323,000)	(614,023,000)	(638,869,000)
Sales of available-for-sale securities	401,109,000	436,316,000	356,071,000
Proceeds from the sale of financing receivables	–	9,896,000	569,579,000
Purchase of financing receivables, net of repayments	–	–	(28,476,000)
Proceeds from notes receivable	20,045,000	–	50,000,000
Other, net	–	–	189,000
Net cash provided by (used in) investing activities	(182,147,000)	(235,208,000)	109,001,000
Cash flows from financing activities:			
Proceeds from issuance of notes payable	–	–	200,000,000
Principal payments on long-term obligations and notes payable	–	–	(3,984,000)
Proceeds from stock issuance	–	–	200,000,000
Payment of preferred dividends	(8,840,000)	(5,878,000)	–
Stock options exercised	1,794,000	367,000	9,431,000
Net cash provided by (used in) financing activities	(7,046,000)	(5,511,000)	405,447,000
Foreign exchange effect on cash and cash equivalents	–	–	2,893,000
Net increase (decrease) in cash and cash equivalents	(116,502,000)	(265,396,000)	247,002,000
Cash and cash equivalents, beginning of year	465,603,000	730,999,000	483,997,000
Cash and cash equivalents, end of year	$ 349,101,000	$ 465,603,000	$ 730,999,000

a. Calculate the following ratios:

ROE, ROC, ROA, Profit Margin, Total Asset Turnover, Receivable Turnover, Inventory Turnover, Payables Turnover Current, Quick, Debt/Equity

b. Calculate the common-size balance sheet and income statement.

c. Comment on the financial health of the two organizations from the point of view of a lender who has been asked to make a $200 million loan to each of the companies.

d. Estimate Dell's and Gateway's 2003 net sales if sales were recognized as cash is collected rather than on the accrual basis. Comment on the significance of the difference between your estimate and reported sales.

e. Suppose you are interested in forecasting future sales for Dell and Gateway. Describe methods that can be used. Forecast Dell's and Gateway's sales for 2006. Justify your answer.

30. Use the data from the financial statement of Home Depot and Lowes to answer the following questions.

HOME DEPOT, INC. Balance Sheet	02/01/2004	02/01/2003
Assets		
Current assets:		
Cash and cash equivalents	$ 2,826,000,000	$ 2,188,000,000
Short-term investments, including current maturities of long-term investments	26,000,000	65,000,000
Receivables, net	1,097,000,000	1,072,000,000
Merchandise inventories	9,076,000,000	8,338,000,000
Other current assets	303,000,000	254,000,000
Total current assets	13,328,000,000	11,917,000,000
Property and equipment, at cost:		
Land	6,397,000,000	5,560,000,000
Buildings	10,920,000,000	9,197,000,000
Furniture, fixtures, and equipment	5,163,000,000	4,074,000,000
Leasehold improvements	942,000,000	872,000,000
Construction in progress	820,000,000	724,000,000
Capital leases	352,000,000	306,000,000
	24,594,000,000	20,733,000,000
Less accumulated depreciation and amortization	4,531,000,000	3,565,000,000
Net property and equipment	20,063,000,000	17,168,000,000
Notes receivable	84,000,000	107,000,000
Cost in excess of the fair value of net assets acquired, net of accumulated amortization of $54 at February 1, 2004 and $50 at February 2, 2003	833,000,000	575,000,000
Other assets	129,000,000	244,000,000
Total assets	$34,437,000,000	$ 30,011,000,000
Liabilities and stockholders' equity		
Current liabilities:		
Accounts payable	$ 5,159,000,000	$ 4,560,000,000
Accrued salaries and related expenses	801,000,000	809,000,000
Sales taxes payable	419,000,000	307,000,000
Deferred revenue	1,281,000,000	998,000,000
Income taxes payable	175,000,000	227,000,000
Current installments of long-term debt	509,000,000	7,000,000
Other accrued expenses	1,210,000,000	1,127,000,000
Total current liabilities	9,554,000,000	8,035,000,000

	02/01/2004	02/01/2003
Long-term debt, excluding current installments	856,000,000	1,321,000,000
Other long-term liabilities	653,000,000	491,000,000
Deferred income taxes	967,000,000	362,000,000
Stockholders' equity		
Common stock, par value $0.05; authorized: 10,000 shares, issued and outstanding 2,373 shares at February 1, 2004 and 2,362 shares at February 2, 2003	119,000,000	118,000,000
Paid-in capital	6,184,000,000	5,858,000,000
Retained earnings	19,680,000,000	15,971,000,000
Accumulated other comprehensive income (loss)	90,000,000	(82,000,000)
Unearned compensation	(76,000,000)	(63,000,000)
Treasury stock, at cost, 116 shares at February 1, 2004 and 69 shares at February 2, 2003	(3,590,000,000)	(2,000,000,000)
Total stockholders' equity	22,407,000,000	19,802,000,000
Total liabilities and stockholders' equity	$34,437,000,000	$30,011,000,000

HOME DEPOT, INC. Income Statement

	02/01/2004	02/01/2003	02/01/2002
Net sales	$64,816,000,000	$58,247,000,000	$53,553,000,000
Cost of merchandise sold	44,236,000,000	40,139,000,000	37,406,000,000
Gross profit	20,580,000,000	18,108,000,000	16,147,000,000
Operating expenses:			
Selling and store operating	12,502,000,000	11,180,000,000	10,163,000,000
Pre-opening	86,000,000	96,000,000	117,000,000
General and administrative	1,146,000,000	1,002,000,000	935,000,000
Total operating expenses	13,734,000,000	12,278,000,000	11,215,000,000
Operating income	6,846,000,000	5,830,000,000	4,932,000,000
Interest income (expense):			
Interest and investment income	59,000,000	79,000,000	53,000,000
Interest expense	(62,000,000)	(37,000,000)	(28,000,000)
Interest, net	(3,000,000)	42,000,000	25,000,000
Earnings before provision for income taxes	6,843,000,000	5,872,000,000	4,957,000,000
Provision for income taxes	2,539,000,000	2,208,000,000	1,913,000,000
Net earnings	$ 4,304,000,000	$3,664,000,000	$3,044,000,000

HOME DEPOT, INC. Cash Flow

	02/01/2004	02/01/2003	02/01/2002
Cash flows from operations:			
Net earnings	$4,304,000,000	$3,664,000,000	$3,044,000,000
Reconciliation of net earnings to net			
Cash provided by operations:			
Depreciation and amortization	1,076,000,000	903,000,000	764,000,000
Decrease (increase) in receivables, net	25,000,000	(38,000,000)	(119,000,000)
Increase in merchandise inventories	(693,000,000)	(1,592,000,000)	(166,000,000)
Increase in accounts payable and accrued liabilities	790,000,000	1,394,000,000	1,878,000,000
Increase in deferred revenue	279,000,000	147,000,000	200,000,000
(Decrease) increase in income taxes payable	(27,000,000)	83,000,000	272,000,000
Increase (decrease) in deferred income taxes	605,000,000	173,000,000	(6,000,000)
Other	186,000,000	68,000,000	96,000,000
Net cash provided by operations	6,545,000,000	4,802,000,000	5,963,000,000
Cash flows from investing activities:			
Capital expenditures, net of $47, $49, and $5 of noncash capital expenditures in fiscal 2003, 2002 and 2001, respectively	(3,508,000,000)	(2,749,000,000)	(3,393,000,000)
Purchase of assets from off-balance sheet financing arrangement	(598,000,000)	–	–
Payments for businesses acquired, net	(215,000,000)	(235,000,000)	(190,000,000)
Proceeds from sales of businesses, net	–	22,000,000	64,000,000
Proceeds from sales of property and equipment	265,000,000	105,000,000	126,000,000
Purchases of investments	(159,000,000)	(583,000,000)	(85,000,000)
Proceeds from maturities of investments	219,000,000	506,000,000	25,000,000
Other	0	0	(13,000,000)
Net cash used in investing activities	(3,996,000,000)	(2,934,000,000)	(3,466,000,000)
Cash flows from financing activities:			
Repayments of commercial paper obligations, net	–	–	(754,000,000)
Proceeds from long-term debt	–	1,000,000	532,000,000
Repayments of long-term debt	(9,000,000)	–	–
Repurchase of common stock	(1,554,000,000)	(2,000,000,000)	–
Proceeds from sale of common stock, net	227,000,000	326,000,000	445,000,000
Cash dividends paid to stockholders	(595,000,000)	(492,000,000)	(396,000,000)
Net cash used in financing activities	(1,931,000,000)	(2,165,000,000)	(173,000,000)
Effect of exchange rate changes on cash and cash equivalents	20,000,000	8,000,000	(14,000,000)
Increase (decrease) in cash and cash equivalents	638,000,000	(289,000,000)	2,310,000,000
Cash and cash equivalents at beginning of year	2,188,000,000	2,477,000,000	167,000,000
Cash and cash equivalents at end of year	2,826,000,000	2,188,000,000	2,477,000,000
Supplemental disclosure of cash payments made for:			
Interest, net of interest capitalized	70,000,000	50,000,000	18,000,000
Income taxes	$2,037,000,000	$1,951,000,000	$1,685,000,000

Lowe's Companies, Inc.
Consolidated Balance Sheets
(In Millions, Except Par Value Data)

	Jan-30-04	Jan-31-03
Assets		
Current assets:		
Cash and cash equivalents	$ 1,446,000,000	$ 853,000,000
Short-term investments (note 3)	178,000,000	273,000,000
Accounts receivable, net (note 1)	131,000,000	172,000,000
Merchandise inventory (note 1)	4,584,000,000	3,968,000,000
Deferred income taxes (note 13)	59,000,000	58,000,000
Other current assets	289,000,000	244,000,000
Total current assets	6,687,000,000	5,568,000,000
Property, less accumulated depreciation (notes 4 and 5)	11,945,000,000	10,352,000,000
Long-term investments (note 3)	169,000,000	29,000,000
Other assets (note 5)	241,000,000	160,000,000
Total assets	$19,042,000,000	$16,109,000,000
Liabilities and shareholders' equity		
Current liabilities:		
Short-term borrowings (note 6)	$ —	$ 50,000,000
Current maturities of long-term debt (note 7)	77,000,000	29,000,000
Accounts payable	2,366,000,000	1,943,000,000
Employee retirement plans (note 12)	74,000,000	88,000,000
Accrued salaries and wages	335,000,000	306,000,000
Other current liabilities (note 5)	1,516,000,000	1,162,000,000
Total current liabilities	4,368,000,000	3,578,000,000
Long-term debt, excluding current maturities (notes 7, 8, and 11)	3,678,000,000	3,736,000,000
Deferred income taxes (note 13)	657,000,000	478,000,000
Other long-term liabilities	30,000,000	15,000,000
Total liabilities	8,733,000,000	7,807,000,000
Shareholders' equity (note 10):		
Preferred stock $5 par value, none issued	—	—
Common stock —$.50 par value; shares issued and outstanding January 30, 2004 — 787 January 31, 2003 — 782	394,000,000	391,000,000
Capital in excess of par value	2,237,000,000	2,023,000,000
Retained earnings	7,677,000,000	5,887,000,000
Accumulated other comprehensive income	1,000,000	1,000,000
Total shareholders' equity	10,309,000,000	8,302,000,000
Total liabilities and shareholders' equity	$19,042,000,000	$16,109,000,000

Lowe's Companies, Inc. Consolidated Statements of Earnings Years Ended on	Jan-30-04	Jan-31-03	Feb-1-02
Net sales	$30,838,000,000	$26,112,000,000	$21,714,000,000
Cost of sales	21,231,000,000	18,164,000,000	15,427,000,000
Gross margin	9,607,000,000	7,948,000,000	6,287,000,000
Expenses:	–	–	–
Selling, general, and administrative (note 5)	5,543,000,000	4,676,000,000	3,857,000,000
Store opening costs	128,000,000	129,000,000	140,000,000
Depreciation	758,000,000	622,000,000	513,000,000
Interest (note 15)	180,000,000	182,000,000	174,000,000
Total expenses	6,609,000,000	5,609,000,000	4,684,000,000
Pre-tax earnings	2,998,000,000	2,339,000,000	1,603,000,000
Income tax provision (note 13)	1,136,000,000	880,000,000	593,000,000
Earnings from continuing operations	1,862,000,000	1,459,000,000	1,010,000,000
Earnings from discontinued operations, net of tax (note 2)	15,000,000	12,000,000	13,000,000
Net earnings	$ 877,000,000	$ 1,471,000,000	$ 1,023,000,000

LOWES COMPANIES, INC. Cash Flow	01/30/2004	01/30/2003	01/30/2002
Cash Flows from operating activities:			
Net earnings	$1,877,000,000	$1,471,000,000	$1,023,000,000
Earnings from discontinued operations, net of tax	(15,000,000)	(12,000,000)	(13,000,000)
Earnings from continuing operations	1,862,000,000	1,459,000,000	1,010,000,000
Adjustments to reconcile net earnings to net cash provided by operating activities:			
Depreciation and amortization	781,000,000	641,000,000	530,000,000
Deferred income taxes	178,000,000	208,000,000	42,000,000
Loss on disposition/write-down of fixed and other assets	31,000,000	18,000,000	39,000,000
Stock-based compensation expense	41,000,000	–	–
Tax effect of stock options exercised	31,000,000	29,000,000	35,000,000
Changes in operating assets and liabilities:			
Accounts receivable, net	2,000,000	(9,000,000)	(5,000,000)
Merchandise inventory	(648,000,000)	(357,000,000)	(326,000,000)
Other operating assets	(45,000,000)	(41,000,000)	(37,000,000)
Accounts payable	423,000,000	228,000,000	1,000,000
Employee retirement plans	(14,000,000)	40,000,000	114,000,000
Other operating liabilities	399,000,000	461,000,000	193,000,000

	01/30/2004	01/30/2003	01/30/2002
Net cash provided by operating activities from continuing operations	3,041,000,000	2,677,000,000	1,596,000,000
Cash flows from investing activities:			
Decrease (increase) in investment assets:			
Short-term investments	139,000,000	(203,000,000)	(30,000,000)
Purchases of long-term investments	(381,000,000)	(24,000,000)	(1,000,000)
Proceeds from sale/maturity of long-term investments	193,000,000	–	3,000,000
Increase in other long-term assets	(95,000,000)	(33,000,000)	(14,000,000)
Fixed assets acquired	(2,444,000,000)	(2,359,000,000)	(2,196,000,000)
Proceeds from the sale of fixed and other long-term assets	45,000,000	44,000,000	42,000,000
Net cash used in investing activities from continuing operations	(2,543,000,000)	(2,575,000,000)	(2,196,000,000)
Cash flows from financing activities:			
Net decrease in short-term borrowings	(50,000,000)	(50,000,000)	(150,000,000)
Long-term debt borrowings	–	–	1,087,000,000
Repayment of long-term debt	(29,000,000)	(63,000,000)	(63,000,000)
Proceeds from employee stock purchase plan	52,000,000	50,000,000	38,000,000
Proceeds from stock options exercised	97,000,000	65,000,000	77,000,000
Cash dividend payments	(87,000,000)	(66,000,000)	(60,000,000)
Net cash provided by (used in) financing activities from continuing operations	(17,000,000)	(64,000,000)	929,000,000
Net cash provided by discontinued operations	112,000,000	16,000,000	14,000,000
Net increase (decrease) in cash and cash equivalents	593,000,000	54,000,000	343,000,000
Cash and cash equivalents, beginning of year	853,000,000	799,000,000	456,000,000
Cash and cash equivalents, end of year	$1,446,000,000	$ 853,000,000	$ 799,000,000

a. Calculate the following ratios:

ROE, ROC, ROA, Profit Margin, Total Asset Turnover, Receivable Turnover, Inventory Turnover, Payables Turnover Current, Quick, Debt/Equity

b. Calculate the common-size balance sheet and income statement.

c. Comment on the financial health of the two organizations from the point of view of a lender who has been asked to make a $200 million loan to each of the companies.

d. Estimate Lowe's and Home Depot's sales for the year ending February 1, 2004 if sales had been recorded as cash is collected rather than on the accrual basis. Comment on the significance of the difference between your estimate and reported sales.

Suppose you are interested in forecasting future sales for Lowes and Home Depot. Describe methods that can be used. Forecast Lowe's and Home Depot's sales for 2006. Justify your answer.

Assuming that the amount forecast for 2006 will continue indefinitely into the future, estimate the market value of Lowes and Home Depot using the free cash flow and residual income approaches. Assume a required rate of return of 10 percent. Hint: The present value of a stream of cash flows that continues into infinity is computed as the amount divided by the required rate of return. For example, the present value of $10 to be received annually forever is 10/.1 = $100 (assuming a 10 percent required rate of return).

BEYOND THE BOOK

31. Prepare a comparative ratio analysis of two competitor companies. At the direction of your instructor, pick either two domestic or one domestic and one foreign competitor. At a minimum, use the set of ratios discussed in the text and at least three years of data. Use any additional ratios that might be commonly used in the industry that you select (you may also need to drop some of the ratios discussed in the book if they are not relevant).

Required: Prepare a written report summarizing your comparative analysis. For the purpose of this report, assume some sort of decision perspective; for instance, you might assume that you are a bank loan officer evaluating the two competitors to decide which has the best lending risk profile.

Outline

Part II: Evaluating Economic Performance of Companies and Projects

- Lecture slides on ratio analysis, discounted cash flows and transform techniques

- Chapters 2 and 3 of "Advanced Engineering Economics" by Park and Sharp-Bette

- Lecture slides on figures of merit

- Chapters 6 and 7 of "Advanced Engineering Economics" by Park and Sharp-Bette

Evaluating Financial Performance

Profitability ratios

➢**Return on Equity (ROE) =** Net income / Shareholders' Equity

➢**Return on Assets (ROA) =** Net income / Assets

➢**Return on Invested Capital (ROIC) =** EBIT (1- Tax rate) / (Interest-bearing debt + Shareholders' equity)

➢**Profit Margin (PM) =** Net income / Sales

➢**Gross Margin (GM) =** Gross profit / Sales

➢**Price to Earnings (P/E ratio) =** Price per share / Earnings per share

Evaluating Financial Performance

ROE = Net income/ Shareholders' Equity

= (Net income/Sales) x (Sales/Assets) x (Assets/Shareholders' Equity)

=   **Profit margin**   **x Asset Turnover x**   **Financial Leverage**

          I.S.   **Left B.S.**   **Right B.S.**

➢ **ROE is not a reliable financial yardstick:**

- **Timing problem**

- **Risk problem**

- **Value problem**

Evaluating Financial Performance

Turnover-control ratios

> **Asset Turnover** = Sales / Assets

> **Fixed-Asset Turnover** = Sales / Net property, plant and equipment

> **Inventory Turnover** = Cost of goods sold / Ending inventory

> **Collection Period** = Accounts receivable / Credit sales per day

(Use sales if credit sales unavailable)

> **Days' Sales in Cash** = Cash and securities / Sales per day

> **Payables Period** = Accounts payable / Credit purchases per day

(Use COGS if credit purchases unavailable))

Evaluating Financial Performance

➤ **Assets to Equity** = Assets / Shareholders' equity

➤ **Debt to Assets** = Total liabilities / Assets

➤ **Debt to Equity** = Total liabilities / Shareholders' equity

➤ **Times Interest Earned** = EBIT / Interest expense

➤ **Current Ratio** = Current assets / Current liabilities

➤ **Acid Test** = (Current assets – Inventory) / Current liabilities

Compounding, Equivalence and Transform Techniques

➢ Payback period and accounting rate of return

➢ Time value of money

➢ Interest rates

➢ Useful formulas

➢ Discrete compounding

➢ Continuous compounding

➢ Equivalence of cash flows

➢ Effect of inflation on cash flow equivalence

➢ Z-transforms and discrete cash flows

➢ Laplace transforms and continuous cash flows

Compounding, Equivalence and Transform Techniques

➢ **Simple interest**

➢ $F_N = P + I = P (1 + N i)$

➢ **Compound interest**

➢ $F_N = P + I = P (1 + i)^N$

➢ **Nominal and effective interest rates**

➢ Annual percentage rate (APR) vs.

Effective annual rate (EAR)

✓ m: number of interest periods per

year

✓ $EAR = (1 + APR / m)^m - 1$

Compounding, Equivalence and Transform Techniques

➤ **4 major types of discrete payments**

- **Single payment**

$$F_N = F \quad \text{and} \quad F_n = 0, \ \forall n \in \{1,..., N-1\}$$

- **Uniform series or equal-payment series**

$$F_n = A, \ \forall n \in \{1,..., N\}$$

- **Arithmetic gradient series**

$$F_n = (n-1)G, \ \forall n \in \{1,..., N\}$$

- **Geometric gradient series**

$$F_n = F_1(1+g)^{n-1}, \ \forall n \in \{1,..., N\}$$

Compounding, Equivalence and Transform Techniques

➢**Compound amount:** $(\,F\,/\,A\,,\,i\,,\,N\,)$

$$F = A\left[\frac{(1+i)^N - 1}{i}\right]$$

➢**Sinking fund:** $(\,A\,/\,F\,,\,i\,,\,N\,)$

$$A = F\left[\frac{i}{(1+i)^N - 1}\right]$$

➢**Present worth:** $(\,P\,/\,A\,,\,i\,,\,N\,)$

$$P = \frac{A}{i}\left[1 - \frac{1}{(1+i)^N}\right]$$

➢**Capital recovery:** $(\,A\,/\,P\,,\,i\,,\,N\,)$

$$A = P\frac{i}{1 - \dfrac{1}{(1+i)^N}}$$

Compounding, Equivalence and Transform Techniques

➤**Present worth:** $(P / G , i , N)$

$$P = G[\frac{1 - \frac{(1 + Ni)}{(1 + i)^N}}{i^2}]$$

➤**Uniform gradient series conversion factor:**
$(A / G , i , N)$

$$A = G[\frac{1}{i} - \frac{N}{(1 + i)^N - 1}]$$

➤**Future worth equivalent of a gradient series:**
$(F / G , i , N)$

$$(F / G, i, N) = \frac{G}{i}[(F / A, i, N) - N]$$

Compounding, Equivalence and Transform Techniques

➢**Present worth:**

$$P = F_1 \frac{1 - (\frac{1+g}{1+i})^N}{i-g}$$

Using $\quad g^{'} = \dfrac{1+i}{1+g} - 1$, we also obtain

$$P = \frac{F_1}{1+g}(P/A, g^{'}, N)$$

Compounding, Equivalence and Transform Techniques

Continuous Compounding

Discrete Payments

➢ Continuous compounding at rate r

- The effective interest rate i is:

  - ✓ $i = e^{r} - 1$

- Use the formulas of discrete compounding

Compounding, Equivalence and Transform Techniques

➢ **Continuous compounding at rate r with flow rate at time t of F_t**

- **Present value**

$$P = \int_0^N F_t e^{-rt}\, dt$$

- **Future value**

$$F = \int_0^N F_t e^{r(N-t)}\, dt$$

Compounding, Equivalence and Transform Techniques

➢**Special case: $F_t = B$**

▪ **Funds flow present worth factor**

$$P = B \int_0^N e^{-rt} dt = B(\frac{1 - e^{-rN}}{r})$$

▪ **Funds flow compound amount factor**

$$F = B \int_0^N e^{rt} dt = B(\frac{e^{rN} - 1}{r})$$

➢ **Two cash flows are equivalent *at interest i* if we can convert one cash flow into the other using proper compound interest factors**

➢ **Cash flow equivalence is used a lot in the stock market and is the basis of the "absence of arbitrage" principle**

Compounding, Equivalence and Transform Techniques

Effect of Inflation on Cash Flow Equivalence

- **Measures of inflation:**

  ➢ CPI (Consumer Price Index) based on market basket

  ➢ GNPIPD (Gross National Product Implicit Price Deflator)

  ➢ PPI (Producer Price Index)

- **These measures tend to overstate inflation as they do not take into account:**

  ➢ Improvements in quality

  ➢ Opportunities for substitution

Compounding, Equivalence and Transform Techniques

- **Explicit and implicit treatments of inflation in discounting**

  - Actual dollars (current dollars, future dollars, inflated dollars, nominal dollars)

  - Constant dollars (real dollars, deflated dollars, todays dollars)

  - Market interest rate i

  - Inflation-free interest rate i' (real interest rate, true interest rate, constant-dollar interest rate)

  - General inflation rate f

$$i' = \frac{i - f}{1 + f}$$

Compounding, Equivalence and Transform Techniques

- **Z- transform of an infinite cash flow $\{f(n)\}$ is:**

$$F(z) = Z\{f(n)\} \equiv \sum_{n=0}^{\infty} f(n)z^{-n}$$

$$F(1+i) = \sum_{n=0}^{\infty} f(n)(1+i)^{-n}$$

- **Properties:**
  - **There is a one to one mapping between an infinite cash flow and its Z-transform**
  - **Linear combinations of cash flows correspond to the same linear combinations of their Z-transforms**
- **Z-transforms have been pre-computed for a large number of cash flows**

261

Compounding, Equivalence and Transform Techniques

- **Laplace transform of an infinite continuous cash flow $\{f(t)\}$ is:**

$$PV(r) = F(z) \equiv \int_0^\infty f(t)e^{-rt}\,dt$$

- **Properties:**
  - ➤ **There is a one to one mapping between an infinite cash flow and its Laplace transform**
  - ➤ **Linear combinations of cash flows correspond to the same linear combinations of their Laplace transforms**
- **Laplace transforms have been pre-computed for a large number of cash flows**

Outline

Part II: Evaluating Economic Performance of Companies and Projects

- Lecture slides on ratio analysis, discounted cash flows and transform techniques

- Chapters 2 and 3 of "Advanced Engineering Economics" by Park and Sharp-Bette

- Lecture slides on figures of merit

- Chapters 6 and 7 of "Advanced Engineering Economics" by Park and Sharp-Bette

2
Interest
and Equivalence

2.1 INTRODUCTION

Engineering economic analysis is primarily concerned with the evaluation of economic investment alternatives. We often describe these investment alternatives by a cash flow diagram showing the amount and timing of estimated future receipts and disbursements that will result from each decision. Because the time value of money is related to the effect of time and interest on monetary amounts, we must consider both the timing and the magnitude of cash flow. When comparing investment alternatives, we must consider the expected receipts and disbursements of these investment alternatives on the same basis. This type of comparison requires understanding of the concepts of equivalence and the proper use of various interest formulas. In this chapter we will examine a number of mathematical operations that are based on the time value of money, with an emphasis on modeling cash flow profiles.

2.2. CASH FLOW PROFILE

An investment project can be described by the amount and timing of expected costs and benefits in the planning horizon. (We will use the terms *project* and *proposal* interchangeably throughout this book.) The terms *costs* and *benefits* represent *disbursements* and *receipts*, respectively. We will use the term *payment* (or *net cash flow*) to denote the receipts less the disbursements that occur at the same point in time. The stream of disbursements and receipts for an investment project over the planning horizon is said to be the *cash flow profile* of the project.

To facilitate the description of project cash flows, we classify them in two categories: (1) discrete-time cash flows and (2) continuous-time flows. The discrete-time cash flows are those in which cash flow occurs at the end of, at the start of, or within discrete time periods. The continuous flows are those in which money flows at a given rate and continuously throughout a given time period. The following notation will be adopted:

F_n = discrete payment occurring at period n,

F_t = continuous payment occurring at time t.

If $F_n < 0$, F_n represents a net disbursement (cash outflow). If $F_n > 0$, F_n represents a net receipt (cash inflow). We can say the same for F_t.

2.3 TIME PREFERENCE AND INTEREST

2.3.1 Time Preference

Cash flows that occur at different points in time have different values and cannot be compared directly with one another. This fact is often stated simply as "money has a time value." There are several reasons why we must assess cash flows in different periods in terms of time preference.

First, money has a potential *earning power,* because having a dollar now gives us an opportunity to invest this dollar in the near future. In other words, equal dollar amounts available at different points in time have different values based on the opportunity to profit from investment activity.

Second, money has a time value because a user may have a different utility of consumption of dollars (i.e., consider them more or less desirable to use) at different times. The preference for consumption in different periods is measured by the rate of time preference. For example, if we have a rate of time preference of i per time period, we are indifferent toward the prospect of either consuming P units now or consuming $P(1 + i)$ units at the end of the period. The rate of time preference is often called the *interest rate* (or *discount rate*) in economic analysis.

Third, money has time value because the *buying power* of a dollar changes through time. When there is inflation, the amount of goods that can be bought for a certain amount of money decreases as the time of purchase is further in the future. Although this change in the buying power of money is important, we limit our concept of time preference to the fact that money has an *earning power,* or utility of consumption. We will treat the effects of inflation explicitly in a later section, and any future reference to the time value of money will be restricted to the first two aspects. Before considering the actual effect of this time value, we will review the types of interest and how they are calculated.

2.3.2 Types of Interest

If an amount of money is deposited in a financial institution, interest accrues (accumulates) at regular time intervals. Each time interval represents an *interest period.* Then the interest earned on the original amount is calculated according to a specified interest rate at the end of the interest period. Two approaches are in use in calculating the earned interest: *simple interest* and *compound interest.*

The first approach considers that the interest earned in any present activity is a linear function of time. Consider the situation in which a present amount P is borrowed from the bank, to be repaid N periods hence by a future amount F. The difference, $F - P$, is simply the interest payment I owed to the bank for the use of the principal P dollars. Because the interest earned is directly proportional to the principal, the interest i is called *simple interest* and is computed from

$$I = F - P$$
$$= (Pi)N$$
$$F = P + (Pi)N$$
$$= \underline{P(1 + iN)} \tag{2.1}$$

The second approach assumes that the earned interest is not withdrawn at the end of an interest period and is automatically redeposited with the original sum in the next interest period. The interest thus accumulated is called *compound interest*. For example, if we deposit $100 in a bank that pays 5% compounded annually and leave the interest in the account, we will have

after 1 year $100 (1.05) = $105.00
after 2 years $105.00 (1.05) = $110.25
after 3 years $110.25 (1.05) = $115.7625

The amount $115.7625 is greater than the original $100 plus the simple interest of $100(0.05)(3), which would be $115.00, because the interest earned during the first and second periods earns additional interest. Symbolically, we can represent a future amount F at time N in terms of a present amount P at time 0, assuming i% interest per period:

$$F_1 = P(1 + i) \qquad \text{after 1 year}$$
$$F_2 = F_1(1 + i) = P(1 + i)^2 \qquad \text{after 2 years}$$
$$\vdots$$
$$F_N = F_{N-1}(1 + i) = P(1 + i)^N \qquad \text{after } N \text{ years}$$

or

$$F = P[(1 + i)^N] \tag{2.2}$$

From Eq. 2.2, the total interest earned over N periods with the compound interest is

$$I = F - P \doteq P[(1 + i)^N - 1] \tag{2.3}$$

The additional interest earned with the compound interest is

$$\Delta I = P[(1 + i)^N - 1] - PiN$$
$$= P[(1 + i)^N - (1 + iN)] \tag{2.4}$$

As either i or N becomes large, ΔI also becomes large, so the effect of compounding is further pronounced.

Example 2.1

Compare the interest earned by $1,000 for 10 years at 9% simple interest with that earned by the same amount for 10 years at 9% compounded annually.

$$\Delta I = 1000[(1 + 0.09)^{10} - (1 + 0.09(10))] = \$467.36$$

The difference in interest payments is $467.36.   □

Unless stated otherwise, practically all financial transactions are based on compound interest; however, the length of the interest period for compounding and the interest rate per period must be specified for individual transactions. In the next section we discuss the conventions used in describing the interest period and the compounding period in business transactions.

2.3.3 Nominal and Effective Interest Rates

In engineering economic analysis, a year is usually used as the interest period, because investments in engineering projects are of long duration and a calendar year is a convenient period for accounting and tax computation. In financial transactions, however, the interest period may be of any duration—a month, a quarter, a year, and so on. For example, the interest charge for the purchase of a car on credit may be compounded monthly, whereas the interest accrued from a savings account in a credit union may be compounded quarterly. Consequently, we must introduce the terms nominal interest rate and effective interest rate to describe more precisely the nature of compounding schemes.

Nominal Interest.   If a financial institution uses more than one interest period per year in compounding the interest, it usually quotes the interest on an annual basis. For example, a year's interest at 1.5% compounded each month is typically quoted as "18% (1.5% × 12) compounded monthly." When the interest rate is stated in this fashion, the 18% interest is called a *nominal interest rate* or *annual percentage rate*. The nominal interest rate, while convenient for a financial institution to use in quoting interest rates on its transactions, does not explain the effect of any compounding during the year. We use the term effective interest rate to describe more precisely the compounding effect of any business transaction.

Effective Interest Rate.   The effective interest rate represents the actual interest earned or charged for a specified time period. In specifying such a time period, we may use the convention of either a year or a time period identical to the payment period. The effective interest rate based on a year is referred to as the *effective annual interest rate* i_a. The effective interest rate based on the payment period is called the *effective interest rate per payment period* i.

We will first look at the expression of the effective annual interest rate. Suppose a bank charges an interest rate of 12% compounded quarterly. This means that the interest rate per period is 3% (12%/4) for each of the 3-month

268

periods during the year. Then interest for a sum of $1 accrued at the end of the year (see Eq. 2.3) is

$$\left(1 + \frac{0.12}{4}\right)^4 - 1 = 0.1255$$

Thus, the effective annual interest rate is 12.55%. Similarly, an interest rate of 12% compounded monthly means that the interest rate per period is 1% (12%/12) for each month during the year. Thus, the effective annual interest rate is

$$\left(1 + \frac{0.12}{12}\right)^{12} - 1 = 0.1268 = 12.68\%$$

Now we can generalize the result as

$$i_a = \left(1 + \frac{r}{M}\right)^M - 1 \tag{2.5}$$

where i_a = the effective annual interest rate,
r = the nominal interest rate per year,
M = the number of interest (compounding) periods per year,
r/M = the interest rate per interest period.

For the special case where $M = 1$ (i.e., one interest period per year, or annual compounding) and $r/M = r$, Eq. 2.5 reduces to $i_a = r = i$. This simply means that with annual compounding we do not need to distinguish between the nominal and effective interest rates.

The result of Eq. 2.5 can be further generalized to compute the effective interest rate in *any payment period*. This results in

$$i = \left(1 + \frac{r}{M}\right)^C - 1$$

$$= \left(1 + \frac{r}{CK}\right)^C - 1 \tag{2.6}$$

where i = the effective interest rate per payment period,
C = the number of interest periods per payment period,
K = the number of payment periods per year,
r/K = the nominal interest rate per payment period.

In deriving Eq. 2.6, we should note the relationships $M \geq C$ and $M = CK$. Obviously, when $K = 1$, C is equal to M, and therefore $i = i_a$. Figure 2.1 illustrates the relationship between the nominal and effective interest rates.

Some financial institutions offer a large number of interest periods per year, such as $M = 365$ (daily compounding). As the number of interest periods M becomes very large, the interest rate per interest period, r/M, becomes very small. If M approaches infinity and r/M approaches zero as a limit, the limiting

Situation: Interest is calculated on the basis of 12% compounded monthly. Payments are made quarterly.

$K = 4$, 4 quarterly payment periods per year
$C = 3$, 3 interest (compounding) periods per quarter
$r = 12\%$
$M = 12$, 12 monthly interest (compounding) periods per year
$r/M = 1\%$, the interest rate per month
$r/K = 3\%$, the nominal interest rate per quarter

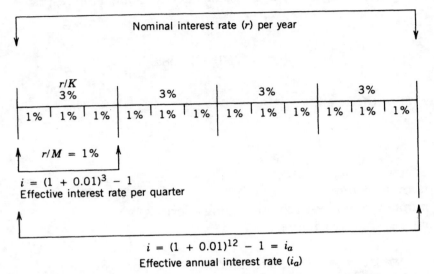

FIGURE 2.1 Functional relationships of r, i, and i_a for monthly compounding with quarterly payments.

condition is equivalent to continuous compounding. By taking limits on both sides of Eq. 2.6, we obtain

$$i = \lim_{M \to \infty}\left[\left(1 + \frac{r}{M}\right)^{M} - 1\right]$$

$$= \lim_{CK \to \infty}\left[\left(1 + \frac{r}{CK}\right)^{C} - 1\right]$$

$$= \lim_{CK \to \infty}\left(1 + \frac{r}{CK}\right)^{C} - 1$$

$$= \lim_{CK \to \infty}\left[\left(1 + \frac{r}{CK}\right)^{CK}\right]^{1/K} - 1$$

$$= (e^r)^{1/K} - 1$$

$$= e^{r/K} - 1 \qquad (2.7)$$

For the effective annual interest rate for continuous compounding, we simply evaluate Eq. 2.7 by setting K to 1. This gives us

$$i_a = e^r - 1 \qquad (2.8)$$

Example 2.2

Find the effective interest rate per quarter at a nominal rate of 18% compounded (1) quarterly, (2) monthly, and (3) continuously.

1. Quarterly compounding

$$r = 18\%, \quad M = 4, \quad C = 1, \quad K = 4$$

$$i = \left(1 + \frac{0.18}{4}\right)^1 - 1 = 4.5\%$$

2. Monthly compounding

$$r = 18\%, \quad M = 12, \quad C = 3, \quad K = 4$$

$$i = \left(1 + \frac{0.18}{12}\right)^3 - 1 = 4.568\%$$

3. Continuous compounding

$$r = 18\%, \quad K = 4, \quad (M = \infty, C = \infty)$$

$$i = e^{0.18/4} - 1 = 4.603\%$$

If we deposit $1,000 in a bank for just one quarter at the interest rate and compounding frequencies specified, our balance at the end of the quarter will grow to $1,045, $1,045.68, and $1,046.03, respectively. □

In Example 2.2 we examined how our deposit balance would grow for a time period of one quarter, but these results can be generalized for deposits of any duration. In the sections ahead, we will develop interest formulas that facilitate the interest compounding associated with various types of cash flow and compounding frequencies. For this presentation, we will group the compound interest formulas into four categories by the type of compounding and type of cash flow. We will first consider discrete compounding in which compounding occurs at a discrete point in time: annual compounding, monthly compounding, and so forth.

2.4 DISCRETE COMPOUNDING

2.4.1 Comparable Payment and Compounding Periods

We first consider the situations for which the payment periods are identical to the compounding periods (annual payments with annual compounding, quarterly payments with quarterly compounding, monthly payments with monthly compounding, and so forth).

___Single Sums.___ In the simplest situation we deposit a single sum of money P in a financial institution for N interest periods. To determine how much can be accumulated by the end of N periods, we may use the result developed in Eq. 2.2,

$$F = P(1 + i)^N \qquad (2.9)$$

The factor $(1 + i)^N$ is called the *single-payment compound amount factor* and is available in tables indexed by i and N. It is represented symbolically by $(F/P, i, N)$. Note that where payment and compounding periods are identical, the effective interest rate is simply $i = r/M$. This transaction can be portrayed by the cash flow diagram shown in Figure 2.2. (Note the time scale convention: the first period begins at $n = 0$ and ends at $n = 1$.)

For example, consider a deposit of $1,000 for 8 years in an individual retirement account (IRA) that earns an interest rate of 11% compounded annually. The balance of the account at the end of 8 years will be

$$F = \$1000(1 + 0.11)^8 = \$2,304.54$$

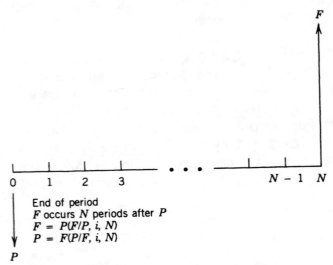

FIGURE 2.2 Cash flow diagram for a single payment.

If the account earns the interest at the rate of 11% compounded quarterly, the balance becomes

$$F = \$1000\left(1 + \frac{0.11}{4}\right)^{32} = \$2{,}382.42$$

If we wish to know what sum P we must deposit with a bank now, at i% compounded periodically, in order to have a future sum F in N periods, we can solve Eq. 2.9 for P.

$$P = F[(1 + i)^{-N}] \tag{2.10}$$

The bracketed term is called the *single-payment present-worth factor*, designated by $(P/F, i, N)$.

For example, we will have \$100 at the end of 3 years if we deposit \$86.38 in a 5% interest-bearing account:

$$P = \$100(\overset{P/F,5\%,3}{0.8638}) = \$86.38$$

Uniform Series. Most transactions with a financial institution involve more than two flows. If we have equal, periodic flows, we can develop formulas for determining beginning and ending balances. For example, an amount A deposited at the *end* of each compounding period in an account paying i% will grow to an amount after N periods of

$$F = A \sum_{n=1}^{N} (1 + i)^{N-n} = A\left[\frac{(1 + i)^N - 1}{i}\right] \tag{2.11}$$

The term in brackets is called the *uniform-series compound amount factor*, or *equal-series compound amount factor*, and is represented by $(F/A, i, N)$. The transaction can be portrayed by the cash flow diagram shown in Figure 2.3. In deriving the summation results in Eq. 2.11, we refer the reader to Table 2.1, which contains closed-form expressions for selected finite summations that are useful in developing interest formulas.

The inverse relationship to Eq. 2.11 yields the *uniform-series sinking-fund factor*, or *sinking-fund factor*,

$$A = F\left[\frac{i}{(1 + i)^N - 1}\right] \tag{2.12}$$

designated by $(A/F, i, N)$. The name derives from a historical practice of depositing a fixed sum at the end of each period into an interest-bearing account (a sinking fund) to provide for replacement moneys for fixed assets.

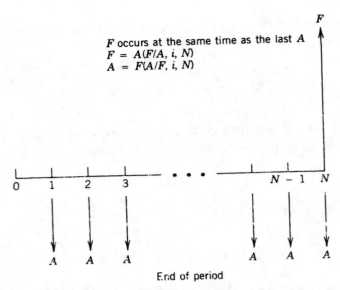

F occurs at the same time as the last A
$F = A(F/A, i, N)$
$A = F(A/F, i, N)$

FIGURE 2.3 Cash flow diagram of the relationship between A and F.

Table 2.1 *Summations Useful in Deriving Interest Formulas*

Geometric series

$$\sum_{n=0}^{N} x^n = 1 + x + x^2 + \cdots + x^N = \frac{1 - x^{N+1}}{1 - x}$$

where $x \neq 1$

    If $-1 < x < 1$, then

$$\sum_{n=0}^{\infty} x^n = 1 + x + x^2 + x^3 + \cdots = \frac{1}{1 - x}$$

Arithmetic–geometric series

$$\sum_{n=0}^{N} nx^n = 0 + x + 2x^2 + \cdots + Nx^N = \frac{x[1 - (N + 1)x^N + Nx^{N+1}]}{(1 - x)^2}$$

where $x \neq 1$

    If $-1 < x < 1$, then

$$\sum_{n=0}^{\infty} nx^n = 0 + x + 2x^2 + 3x^3 + \cdots = \frac{x}{(1 - x)^2}$$

Educational endowment funds can be constructed conveniently by using the sinking-fund factor: to build a $12,000 fund in 18 years at 5% compounded annually requires

$$A = \overset{A/F,5\%,18}{\$12,000(0.0356)} = \$427.20 \quad \text{at the end of each year}$$

The relationships among P, F, and A can be manipulated to relate a series of equal, periodic flows (defined by A) to a present amount P. Substituting Eq. 2.11 into Eq. 2.9 yields

$$P = A\left[\frac{(1 + i)^N - 1}{i(1 + i)^N}\right] \qquad \text{US PWF} \tag{2.13}$$

and its inverse

$$A = P\left[\frac{i(1 + i)^N}{(1 + i)^N - 1}\right] \qquad \text{US CRF} \tag{2.14}$$

The bracketed term in Eq. 2.13 is the *uniform-series present worth factor*, designated by $(P/A, i, N)$. The term in Eq. 2.14 is the *uniform-series capital recovery factor*, or simply the *capital recovery factor*, represented by $(A/P, i, N)$. Figure 2.4 shows the cash flow transactions associated with these factors. The latter factor can be used to determine loan repayment schedules so that principal and interest are repaid over a given time period in equal end-of-period amounts.

To illustrate the use of A/P and P/A factors, consider a commercial mortgage at 8% over 20 years, with a loan principal of $1 million. If equal year-end payments are desired, each annual payment must be

$$\overset{A/P,8\%,20}{\$1,000,000(0.10185)} = \$101,850$$

The loan schedule can then be constructed as in Table 2.2. The interest due at $n = 1$ is 8% of the $1 million outstanding during the first year. The $21,850 left over is applied to the principal, reducing the amount outstanding in the second year to $978,150. The interest due in the second year is 8% of $978,150, or $78,252, leaving $23,598 for repayment of the principal. At $n = 20$, the last $101,850 payment is just sufficient to pay the interest on the outstanding loan principal and to repay the outstanding principal.

Such an equal-payments scheme is also common for home mortgages and automobile loans. In each period a decreasing amount of interest is paid, leaving a larger amount to reduce the principal. Each reduction of loan principal increases an owner's equity in the item by a corresponding amount.

The series present worth factor can be useful for determining the outstanding balance of a loan at any time, as portrayed in Table 2.2. At the end of the fifth year, for example, we still owe 15 payments of $101,850. The value of those

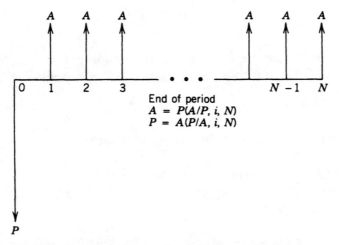

FIGURE 2.4 Equal-payment series and single present amount.

Table 2.2 *A Loan Repayment Schedule Showing Principal and Interest Payments*

Year	Beginning Loan Balance	Interest Payment	Principal Payment	Total Payment
1	1,000,000*	80,000	21,850	101,850
2	978,150	78,252	23,598	101,850
3	954,552	76,364	25,486	101,850
4	929,066	74,325	27,525	101,850
5	901,541	72,123	29,727	101,850
6	871,814	69,745	32,105	101,850
7	839,709	67,177	34,673	101,850
8	805,036	64,403	37,447	101,850
9	767,589	61,407	40,443	101,850
10	727,146	58,172	43,678	101,850
11	683,468	54,677	47,173	101,850
12	636,295	50,904	50,946	101,850
13	585,349	46,828	55,022	101,850
14	530,327	42,426	59,424	101,850
15	470,903	37,672	64,178	101,850
16	406,725	32,538	69,312	101,850
17	337,413	26,993	74,857	101,850
18	262,556	21,005	60,845	101,850
19	181,711	14,537	87,313	101,850
20	94,398	7,452	94,398	101,850

*All figures are rounded to nearest dollars.
NOTE: Loan Amount = $1,000,000
    Loan life = 20 years
    Loan interest = 8% compounded annually
    Equal annual payment size = $1,000,000(A/P, 8%, 20)
                        = $1,000,000(0.10185)
                        = $101,850

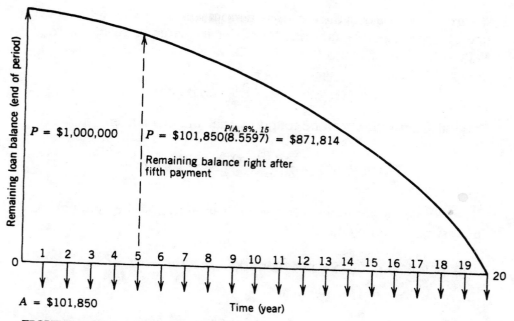

FIGURE 2.5 loan balance as a function of time (n).

payments at time 5 can be represented as in Figure 2.5 with the time scale shifted by 5 and is found from the equation to be

$$P = \$101,850 \overset{P/A,8\%,15}{(8.5595)} = \$871,785$$

which is the same as the \$871,814 in Table 2.2.

Example 2.3

Suppose we are in the market for a medium-sized used car. We have surveyed the dealers' advertisements in the newspaper and have found a car that should fulfill our needs. The asking price of the car is \$7,500, and the dealer proposes that we make a \$500 down payment now and pay the rest of the balance in equal end-of-month payments of \$194.82 each over a 48-month period. Consider the following situations.

1. Instead of using the dealer's financing, we decide to make a down payment of \$500 and borrow the rest from a bank at 12% compounded monthly. What would be our monthly payment to pay off the loan in 4 years? To find A,

$$i = \frac{12\%}{12 \text{ periods}} = 1\% \text{ per month}$$

$$N = (4 \text{ years})(12 \text{ periods per year}) = 48 \text{ periods}$$

$$A = P(A/P, i, N) = (\$7,500 - \$500)\overset{A/P,1\%,48}{(0.0263)} = \$184.34$$

2. We are going to accept the dealer's offer but we want to know the effective rate of interest per month that the dealer is charging. To find i, let $P = \$7{,}000$, $A = \$194.82$, and $N = 48$.

$$\$194.82 = \$7{,}000(A/P, i, 48)$$

The satisfying value i can be found by trial and error from

$$(A/P, i, 48) = \frac{i(1 + i)^{48}}{(1 + i)^{48} - 1} = 0.0278$$

to be $i = 1.25\%$ per month. This value is used to find the nominal annual interest rate used by the dealer.

$$r = (i)(M) = (1.25\% \text{ per month})(12 \text{ months per year})$$
$$= 15\% \text{ per year}$$

Then the effective annual interest used by the dealer is simply

$$i_a = \left(1 + \frac{0.15}{12}\right)^{12} - 1 = 16.08\% \quad \square$$

Linear Gradient Series. Many engineering economy problems, particularly those related to equipment maintenance, involve cash flows that change by a constant amount (G) each period. We can use the gradient factors to convert such gradient series to present amounts and equal annual series. Consider the series

$$F_n = (n - 1)G, \qquad n = 1, 2, \ldots, N \tag{2.15}$$

As shown in Figure 2.6, the gradient G can be either positive or negative. If $G > 0$, we call the series an increasing gradient series. If $G < 0$, we have a decreasing gradient series. We can apply the single-payment present-worth factor to each term of the series and obtain the expression

$$P = \sum_{n=1}^{N} (n - 1)G(1 + i)^{-n} \tag{2.16}$$

Using the finite summation of a linear function in Table 2.1, we obtain

$$P = G\left[\frac{1 - (1 + Ni)(1 + i)^{-N}}{i^2}\right] \tag{2.17}$$

The resulting factor in brackets is called the *gradient series present-worth factor* and is designated $(P/G, i, N)$.

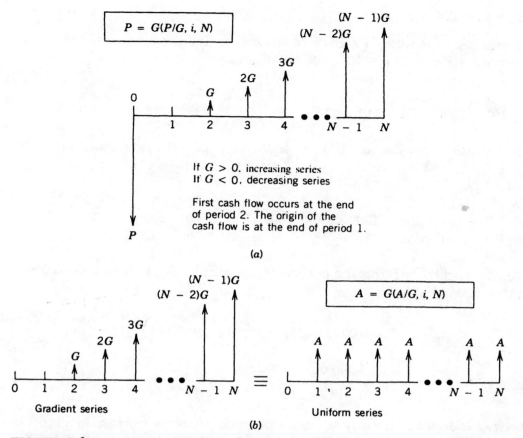

$$P = G(P/G, i, N)$$

$(N-1)G$

$(N-2)G$

$3G$

$2G$

G

0
1   2   3   4   •••   N-1   N

P

If $G > 0$. increasing series
If $G < 0$. decreasing series

First cash flow occurs at the end
of period 2. The origin of the
cash flow is at the end of period 1.

(a)

$(N-1)G$

$(N-2)G$

$3G$

$2G$

G

0 1 2 3 4 ••• N-1 N

Gradient series

$$A = G(A/G, i, N)$$

A A A A   A A

0 1 2 3 4 ••• N-1 N

Uniform series

(b)

FIGURE 2.6 Cash flow diagram for a gradient series. (*a*) A strictly gradient series. (*b*) Conversion factor from a gradient series to a uniform series.

A uniform series equivalent to the gradient series can be obtained by substituting Eq. 2.17 into Eq. 2.14 for P,

$$A = G\left[\frac{1}{i} - \frac{N}{(1+i)^N - 1}\right] \tag{2.18}$$

where the resulting factor in brackets is referred to as the *gradient-to-uniform-series conversion factor* and is designated ($A/G, i, N$).

To obtain the future-worth equivalent of a gradient series, we substitute Eq. 2.18 into Eq. 2.14 for A.

$$F = \frac{G}{i}\left[\frac{(1+i)^N - 1}{i} - N\right]$$

$$= \frac{G}{i}\left[(F/A, i, N) - N\right] \tag{2.19}$$

Example 2.4

An example of the use of a gradient factor is to find the future amount of the following series with $i = 10\%$ per period.

n	0	1	2	3	4	5	6	7	8
F_n	0	100	106	112	118	124	130	136	142

The constant portion of 100 is separated from the gradient series of $0,0,6,12, \ldots , 42$.

n	0	1	2	3	4	5	6	7	8
F_n	0	100	100	100	100	100	100	100	100
	0	0	6	12	18	24	30	36	42

We can quickly verify that the portion of the strict gradient series will accumulate to \$206.15.

$$F = 100 \overset{F/A,10\%,8}{(11.436)} + \frac{6}{0.1} \overset{F/A,10\%,8}{[(11.436)} - 8]$$

$$= 1{,}143.60 + 206.15$$

$$= 1{,}349.76 \quad \square$$

Geometric Series. In many situations periodic payments increase or decrease over time, not by a constant amount (gradient) but by a constant percentage (geometric growth). If we use g to designate the percentage change in the payment from one period to the next, the magnitude of the nth payment, F_n, is related to the first payment, F_1, by

$$F_n = F_1(1 + g)^{n-1}, \qquad n = 1, 2, \ldots, N \tag{2.20}$$

As illustrated in Figure 2.7, g can be either positive or negative, depending on the type of cash flow. If $g > 0$ the series will increase, and if $g < 0$ the series will decrease.

To find an expression for the present amount P, we apply the single-payment present-worth factor to each term of the series

$$P = \sum_{n=1}^{N} F_1(1 + g)^{n-1}(1 + i)^{-n} \tag{2.21}$$

Bringing the term $F_1(1 + g)^{-1}$ outside the summation yields

$$P = \frac{F_1}{1 + g} \sum_{n=1}^{N} \left(\frac{1 + g}{1 + i}\right)^n \tag{2.22}$$

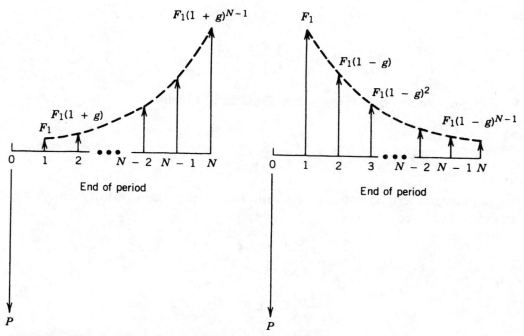

FIGURE 2.7 Cash flow diagram of the geometric series.

The summation in Eq. 2.22 represents the first N terms of a geometric series, and the closed-form expression for the partial geometric summation yields the following relationship.

$$P = \begin{cases} F_1\left[\dfrac{1 - (1 + g)^N(1 + i)^{-N}}{i - g}\right] & i \neq g \\[2em] \dfrac{NF_1}{1 + i} & i = g \end{cases} \tag{2.23}$$

This present-worth factor is designated $(P/A, g, i, N)$.

The future-worth equivalent of the geometric series is obtained by substituting Eq. 2.23 into Eq. 2.5 to find $(F/A, g, i, N)$.

$$F = \begin{cases} F_1\left[\dfrac{(1 + i)^N(1 + i)^{-N}}{i - g}\right] & i \neq g \\[2em] NF_1(1 + i)^{N-1} & i = g \end{cases} \tag{2.24}$$

We may use an alternative expression of Eq. 2.23 as shown in [4]. In Eq. 2.22 we may rewrite the term $(1 + g)/(1 + i)$ as

$$\frac{1 + g}{1 + i} = \frac{1}{1 + g'} \tag{2.25}$$

or

$$g' = \frac{1 + i}{1 + g} - 1$$

We then substitute Eq. 2.25 back into Eq. 2.22 to obtain

$$P = \frac{F_1}{1 + g} \sum_{n=1}^{N} (1 + g')^{-n} \tag{2.26}$$

The summation term constitutes the uniform-series present-worth factor for N periods. Therefore,

$$P = \frac{F_1}{1 + g} \left[\frac{g'(1 + g')^N}{(1+g') - 1} \right]$$

$$= \frac{F_1}{1 + g}(P/A, g', N), g \neq i \tag{2.27}$$

If $g < i$, then $g' > 0$, and we can use the $(P/A, g', N)$ factor to find P. If $g = i$, then $g' = 0$, and the value of $(P/A, g', N)$ will be N. The geometric-series factor thus reduces to $P = F_1 N/(1 + g)$. If $g > i$, then $g' < 0$. In this case, no table values can be used to evaluate the P/A factor, and it will have to be calculated directly from a formula. Table 2.3 summarizes the interest formulas developed in this section and the cash flow situations in which they should be used.

Example 2.5

A mining company is concerned about the increasing cost of diesel fuel for their mining operation. A special piece of mining equipment, a tractor-mounted ripper, is used to loosen the earth in open-pit mining operations. The company thinks that the diesel fuel consumption will escalate at the rate of 10% per year as the efficiency of the equipment decreases. The company's records indicate that the ripper averages 18 gallons per operational hour in year 1, with 2,000 hours of operation per year. What would the present worth of the cost of fuel for this ripper be for the next five years if the interest rate is 15% compounded annually?

Assuming that all the fuel costs occur at the end of each year, we determine the present equivalent fuel cost by calculating the fuel cost for the first year:

$$F_1 = (\$1.10/\text{gal})(18 \text{ gal/hr})(2,000 \text{ hr/year}) = \$39,600/\text{year}$$

$$(g = 0.10, N = 5, i = 0.15)$$

Then, using the appropriate factors in Eq. 2.23, we compute

$$P = \$39,600 \left[\frac{1 - (1 + 0.10)^5(1 + 0.15)^{-5}}{0.15 - 0.10} \right] = \$157,839.18$$

Table 2.3 *Summary of Discrete Compounding Formulas with Discrete Payments*

Flow Type	Factor Notation	Formula	Cash Flow Diagram
Single	Compound amount $(F/P, i, N)$	$F = P(1 + i)^N$	
	Present worth $(P/F, i, N)$	$P = F(1 + i)^{-N}$	
Equal payment series	Compound amount $(F/A, i, N)$	$F = A\left[\dfrac{(1 + i)^N - 1}{i}\right]$	
	Sinking fund $(A/F, i, N)$	$A = F\left[\dfrac{i}{(1 + i)^N - 1}\right]$	
	Present worth $(P/A, i, N)$	$P = A\left[\dfrac{(1 + i)^N - 1}{i(1 + i)^N}\right]$	
	Capital recovery $(A/P, i, N)$	$A = P\left[\dfrac{i(1 + i)^N}{(1 + i)^N - 1}\right]$	
Gradient series	Uniform gradient Present worth $(P/G, i, N)$	$P = G\left[\dfrac{(1 + i)^N - iN - 1}{i^2(1 + i)^N}\right]$	
	Geometric gradient Present worth $(P/A, g, i, N)$	$P = \begin{cases} F_1\left[\dfrac{1 - (1 + g)^N(1 + i)^{-N}}{i - g}\right] \\ \dfrac{NF_1}{1 + i} \quad (\text{if } i = g) \end{cases}$	

Source: Park [3].

283

Using the alternative formula in Eq. 2.27, we first compute

$$g' = \frac{1.15}{1.10} - 1 = 0.04545$$

We then obtain

$$P = \frac{39,600}{1.10} \overset{P/A,\ 4.545\%,5}{(4.38442)} = 157,839.20$$

Although Eq. 2.27 looks more compact than Eq. 2.23, it does not provide any computational advantage in this example. □

All the interest formulas developed in Table 2.3 are applicable only to situations in which the compounding period coincides with the payment period. In the next section we discuss situations in which we have noncomparable payment and compounding periods.

2.4.2 Noncomparable Payment and Compounding Periods

Whenever the payment period and the compounding period do not correspond, we approach the problem by finding the effective interest rate based on the payment period and then using this rate in the compounding interest formulas in Table 2.3.

The specific computational procedure for noncomparable compounding and payment periods is as follows.

1. Identify the number of compounding periods per year (M), the number of payment periods per year (K), and the number of interest periods per payment period (C).

2. Compute the effective interest rate per payment period, using Eq. 2.6.

$$i = \left(1 + \frac{r}{M}\right)^C - 1$$

3. Find the total number of payment periods.

$$N = K\,(\text{number of years})$$

4. Use i and N in the appropriate formula given in Table 2.3.

Example 2.6

What is the present worth of a series of equal quarterly payments of $1,000 that extends over a period of 5 years if the interest rate is 8% compounded monthly? The variables are

$K = 4$ payment periods per year

$M = 12$ compounding periods per year

$C = 3$ interest periods per payment period (quarter)

$r = 8\%$

$$i = \left(1 + \frac{r}{M}\right)^C - 1 = \left(1 + \frac{0.08}{12}\right)^3 - 1 = 2.0133\% \text{ per quarter}$$

$N = (5)(4) = 20$ payment periods

Then the present amount is

$$P = A(P/A, i, N)$$
$$= \$1000(P/A, 2.0133\%, 20) = \$16,330.37 \quad \square$$

In certain situations the compounding periods occur *less* frequently than the payment periods. Depending on the financial institution involved, no interest may be paid for funds deposited during an interest period. The accounting methods used by most firms record cash transactions at the end of the period in which they have occurred, and any cash transactions that occur within a compounding period are assumed to have occurred at the end of that period. Thus, when cash flows occur daily but the compounding period is monthly, we sum the cash flows within each month (ignoring interest) and place them at the end of each month. The modified cash flows become the basis for any calculations involving the interest factors.

In the extreme situation in which payment occurs more frequently than compounding, we might find that the cash flows continuously throughout the planning horizon on a somewhat uniform basis. If this happens, we can also apply the approach discussed earlier (integrating instead of summing all cash flows that occur during the compounding period and placing them at the end of each compounding period) to find the present worth of the cash flow series. In practice, we avoid this cumbersome approach by adopting the funds flow concept, which is discussed in the next section.

Example 2.7

Consider the cash flow diagram shown in Figure 2.8*a*, where the time scale is monthly. If interest is compounded quarterly, the cash flows can be relocated as shown in Figure 2.8*b*. The cash flow shown in Figure 2.8*b* is equivalent to the cash flow in Figure 2.8*a* for quarterly compounding. After the equivalent cash flow is determined, we can proceed as previously discussed for the situation in which the compounding periods and the payment periods coincide.

Let $i = 3\%$ per quarter. Then the present worth of cash flow given in Figure 2.8*a* is equivalent to the present worth of cash flow given in Figure 2.8*b*. Since $G = \$90$,

$$P = \$330\underset{P/A,3\%,8}{(7.0197)} + \$90\underset{P/G,3\%,8}{(23.4806)} = \$4,429.76 \quad \square$$

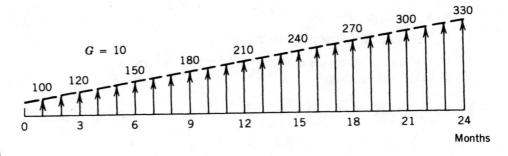

(a)

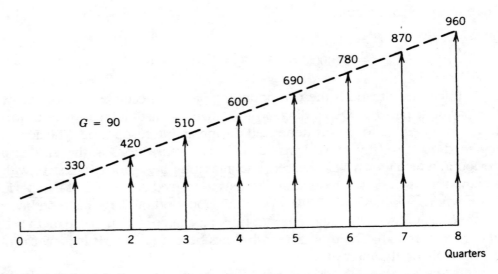

(b)

FIGURE 2.8 Example of cash flows where compounding is less frequent than payment. (*a*) Original cash flows. (*b*) Equivalent quarterly cash flows.

2.5 CONTINUOUS COMPOUNDING

2.5.1 Discrete Payments

When payments occur at discrete points in time but interest is permitted to compound an infinite number of times per year (that is, continuously in time), we have the special instance of more frequent compounding than payments discussed in Section 2.4.2. Therefore, we approach the problem in the following way.

1. Identify the payment periods per year (K). 4
2. Compute $i = e^{r/K} - 1$ by using Eq. 2.7.
3. Find the total number of payment periods.

$$N = K \quad \text{(number of years)}$$

4. Use i and N in the appropriate interest formulas given in Table 2.3.

We can derive a new family of interest factors under continuous compounding by substituting $e^r - 1$ for i when payments are annual and $e^{r/K} - 1$

286

Table 2.4 *Summary of Continuous Compounding Formulas with Annual Payments*

Flow Type	Factor Notation	Formula	Cash Flow Diagram
Single	Compound amount $(F/P, r, N)$	$F = P(e^{rN})$	
	Present worth $(P/F, r, N)$	$P = F(e^{-rN})$	
Equal payment series	Compound amount $(F/A, r, N)$	$F = A\left(\dfrac{e^{rN} - 1}{e^{r} - 1}\right)$	
	Sinking fund $(A/F, r, N)$	$A = F\left(\dfrac{e^{r} - 1}{e^{rN} - 1}\right)$	
	Present worth $(P/A, r, N)$	$P = A\left[\dfrac{e^{rN} - 1}{e^{rN}(e^{r} - 1)}\right]$	
	Capital recovery $(A/P, r, N)$	$A = P\left[\dfrac{e^{rN}(e^{r} - 1)}{e^{rN} - 1}\right]$	
Gradient series	Uniform gradient Present worth $(P/G, r, N)$	$P = G\left[\dfrac{e^{rN} - 1 - N(e^{r} - 1)}{e^{rN}(e^{r} - 1)^2}\right]$	
	Geometric gradient Present worth $(P/A, g, r, N)$	$P = \begin{cases} F_1\left[\dfrac{1 - e^{(g-r)N}}{e^{r} - e^{g}}\right] \\ \dfrac{NF_1}{e^{r}} \quad (\text{if } g = e^{r} - 1) \end{cases}$	

Source: Park [3].

for i when payments are more frequent than annual. Table 2.4 summarizes the resulting compound interest factors for annual payments.

Example 2.8

What is the present worth of a uniform series of year-end payments of $500 each for 10 years if the interest rate is 8% compounded continuously?

Let $r = 0.08$

$\qquad i = e^r - 1 = 8.33\%$

$\qquad N = 10$

$\qquad A = \$500$

Then

$$P = A\left[\frac{e^{rN} - 1}{e^{rN}(e^r - 1)}\right] = \$500(6.6117) = \$3,305.85$$

Using the discrete compounding formula with $i = 8.33\%$, we also find that

$$P = A(\overset{P/A,8.33\%,10}{6.6117}) = \$3,305.85 \quad \square$$

Example 2.9

A series of equal quarterly payments of $1,000 extends over a period of 5 years. What is the present worth of this quarterly time series at 8% interest compounded continuously?

Since the payments are quarterly, the calculations must be quarterly. The required calculations are

$$\frac{r}{K} = \frac{8\%}{4 \text{ quarters}} = 2\% \text{ per quarter compounded continuously}$$

$$i = e^{r/K} - 1 = e^{0.02} - 1 = 0.0202 = 2.02\% \text{ per quarter}$$

$$N = (4 \text{ payment periods per year})(5 \text{ years}) = 20 \text{ periods}$$

$$P = A\left[\frac{e^{(r/K)N} - 1}{e^{(r/K)N}(e^{r/K} - 1)}\right] = \$1,000(15.3197) = \$16,319.70$$

Using the discrete compounding formula with $i = 2.02\%$, we also find that

$$P = A(\overset{P/A,2.02\%,20}{16.3197}) = \$16,319.70 \quad \square$$

2.5.2 Continuous Cash Flows

It is often appropriate to treat cash flows as though they were continuous rather than discrete. An advantage of the continuous flow representation is its

Table 2.5 *Summary of Interest Factors for Continuous Cash Flows with Continuous Compounding*

Type of Cash Flow	Cash Flow Function	Parameters To Find	Parameters Given	Algebraic Notation	Factor Notation
Uniform (step)	$F_t = \bar{A}$	P	$\bar{A}$	$\bar{A}\left(\dfrac{e^{rN}-1}{re^{rN}}\right)$	$(P/\bar{A},\, r,\, N)$
		$\bar{A}$	P	$P\left(\dfrac{re^{rN}}{e^{rN}-1}\right)$	$(\bar{A}/P,\, r,\, N)$
		F	$\bar{A}$	$\bar{A}\left(\dfrac{e^{rN}-1}{r}\right)$	$(F/\bar{A},\, r,\, N)$
		$\bar{A}$	F	$F\left(\dfrac{r}{e^{rN}-1}\right)$	$(\bar{A}/P,\, r,\, N)$
Gradient (ramp)	$F_t = Gt$	P	G	$\dfrac{G}{r^2}(1 - e^{-rN})$ $-\dfrac{G}{r}(Ne^{-rN})$	
Decay	$F_t = ce^{-jt}$ $j =$ decay rate with time	P	c, j	$\dfrac{c}{r+j}(1 - e^{-(r+j)N})$	
Exponential	$F_t = ce^{jt}$	P	c, j	$\dfrac{c}{r-j}(1 - e^{-(r-j)N})$	
Growth	$F_t = c(1 - e^{jt})$	P	c, j	$\dfrac{c}{r}(1 - e^{-rN})$ $-\dfrac{c}{r+j}(1 - e^{-(r+j)N})$	

flexibility for dealing with patterns other than the uniform and gradient ones. Some of the selected continuous cash flow functions are shown in Table 2.5.

To find the present worth of a continuous cash flow function under continuous compounding, we first recognize that the present-worth formula for a discrete series of cash flows with discrete compounding is

$$P = \sum_{n=0}^{N} F_n(1 + i)^{-n}$$

Since F_n becomes a continuous function F_t and the effective annual interest rate i for continuous compounding is $e^r - 1$, integration of the argument instead of summation yields

$$P = \int_0^N (F_t)e^{-rt} \, dt \tag{2.28}$$

[Note that $n \to t$, $F_n \to F_t$, $\sum_{n=0}^{N} \to \int_0^N$, and $(1 + i)^{-n} \to e^{-rt}$.] Then the future value equivalent of F_t over N periods is simply

$$F = \int_0^N F_t e^{rt} \, dt \tag{2.29}$$

To illustrate the continuous flow concept, consider F_t to be a uniform flow function when an amount flows at the rate $\bar{A}$ per period for N periods. (This cash flow function is presented in Table 2.5 and is expressed as $F_t = \bar{A}$, $0 \le t \le N$.) Then the present-worth equivalent is

$$P = \int_0^N \bar{A}e^{-rt} \, dt = \bar{A}\left(\frac{e^{rN} - 1}{re^{rN}}\right) = \bar{A}\left(\frac{1 - e^{-rN}}{r}\right) \tag{2.30}$$

The resulting factor in parenthesis in (2.30) is referred to as the *funds flow present-worth factor* and is designated $(P/\bar{A}, r, N)$. The future-worth equivalent is obtained from

$$F = \int_0^N \bar{A}e^{rt} \, dt = \bar{A}\left(\frac{e^{rN} - 1}{r}\right) \tag{2.31}$$

The resulting factor $(e^{rN} - 1)/r$ is called the *funds flow compound amount factor* and is designated $(F/\bar{A}, r, N)$. Since the relationships of $\bar{A}$ to P and F are given by Eqs. 2.30 and 2.31, we can easily solve for $\bar{A}$ if P or F is given. Table 2.5 summarizes all the funds flow factors necessary to find present-worth and future-worth equivalents for a variety of cash flow functions.

As a simple example, we compare the present-worth figures obtained in two situations. We deposit $10 each day for 18 months in a savings account that has an interest rate of 12% compounded daily. Assuming that there are 548 days in the 18-month period, we compute the present worth.

$$P = 10(\overset{P/A,0.032877\%,548}{501.4211}) = \$5,014.21$$

Now we approximate this discrete cash flow series by a uniform continuous cash flow profile (assuming continuous compounding). In doing so, we may define $\bar{A}$ as

$$\bar{A} = 10(365) = \$3,650/\text{year}$$

Note that our time unit is a year. Thus, an 18-month period is 1.5 years. Substituting these values back into Eq. 2.30 yields

$$P = \int_0^{1.5} 3,650e^{-0.12t} = \frac{3,650}{0.12}\left(1 - e^{-0.18}\right)$$

$$= \$5,010.53$$

The discrepancy between the values obtained by the two methods is only $3.68.

Example 2.10

A county government is considering building a road from downtown to the airport to relieve congested traffic on the existing two-lane divided highway. Before allowing the sale of a bond to finance the road project, the court has requested an estimate of future toll revenues over the bond life. The toll revenues are directly proportional to the growth of traffic over the years, so the following growth cash flow function (with units in millions of dollars) is assumed to be reasonable.

$$F_t = 5(1 - e^{-0.10t})$$

Find the present worth of toll revenues at 6% interest compounded continuously over a 25-year period.

Expanding F_t gives us

$$F_t = 5 - 5e^{-0.10t}$$

If we let $f(t)_1 = 5$ and $f(t)_2 = -5e^{-0.10t}$, the present-worth equivalent for each function would be

$$P_1 = \int_0^{25} 5e^{-0.06t}\, dt = 5\left[\frac{e^{0.06(25)} - 1}{(0.06)e^{0.06(25)}}\right] = \$64.74$$

$$P_2 = \int_0^{25} -5e^{-(0.10 + 0.06)t}\, dt = -5\left[\frac{e^{0.16(25)} - 1}{(0.16)e^{0.16(25)}}\right] = -\$30.68$$

and

$$P = P_1 + P_2 = \$34.06$$

The present worth of toll revenues over a 25-year period amounts to \$34.06 million. This figure could be used for bond validation. □

2.6 EQUIVALENCE OF CASH FLOWS

2.6.1 Concept of Equivalence

When we compare two cash flows, we must compare their characteristics on the same basis. By definition, two cash flows are equivalent if they have the same economic effect. More precisely, two cash flows are equivalent at interest i if we can convert one cash flow into the other by using the proper compound interest factors. For example, if we deposit \$100 in a bank for 3 years at 8% interest compounded annually, we will accumulate \$125.97. Here we may say that, at 8% interest, \$100 at time 0 is equivalent to \$125.97 at time 3.

Consider another example in which an individual has to choose between two options. Option I is to receive a lump sum of \$1,000 now. Option II is to receive \$600 at the end of each year for 2 years, which provides \$1,200 over the 2-year period. Our question is what interest rate makes these two options equivalent. To answer the question, we need to establish a common base in time to convert the cash flows. Three common bases are the equivalent future value F, the equivalent present value P, and the equivalent annual value A. Future value is a measure of the cash flow relative to some "future planning horizon," considering the earning opportunities of the intermediate cash receipts. The present value represents a measure of future cash flow relative to the time point "now" with provisions that account for earning opportunities. The annual equivalent value determines the equal payments on an annual basis. The uniform cash flow equivalent might be the more appropriate term to use. The conceptual transformation from one type of cash flow to another is depicted in Figure 2.9.

For our example, we will use F as a base of reference value and set the planning horizon at the end of year 2. To find the future value of option I, we may use an $(F/P, i, A)$ factor.

$$F_I = 1000(F/P, i, 2) = 1000(1 + i)^2$$

For option II, we may use an $(F/A, i, n)$ factor.

$$F_{II} = 600(F/A, i, 2) = 600(1 + i) + 600$$

If we specify i, we can easily evaluate F_I and F_{II}. Table 2.6 summarizes these values at selected interest rates. We observe from the table that $F_I = F_{II} = \$1,278$ at $i = 13\%$. In other words, the two options are equivalent if the individual can earn a 13% interest from the investment activity. We also observe that at $i = 13\%$ $P_I = P_{II}$ and $A_I = A_{II}$. This is not surprising, because the present value amount is merely the future amount times a constant. The same can be said for the annual

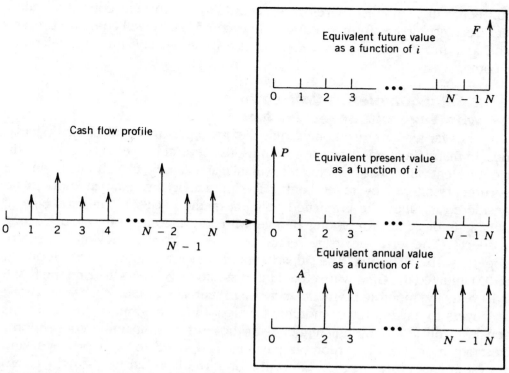

FIGURE 2.9 Conversion to equivalent bases.

Table 2.6 *Equivalence Calculations*

i (%)	Option I $F_I = 1{,}000(1 + i)^2$	Option II $F_{II} = 600(1 + i) + 600$	Equivalence
0	$1,000	$1,200	
5	1,103	1,230	
7	1,145	1,242	$F_I < F_{II}$
12	1,254	1,272	
13	1,277	1,277	$F_I = F_{II}$
15	1,323	1,290	$F_I > F_{II}$
20	1,440	1,320	

Option I

$1,000

0   1   2

Option II

$600 $600

0   1   2

equivalent value amount. Therefore, we should expect that any equivalent value that directly compares future value amounts could just as well compare present value amounts or annual equivalent amounts without affecting the selection outcome.

2.6.2 Equivalence Calculations with Several Interest Factors

Thus far we have used only single factors to perform equivalence calculations. In many situations, however, we must use several interest factors to obtain an equivalent value. To show this, we will take an example from home financing instruments offered by many banks. The particular financing method to be considered is called the graduated-payment method (GPM). This mortgage financing is designed for young people with low incomes but good earning prospects. (The term mortgage refers to a special loan for buying a piece of property such as a house.) The Department of Housing and Urban Development (HUD) initiated the GPM with a fixed interest rate for 30 years. During the first 5 or 10 years the monthly payments increase in stair-step fashion each year, allowing buyers to make a lower monthly payment in the beginning; the payments then level off at an amount higher than those of a comparable conventional fixed-rate mortgage. The monthly payment is applied to both principal and interest and can carry negative amortization. (The loan balance actually grows instead of decreasing under negative amortization when monthly payments are lower than monthly loan interests.) Our question is how the monthly payments are computed for a certain loan amount, interest rate, and life of the loan.

Let

P = loan amount,

A = monthly payment for the first year,

i = loan interest rate per month,

g = annual rate of increase in the monthly payment,

K = number of years the payment will increase,

N = number of months to maturity of the loan.

Figure 2.10*a* illustrates the cash flow transactions associated with the GPM. From the lender's view, lending the amount P now should be equivalent to a transaction in which the monthly payments are as shown in Figure 2.10*a*. To establish the equivalence relation between P and A with fixed values of i, g, K, and N, we convert each group of 12 equal monthly payments to a single present equivalent amount at the beginning of each year. Then the remaining $(N - 12K)$ equal payments are converted to a single present equivalent amount at $n = 12K$. The equivalent cash flow after this transformation should look like Figure 2.10*b*. To find the present equivalent value of this transformed cash flow, we simply calculate

$$P = A(P/A, i, 12) + A(1 + g)(P/A, i, 12)(P/F, i, 12)$$

$$+ A(1 + g)^2(P/A, i, 12)(P/F, i, 24) + \cdots$$

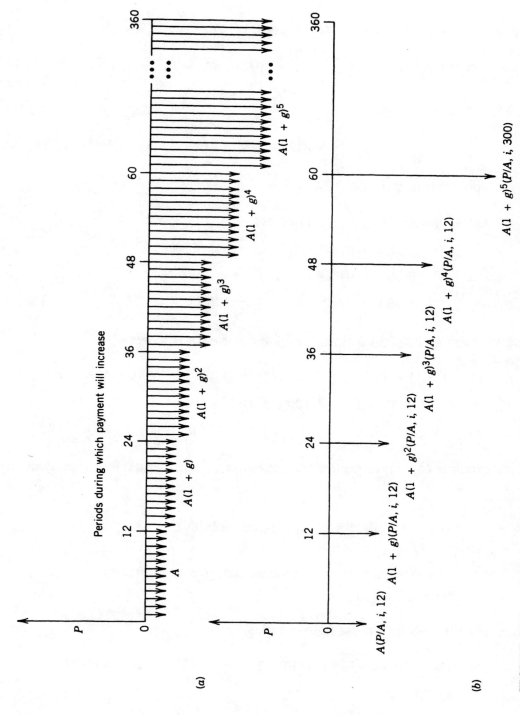

(a)

(b)

FIGURE 2.10 Cash flow diagram of a typical GPM loan. (*a*) Loan transactions (monthly). (*b*) Equivalent transactions.

$$+ A\{(1 + g)^{K-1} (P/A, i, 12)[P/F, i, 12(K - 1)]\}$$

$$+ A(1 + g)^K(P/A, i, N - 12K)(P/F, i, 12K) \qquad (2.32)$$

We multiply each term by $(1 + i)^{12}$ or $(F/P, i, 12)$.

$$P(1 + i)^{12} = A(P/A, i, 12)(1 + i)^{12} + A(1 + g)(P/A, i, 12)$$
$$+ A(1 + g)^2(P/A, i, 12)(1 + i)^{-12} + \cdots$$
$$+ A(1 + g)^{K-1}(P/A, i, 12)(1 + i)^{-12(K-2)}$$
$$+ A(1 + g)^K(P/A, i, N - 12K)(1 + i)^{-12(K+1)} \quad (2.33)$$

We multiply each term in Eq. 2.32 by $1 + g$.

$$P(1 + g) = A(1 + g)(P/A, i, 12) + A(1 + g)^2(P/A, i, 12)(1 + i)^{-12}$$
$$+ A(1 + g)^3(P/A, i, 12)(1 + i)^{-24} + \cdots$$
$$+ A(1 + g)^K(P/A, i, 12)(1 + i)^{-12(K-1)}$$
$$+ A(1 + g)^{K+1}(P/A, i, N - 12K)(1 + i)^{-12K} \qquad (2.34)$$

Now we subtract Eq. 2.34 from Eq. 2.33 and solve for A to get

$$A = P[(1 + i)^{12} - (1 + g)]\{(1 + g)^K(1 + i)^{-12(K+1)}[(P/A, i, N - 12K)$$
$$- (P/A, i, 12)] + [(P/A, i, 12)(1 + i)^{12}$$
$$- (1 + g)^{K+1}(P/A, i, N - 12K)(1 + i)^{-12K}]\}^{-1} \qquad (2.35)$$

For an example of such an equivalence calculation, consider the following data:

$P = \$45,000,$

$i = \frac{3}{4}\%$ per month (9% compounded monthly),

$g = 5\%$ per year,

$K = 5$ years (no further increase in monthly payment after the sixth year),

$N = 360$ months (30 years).

Evaluating Eq. 2.35 with these figures yields

$$A = 45,000[0.04387]\{0.8916 [107.7267] + 12.5076 - 101.9927\}^{-1}$$

$$= \$300.18/\text{month}$$

Then the monthly payment will increase the second year to \$315.19, the third year to \$330.95, the fourth year to \$347.50, the fifth year to \$364.87, and for the remaining years to \$383.11.

Example 2.11

The following two cash flow transactions are said to be equivalent in terms of economic desirability at an interest rate of 10% compounded annually. Determine the unknown value A.

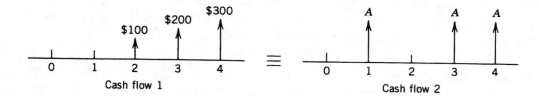

Cash flow 1 $\equiv$ Cash flow 2

We will first use the present equivalent as the basis of comparison. Cash flow 1 represents a strict gradient series, whereas cash flow 2 can be viewed as an equivalent payment series with the second payment missing. Therefore, the equivalence would be expressed by

$$100\overset{P/G,10\%,4}{(4.3781)} = A\left[\overset{P/F,10\%,1}{(0.9091)} + \overset{P/F,10\%,3}{(0.7513)} + \overset{P/F,10\%,4}{(0.6830)}\right]$$

Solving for A yields

$$A = \$186.83$$

If we use the annual equivalent as the basis of comparison, we compute

$$100\overset{A/G,10\%,4}{(1.3812)} = A - A\overset{P/F,10\%,2}{(0.8264)}\overset{A/P,10\%,4}{(0.3155)}$$

Solving for A yields $A = \$186.83$ again. The second approach should be computationally more attractive because it takes advantage of the cash flow pattern and thus requires fewer interest factors in the computation. □

2.7 EFFECT OF INFLATION ON CASH FLOW EQUIVALENCE

Up to this point we have shown how we properly account for the time value of money in equivalence calculations in the absence of inflation. In this section we present methods that incorporate the effect of inflation in our equivalence calculations.

2.7.1 Measure of Inflation

Definition. Before discussing the effect of inflation on equivalence calculations, we need to discuss how we measure inflation. In simple terms, the results of investment activity are stated in dollars, but the dollar is an imperfect unit of measure because its value changes from time to time. Inflation is the term used to describe a decline in the value of the dollar. For example, if we deposit $1,000 in a one-year savings certificate and withdraw $1,090 a year later, we say that our rate of return has been 9%—and it has, as long as those dollars we withdraw at year's end actually purchase 9% more. If inflation has reduced the value of the dollar by 10%, our 9% positive investment return in dollars is actually about a 1% loss in economic value or purchasing power. Inflation is thus a measure of the decline in the purchasing power of the dollar.

Measure. The decline in purchasing power can be measured in many ways. Consumers may judge inflation in terms of the prices they pay for food and other goods; economists record this measure in the form of the consumer price index (CPI), which is based on sample prices in a "market basket" of purchases. We should note that consumer prices do not always behave like wholesale prices or commodity prices, and as a result, a dollar's worth varies depending on what is bought.

There is another measure of the dollar's value that reflects the average purchasing power of the dollar as it applies to all goods and services in the economy—the gross national product implicit price deflator (GNPIPD). The GNPIPD is computed and published quarterly by the U.S. Department of Commerce, Bureau of Economic Analysis.

Various cost indices are also available to the estimator. A government index listing is given by the *Statistical Abstract of the United States,* a yearly publication that includes material, labor, and construction costs. The Bureau of Labor Statistics publishes the monthly *Producer Price Index* and covers some 3,000 product groupings.

Average Inflation Rate. To account for the effect of inflation, we utilize an annual percentage rate that represents the annual increase in prices over a one-year period. Because the rate each year is based on the previous year's price, this inflation rate has a compounding effect. For example, prices that increase at the rate of 5% per year in the first year and 8% per year in the second year, with a starting base price of $100, will increase at an average inflation rate of 6.49%.

$$100(1 + 0.05)(1 + 0.08) = 113.40$$

first year

second year

Let f be the average annual inflation rate. Then we equate

$$100(1 + f)^2 = 113.40$$

$$f = 6.49\%$$

The inflation rate itself may be computed from any of the several available indices. With the CPI value, the annual inflation rate may be calculated from the expression

$$\text{Annual inflation rate for year } n = \frac{CPI_n - CPI_{n-1}}{CPI_{n-1}} \qquad (2.36)$$

For example, with $CPI_{1990} = 270$ and $CPI_{1989} = 260$, the annual inflation rate for year 1990 is

$$\frac{270 - 260}{260} = 0.0385 \text{ or } 3.85\%$$

As just indicated, we can easily compute the inflation rates for the years with known CPI values. However, most equivalence calculations for projects require the use of cash flow estimates that depend on expectations of *future* inflation rates. The methods used by economists to estimate future inflation rates are many and varied. Important factors to consider may include historical trends in rates, predicted economic conditions, professional judgment, and other elements of economic forecasting. The estimation of future inflation rates is certainly a difficult task; a complete discussion of this subject is beyond the scope of this text but can be found elsewhere [1]. Our interest here is in how we use these rates in equivalence calculations, when they are provided.

2.7.2 Explicit and Implicit Treatments of Inflation in Discounting

We will present three basic approaches for calculating equivalence values in an inflationary environment that allow for the simultaneous consideration of changes in earning power and changes in purchasing power. The three approaches are consistent and, if applied properly, should result in identical solutions. The first approach assumes that cash flow is estimated in terms of *actual dollars,* and the second uses the concept of *constant dollars.* The third approach uses a combination of actual and constant dollars and is discussed in Section 2.7.3.

Definition of Inflation Terminology. To develop the relationship between actual-dollar analysis and constant-dollar analysis, we will give precise definitions of several inflation-related terms, borrowed from Thuesen and Fabrycky [4].

Actual dollars represent the out-of-pocket dollars received or expended at any point in time. Other names for them are then-current dollars, current dollars, future dollars, inflated dollars, and nominal dollars.

Constant dollars represent the hypothetical purchasing power of future receipts and disbursements in terms of the purchasing dollars in some base year. (The base year is normally time zero, the beginning of the investment.) We will assume that the base year is always time zero unless specified otherwise. Other names are real dollars, deflated dollars, and today's dollars.

Market interest rate (i) represents the opportunity to earn as reflected by the actual rates of interest available in the financial market. The interest rates used in previous sections are actually market interest rates. (The designation i is used consistently throughout this book to represent interest rates available in the marketplace.) When the rate of inflation increases, there is a corresponding upward movement in market interest rates. Thus, the market interest rates include the effects of both the earning power and the purchasing power of money. Other names are combined interest rate, nominal interest rate, minimum attractive rate of return, and inflation-adjusted discount rate.

Inflation-free interest rate (i') represents the earning power of money isolated from the effects of inflation. This interest rate is not quoted by financial institutions and other investors and is therefore not generally known to the public. This rate can be computed, however, if the market interest rate and inflation rate are known. Naturally, if there is no inflation in an economy, i and i' should be identical. Other names are real interest rate, true interest rate, and constant-dollar interest rate.

General inflation rate (f) represents the average annual percentage of increase in prices of goods and services. The market inflation rate is expected to respond to this general inflation rate. *Escalation rate* (e) represents a specific inflation rate applicable to a specific segment of the economy. It is sometimes used in contracts.

It is important to recognize that there is a relationship between inflation and interest rate. For example, the historical rate on AAA bonds is about 2.5% to 3% above the general inflation rate as measured by the CPI [1]. In addition, the rate of return (ROR) required by well-managed companies on their investments must be at some level above the inflation rate. In the next section we will derive the mathematical relationships of i, i', and f.

Relationships of i, i', and f.   We must first establish the relationship between actual dollars and constant dollars. Suppose we estimate a future single payment F' that occurs at the end of the nth period in terms of constant dollars (primes indicate constant dollars). To translate this constant-dollar amount into the actual dollars at the end of the nth period, we use

$$F = F'(1 + f)^n$$

Solving for F' yields

$$F' = F(1 + f)^{-n} \qquad (2.37)$$

where F' = constant-dollar expression for the cash flow at the end of the nth period,

F = actual-dollar expression for the cash flow at the end of the nth period.

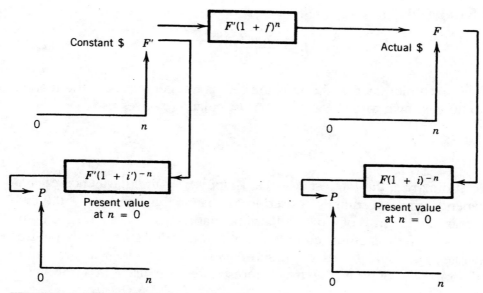

FIGURE 2.11 Relationships of i, i^1 and f.

As shown in Figure 2.11, to find the present value equivalent of this actual dollar, we should use the market interest rate i in

$$P = F(1 + i)^{-n} \qquad (2.38)$$

If the cash flow is already given in constant dollars with the inflation effect removed, we should use i' to account for only the earning power of the money. To find the present value equivalent of this constant dollar at i', we use

$$P = F'(1 + i')^{-n} \qquad (2.39)$$

The P values must be equal at time zero, and equating the results of Eqs. 2.38 and 2.39 yields

$$F(1 + i)^{-n} = F'(1 + i')^{-n}$$
$$= F(1 + f)^{-n}(1 + i')^{-n}$$
$$(1 + i)^{-n} = (1 + f)^{-n}(1 + i')^{-n}$$
$$(1 + i) = (1 + f)(1 + i')$$
$$= 1 + f + i' + i'f$$

or

$$i = i' + f + i'f \qquad (2.40)$$

Solving for i' yields

$$i' = \frac{i - f}{1 + f} \qquad\qquad (2.41)$$

As an example, say that the inflation rate is 6% per year and the market interest rate is known to be 15% per year. Calculating i' gives us

$$i' = \frac{0.15 - 0.06}{1 + 0.06} = 8.49\%$$

To summarize, the interest rate that is applicable in equivalence calculations depends on the assumptions used in estimating the cash flow. If the cash flow is estimated in terms of actual dollars, the market interest rate (i) should be used. If the cash flow is estimated in terms of constant dollars, the inflation-free interest rate (i') should be used. In subsequent sections we will give more detailed examples of how the two interest rates are used in equivalence calculations.

Actual-Dollar versus Constant-Dollar Analysis. If cash flow is represented in constant dollars (such as 1990 dollars), an inflation-free discount rate i (say 5% to 15%) may be appropriate for a profitable business. If cash flow is represented in inflated dollars, a market interest rate (say 15% to 25%) may be appropriate. Often, the difficulty lies in determining the nature of the cash flow. In this section, we will consider two cases and explain how the analyses in terms of actual and constant dollars can be used.

Case 1: Projections in physical units can often be translated into constant-dollar projections by using a constant-dollar price per unit and then converted to present value by using an inflation-free discount rate.

Example 2.12

SM Manufacturing Company makes electric meters of the type with which utility companies measure electricity consumption by users. SM has projected the sale of its meters by using data on new housing starts and deterioration and replacement of existing units. The price per unit should keep up with the wholesale price index (WPI). In 1990 the price per unit is $25. To achieve the production and sales projected in the following, SM needs to invest $75,000 now (in 1990). Other costs remain unchanged.

n	0	1	2	3	4	5	6	7
Unit Sales	—	1,000	1,100	1,200	1,200	1,300	1,300	1,200
$ Inflow	—	25,000	27,500	30,000	30,000	32,500	32,500	30,000

SM thinks it should earn a 5% inflation-free rate of return (ROR) on any investment.

This is an easy problem because all figures are in constant (1990) dollars. Just discount the dollar inflows at 5%. For example, present value would be

$$P = -75{,}000 + 25{,}000(1/1.05) + 27{,}500(1/1.05)^2$$
$$+ 30{,}000(1/1.05)^3 + 30{,}000(1/1.05)^4 + 32{,}500(1/1.05)^5$$
$$+ 32{,}500(1/1.05)^6 + 30{,}000(1/1.05)^7$$
$$= 95{,}386 \text{ in 1990 dollars} \quad \square$$

Case 2: If projections in dollars are made with numerical and statistical techniques, they will very likely reflect some inflationary trend. If they do, we should use a market interest rate or a two-step approach in which we first convert to constant dollars and then compute present value by using an inflation-free discount rate.

Example 2.13

U.S. Cola Company (USCC) is studying a new marketing scheme in southeast Georgia. By examining a similar project conducted from 1977 to 1989 and using nonlinear statistical regression, the analysts have projected additional dollar profits from this new marketing practice as follows.

Year	1 (1991)	2	3	4	5	6
Additonal Profit	100,000	120,000	150,000	200,000	150,000	100,000

An investment of $500,000 is required now (1990) to fund the project. USCC is accustomed to obtaining a 20% ROR on its projects during these inflation-ridden times.

Statistical regression on dollar sales inevitably reflects any inflationary trends during the study period (1977 to 1989 in this example), so we may conclude that the dollar profits are represented in inflated, actual dollars. The 20% discount rate was developed for today's inflationary economy, so it can be used to compute a present value:

$$P = -500{,}000 + 100{,}000(1/1.2) + 120{,}000(1/1.2)^2$$
$$+ 150{,}000(1/1.2)^3 + 200{,}000(1/1.2)^4$$
$$+ 150{,}000(1/1.2)^5 + 100{,}000(1/1.2)^6$$
$$= -56{,}306 \text{ in 1990 dollars}$$

(Note that in the sign convention used a minus sign means cash outflow.) $\quad \square$

Example 2.14

The scenario is the same as in example 2.13, but we assume that inflation is projected to be 9% per year, and we do the analysis by first converting to constant dollars. USCC expects at least a 10% inflation-free return on its investments. Noting that

$$(1 + 0.1)(1 + 0.09) = 1.990 \cong (1 + 0.2)$$

$$1.199$$

we judge this to be a reasonable translation. We first deflate the cash flow at 9%.

n	1	2	3	4	5	6
F'_n	91,743	101,002	115,828	141,685	97,490	59,627

Now we compute a present value using the constant-dollar cash flow with appropriate interest rate of 10%:

$$
\begin{aligned}
P = {} & -500,000 + 91,743(1/1.1) + 101,002(1/1.1)^2 \\
& + 115,828(1/1.1)^3 + 141,685(1/1.1)^4 \\
& + 97,490(1/1.1)^5 + 59,627(1/1.1)^6 \\
= {} & -55,137 \text{ in 1990 dollars}
\end{aligned}
$$

This value agrees closely with that obtained by using actual dollars and the market interest rate of 20%; the discrepancy comes from the fact that $1.199 \neq 1.200$. □

Composite Cash Flow Elements with Different Escalation Rates. The equivalence calculation examples in the previous sections were all based on the assumption that all cash flows respond to the inflationary trend in a uniform manner. Many project cash flows, however, are composed of several cash flow elements with different degrees of responsiveness to the inflationary trend. For example, the net cash flow elements for a certain project may comprise sales revenue, operating and maintenance costs, and taxes. Each element may respond to the inflationary environment to a varying degree. In computing the tax element alone, we need to isolate the depreciation element. With inflation, sales and operating costs are assumed to increase accordingly. Depreciation would be unchanged, but taxes, profits, and thus the net cash flow usually would be higher. (A complete discussion of the effect of inflation on the after-tax cash flow will be given in Chapter 4.) Now we will discuss briefly how we compute the equivalence value with such cash flows.

In complex situations there may be several inflation rates. For example, an apartment developer might project physical unit sales, building costs in actual dollars using a building cost index, and sales revenue in actual dollars using a real estate price index, and then find the equivalent present value using an interest rate that reflects the consumer price index.

Example 2.15

This more complex example illustrates the apartment building project. Base year cost per unit is $15,000 and selling price per unit is $20,000. The building cost index is projected to increase 11% next year and 10% more the following year. The real estate price index is expected to jump 15% next year and then level off at a 13% increase per year. We will use a market interest rate of 15%, hoping that it will yield an inflation-free return of 5% when the general inflation rate is 9% to 10% (to be precise, $f = 9.52\%$).

Item	n: 0	1	2	3
Units built	200	250	200	—
Units sold	—	200	250	200
Costs (thousands)	3,000	3,750(1.11)	3,000(1.11)(1.1)	—
Revenues (thousands)	—	4,000(1.15)	5,000(1.15)(1.13)	4,000(1.15)(1.13)^2
Net flow (thousands) (actual $)	−3,000	+438	+2,835	+5,874
$(P/F, 15\%, n)$	1	0.8696	0.7561	0.6575

$$P = -3,000 + 438(0.8696) + 2,835(0.7561) + 5,874(0.6575)$$

$$P = \$3,387,000 \text{ in base year (time 0) dollars} \quad \square$$

2.7.3 Home Ownership Analysis during Inflation

A personal decision of wide and continuing interest is whether it is more economical to buy a home or to rent during an inflationary environment. In this section we will illustrate how this decision can be made on a rational basis by applying the concepts of actual and constant dollars.

Renting a House. To make a meaningful comparison, let's estimate the current rent of a two-bedroom apartment as $400 per month plus $60 per month for basic utilities (heating and cooling but not telephone, water, and sewer). Both costs have a tendency to increase with inflation, so let's project a 10% inflation rate, which gives us the following monthly costs per year.

n	1	2	3		10
Rent	400	440	484	· · ·	943
Utilities	60	66	73	· · ·	141

We selected a planning period of 10 years because realtors tell us that very few people live in the same house for the period of a home mortgage (typically 25 to 30 years). Of course, when you rent an apartment you are free to switch every year, and we'll assume a fairly uniform market of rents with no rent control (this situation occurs when the vacancy rate is 5% to 10%). Let's use a market interest rate of 15% (annual compounding) to compute the present value of apartment living costs (approximate, since we collapse all monthly flows to the year's end).

$$P = (-460)(12)/1.15 + (-506)(12)/(1.15)^2 + \cdots + (-1{,}084)(12)/(1.15)^{10}$$

$$= -39{,}610 \text{ in time 0 dollars}$$

Alternatively, we can compute an inflation-free discount rate i' to be used with constant dollars by applying Eq. 2.40.

$$0.15 = i' + 0.1 + 0.1i'$$

$$i' = 0.0455$$

We must also convert 460 to $460/1.1 = 418.18$. Thus, a present value using the constant-dollar cash flow is

$$P = (-418.18)(12)(P/A,\ 4.55\%, 10)$$

and

$$= \frac{F_1 (P/A,\ \bar{a}',\ N)}{(1+g)}$$

$$(P/A,\ 4.55\%,\ 10) = \left[\frac{(1.0455)^{10} - 1}{0.0455(1.0455)^{10}} \right] = 7.8933$$

so

$$P = (-418.18)(12)(7.8933)$$

$$= -39{,}610 \text{ in time 0 dollars}$$

Buying a House. Now we must estimate the cash flow for a house or condominium. The purchase cost will be $60,000. "Wait a minute!" you say. "I've seen those $60,000 units and they're too old, too small, or too far away, or built like apartments." Right. It's difficult to compare the space and quality of an apartment with those of a house, but it is not fair to compare a two-bedroom apartment with a new, close-in home or condominium containing 1,500 or more square feet. Therefore, the $60,000 home is a more appropriate comparison. If you finally decide to spend $80,000, you're allocating more money to your residence than when you lived in apartments, but you'll get more space, privacy, convenience, return, and so forth.

We will try for 95% financing, which means that we need a $3,000 down payment plus about another $3,000 for closing costs, for a cash requirement of about $6,000.

The mortgage interest rate might be 14.5% (total $14.5/12 = 1.208\%$ per month) on a fixed-rate 30-year mortgage. So the monthly payment is

$$57,000 \ (A/P, \ 1.208\%, \ 360) = (57,000)\left[\frac{0.01208(1.01208)^{360}}{(1.01208)^{360} - 1} \right]$$

$$= (57,000)(0.012242)$$

$$= \$697.815 = \$698/\text{month}$$

The mortgage balance remaining after our 10-year comparison period is

$$697.815(P/A, \ 1.208\%, \ 240) = 697.815\left[\frac{(1.01208)^{240} - 1}{0.01208(1.1208)^{240}} \right]$$

$$= (697.815)(78.143) = \$54,529$$

We will have paid off less than 5% of the loan in 10 years, which is not unusual for these mortgages. Approximately 97% of our monthly payments will be interest, which is tax deductible:

$$
\begin{aligned}
(698)(12)(10) &= \$83,760 \quad \text{total payments} \\
57,000 - 54,529 &= \underline{\$\ 2,471} \quad \text{principal repayments} \\
&\ \ \$81,289 \quad \text{interest payments}
\end{aligned}
$$

We will assume a 40%[1] marginal income tax rate (federal plus state) and sufficient other deductions to make the interest reduce our tax by

$$(698)(0.97)(0.40) = \$271/\text{month}$$

So the after-tax cost of the mortgage is only $698 − $271 = $427.

Real estate taxes are estimated to be $600 per year, or $50/month, and these are also tax deductible, which saves us $20/month for an after-tax cost of $30/month. These taxes will increase at about 10% per year.

Basic taxes and utilities will be about $60/month for a condominium and $100/month for a house, so let's use $80/month, with 10% inflation. Homeowner's insurance is slightly higher than renter's insurance, so we allow $100 per year. Maintenance can be another $300 per year. The monthly total of these items is $33/month, inflating at 10%. Our home will appreciate in value at about 7% per year and sell at

$$60,000(1.07)^{10} = \$118,029$$

After paying a 6% realtor's commission and the mortgage balance, we keep

$$(118,029)(0.94) - 54,529 = \$56,418$$

---

[1] A 30% tax rate may be more reasonable for many homeowners. We will leave this for the reader to do as an exercise (see Problem 2.23).

(We assume no capital gain tax on this amount.) Now we're ready to compute P.

$$P = -6,000 \qquad \text{constant dollars}$$

$$- (427)(12)(P/A, 15\%, 10) \qquad \text{actual dollars}$$

$$\left. \begin{array}{l} - (30/1.1)(12)(P/A, 4.55\%, 10) \\ - (80/1.1)(12)(P/A, 4.55\%, 10) \\ - (33/1.1)(12)(P/A, 4.55\%, 10) \end{array} \right\} \text{constant dollars}$$

$$+ 56,418(P/F, 15\%, 10) \qquad \text{actual dollars}$$

Note carefully that we use 15% for actual-dollars expenses and 4.55% for constant-dollars expenses. We could convert the real estate taxes, utilities, incremental insurance, and maintenance to actual dollars by using 10% and then using 15% for discounting, but that is too much work. Our method produces the same numerical results.

$$P = -6,000$$

$$- (427)(12)(5.0188)$$

$$- (130)(12)(7.8933)$$

$$+ (56,418)(0.2472)$$

$$= -30,080 \text{ in constant dollars}$$

This cost is $9,530 *less* than renting. In this example the present value costs in constant dollars for home ownership are about 76% of the present value costs for renting. The big difference comes from the fact that you are using $57,000 of someone else's money to buy an asset that resells at two times its purchase price. You pay interest on the loan, but this is partly offset by the rent you would pay in an apartment.

Notice that the house was assumed to appreciate at 7%, compared with a mortgage interest rate of 14.5% nominal (15.5% effective per year). Many people think home ownership makes sense only if the mortgage interest rate is below the real estate appreciation rate. This is not true, as the example demonstrates.

We also used a 15% market interest rate, versus 10% general inflation and 7% real estate inflation. We might question the sensitivity of the results to these factors. In Table 2.7 we show some results of a sensitivity analysis in which we vary the inflation rate, the real estate appreciation rate, and the rent. We can see that there is a wide range of parameter values where buying is better. In fact, many people have benefited financially from home ownership during inflation. The home ownership analysis could be based on the principle of monthly payment and monthly compounding without collapsing all monthly flows to year end. We will leave this for the reader to do as an exercise (see Problem 2.22).

Table 2.7 Sensitivity Analysis: Buy versus Rent Decision

Inflation f:	5%			10%			15%		
Market Interest i:	10%			15%			20%		
Real Estate Appreciation Rate: Rent	0%	2.5%	5%	5%	7.5%	10%	5%	10%	15%
350	−36.6 −49.6 136	−36.6 −43.5 119	−36.6 −35.9 98	−35.3 −34.8 99	−35.3 −28.8 82	−35.3 −21.4 61	−34.1 −34.1 98	−34.1 −24.6 72	−34.1 −11.4 33
400	−41.1 −49.6 121	−41.1 −43.5 106	−41.1 −35.9 87	−39.6 −34.8 88	−39.6 −28.8 73	−39.6 −21.4 54	−38.3 −33.4 87	−38.3 −24.6 64	−38.3 −11.4 30
450	−45.5 −49.6 109	−45.5 −43.5 96	−45.5 −35.9 79	−43.9 −34.8 79	−43.9 −28.8 66	−43.9 −21.4 49	−42.4 −33.4 79	−42.4 −24.6 58	−42.4 −11.4 27

NOTES: Each triplet of entries consists of present value of rental cash flow in thousands, present value of ownership cash flow in thousands, and percentage ratio of ownership flow to rental flow.

Other parameters:

5% down	$60,000 home cost	$80/month utilities (home)	$300/year maintenance (home)
5% closing costs	14.5% mortgage rate	$600/year real estate taxes	6% realtor's commission
30-year mortgage	40% marginal tax rate	$100/year incremental insurance	10-year planning period

2.8 SUMMARY

In this chapter we have examined the concept of the time value of money and the equivalence of cash flows. Discrete compound interest formulas have been derived for converting present sums, future sums, uniform series, gradient series, and geometric series to specified points in time. We also discussed the concepts of nominal interest rate and effective interest rate, which led to the idea of continuous compounding. Continuous-compounding formulas were then derived for both discrete and continuous cash flows.

We discussed the measures of inflation and the effects of inflation on equivalence calculations. We presented two basic approaches that may be used in equivalence calculations to offset the effects of changes in purchasing power. In the actual-dollar analysis, we include an inflation component in estimating cash flows so that a market interest rate is used to find the equivalence value. In the constant-dollar approach we express the cash flows in terms of base-year dollars and use an inflation-free interest rate to compute the equivalent value at the specified points in time. We also showed that if these approaches are applied correctly, they should lead to identical results.

REFERENCES

1. BUCK, J. R., and C. S. PARK, *Inflation and Its Impact on Investment Decisions,* Industrial Engineering and Management Press, Institute of Industrial Engineers, Norcross, Ga., 1984.

2. FLEISCHER, G. A., and T. L. WARD, "Classification of Compound Interest Models in Economic Analysis," *The Engineering Economist,* Vol. 23, No. 1, pp. 13–29, Fall 1977.

3. PARK, C. S., *Modern Engineering Economic Analysis,* Addison–Wesley, Reading, Mass., 1990.

4. THUESEN, G. J., and W. J. FABRYCKY, *Engineering Economy,* 7th edition, Prentice–Hall, Englewood Cliffs, N.J., 1989.

5. WHITE, J. A., M. H. AGEE, and K. E. CASE, *Principles of Engineering Economic Analysis,* 3rd edition, Wiley, New York, 1989.

PROBLEMS

2.1. A typical bank offers you a Visa credit card that charges interest on unpaid balance at a 1.5% per month compounded monthly. This means that the nominal interest (annual percentage) rate for this account is A and the effective annual interest rate is B. Suppose your beginning balance was $500 and you make only the required minimum *monthly* payment (payable at the end of each month) of $20 for next 3 months. If you made no new purchases with this card during this period, your unpaid balance will be C at the end of 3 months. What are the values of A, B, and C?

2.2. In January 1989, C&S, the largest mutual savings bank in Georgia, published the following information: interest, 7.55%; effective annual yield, 7.842%. The bank did not explain how the 7.55% is connected to the 7.842%, but you can figure out that the compounding scheme used by the bank should be _____.

2.3. How many years will it take an investment to double if the interest rate is 12% compounded (a) annually, (b) semiannually, (c) quarterly, (d) monthly, (e) weekly, (f) daily, and (g) continuously?

2.4. Suppose that $1,000 is placed in a bank account at the end of each *quarter* over the next 10 years. Determine the total accumulated value (future worth) at the end of 10 years where the interest rate is 8% compounded *quarterly*.

2.5. What equal-payment series is required to repay the following present amounts?
  a. $10,000 in 4 years at 10% interest compounded annually with 4 annual payments.
  b. $5,000 in 3 years at 12% interest compounded semiannually with 6 semiannual payments.
  c. $6,000 in 5 years at 8% interest compounded quarterly with 20 quarterly payments.
  d. $80,000 in 30 years at 9% interest compounded monthly with 360 monthly payments.

2.6. Suppose that $5,000 is placed in a bank account at the end of each quarter over the next 10 years. Determine the total accumulated value (future worth) at the end of 10 years when the interest rate is
  a. 12% compounded annually.   c. 12% compounded monthly.
  b. 12% compounded quarterly.   d. 12% compounded continuously.

2.7. What equal *quarterly* payments will be required to repay a loan of $10,000 over 3 years if the rate of interest is 8% compounded *continuously?*

2.8. Compute the present worth of cash flow that has a triangular pattern with 12% interest compounded continuously.

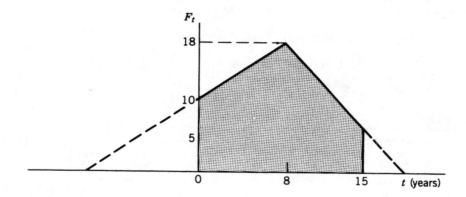

2.9. Suppose a uniformly increasing continuous cash flow (a ramp) accumulates $600 over 3 years. Find the present worth of this cash flow under continuous compounding at $r = 12\%$.

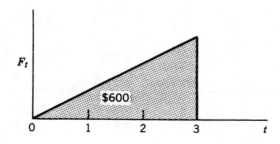

2.10. For computing the equivalent equal-payment series (*A*) of the following cash flow with *i* = 10%, which of the following statements is (are) correct?

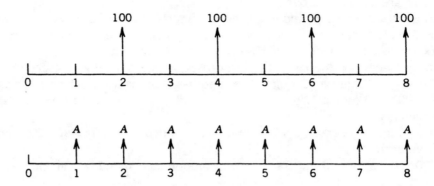

a. $A = 100(P/A, 10\%, 4)(A/P, 10\%, 8)$

b. $A = [100(P/F, 10\%, 2) + 100(P/F, 10\%, 4) + 100(P/F, 10\%, 6)$
$\qquad + 100(P/F, 10\%, 8)](A/P, 10\%, 8)$

c. $A = 100(A/F, 10\%, 2)$

d. $A = 100(P/A, 21\%, 4)(A/P, 10\%, 8)$

e. $A = 100(F/A, 10\%, 4)(A/F, 10\%, 8)$

f. $A = 100(F/A, 21\%, 4)(A/F, 10\%, 8)$

2.11. The following equation describes the conversion of a cash flow into an equivalent equal-payment series with *n* = 8. Draw the original cash flow diagram. Assume an interest rate of 10% compounded annually.

$A = [-1,000 - 1,000(P/F, 10\%, 1)](A/P, 10\%, 8)$

$\quad + [3,000 + 500(A/G, 10\%, 4)](P/A, 10\%, 4)(P/F, 10\%, 1)(A/P, 10\%, 8)$

$\quad + 750(F/A, 10\%, 2)(A/F, 10\%, 8)$

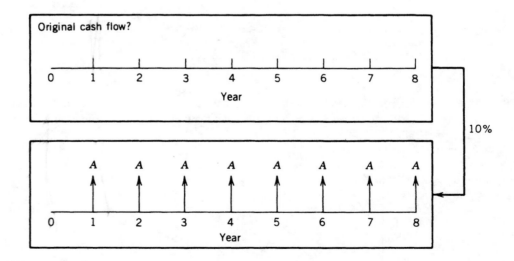

2.12. The following two cash flow transactions are said to be equivalent at 10% interest compounded annually. Find the unknown value X that satisfies the equivalence.

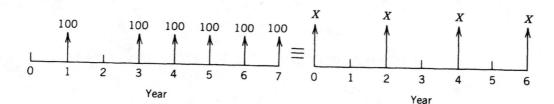

2.13. Suppose you have the choice of investing in (1) a zero-coupon bond that costs $513.60 today, pays nothing during its life, and then pays $1,000 after 5 years or (2) a municipal bond that costs $1,000 today, pays $67 in interest *semiannually*, and matures at the end of 5 years. Which bond would provide the higher *yield to maturity* (or return on your investment)?

2.14. You borrow B dollars from your bank, which adds on the total interest before computing the monthly payment (add-on interest). Thus, if the quoted nominal interest rate (annual percentage rate) is r% and the loan is for N months, the total amount that you agree to repay is

$$B + B(N/12)(r/100)$$

This is divided by N to give the amount of each payment, A.

$$A = B(1/N + r/1200)$$

This is called an add-on loan. But the true rate of interest that you are paying is somewhat more than r%, because you do not hold the amount of the loan for the full N months.
a. Find the equation to determine the true rate of interest i per month.
b. Plot the relationship between r and i as a function of N.
c. For $B = \$10,000$, $N = 36$ months, and $r = 8\%$, find the effective annual borrowing rate per year.
d. Identify the lending situation in which the true interest rate i per month approaches to $r/12$.

2.15. John Hamilton is going to buy a car worth $10,000 from a local dealer. He is told that the add-on interest rate is only 1.25% per month, and his monthly payment is computed as follows:

Installment period = 30 months
Interest = 30(0.0125)($10,000) = $3,750
Credit check, life insurance, and processing fee = $50
Total amount owed = $10,000 + $3,750 + $50 = $13,800
Monthly payment size = $13,800/30 = $460 per month

What is the effective rate that John is paying for his auto financing?
a. Effective interest rate per month?
b. Effective annual interest rate?
c. Suppose that John bought the car and made 15 such monthly payments ($460). Now he decides to pay off the remaining debt with one lump sum payment at the time of the sixteenth payment. What should the size of this payment be?

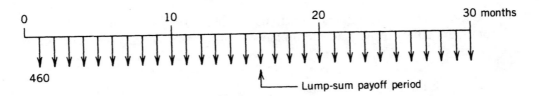

2.16. A pipeline was built 3 years ago to last 6 years. It develops leaks according to the relation

$$\log N = 0.07T - 2.42, \qquad T > 30$$

where N is the total number of leaks from installation and T is the time in months from installation. It costs $500 to repair a leak. If money is worth 8% per year, and without considering any tax effect, how much can be spent now for a cathodic system that will reduce leaks by 75%? (Adapted from F. C. Jelen and J. H. Black, *Cost and Optimization*, McGraw–Hill, New York, 1983.)

2.17. A market survey indicates that the price of a 10-oz jar of instant coffee has fluctuated over the last few years as follows:

Period	−4	−3	−2	−1	0	1
Price ($)	2.83	3.13	3.47	4.67	5.83	?

a. Assuming that the base period (price index = 100) is period −4 (four periods ago), compute the average price index for this instant coffee.

b. Estimate the price at time period 1, if the current price trend is expected to continue.

2.18. The annual operating costs of a small electrical generating unit are expected to remain the same ($200,000) if the effects of inflation are not considered. The best estimates indicate that the annual inflation-free rate of interest (i') will be 5% and the annual inflation rate (f) 6%. If the generator is to be used 3 more years, what is the present equivalent of its operating costs using *actual-dollar analysis?*

2.19. You want to know how much money to set aside now to pay for 1,000 gallons of home heating oil each year for 10 years. The current price of heating oil is $1.00 per gallon, and the price is expected to increase at a 10% compound price change each year for the next 10 years. The money to pay for the fuel oil will be set aside now in a bank savings account that pays 6% annual interest. How much money do you have to place in the savings account now, if payment for the fuel is made by end-of-year withdrawals?

2.20. An investment of $100,000 is required to expand a certain production facility in a manufacturing company. The firm estimates that labor costs will be $150,000 for the first year but will increase at the rate of 8% over the previous year's expenditure. Material costs, on the other hand, will be $400,000 for the first year but will increase at the rate of 10% per year due to inflation. If the firm's inflation-free interest rate (i') is 10% and the average general inflation rate (f) is expected to be 5% over the next 5 years, determine the total present equivalent operating expenses (with no tax consideration) for the project.

2.21. A couple with a 7-year-old daughter want to save for their child's college expenses in advance. Assuming that the child enters college at age 18, they estimate that an amount of $20,000 per year in terms of today's dollars will be required to support the child's college expenses for 4 years. The future inflation rate is estimated to be

6% per year and they can invest their savings at 8% compounded quarterly.

    a. Determine the equal quarterly amounts the couple must save until they send their child to college.

    b. If the couple has decided to save only $500 each quarter, how much will the child have to borrow each year to support her college education?

2.22. Consider the problem of renting versus buying a home given in Section 2.7.3. Recall that the analysis was performed on the basis of annual payments with annual compounding. Repeat the analysis using monthly payments and monthly compounding.

2.23. Consider again the problem of renting versus buying a home given in Section 2.7.3. Recall that the tax rate used in the analysis was 40%, which seems too high. Repeat the analysis using a tax rate of 30%. Does a lower tax rate make the buying option more attractive?

3
Transform Techniques in Cash Flow Modeling

3.1 INTRODUCTION

In Chapter 2 equivalence calculations were made by the proper use of the various interest formulas. In particular, with the interest rate and the compounding schemes specified, we showed how to convert various cash flow profiles into equivalent present values. In many situations, however, the cash flow patterns may take more complex forms than those discussed in Chapter 2. If they do, transform methods are often used to accomplish the same equivalence calculations with less computational effort and in a more routine manner. These methods are the Z-transform and Laplace transform methods. We will show in this chapter how they may be used in the modeling and analysis of economic situations involving either a discrete or a continuous time series of cash flow.

We will first discuss the concept of present value and its relationship to transform theory. Some useful properties of transforms will be presented, and their applications to economic model building will be discussed. Many examples are offered to aid the reader in understanding these powerful techniques. The reader will see that application of these transform formulas eliminates many of the calculations that are required when conventional interest formulas are used in complicated equivalence calculations.

3.2 Z-TRANSFORMS AND DISCRETE CASH FLOWS

3.2.1 The Z-Transform and Present Value

Consider that the function $f(n)$ describes the cash flow magnitude at the discrete point in time n. Then the equivalent present value of this cash flow series over an infinite time horizon at an interest rate i, assuming a discrete compounding principle, is

$$PV(i) = \sum_{n=0}^{\infty} f(n)(1 + i)^{-n} \tag{3.1}$$

Hill and Buck [6] recognized that the general form of the summation in (3.1) bears a striking resemblance to the definition of Z-transforms, the only difference being a definition of variables. That is, when a general discrete time series is described by a function $f(nT)$, where T is an equidistant time interval and n is an integer, the Z-transform of the time series $f(nT)$ is defined as

$$F(z) = \sum_{n=0}^{\infty} f(nT)z^{-n} \tag{3.2a}$$

With $T = 1$,

$$F(z) = \sum_{n=0}^{\infty} f(n)z^{-n} = Z\{f(n)\} \tag{3.2b}$$

where z is a complex variable. If we replace z with the interest rate $1 + i$ and set the constant-length time interval T to unity (that is, the compounding period is the unit of time, monthly or yearly), Eq. 3.2 becomes

$$F(z) = \sum_{n=0}^{\infty} f(n)(1 + i)^{-n} \tag{3.3}$$

where i is the interest rate for a compounding period. Throughout this chapter the value of T will be set to unity so that the compounding period can be assumed to be the unit of time. In the literature of mathematics, we find a transformation essentially the same as our Z-transform but expressed in positive powers of z:

$$F'(z) = \sum_{n=0}^{\infty} f(n)z^{n} \tag{3.4}$$

In this book we use the definition in (3.2) because the expressions for the corresponding Z-transform are analogous to those for present values. It should be obvious, however, that both transformations have the same purpose and application, and that one transform is converted to the other by the relations

$$F'(z) = F\left(\frac{1}{z}\right), \qquad F(z) = F'\left(\frac{1}{z}\right) \tag{3.5}$$

In the construction of Z-transforms, the following notation will be used. If $f(n)$ represents the discrete f function, $F(z)$ will represent the transform. In addition, as a shorthand notation, the transform pair will be denoted by $f(n) \leftrightarrow F(z)$. This double arrow is symbolic of the uniqueness of the one-to-one correspondence between $f(n)$ and $F(z)$. Thus, if $Z\{g(n)\} = G(z)$, we write $g(n) \leftrightarrow G(z)$. This lowercase–uppercase correspondence will be adhered to throughout this chapter.

For a cash flow sequence of infinite duration, the resulting Z-transform will be an infinite series involving inverse powers of z. This series can be expressed as a rational fraction in z, provided that the series converges. These so-called closed-form expressions will be especially convenient for our computations. For expressing a Z-transform as a ratio of polynomials in z, two important identities of infinite series will be needed:

$$\sum_{n=0}^{\infty} a^n = \frac{1}{1-a} \quad \text{provided } |a| < 1 \tag{3.6}$$

and

$$\sum_{n=0}^{\infty} (1+n)a^n = \frac{1}{(1-a)^2} \quad \text{provided } |a| < 1 \tag{3.7}$$

Now consider the sequence of function $f(n) = a^n$. The Z-transform is

$$F(z) = \sum_{n=0}^{\infty} f(n)z^{-n} = \sum_{n=0}^{\infty} a^n z^{-n} = \sum_{n=0}^{\infty} \left(\frac{a}{z}\right)^n$$

Using Eq. 3.6, we obtain

$$F(z) = \frac{1}{1-a/z} = \frac{z}{z-a} \quad \text{if } \left|\frac{a}{z}\right| < 1 \tag{3.8}$$

In other words, the infinite geometric series a^n converges to $z/(z-a)$ if $|z| > |a|$. For ease of conversion, the table of transform pairs of $f(n)$ and $F(z)$ is provided (see Table 3.1).

Many cash flow transactions have a finite time duration. Because transforms are defined for series with infinite time horizons, it is necessary to introduce additional techniques to provide a methodology that is applicable to finite time horizons. We will examine some properties of the Z-transform in the following section.

3.2.2 Properties of the Z-Transform

Many useful properties of the Z-transform are discussed in the literature of mathematics, probability theory, and operations research [4,5,7]. We will focus on two important properties that are most relevant in equivalence calculations: linearity and translation.

Table 3.1 *A Short Table of Z-Transform Pairs*

Standard Pattern	Original Function, $f(n)$	Z-Transform, $F(z)$	Present Value of $f(n)$ Starting at $n=0$ and Continuous over the Infinite Time Horizon
Step (uniform series)	C	$C\left(\dfrac{z}{z-1}\right)$	$C\left(\dfrac{1+i}{i}\right)$
Ramp (gradient series)	Cn	$C\left[\dfrac{z}{(z-1)^2}\right]$	$C\left(\dfrac{1+i}{i^2}\right)$
Geometric	Ca^n	$C\left(\dfrac{z}{z-a}\right)$	$C\left(\dfrac{1+i}{1+i-a}\right)$
Decay	Ce^{-jn}	$C\left(\dfrac{z}{z-e^{-j}}\right)$	$C\left(\dfrac{1+i}{1+i-e^{-j}}\right)$
Growth	$C(1-e^{-jn})$	$C\left(\dfrac{z}{z-1}-\dfrac{z}{z-e^{-j}}\right)$	$C\left(\dfrac{1+i}{i}-\dfrac{1+i}{1+i-e^{-j}}\right)$
Impulse (single payment)	$C\delta(n-k)$	$C\left(z^{-k}\right)$	$C(1+i)^{-k}$

NOTE: C = pattern scale factor
  n = time index for compounding periods
  i = effective interest rate for a compounding period.
  a = pattern base factor
  j = pattern rate factor
  δ = impulse function
  k = number of time periods before the impulse occurs

Linearity.   The Z-transform is a linear operation. Thus, when a sequence can be expressed as a sum of other sequences, the following result will be useful.

$$f(n) = C_1 f_1(n) + C_2 f_2(n) \leftrightarrow F(z)$$

$$f_1(n) \leftrightarrow F_1(z)$$

$$f_2(n) \leftrightarrow F_2(z)$$

then

$$F(z) = C_1 F_1(z) + C_2 F_2(z) \qquad (3.9)$$

This linearity property makes it possible to combine component time forms and to amplify general time patterns by the scale factor C to represent the

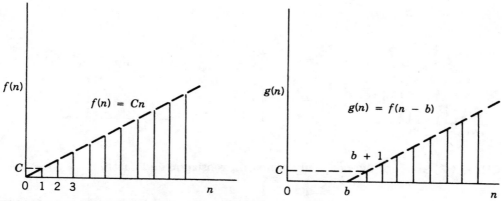

FIGURE 3.1 Ramp pattern transaction (gradient series).

proportion of the component. By adding it to or subtracting it from the scaled transforms of other components, we are able to describe the composite Z-transform of the entire stream of components.

Translation with Time Advance. To consider a composite of cash flows that start at various points in time, we seek the relation between the Z-transform of sequences and their shifted version. Consider the sequence $g(n)$ obtained from $f(n)$ by shifting $f(n)$ to the right by b units of time. This situation is illustrated in Figure 3.1, in which the function $f(n)$ takes a ramp pattern. Since the sequence $g(n)$ is 0 for $n < b$, we can define the sequence $g(n)$ in terms of $f(n)$ as

$$g(n) = \begin{cases} f(n - b) & \text{for } n \geq b \\ 0 & \text{for } n < b \end{cases} \tag{3.10}$$

To find the transform of this time-shifted function, we use the property of the unit step function. If we take the unit step function and translate it b units to the right to get $u(n - b)$, we obtain the function shown in Figure 3.2a. Mathematically, we denote this by

$$u(n - b) = \begin{cases} 1 & \text{for } n \geq b \\ 0 & \text{for } n < b \end{cases} \tag{3.11}$$

Notice that the shifted unit step function in Figure 3.2a has no values for $n < b$ but is equal to 1 for $n \geq b$. The product $f(n - b)u(n - b)$ will be zero for $n < b$ and will equal $f(n - b)$ for $n \geq b$. This product form shown in Figure 3.2c defines precisely the shifted ramp function we defined in Figure 3.1b. More generally, we define such a function as

$$g(n) = f(n - b)u(n - b) = \begin{cases} f(n - b) & \text{for } n \geq b \\ 0 & \text{for } n < b \end{cases} \tag{3.12}$$

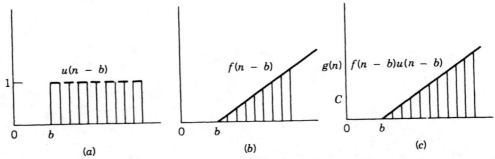

FIGURE 3.2 Graph of the ramp function with translation and cutoff.

Then the Z-transform of the above expression is defined as

$$G(z) = z^{-b} F(z) = (1 + i)^{-b} F(z) \tag{3.13}$$

The quantity z^{-b} in the Z-transform simply reflects the fact that the start of the function $f(n)$ has been shifted forward in time by b units. Thus, if $f(n) = Cn$, shifting $f(n)$ to the right by b units and taking its Z-transform generates $z^{-b}[Cz/(z-1)^2]$. Expressing this in terms of the present value and replacing z with $(1 + i)$, we obtain $PV(i) = [C(1 + i)^{1-b}]/i^2$.

Translation with Cutoff.   Many realistic cash flow functions extend over finite time horizons. Another scheme of translation property is useful in finding the Z-transforms for these translated cash flow functions. Consider the function $g(n)$ shown in Figure 3.3c. This function is basically the truncated ramp function $f(n)$ in Figure 3.3b with the added feature of a delayed turn-on at time b, where b is an integer. By using the translation property discussed in the last section and multiplying the ramp function $f(n)$ by a unit step, we can express the desired truncated function $g(n)$ as

$$g(n) = f(n)u(n - b) = \begin{cases} f(n) & \text{for } b \le n \\ 0 & \text{otherwise} \end{cases} \tag{3.14}$$

and the Z-transform of this product expression is

$$G(z) = z^{-b}Z\{f(n + b)\} \tag{3.15}$$

Unlike the situation in Figure 3.2c, the origin of the function $f(n)$ remains unchanged, but the first transaction begins at time b. Thus, it is important to recognize the functional distinction between $f(n)u(n - b)$ and $f(n - b)u(n - b)$. That is, an expression $f(n - b)u(n - b)$ similar to the one illustrated by Figure 3.2c will appear in shifting the sequence $f(n)$ to the right by b units in time; and its first transaction also starts at time b.

Now the Z-transform and present value expression for the ramp function

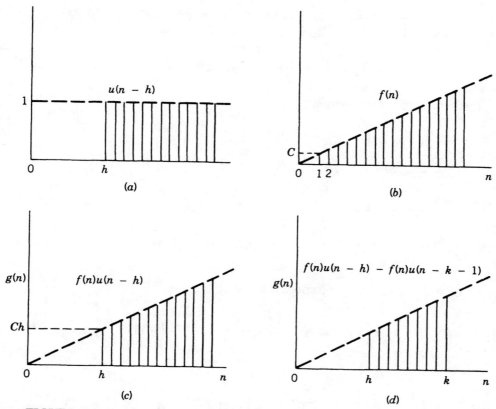

FIGURE 3.3 Ramp function with translation and cutoff.

with a delayed turn-on at time h shown in Figure 3.3c can easily be found. Since $f(n) = Cn$, the transform of $g(n)$ is

$$G(z) = z^{-h}Z\{f(n + h)\}$$

$$= z^{-h}Z\{Cn + Ch\}$$

$$= Cz^{-h}\left[\frac{z}{(z - 1)^2} + \frac{hz}{z - 1}\right]$$

$$= \frac{Cz^{1-h}}{(z - 1)^2}[1 + h(z - 1)] \tag{3.16}$$

By replacing z with $(1 + i)$, we obtain the present value expression

$$PV(i) = \frac{C(1 + i)^{1-h}}{i^2}(1 + hi) \tag{3.17}$$

Suppose we want to find the present value of the series shown in Figure 3.3d. This function is the same ramp function with the delayed turn-on at time h but also with a turn-off at time k, where h and k are integers. By using the property of the unit step function, we can express the desired ramp translation with turn-on and turn-off as follows.

$$g(n) = f(n)u(n - h) - f(n)u(n - k - 1) \qquad (3.18)$$

The transform of this function will be

$$
\begin{aligned}
G(z) &= z^{-h}Z\{f(n + h)\} - z^{-(k+1)}Z\{f(n + k + 1)\} \\
&= z^{-h}Z\{Cn + Ch\} - z^{-(k+1)}Z\{Cn + C(k + 1)\} \\
&= Cz^{-h}\left[\frac{z}{(z - 1)^2} + \frac{hz}{z - 1}\right] - Cz^{-(k+1)}\left[\frac{z}{(z - 1)^2} + \frac{(k + 1)z}{z - 1}\right] \\
&= \frac{C}{(z - 1)^2}(z^{1-h} - z^{-k}) + \frac{C}{z - 1}[hz^{1-h} - (k + 1)z^{-k}] \qquad (3.19)
\end{aligned}
$$

In terms of the present value expression, we have

$$PV(i) = \frac{C}{i^2}[(1 + i)^{1-h} - (1 + i)^{-k}] + \frac{C}{i}[h(1 + i)^{1-h} - (k + 1)(1 + i)^{-k}] \qquad (3.20)$$

Example 3.1

As an example of the use of Eq. 3.20, suppose that estimates of certain end-of-year expenses are \$300 for the third year, \$400 for the fourth year, and \$500 for the fifth year. If the effective interest rate is 15%, what is the equivalent present value?

The gradient series can be expressed as

$$f(n) = 100n \quad \text{where } 3 \leq n \leq 5$$

With $C = 100$, $h = 3$, $k = 5$, and $i = 0.15$, we obtain

$$
\begin{aligned}
PV(15\%) &= \frac{100}{(0.15)^2}[(1.15)^{-2} - (1.15)^{-5}] + \frac{100}{0.15}[3(1.15)^{-2} - 6(1.15)^{-5}] \\
&= \$674.54 \quad \square
\end{aligned}
$$

Translation with Impulses. Suppose we want to find the transform of an impulse function $g(n)$ as given in Figure 3.4c. This type of impulse function may represent the salvage value of an item at time h, when the salvage value $f(n)$ decreases exponentially over time. To obtain the transforms of such impulse functions, we need to define a Kronecker delta function that corresponds to a unit impulse function as shown in Figure 3.4c. That is,

$$\delta(n - h) = \begin{cases} 1 & \text{for } n = h \\ 0 & \text{otherwise} \end{cases} \qquad (3.21)$$

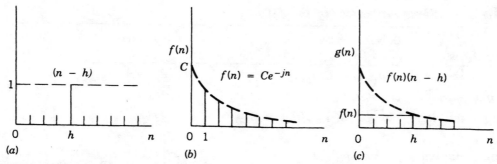

FIGURE 3.4 Kronecker delta function and translation with impulse.

By multiplying the salvage value function $f(n)$ by the unit impulse function, we obtain an expression in which the salvage value occurs only at time h, as desired. Formally, we may write this product expression as

$$g(n) = f(n)\delta(n - h) = \begin{cases} f(h) & \text{for } n = h \\ 0 & \text{otherwise} \end{cases} \tag{3.22}$$

Since $f(h)$ is a constant and the transform of the shifted unit impulse function $\delta(n - h)$ is z^{-h}, the transform of the product form yields

$$G(z) = z^{-h}f(h) = f(h)(1 + i)^{-h} \tag{3.23}$$

and this is exactly the present value expression for a single payment. If we define $f(h) = Ce^{-jh}$, we can find the present value expression

$$PV(i) = Ce^{-jh}(1 + i)^{-h} \tag{3.24}$$

where j is the pattern rate factor for a decay function.

The linearity and translation properties just discussed provide many of the necessary analytical tools for finding the Z-transforms of realistic discrete time series encountered in economic analysis. Table 3.2 summarizes some other useful operational rules for the Z-transform. (See [7].)

3.2.3 Development of Present Value Models

We develop two types of present value models that correspond to the timing of the start of the original cash flow function. They are the extensive models and the simplified models.

Extensive Present Value Models. The extensive models represent cash flow functions that are shifted forward in time but switched on only at time h ($h \geq b$) and then terminated at time k ($k > h$) (see Figure 3.5). This function is basically the shifted ramp (gradient series) in Figure 3.1b with a delayed turn-on at time h and a turn-off at time k, where h and k are integers.

Table 3.2 *Some Properties of the Z-Transform*

Operational Rule	Original Function, $f(n)$	Z-Transform, $F(z)$
Linearity	$C_1 f_1(n) + C_2 f_2(n)$	$C_1 F_1(z) + C_2 F_2(z)$
Damping	$a^{-n} f(n)$	$F(az)$
Shifting to the right	$f(n - k)u(n - k), k \geq 0$	$z^{-k}F(z)$
Shifting to the left	$f(n+k), k \geq 0$	$z^k \left[F(z) - \sum_{n=0}^{k-1} f(n)z^{-n} \right]$
Differencing of $f(n)$	$\Delta f(n) = f(n + 1) - f(n)$	$(z - 1)F(z) - zf(0)$
	$\nabla f(n) = f(n) - f(n - 1)u(n - 1)$	$\dfrac{z - 1}{z}F(z)$
Summation of $f(n)$	$\displaystyle\sum_{j=0}^{n} f(j)$	$\dfrac{z}{z - 1}F(z)$
Periodic sequences	$f(n + k) = f(n)$, period k	$\dfrac{z^k}{z^k - 1} \displaystyle\sum_{n=0}^{k-1} f(n)z^{-n}$
Convolution	$f(n) * g(n)$	$F(z) * G(z)$

To find the correct transform, we use the translation properties of Eqs. 3.12 and 3.14. The function $g(n)$ can then be expressed by multiplying the shifted gradient series by a unit step function. The resulting functional expression is

$$g(n) = [u(n - b) - u(n - k - 1)]f(n - b) \tag{3.25}$$

Since $f(n) = Cn$ (gradient series), we may rewrite $f(n - b)$ as

$$f(n - b) = C(n - b) = Cn - Cb = f(n) - f(b)$$

Thus, we may also rewrite $g(n)$ as

$$g(n) = f(n)[u(n - b) - u(n - k - 1)]$$
$$+ f(b)[u(n - k - 1) - u(n - b)] \tag{3.26}$$

Note that $f(b)$ is a constant Cb. Using the transform results of Eq. 3.18, we obtain

$$G(z) = \frac{C}{(z - 1)^2}(z^{1-b} - z^{-k}) + \frac{C}{z - 1}[(b - b)z^{1-b}$$
$$- (k + 1 - b)z^{-k}] \tag{3.27}$$

By replacing z with $1 + i$, we obtain the present value expression of this extensive model.

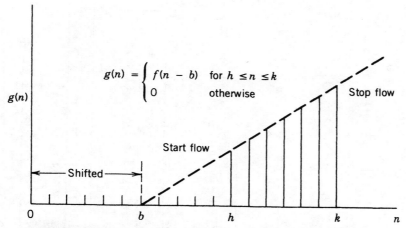

$$g(n) = \begin{cases} f(n - b) & \text{for } h \leq n \leq k \\ 0 & \text{otherwise} \end{cases}$$

FIGURE 3.5 Extensive model of ramp time pattern.

$$PV(i) = \frac{C}{i^2}[(1 + i)^{1-b} - (1 + i)^{-k}] + \frac{C}{i}[(h - b)(1 + i)^{1-b}]$$
$$- (k + 1 - b)(1 + i)^{-k}] \qquad (3.28)$$

If we use the conventional engineering economy notation, the present value of this shifted-gradient series is

$$PV(i) = [Cb(P/A, i, k - h + i) + C(P/G, i, k - h + 1)] (P/F, i, b - 1) \quad (3.29)$$

If we converted these factor notations to algebraic form, the final form would be as long an expression as Eq. 3.28. Table 3.3 provides the extensive models of other discrete cash flow patterns.

Example 3.2

A 20-MW oil-burning power plant now under construction is expected to be in full commercial operation in 4 years from now. The fuel cost for this new plant is a function of plant size, thermal conversion efficiency (heat rate), and plant utilization factor. Because of inflation, the future price of oil will increase. The annual fuel cost is then represented by the following expression,

$$f(n) = (S)(H)(U) \left(\frac{8{,}760 \text{ hr/year}}{10^6} \right) P_0 (1 + f)^{n-1}$$

where $f(n)$ = annual fuel cost at the end of the nth operating year,
    S = plant size in kW (1 MW = 1,000 kW),
    H = heat rate (Btu/kW·hr),
    U = plant utilization factor,
    f = average annual fuel inflation rate,
    P_0 = starting price of fuel per million Btu during the first year of operation.

Table 3.3 Extensive Discrete Present Value Models

Cash Flow Pattern	Function	Typical Cost Example	Present Value, $PV(i)$
Step	$g(n) = f(n-b)$ $= C$	Operating costs	$\dfrac{C}{i}[(1+i)^{1-b} - (1+i)^{-k}]$
Ramp (slope = C)	$g(n) = f(n-b)$ $= C(n-b)$	Maintenance and deterioration	$\dfrac{C}{i^2}[(1+i)^{1-b} - (1+i)^{-k}]$ $+ \dfrac{C}{i}[(b-b)(1+i)^{1-b} - (k+1-b)(1+i)^{-k}]$
Decreasing Ramp (Slope = $-C$)	$g(n) = f(n-b)$ $= A - C(n-b)$	Value depreciation costs	$\dfrac{(1+i)^{1-b}}{i}\left[A - \dfrac{C}{i} - C(b-b)\right]$ $- \dfrac{(1+i)^{-k}}{i}\left[A - \dfrac{C}{i} - C(k+1-b)\right]$
Geometric series	$g(n) = f(n-b)$ $= Ca^{(n-b)}$	Inflationary costs	$\dfrac{Ca^{p-b}}{1+i-a}[(1+i)^{1-b} - a^{k+1-b}(1+i)^{-k}]$
Decay	$g(n) = f(n-b)$ $= Ce^{-f(n-b)}$	Start-up and learning costs	$\dfrac{C(1+i)}{1+i-e^{-f}}\left[\dfrac{e^{-f(b-b)}}{(1+i)^b} - \dfrac{e^{-f(k+1-b)}}{(1+i)^{k+1}}\right]$
Growth	$g(n) = C(1 - e^{-f(n-b)})$	Wear-in maintenance costs	$\dfrac{C(1+i)}{i(1+i-e^{-f})}\left[\dfrac{(1+i-e^{-f}) - ie^{-f(b-b)}}{(1+i)^b} - \dfrac{(1+i-e^{-f}) - ie^{-f(k+1-b)}}{(1+i)^{k+1}}\right]$

Assume that $S = 20,000$ kW, $H = 10,000$ Btu/kW·hr, $U = 0.20, f = 0.07$, and $P_0 = \$4.5$ per million Btu during year 4. The expected life of the plant is 15 years. What is the present value of the total fuel cost at the beginning of construction (now) if the annual market rate of interest is 18%?

With the parameters as specified, the annual fuel cost function is

$$f(n) = 1,576,800 \, (1 + 0.07)^{n-1}, \qquad 1 \le n \le 15$$

To find the present value of the total fuel cost at the beginning of construction, we rewrite $f(n)$ to obtain $g(n)$.

$$g(n) = f(n - 4)$$
$$= 1,576,800 \, (1 + 0.07)^{n-5}, \qquad 5 \le n \le 19$$
$$= 1,473,645(1.07)^{n-4}$$

Now we can use the geometric series formula given in Table 3.3. We identify $C = 1,473,645$, $a = 1.07$, $b = 4$, $b = 5$, $k = 19$, and $i = 0.18$, which yield

$$PV(18\%) = \frac{1,473,645(1.07)}{0.11}[(1.18)^{-4} - (1.07)^{15}\,(1.18)^{-19}]$$
$$= \$5,689,941 \quad \square$$

Simplified Present Value Models. The simplified models are defined as those with cash flows that have no delayed turn-on ($b = 0$) and that terminate after k time units. The procedure for finding the Z-transform for this type of simplified form was illustrated in the previous section (see Figure 3.3d). Table 3.4 summarizes the present value models for some other common cash flow patterns. These simplified present value models correspond, in fact, to the traditional tabulated interest factors found in engineering economy textbooks. They simplify the use of this transform methodology when the modified features of cash flow patterns are not required.

3.2.4 Extension to Future and Annual Equivalent Models

The future equivalent values at the end of period N can easily be obtained from the present values shown in Tables 3.3 and 3.4 by multiplying through by $(1 + i)^N$. Similarly, annual equivalent values over period N are determined by multiplying the present values by the factor $i/[1 - (1 + i)^{-N}]$.

$$FV(i) = PV(i)[(1 + i)^N]$$
$$AE(i) = PV(i) \left[\frac{i}{1 - (1 + i)^{-N}} \right]$$

Consequently, all the Z-transforms in Tables 3.3 and 3.4 may be directly converted to a future or annual equivalent value by applying these elementary algebraic

Table 3.4 Simplified Discrete Present Value Models

Cash Flow Pattern	Function	Typical Cost Example	Present Value, $PV(i)$
	$f(n) = C$	Operating costs	$\frac{C}{i}[1 - (1+i)^{-k}]$
	$f(n) = Cn$	Maintenance and deterioration	$\frac{C}{i^2}[1 - (1+i)^{-k}] + \frac{C}{i}[1 - (k+1)(1+i)^{-k}]$
	$f(n) = A - Cn$	Value depreciation costs	$\frac{1}{i}\left(A - \frac{C}{i} - C\right) - \frac{(1+i)^{-k}}{i}\left[A - \frac{C}{i} - C(k+1)\right]$
	$f(n) = Ca^n$	Inflationary costs	$\frac{Ca}{1+i-a}[1 - a^k(1+i)^{-k}]$
	$f(n) = Ce^{-jn}$	Start-up and learning costs	$\frac{C(1+i)}{1+i-e^{-j}}\left[\frac{e^{-j}}{1+i} - \frac{e^{-j(k+1)}}{(1+i)^{k+1}}\right]$
	$f(n) = C(1 - e^{-jn})$	Wear-in maintenance costs	$\frac{C(1+i)}{1+i-e^{-j}}\left[\frac{1-e^{-j}}{i} - \frac{1+i-e^{-j}-ie^{-j(k+1)}}{i(1+i)^{k+1}}\right]$

manipulations as needed. All the Z-transforms derived in the previous sections are based on the assumption that the compounding periods and the payment occurrences coincide. In situations in which the compounding periods occur more frequently than the receipt of payments, one can find the effective interest rate for the payment period and use it in the Z-transforms developed in Tables 3.3 and 3.4 (see Section 2.4.2).

3.2.5 Applications of Z-Transforms

In this section we will demonstrate the application of the Z-transform to the solution of equivalence problems. Two uses will be illustrated: profit margin analysis and calculation of the present value of interest payments.

Profit Margin Analysis. Consider that a new production facility under construction is expected to be in full commercial operation 2 years from now. The plant is expected to have an initial profit margin of $5 million per year. Find the present value of the total profit margin at 10% interest compounded annually for 20 years of operation if

i. Profit margin and plant performance stay level.

$$g(n) = 5, \quad 3 \le n \le 22$$

ii. Performance traces a learning curve whereby the profit margin grows in each year.

$$g(n) = 5(2 - e^{-0.10(n-3)}), \quad 3 \le n \le 22$$

iii. Performance traces the same growth curve, but the profit margin shrinks at a rate of $e^{-0.03(n-3)}$ so that

$$g(n) = 5e^{-0.03(n-3)}(2 - e^{-0.10(n-3)}), \quad 3 \le n \le 22$$

These three cases are illustrated in Figure 3.6.

For case i, the cash flow diagram is a shifted step function with $C = 5$, $b = 3$, $b = 3$, and $k = 22$. From Table 3.3 the equivalent present value for this shifted step function is

$$PV(i) = \frac{5}{0.1} [(1.1)^{-2} - (1.1)^{-22}] = 50(0.7036) = \underline{\$35.18}$$

For case ii, the growth cash flow function may be regarded as a linear combination of a shifted step function and a shifted decay function. That is,

$$\begin{array}{ccccc} \text{Growth function} & = & \text{Step function} & - & \text{Decay function} \\ g(n) & = & 5(2) & - & 5e^{-0.10(n-3)} \end{array}$$

Thus, for the step function, the corresponding parameters would be $C = 10$, $b = 3$, $b = 3$, and $k = 22$, and for the decay function they would be $C = 5$, $j = 0.10$,

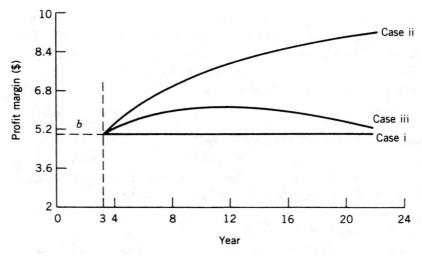

n	Case i	Case ii	Case iii
3	5	5	5
4	5	5.475813	5.313978
5	5	5.906346	5.562387
6	5	6.295909	5.754028
7	5	6.6484	5.896602
8	5	6.967347	5.996851
9	5	7.255942	6.060672
10	5	7.517073	6.093221
11	5	7.753355	6.099005
12	5	7.967152	6.08196
13	5	8.160603	6.045523
14	5	8.335645	5.992693
15	5	8.494029	5.926083
16	5	8.637341	5.847972
17	5	8.767016	5.76034
18	5	8.884349	5.664912
19	5	8.990518	5.563184
20	5	9.086582	5.456453
21	5	9.173506	5.345845
22	5	9.252158	5.232331

FIGURE 3.6 Profit margin analysis.

$b = 3$, $b = 3$, and $k = 22$. From Table 3.3 we obtain the Z-transform of this composite function as follows.

$$PV(i) = \frac{10}{0.1}\left[(1.1)^{-2} - (1.1)^{-22}\right] - \frac{5(1.1)}{1.1 - e^{-0.1}}\left[\frac{1}{(1.1)^3} - \frac{e^{-2.0}}{(1.1)^{23}}\right]$$

$$= 70.36 - 20.74 = \underline{\$49.61}$$

As expected, the total profit margin has increased significantly compared with case i, where no learning effect is appreciable.

For case iii, $g(n)$ is also a linear combination of two similar types of decay function. That is,

$$g(n) = 10e^{-0.03(n-3)} - 5e^{-0.13(n-3)}$$

The first decay function has parameter values of $C = 10$, $b = 3$, $h = 3$, $j = 0.03$, and $k = 22$. The second decay function has $C = 5$, $b = 3$, $h = 3$, $j = 0.13$, and $k = 22$. Thus, from Table 3.3 the Z-transform of this combination yields

$$PV(i) = \frac{10(1.1)}{1.1 - e^{-0.03}}\left[\frac{1}{(1.1)^3} - \frac{e^{-0.60}}{(1.1)^{23}}\right]$$

$$- \frac{5(1.1)}{1.1 - e^{-0.13}}\left[\frac{1}{(1.1)^3} - \frac{e^{-2.60}}{(1.1)^{23}}\right]$$

$$= 58.58 - 18.41 = \$40.17$$

Analysis of Loan Transactions. The repayment schedule for most loans is made up of a portion for the payment of principal and a portion for the payment of interest on the unpaid balance. In economic analysis the interest paid on borrowed capital is considered as a deductible expense for income tax computation. Therefore, it is quite important to know how much of each payment is interest and how much is used to reduce the principal amount borrowed initially. To illustrate this situation, suppose that we want to develop an expression for the present value of the interest components of a uniform repayment plan. Let

A = the equal annual repayment amount,

B = the amount borrowed,

i_b = the borrowing interest rate per period,

N = the maturity of the loan (period).

Then the annual payments will be

$$A = B(A/P, i_b, N) = B\frac{i_b(1 + i_b)^N}{(1 + i_b)^N - 1} \tag{3.30}$$

Each payment is divided into an amount that is interest and a remaining amount for reduction of the principal. Let

I_n = portion of payment A at time n that is interest,

B_n = portion of payment A at time n that is used to reduce the remaining balance,

$$A = I_n + B_n, \text{ where } n = 1, 2, \ldots, N,$$

U_n = unpaid balance at the end of period n, with $U_0 = B$.

The relation of these parameters is illustrated in Figure 3.7. Since the interest payment is based on the unpaid principal that remains at the end of each period, the interest accumulation in the first year is simply $i_b B$. Thus, the first payment A consists of an interest payment $i_b B$ and a principal payment of $A - i_b B$. The unpaid balance remaining after the first payment would be $U_1 = B - (A - i_b B) = B(1 + i_b) - A$. Consequently, the interest charge for the second year would be $i_b U_1$, and the size of the net principal reduction associated with the second payment would be $A - i_b U_1$. In other words, the unpaid balance remaining after the second payment would be

$$\begin{aligned} U_2 &= U_1 - (A - i_b U_1) \\ &= U_1(1 + i_b) - A \end{aligned} \tag{3.31}$$

The amount of principal remaining to be repaid right after making the nth payment can be found with the recursive relationship

$$U_n = U_{n-1}(1 + i_b) - A$$

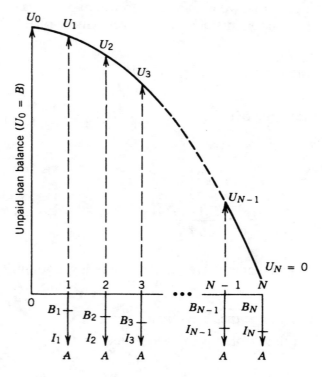

FIGURE 3.7 Loan transactions— unpaid balance as functions of B_n and I_n.

It follows immediately that

$$U_n = B(1 + i_b)^n - A[(1 + i_b)^{n-1} + (1 + i_b)^{n-2} + \cdots + 1]$$

$$= B(1 + i_b)^n - \frac{A}{i_b}[(1 + i_b)^n - 1]$$

$$= \left(B - \frac{A}{i_b}\right)(1 + i_b)^n + \frac{A}{i_b}, \qquad n = 0, 1, \ldots, N - 1 \qquad (3.32)$$

Now we can express the amount of interest payment required at the end of period $n + 1$.

$$I_{n+1} = i_b U_n$$

$$= \underbrace{(Bi_b - A)(1 + i_b)^n}_{\substack{\text{geometric} \\ \text{series}}} + \underbrace{A}_{\substack{\text{step} \\ \text{function}}}, \qquad n, = 0, 1, \ldots, N - 1 \qquad (3.33)$$

Finally, the total present value of these interest payments at an interest rate of i over the loan life of N periods is defined as

$$PV(i) = \sum_{n=0}^{N-1} I_{n+1}(1 + i)^{-(n+1)} \qquad (3.34)$$

Let $g(n) = I_{n+1}$, where $g(n)$ is the sum of a geometric and a uniform series. From Table 3.4, the Z-transform of the geometric series portion is obtained by letting $a = (1 + i_b)$, $C = Bi_b - A$, $b = h = 1$, and $k = N$.

$$PV_1(i) = \frac{Bi_b - A}{i - i_b}[1 - (1 + i_b)^N(1 + i)^{-N}], \quad \text{where } i \neq i_b \qquad (3.35)$$

The transform of the step function portion is found by substituting $C = A$, $b = h = 1$, and $k = N$.

$$PV_2(i) = \frac{A}{i}[(1 - (1 + i)^{-N}] \qquad (3.36)$$

Finally, the transform of $g(n)$ *is found to be*

$$PV(i) = PV_1(i) + PV_2(i) \qquad .$$

$$= \frac{Bi_b - A}{i - i_b}\left[1 - \left(\frac{1 + i_b}{1 + i}\right)^N\right] + \frac{A}{i}[1 - (1 + i)^{-N}] \qquad (3.37)$$

To illustrate the use of this formula, suppose that \$50,000 is borrowed at 8% annual interest and is to be repaid in ten equal annual payments. Determine the total present value of these interest payments associated with the loan transaction at a discount rate of 15%. Since we have $B = \$50,000$, $i_b = 8\%$, $N = 10$ years, and $i = 15\%$, the payment size A is

$$A = \$50,000(A/P,\ 8\%,\ 10) = \$7,451.47$$

Then the total present value is

$$PV(15\%) = \frac{\$50,000(0.08) - \$7,451.57}{0.15 - 0.08}\left[1 - \left(\frac{1.08}{1.15}\right)^{10}\right]$$
$$+ \frac{\$7,451.47}{0.15}\left[1 - \frac{1}{(1.15)^{10}}\right]$$
$$= -\$49,306.70(1 - 0.53365) + \$49,676.47(1 - 0.24718)$$
$$= \$14,403.26$$

It may be of interest to compare the use of Eq. 3.37 with that of the conventional discounting formula developed by Brooking and Burgess [1]. They use the expression

$$PV(i) = B\left\{(A/P,\ i_b,\ N)\left[(P/A,\ i,\ N) - \frac{(P/F,\ i_b,\ N) - (P/F,\ i,\ N)}{i - i_b}\right]\right\}$$
$$= A\left[\frac{1 - (1 + i)^{-N}}{i} - \frac{(1 + i_b)^{-N} - (1 + i)^{-N}}{i - i_b}\right] \tag{3.38}$$

Our method may be numerically verified with the traditional method as follows.

$$PV(15\%) = \$7,451.47\left(5.0188 - \frac{0.4632 - 0.2472}{0.07}\right)$$
$$= \$7,451.47(5.0188 - 3.0857)$$
$$= \$14,404.47$$

The slight difference is due to rounding errors.

3.3 LAPLACE TRANSFORMS AND CONTINUOUS CASH FLOWS

Up to this point we have discussed only discrete cash flow functions. In this section we will extend the modeling philosophy to continuous cash flow functions. The Laplace transform method offers a modeling flexibility similar to that of the Z-transform for computing present values for many forms of continuous cash flow functions.

3.3.1 Laplace Transform and Present Value

As shown in Section 2.5.2, the present value of the infinite continuous cash flow streams, assuming continuous compounding, is given by the expression

$$PV(r) = \int_0^\infty f(t)e^{-rt}\, dt \tag{3.39}$$

where $f(t)$ = continuous cash flow function of the project,

r = nominal interest rate $[r = \ln(1 + i)]$,

t = time expressed in years,

e^{-rt} = discount function.

As Buck and Hill [2] recognized, the general form of this integral bears a close resemblance to the definition of the Laplace transforms. That is, if the function $f(t)$ is considered to be piecewise continuous, then the Laplace transform of $f(t)$, written $L\{f(t)\}$, is defined as a function $F(s)$ of the variable s by the integral

$$L\{f(t)\} = F(s) = \int_0^\infty f(t)e^{-st}\, dt \tag{3.40}$$

over the range of values of s for which the integral exists. Replacing s in Eq. 3.40 with the continuous compound interest rate r simply generates Eq. 3.39; thus, taking a Laplace transform on the cash flow function $f(t)$ is equivalent to computing the present value of the cash flow streams over an infinite horizon time.

In the construction of Laplace transforms, we will use the following notation. If $f(t)$ represents the time domain continuous function, then $F(s)$ will represent its transform. As for the Z-transform, this lowercase–uppercase correspondence will be used throughout the text. As a shorthand notation, the transform pair will be denoted by

$$f(t) \leftrightarrow F(s)$$

For example, to find the transform of a linear function $f(t) = t, t > 0$, we directly evaluate Eq. 3.40.

$$F(s) = \int_0^\infty te^{-st}\, dt = \frac{1}{s^2} \tag{3.41}$$

and find that the transform pair is

$$t \leftrightarrow \frac{1}{s^2}$$

The transforms of some causal time functions that are typically encountered are shown in Table 3.5. The function $u(t)$ in this table represents the unit

Table 3.5 *A Short Table of Laplace Transform Pairs**

Standard Cash Flow Pattern	Cash Flow Function, $f(t)$	Laplace Transform, $F(s)$	Present Value, (Infinite), $PV(r)$
Unit step	$f(t) = u(t) = \begin{cases} 1 & t > 0 \\ 0 & \text{otherwise} \end{cases}$	$1/s$	$1/r$
Delayed unit step	$f(t) = u(t - b) \quad b > 0$	e^{-bs}/s	e^{-br}/r
Ramp	$f(t) = t$	$1/s^2$	$1/r^2$

Table 3.5 (Continued)

Standard Cash Flow Pattern	Cash Flow Function, $f(t)$	Laplace Transform, $F(s)$	Present Value, (Infinite), $PV(r)$
Decay	$f(t) = e^{-jt}$	$1/(s + j)$	$1/(r + j)$
Exponential	$f(t) = e^{jt}$	$1/(s - j)$	$1/(r - j)$
Growth	$f(t) = 1 - e^{-jt}$	$\dfrac{1}{s} - \dfrac{1}{s + j}$	$j/r(r + j)$

*See [7] for a complete Laplace function table.

step function with jump at $t = 0$, and $u(t - a)$ denotes the unit step function with jump at $t = a$. The special property of this function is discussed in the next section.

3.3.2 Properties of Laplace Transforms

In this section we will examine some useful operational properties of the Laplace transform. As in the Z-transform analysis, the properties most relevant to modeling cash flows are linearity and translation.

Linearity. If we define

$$f_1(t) \leftrightarrow F_1(s) \quad \text{and} \quad f_2(t) \leftrightarrow F_2(s)$$

then

$$c_1 f_1(t) + c_2 f_2(t) \leftrightarrow c_1 F_1(s) + c_2 F_2(s) \tag{3.42}$$

This follows from the linearity property of integrals of Eq. 3.40. Suppose we define $f(t)$ as

$$f(t) = 1 + t + \tfrac{1}{2} t^2$$

The transform is

$$L\{f(t)\} = L\{1\} + L\{t\} + L\{\tfrac{1}{2} t^2\}$$

Using Eqs. 3.42 and 3.40 along with the transform results in Table 3.5, we obtain

$$F(s) = \frac{1}{s} + \frac{1}{s^2} + \frac{1}{s^3}$$

Translation with Time Delay. Consider Figure 3.8, in which the function $g(t)$ is obtained from $f(t)$ by shifting the graph of $f(t)$ b units on the time scale to the right. Mathematically, we define such a function as

$$g(t) = \begin{cases} f(t - b) & \text{for } t \geq b \\ 0 & \text{for } t < b \end{cases} \tag{3.43}$$

To find the transform of this type of cash flow function that starts after a delay of b time units, we utilize the property of the unit step function $u(t)$. If we take the unit step function and translate it b units to the right to get $u(t - b)$, we obtain the function shown in Table 3.5. Mathematically, we denote this by

$$u(t - b) = \begin{cases} 1 & \text{for } t \geq b \\ 0 & \text{for } t < b \end{cases} \tag{3.44}$$

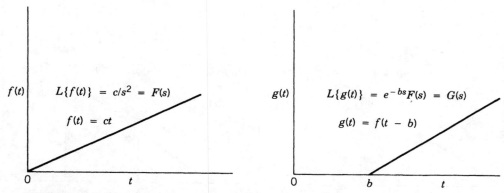

FIGURE 3.8 Translation of continuous ramp pattern.

Then the product $g(t)u(t - b)$ or $f(t - b)u(t - b)$ will be defined as

$$g(t) = f(t - b)u(t - b) = \begin{cases} f(t - b) & \text{for } t \geq b \\ 0 & \text{for } t < b \end{cases} \tag{3.45}$$

The Laplace transform of $g(t)$ given by Eq. 3.45 is

$$L\{g(t)\} = e^{-bs}F(s) \tag{3.46}$$

Accordingly, a cash flow that starts later than $t = 0$ can be treated as if it started immediately and then a correction for the delayed start can be made with the discount factor e^{-sb} ($= e^{-rb}$). This feature proves to be very useful when developing present value models with a composite of delayed turn-on cash flows.

Translation with Cutoff. Another translation property of interest is turning cash flow streams on and off as desired. To illustrate the concept, suppose we wish to find the Laplace transform of a ramp function with features of a delayed turn-on at time b and a turn-off at time k. This function is illustrated in Figure 3.9. Mathematically, we denote such a function by

$$g(t) = f(t)[u(t - b) - u(t - k)] \tag{3.47}$$

The first unit step begins the transactions at $t = b$ and the second stops the transactions at $t = k$. The Laplace transform of this $g(t)$ is defined by

$$G(s) = (e^{-bs} - e^{-ks})\left[F(s) + \frac{f(b)}{s}\right] \tag{3.48}$$

Some care must be exercised in using the time delay theorem. The reader should note the subtle functional difference that $f(t)u(t - b)$ is not a simple time-shifted function $[f(t - b)u(t - b)]$.

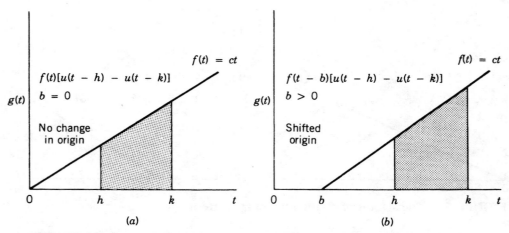

FIGURE 3.9 A continuous ramp function with translation and cutoff.

$$f(t)u(t - b) \neq f(t - b)u(t - b)$$

This difference is illustrated in Fig. 3.10. We can rewrite the function as

$$f(t)u(t - b) = f(t - b)u(t - b) + f(b)u(t - b) \qquad (3.49)$$

Since $f(b)$ is a constant, the Laplace transform of Eq. 3.49 is found by using Eq. 3.46:

$$L\{f(t)u(t - b)\} = e^{-bs}F(s) + \frac{f(b)e^{-bs}}{s}$$

$$= e^{-bs}L\{f(t + b)\} \qquad (3.50)$$

Therefore, the transform of Eq. 3.47 can be expressed as

$$L\{g(t)\} = G(s) = e^{-bs}L\{f(t + b)\} - e^{-ks}L\{f(t + k)\} \qquad (3.51)$$

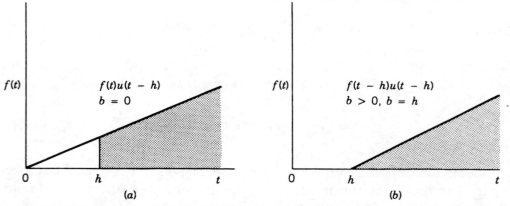

FIGURE 3.10 Functional difference between $f(t)u(t - b)$ and $f(t - b)u(t - b)$.

Example 3.3

Suppose a cash flow function is given by

$$f(t) = 5t, \qquad 10 \leq t \leq 20$$

Using Eq. 3.48 and Table 3.5, we obtain

$$G(s) = e^{-10s}L\{5(t + 10)\} - e^{-20s}L\{5(t + 20)\}$$

$$= e^{-10s}\left(\frac{5}{s^2} + \frac{50}{s}\right) - e^{-20s}\left(\frac{5}{s^2} + \frac{100}{s}\right)$$

$$= \frac{5}{s^2}\left(e^{-10s} - e^{-20s}\right) + \frac{50}{s}\left(e^{-10s} - 2e^{-20s}\right)$$

With a nominal interest rate of 10% ($r = s = 0.1$), the total present value is

$$PV(10\%) = \frac{5}{(0.1)^2}\,(e^{-1} - e^{-2}) + \frac{50}{0.1}(e^{-1} - 2e^{-2})$$

$$= 116.27 + 48.60 = \$164.87$$

Our method may be numerically verified by direct integration of the cash flow function.

$$PV(10\%) = \int_{10}^{20} 5te^{-0.1t}\,dt = \$165$$

Once again, the slight difference is due to rounding errors.   □

Translations with Impulses.   Suppose we want to find the transform of an impulse function $f(t)$ shown in Figure 3.11. This type of impulse function may represent the salvage value of an asset at $t = h$ when the salvage value $f(t)$ decreases exponentially over time. To obtain the transform of such an impulse function, we need to define a Kronecker delta function that corresponds to a unit impulse at $t = h$. That is,

$$\delta(t - h) = \begin{cases} 1 & \text{for } t = h \\ 0 & \text{otherwise} \end{cases} \tag{3.52}$$

By multiplying the salvage value function $f(t)$ by the unit impulse function, we obtain

$$g(t) = f(t)\delta(t - h) = \begin{cases} f(h) & \text{for } t = h \\ 0 & \text{otherwise} \end{cases} \tag{3.53}$$

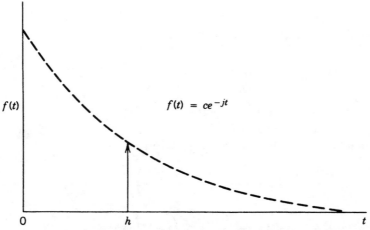

FIGURE 3.11 Example of an impulse cash flow function—decay.

Since $f(b)$ is a constant, the transform of the product form yields

$$g(s) = e^{-bs}f(b) \qquad (3.54)$$

which is the present value expression for a single payment.

Many other useful operational rules can be used in modeling continuous cash flow functions, such as scaling, periodic functions, and convolutions. These are summarized in Table 3.6. (See also Muth [7].)

3.3.3 Development of Continuous Present Value Models

Two types of present value models are needed, corresponding to the start of the original cash flow function. These are the extensive models and the simplified models. Figure 3.12 illustrates the modeling concept of both the extensive and the simplified forms of the ramp time form.

Extensive Present Value Models. The computational procedure for finding the correct extensive present value model was discussed in the previous section. Formulas for directly computing the present values of these extensive models of five common cash flow time forms are presented in Table 3.7. To examine the modeling concept again, consider the exponential time forms of cash flow given in Table 3.7.

Let $f(t) = ce^{jt}$, where c is the scale factor and j is the growth rate with time. To obtain a geometric time form shifted to the right by b time units, we define $g(t) = f(t - b)$. To denote the added feature of a delayed turn-on at $t = b$ and a turn-off at $t = k$, we write

$$g(t) = f(t - b)[u(t - b) - u(t - k)]$$

344

Table 3.6 *Summary of Operational Rules of the Laplace Transform*

Operational Rule	Original Function	Laplace Transform
Linearity	$C_1 f_1(t) + C_2 f_2(t)$	$c_1 F_1(s) + c_2 F_2(s)$
Change of scale	$f(at), \quad a > 0$	$\dfrac{1}{a} F(s)$
Shifting to the right	$f(t - a)u(t - a), \quad a > 0$	$e^{-as} F(s)$
Shifting to the left	$f(t + a), \quad a < 0$	$e^{as}\left[F(s) - \displaystyle\int_0^a e^{-st} f(t)\, dt \right]$
Damping	$e^{-at} f(t)$	$F(s + a)$
Differentiation of $F(s)$ function	$tf(t)$	$-\dfrac{d}{ds} F(s)$
Integration of $F(s)$ function	$\dfrac{f(t)}{t}$	$\displaystyle\int_s^\infty F(u)\, du$
Differentiation of $f(t)$	$\dfrac{d}{dt} f(t)$	$sF(s) - f(0+)$
	$\dfrac{d^n}{dt^n} f(t)$	$s^n F(s) - s^{n-1} f(0+)$ $- s^{n-2} f E(0+) - \cdots$ $- f^{(n-1)}(0+)$
Integration of f(t)	$\displaystyle\int_0^t f(u)\, du$	$\dfrac{1}{s} F(s)$
Periodic function	$f(t) = f(t + T), \quad T = \text{period}$	$F(s) = \dfrac{1}{1 - e^{-sT}} \displaystyle\int_0^T e^{-st} f(t)\, dt$
Convolution	$f_1(t) * f_2(t)$	$F_1(s) F_2(s)$

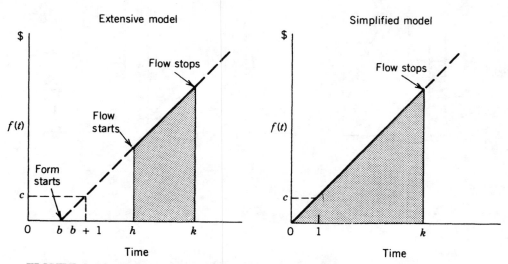

FIGURE 3.12 Features of extensive and simplified continuous models.

Table 3.7 *Extensive Continuous Present Value Models*

Time Form	$f(t)$	$PV(r)$	
Step	c	$\dfrac{c}{r}(e^{-br} - e^{-kr})$	
Ramp	ct	$\dfrac{c}{r^2}(e^{-br} - e^{-kr}) + \dfrac{c}{r}[(b-b)e^{-br} - (k-b)e^{-kr}]$	
Decay	ce^{-jt}	$\dfrac{ce^{+bj}}{r+j}(e^{-b(j+r)} - e^{-k(j+r)})$	
Growth	$c(1 - e^{-jt})$	$\dfrac{c}{r}(e^{-br} - e^{-kr}) - \dfrac{ce^{bj}}{r+j}(e^{-b(j+r)} - e^{-k(j+r)})$	
Exponential	ce^{jt}	$\dfrac{ce^{-bj}}{r-j}(e^{b(j-r)} - e^{k(j-r)}), \quad j \neq r$	

346

Since $f(t) = ce^{jt}$, $f(t - b) = ce^{j(t-b)}$. Therefore, we may rewrite $g(t)$ as

$$
\begin{aligned}
g(t) &= ce^{j(t-b)}[u(t - b) - u(t - k)] \\
&= (e^{-bj})(ce^{jt})[u(t - b) - u(t - k)] \\
&= (e^{-bj})f(t)[u(t - b) - u(t - k)]
\end{aligned} \tag{3.55}
$$

From Eq. 3.47, the transform of $g(t)$ yields

$$
L\{g(t)\} = e^{-bj}[e^{-bs}L\{f(t + b) - e^{-ks}L\{f(t + k)\}]
$$

To evaluate $L\{f(t + b)\}$ and $L\{f(t + k)\}$, we simply expand the original function $f(t) = ce^{jt}$

$$
L\{f(t + b)\} = \{ce^{j(t+b)}\} = ce^{jb}L\{f(t)\} = ce^{jb}F(s)
$$

$$
L\{f(t + k)\} = \{ce^{j(t+k)}\} = ce^{jk}L\{f(t)\} = ce^{jk}F(s)
$$

Since $F(s) = 1/(s - j)$ for $f(t) = e^{jt}$, but with $s = r$, we have

$$
L\{g(t)\} = \frac{ce^{-bj}}{r - j}\left(e^{b(j-r)} - e^{k(j-r)}\right) \tag{3.56}
$$

Example 3.4

Consider a cash inflow stream that starts at $t = 2$ (years) and increases \$1,000 per year uniformly until $t = 10$. Table 3.7 reveals that the ramp is the proper time form for the cash flow. This time form has the scale parameter of $c = \$1,000$. Assume that the pattern starts at $b = 2$, the cash flow begins immediately after that at $b = 2$, and the flow stops at $k = 10$. The present value at the nominal rate of interest 10% is

$$
PV(10\%) = \frac{\$1,000}{(0.1)^2}(e^{-0.2} - e^{-1}) + \frac{\$1,000}{0.1}(0 - 8e^{-1})
$$

$$
= \$45,085.13 - \$29,430.35 = \$15,654.78 \quad \square
$$

Simplified Present Value Models. When there is no shift in time form and no delayed turn-on, the extra factors in the extensive model become cumbersome. In other words, if $b = b = 0$, we can further simplify the formulas in Table 3.7. The reader may notice that the simplified models correspond to the traditional tabulated interest factors (funds flow factors) used in most engineering economy textbooks. These are summarized in Table 3.8.

Present Values of Impulse Cash Flows. Single instantaneous cash flows are referred to as "impulses" to distinguish them from the continuous flow streams examined in the previous sections. Frequently, it is necessary to describe a cash

Table 3.8 *Simplified Continuous Present Value Models*

Time Form	$f(t)$	$PV(r)$
Step	c	$\dfrac{c}{r}(1 - e^{-kr})$
Ramp	ct	$\dfrac{c}{r^2}(1 - rke^{-kr})$
Decay	ce^{-jt}	$\dfrac{c}{r+j}(1 - e^{-k(j+r)})$
Growth	$c(1 - e^{-jt})$	$\dfrac{c}{r}(1 - e^{-kr}) - \dfrac{c}{r+j}(1 - e^{-k(j+r)})$
Exponential	ce^{jt}	$\dfrac{c}{r-j}(1 - e^{k(j-r)})$

impulse that changes in magnitude over time according to some time form. As an example, a salvage value from the sale of a machine decreases gradually with the age of the machine, but the actual value received is a single flow at the time of disposal. Present value formulas corresponding to such a cash impulse, following the four time forms but occurring only at time T, are summarized in Table 3.9. These present value formulas are derived from Eq. 3.54.

Example 3.5

Suppose that the salvage value of an automobile can be described by a decay time form with an initial value of $6,000. The decay rate with time is given as 0.3. Find the present value of the salvage value that occurs at the end of 5 years at a nominal interest rate of 10% compounded continuously. Let $c = 6,000$, $r = 0.3$, $j = 0.1$, and $T = 5$. Then

$$PV(10\%) = ce^{-(j + r)T} = \$6,000e^{-2.0} = \$812.01 \quad \square$$

Table 3.9 Present Values of Impulse Cash Flows

Time Form		PV(r)

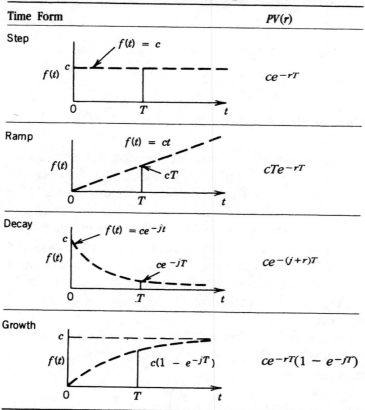

Step	ce^{-rT}
Ramp	cTe^{-rT}
Decay	$ce^{-(j+r)T}$
Growth	$ce^{-rT}(1 - e^{-jT})$

3.3.4 Extension to Future and Annual Equivalent Models

The future equivalent values at the end of period T can easily be obtained from the present value formulas shown in Tables 3.7, 3.8, and 3.9 simply by multiplying through by e^{rT}. Similarly, annual values of equivalent cash flow streams are defined here as the annual cash flow of a step time form starting immediately, terminating at the same time as the equivalent stream, and possessing equal present value. Accordingly, the present value of a step (uniform) time form with the annual cash flow of $\bar{A}$ dollars may be equated to the present value formulas of the other time forms. Solving for $\bar{A}$ gives us the equivalent annual value.

Example 3.6

Consider Example 3.5 and find the equivalent annual value at a nominal interest rate of 10% compounded continuously. Since the present value of the ramp time form that extends over a 10-year period is \$15,654.78, the annual equivalent cash flow stream of $\bar{A}$ dollars per year is determined as follows. From Table 3.8, the present value of the step time form with $b = h = 0$, $c = \bar{A}$, $k = 10$, and $r = 0.1$ yields

$$\frac{\bar{A}}{0.1}(1 - e^{-1}) = \$15,654.78$$

The satisfying value of $\bar{A}$ is the equivalent annual value, which is $\bar{A} = \$2,476.55$. □

3.3.5 Application of the Laplace Transform

Description of the Basic Inventory System. Consider the simplest imaginable type of inventory system in which there is only a single item. The demand rate for this item is assumed to be deterministic and a constant λ units per year. The fixed cost of placing an order in dollars is A. The unit cost of the item in dollars is C. Let I_0 be the inventory carrying charge (measured in the units of dollars per year per dollar of investment in inventory) exclusive of the rate of return (i.e., of the opportunity cost). We will further assume that the procurement lead time is a constant and that the system is not allowed to be out of stock at any point in time. Orders for the item are received in lots of Q units. The problem is to determine the optimal value of Q.

Figure 3.13 depicts the inventory behavior of this model with respect to time. Since the order quantity Q and the demand rate λ are constant, the inventory level of the first cycle T is

$$I(t) = Q - \lambda t, \qquad 0 \le t \le T \tag{3.57}$$

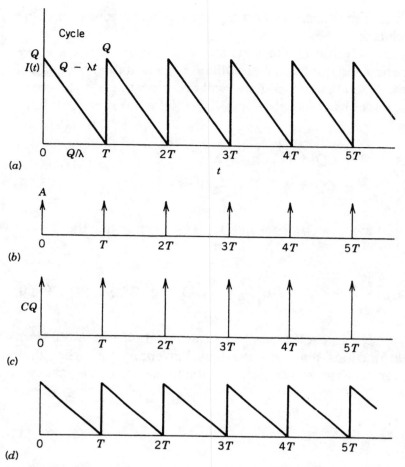

FIGURE 3.13 Inventory behavior: quantity and const as functions of time. (*a*) Inventory positions. (*b*) Ordering costs. (*c*) Purchase costs. (*d*) Inventory costs.

Note that $I(t) = 0$ at $t = T$ and $T = Q/\lambda$. Let

r = the nominal interest rate,

$f(t)_1$ = the ordering cost per cycle,

$f(t)_2$ = the purchase cost per cycle,

$f(t)_3$ = the inventory carrying cost per cycle.

Then the inventory cost for the first cycle is given by

$$f(t) = f(t)_1 + f(t)_2 + f(t)_3 \qquad (3.58)$$

where
$$f(t)_1 = A,$$
$$f(t)_2 = CQ,$$

$$f(t)_3 = I_0 C \int_0^T (Q - \lambda t)\, dt.$$

Equation 3.58 represents the inventory cost per cycle *without* considering the effect of the time value of money.

To find the present value of the inventory cost for the first cycle, we assume that the ordering and purchase costs will occur only at the beginning of the cycle, but that the inventory carrying cost will occur continuously over the cycle. With these assumptions, the Laplace transform of the inventory cost function is

$$F(s) = A + CQ + L\{I_0C(Q - \lambda t)\}$$
$$= A + CQ + I_0C\left[\frac{Q}{s} - \frac{\lambda}{s^2}(1 - e^{-sT})\right] \qquad (3.59)$$

After substituting $s = r$ and $T = Q/\lambda$ back into Eq. 3.59, we find that the present value expression is

$$PV(r)_{cycle} = A + CQ + I_0C\left[\frac{Q}{r} - \frac{\lambda}{r^2}(1 - e^{-rQ/\lambda})\right] \qquad (3.60)$$

Since the cycle repeats itself forever, we can use the Laplace transform property of periodic functions. If we denote the total inventory cost over infinite cycles as $g(t)$, $G(s)$ can be expressed in terms of the transform of the first cycle $F(s)$.

$$G(s) = F(s)\frac{1}{1 - e^{-sT}} \qquad (3.61)$$

$$PV(r)_{total} = PV(r)_{cycle}\left(\frac{1}{1 - e^{-rQ/\lambda}}\right)$$
$$= \frac{1}{1 - e^{-rQ/\lambda}}\left(A + CQ + \frac{I_0CQ}{r}\right) - \frac{I_0C\lambda}{r^2} \qquad (3.62)$$

Differentiating $PV(r)_{total}$ with respect to Q and equating the result to zero gives us

$$(1 - e^{-rQ/\lambda})\left(C + \frac{I_0C}{r}\right) - \left(A + CQ + \frac{I_0CQ}{r}\right)\left(\frac{r}{\lambda}e^{-rQ/\lambda}\right) = 0 \qquad (3.63)$$

An exact analytical solution of (3.63) for Q is not normally possible, but a numerical solution may be obtained by using the Newton–Raphson method [8]. An approximate solution (within about 2%) can be obtained more easily, however, by using a second-order approximation for the exponential term.

$$e^{-rQ/\lambda} = 1 - \left(\frac{r}{\lambda}\right)Q + \left(\frac{r}{\lambda}\right)^2 Q^2 \frac{1}{2!}$$
$$- \left(\frac{r}{\lambda}\right)^3 Q^3 \frac{1}{3!} + \cdots \qquad (3.64)$$

Since $0<r<1$ (in general), we can ignore the terms $(r/\lambda)^3$ and higher. Then, substituting the first three terms into Eq. 3.63 and solving for Q, we obtain

$$Q^* \triangleq \left[\frac{2A}{(I_0 + r)C} \right]^{1/2} \tag{3.65}$$

With $A = \$10$, $C = \$5/\text{unit}$, $I_0 = 0.1$, $r = 0.1$, and $\lambda = 100$ units per year, the optimal order quantity is about

$$Q^* \triangleq \left[\frac{2(15)(100)}{(0.1 + 0.2)5} \right]^{1/2} = 36.51$$

The numerical solution obtained by the Newton–Raphson method would be $Q^* = 36.23$.

3.4 SUMMARY

The Z-transform and the Laplace transform can be used in a wide variety of cash flow models, and in many situations these methodologies are more efficient than the traditional approach. This chapter was intended to (1) introduce the transform methodologies, (2) provide alternative techniques for modeling cash flows that are interrupted or impulses that follow a particular time form, and (3) demonstrate the use of this methodology in equivalence calculations. We do not recommend the transform analysis for modeling simple cash flow transactions because there is not much savings in computation. The transform analysis will provide definite computational advantages, however, for complex cash flow functions.

REFERENCES

1. BROOKING, S. A., and A. R. BURGESS, "Present Worth of Interest Tax Credit," *The Engineering Economist,* Vol. 21, No. 2, Winter 1976, pp. 111–117.

2. BUCK, J. R., and T. W. HILL, "Laplace Transforms for the Economic Analysis of Deterministic Problems in Engineering," *The Engineering Economist,* Vol. 16, No. 4, 1971, pp. 247–263.

3. BUCK, J. R., and T. W. HILL, "Additions to the Laplace Transform Methodology for Economic Analysis," *The Engineering Economist,* Vol. 20, No. 3, 1975, pp. 197–208.

4. GIFFIN, W. C., *Transform Techniques for Probability Modeling,* Academic Press, New York, 1975.

5. GRUBBSTROM, R. W., "On the Application of the Laplace Transform to Certain Economic Problems," *Management Science,* Vol. 13, No. 7, 1967, pp. 558–567.

6. HILL, T. W., and J. R. BUCK, "Zeta Transforms, Present Value, and Economic Analysis," *AIIE Transactions,* Vol. 6, No. 2, 1974, pp. 120–125.

7. MUTH, E. J., *Transform Methods with Applications to Engineering and Operations Research,* Prentice–Hall, Englewood Cliffs, N.J., 1977.

8. PARK, C. S., and Y. K. SON, "The Effect of Discounting on Inventory Lot Sizing Models," *Engineering Costs and Production Economics,* Vol. 16, No. 1, 1989, pp. 35–48.

9. REMER, D. S., J. C. TU, D. E. CARSON, and S. A. GANTY, "The State of the Art of Present Worth Analysis of Cash Flow Distributions," *Engineering Costs and Production Economics,* Vol. 7, No. 4, 1984, pp. 257–278.

PROBLEMS

3.1. Consider a cash flow stream for which the monthly profits are $\$1,000e^{-0.1n}$ for $n = 1, 2, 3, \ldots , 12$ months and the nominal interest rate is 12%. Find the present value under

    a. 12% compounded annually.   c. 12% compounded monthly.

    b. 12% compounded quarterly.   d. 12% compounded continuously.

3.2. Consider the discrete cash flow patterns shown in the accompanying illustration.

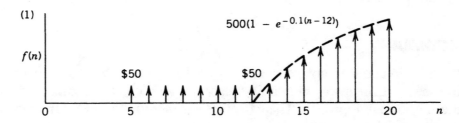

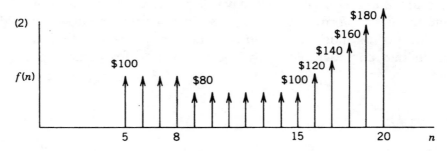

    a. Compute the present value of each cash flow series using the conventional interest formulas at $i = 10\%$.

    b. Compute the present value of each cash flow series using the discrete transform results at $i = 10\%$.

    c. Compute the annual equivalent value of each cash flow series over 20 years.

3.3. Consider the retirement schedule for a $100,000 bond issue by a city, which is to be proportional to the city's anticipated growth. If this anticipated growth tends to follow the general growth pattern of

$$f(n) = C(1 - e^{-0.087n})$$

and the bond interest rate is 5%, find an increasing repayment over 20 years.

3.4. Suppose you borrow $100,000 at an interest rate of 9% compounded monthly over 30 years to finance a home. If your interest rate is 1% per month, compute the present value of the total interest payment of the loan.

3.5. Consider the following cost and return components of a machine tool.
   a. The initial cost of $8,000.
   b. A uniform operating cost of $800 each year.
   c. Maintenance costs, which increase at a rate of $400 each year.
   d. Annual start-up costs, which decay at the rate of 1.0 from an upper limit of $1,000 initially.
   e. A single salvage value return, which decays at the rate of 0.5 with age from the initial cost of $8,000. Assume $i = 8\%$.
   Compute the present value of these five cash flow components over 10 years.

3.6. Consider a machine that now exists in condition j and generates earnings at the uniform continuous rate of A_j dollars per year. If at some time T the machine's condition changes from j to k, its earning rate will instantaneously change from A_j to A_k. We will inspect the machine exactly one year from now. You may treat the time value of money in terms of a nominal interest rate of r compounded continuously.
   a. If the machine's condition changes to k at time T, where T is in time interval between 0 and 1, what is the present value of its earnings for the year?
   b. If the machine remains in condition j for the entire year, what is the present value of its earnings for the year?

3.7. Suppose a uniformly increasing continuous cash flow (a ramp) accumulates $1,000 over 4 years. The continuous cash flow function is expressed as

$$f(t) = ct, \qquad 0 \le t \le 4$$

Assume that $r = 12\%$ compounded continuously.
   a. Find the slope c.
   b. Compute the present equivalent of this continuous series.
   c. Compute the future value of this continuous series.

3.8. Find the present value of the following quadratic cash flow at 10% interest compounded continuously,

$$f(t) = \$200 + 45t - 3t^2$$

   a. if $0 \le t \le 10$.
   b. if $0 \le t \le \infty$.

3.9. A chemical process for an industrial solvent generates a continuous after-tax cash flow $f(t)$ of $250,000 per year for a 10-year planning horizon.
   a. Find the present value of this cash flow stream over 10 years if money is worth 12% compounded continuously.
   b. The profit per year is expected to increase continuously because of increased productivity and can be expressed as

$$f(t) = 250,000(2.0 - e^{-0.2t})$$

   where t is time in years. Find the present value of this cash flow stream.
   c. Productivity increases as in part b, but competition reduces the profit continuously by 8% per year. Find the present value of the cash flow.

3.10. Consider the following simple inventory system. A stock of Q units is produced at a rate of a_p units per day for a period T_p. It is then necessary to leave the batch in stock for a period of T_d, during which sorting, inspection, and painting are carried out. A quantity Q_1 is then supplied to the assembly line at the rate of a units per day for a period T_c. The supply to the assembly is intermittent, so that after a supply period T_c there is an interval T_0 before supply is resumed for another period T_c, and so on. Assuming that the relationship between Q and a is defined as $Q = ka$, k is an integer, and b stands for a holding cost of one unit per unit time, answer the following questions.

  a. Draw the level of inventory position as a function of time t.

  b. Assuming continuous compounding at a nominal rate of r, find the expression of present value of the total inventory cost over one complete cycle. (One cycle is defined as a time interval in which the entire stock Q is depleted.)

  c. With $Q = 1,000$ units, $a_p = 10$ units/day, $T_p = 100$ days, $T_d = 50$ days, $a = 5$ units/day, $T_c = 80$ days, $T_0 = 55$ days, $b = \$5$ per unit per year, and $r = 12\%$ compounded continuously, find the total present value using the formula developed in part b.

3.11. Consider an inventory system in which an order is placed every T units of time. It is desired to determine the optimal value of Q by maximizing the average annual profit. This profit is the revenue less the sum of the ordering, purchasing, and inventory carrying costs. All demands will be met from inventory so that there are never any back orders or lost sales. We assume that the demand rate λ is known with certainty and does not change with time. If the on-hand inventory does not continually increase or decrease with each period, the quantity ordered each time will be $Q = \lambda T$. To minimize carrying charges, the on-hand inventory when a procurement arrives should be zero. Suppose that A is the fixed cost of placing an order, C is the cost of one unit, I is the inventory carrying charge, and R is the unit sales price. For simplicity, we select the time origin as a point just prior to the arrival of an order so that nothing is on hand at the time origin.

  a. If r is the nominal interest compounded continuously, find the optimal Q that maximizes the present value of all future profits.

  b. As a specific example, consider a situation in which $A = \$15$, $C = \$35$, $I = 0.10$, $r = 10\%$, $\lambda = 1,500$ units per year, and $R = \$60$ per unit.

3.12. Develop the Z-transform result for the decay function, $g(n) = Ce^{-j(n-b)}$, shown in Table 3.3.

3.13. Develop the Z-transform result for the growth function, $g(n) = C(1 - e^{-j(n-b)})$, shown in Table 3.3. Knowing that this growth function is the sum of C and $-Ce^{-j(n-b)}$, use the linearlity property.

3.14. Develop the Laplace transform result for the growth function shown in Table 3.7.

Outline

Part II: Evaluating Economic Performance of Companies and Projects

- Lecture slides on ratio analysis, discounted cash flows and transform techniques

- Chapters 2 and 3 of "Advanced Engineering Economics" by Park and Sharp-Bette

- Lecture slides on figures of merit

- Chapters 6 and 7 of "Advanced Engineering Economics" by Park and Sharp-Bette

Figures of Merit

➤ **The Net Present Value Criterion**

➤ **The Future Value Criterion**

➤ **The Annual Equivalence Criterion**

➤ **The Internal Rate of Return Criterion**

➤ **Solomon's Average Rate of Return Criterion**

➤ **The Modified Internal Rate of Return Criterion**

➤ **The Benefit-Cost Ratios Criteria**

➤ **The Discounted Payback Period**

➤ **The Project Balance Concept**

➤ **Conventional, Potentially Profitable, Pure and Mixed Investments**

Figures of Merit

➢ **A project net present value (NPV) is:**

$$NPV\ (i) = \sum_{n=0}^{N} \frac{F_n}{(1+i)^n}$$

▪ **NPV Criterion:**

➢ Accept the project if $NPV(i) > 0$

➢ Remain indifferent if $NPV(i) = 0$

➢ Reject the project if $NPV(i) < 0$

Figures of Merit

➤ **"The" internal rate of return (IRR) of a project is "the" rate $i*$ for which:**

$$NPV(i*) = 0$$

- **IRR Criterion:**
  - ➤ Accept the project if $i* > MARR$
  - ➤ Remain indifferent if $i* = MARR$
  - ➤ Reject the project if $i* < MARR$

Figures of Merit

➢ **A project NPV is:**

$$NPV(i) = \sum_{n=0}^{N} \frac{F_n}{(1+i)^n} = \sum_{n=0}^{N} \frac{b_n}{(1+i)^n} - \sum_{n=0}^{N} \frac{c_n}{(1+i)^n} = B - C$$

- **Aggregate B/C Ratio:**

$$R_A = \frac{B}{C}$$

- **Aggregate B/C Ratio Criterion:**

  ➢ Accept the project if $R_A > 1$

  ➢ Remain indifferent if $R_A = 1$

  ➢ Reject the project if $R_A < 1$

Figures of Merit

➤ **A project's outflows can be decomposed into two parts:**

- **I : the initial investment**

- **O = C – I : consists of annual operating and maintenance costs**

- **Netted B/C Ratio:**

$$R_N = \frac{B - O}{I}$$

- **Netted B/C Ratio Criterion:**

  ➢ Accept the project if $R_N > 1$

  ➢ Remain indifferent if $R_N = 1$

  ➢ Reject the project if $R_N < 1$

Figures of Merit

- **Lorie-Savage Ratio:**

$$L - S = \frac{B - C}{I}$$

- **Lorie-Savage Ratio Criterion:**

  ➤ Accept the project if $L\text{-}S > 0$

  ➤ Remain indifferent if $L\text{-}S = 0$

  ➤ Reject the project if $L\text{-}S < 0$

Figures of Merit

- **Generalized Project balance (PB):**

$$PB(i, j)_0 = F_0$$

$$PB(i, j)_n = \begin{cases} PB(i, j)_{n-1}(1+i) + F_n, \text{if } PB(i, j)_{n-1} \leq 0 \\ PB(i, j)_{n-1}(1+j) + F_n, \text{if } PB(i, j)_{n-1} > 0 \end{cases}$$

Where **j** is a conservative rate at which a company can invest recovered balances

- **GPB Criterion:**

  ➢ Accept the project if $PB(i, j)_N > 0$

  ➢ Remain indifferent if $PB(i, j)_N = 0$

  ➢ Reject the project if $PB(i, j)_N < 0$

- **Investment:** $F_0 < 0$

- **Conventional (or simple) Investment:** investment with only one change in the sign of the cash flows

- **Potentially Profitable Investment:** investment with a positive sum of net cash flows

- **Proposition:** a **potentially profitable conventional investment has a unique positive root**

- **Pure Investment:** no over-recovered balances at its largest root

  ➤ NPV $(i^*) = 0$, NPV (i) <> 0 for $i > i^*$ and PB $(i^*)_n \leq 0$ for n=0,1,…,N-1

  $\Rightarrow$ All conventional investments are pure

- **Mixed Investment:** investment that is not pure

  ➤ Let j be the investment rate for over-recovered balances

  ➤ Let $i(j)$ be the interest rate at which the ending balance is zero: PB $(i(j), j)_N = 0$

- **Generalized IRR criterion:**

  ➤ Accept the project if $i(j) > \mathbf{MARR}$

  ➤ Remain indifferent if $i(j) = \mathbf{MARR}$

  ➤ Reject the project if $i(j) < \mathbf{MARR}$

Incremental Approach

- **Rule:**

  ➢ Sort potentially profitable conventional investments by increasing order of the sum of their cash flows

  ➢ Compute incremental IRR and use IRR criterion to switch projects

Outline

Part II: Evaluating Economic Performance of Companies and Projects

- Lecture slides on ratio analysis, discounted cash flows and transform techniques

- Chapters 2 and 3 of "Advanced Engineering Economics" by Park and Sharp-Bette

- Lecture slides on figures of merit

- Chapters 6 and 7 of "Advanced Engineering Economics" by Park and Sharp-Bette

6

Measures
of Investment Worth
—Single Project

6.1 INTRODUCTION

In this chapter we focus primarily on evaluating individual projects by the application of various numerical criteria. In our analysis we treat investment projects as almost the same as securities (stocks, bonds, and so on). Both investment projects and securities normally require initial outlays in order to provide a later sequence of cash receipts. The major difference is that investment projects are not marketable and securities are. When it is necessary to distinguish between projects and securities in our discussion, it will be done. Otherwise, the assumption can be made that the analyses are identical.

Ten different criteria are discussed in this chapter. The net present value (*PV*) criterion is considered the standard measure of investment, and the other measures are discussed and compared with it. The *PV* criterion and its economic interpretation by means of the project balance concept are discussed in Section 6.2. The internal rate of return (*IRR*) criterion, Solomon's average rate of return (*ARR*) criterion, and modified internal rate of return (*MIRR*) criterion are defined in Section 6.3 and are compared with the *PV* criterion. In Section 6.4 alternative measures, benefit–cost ratios, are presented, and again they are compared with the *PV* criterion. The payback period of an investment is discussed in Section 6.5. Finally, the time-dependent measure of investment worth is developed in Section 6.6. In discussing the various measures, we need to make certain assumptions about the investment settings.

6.1.1 Initial Assumptions

In the following investment worth analysis, we assume that the *MARR* (or cost of capital) is known to the decision maker. We also assume a stable, perfect capital market and complete certainty about investment outcomes. In a perfect capital market a firm can raise as much cash as it wants at the going rate of interest, or the firm has sufficient funds to accept all profitable investments. A perfect capital market makes it possible for a firm to invest as much cash as it wants at the market rate of interest. Since the firm may already have undertaken all profitable investments, the market rate of interest is assumed to measure the return on the firm's marginal investment opportunities. Having complete certainty about an investment means that the firm has perfect knowledge of the present and future cash flows associated with the project. Because of this knowledge, the firm finds it unnecessary to make any allowance for uncertainty in project evaluation.

These assumptions describe what might be called the ideal investment situation, quite different from the real-world situation. By setting aside certain complications, however, these assumptions will allow us to introduce the topic of investment analysis at a much simpler level than we otherwise could. In later chapters these assumptions will be removed and the analysis extended to more realistic situations, in which none of these assumptions is fully satisfied.

6.1.2 Notation

To discuss the various evaluation criteria, we will use the following common notation for cash flow representation.

n time, measured in discrete compounding periods

i opportunity interest rate (*MARR*), or market interest rate

C_0 initial investment at time 0, a positive amount

b_n revenue at end of period n, $b_n \geq 0$

c_n expense at the end of period n, $c_n \geq 0$

N project life

F_n net cash flow at the end of period n ($F_n = b_n - c_n$; if $b_n \geq c_n$, then $F_n \geq 0$; if $b_n < c_n$, then $F_n < 0$)

Figure 6.1 illustrates this notation with a cash flow diagram. Additional notation pertaining to a specific criterion will be defined later as necessary. It must be emphasized that all cash flows represent the *cash flows after taxes*.

6.2 THE NET PRESENT VALUE CRITERION

We will use the concept of equivalence to develop the net present value (*PV*) criterion for evaluating investment worth. The future value and annual equivalent criteria are variations of the *PV* criterion found by converting the *PV* into either the future value or the annual equivalent by using the same interest rate. In this section we define and discuss the interpretation of these three criteria.

6.2.1 Mathematical Definition

The **PV** *Criterion.*   Consider a project that will generate cash receipts of b_n at the end of each period n. The present value of cash receipts over the project life, B, is expressed by

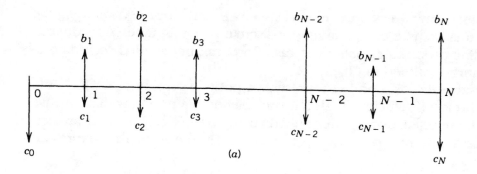

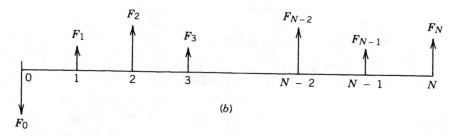

FIGURE 6.1. Notation conventions. (a) Gross cash flow. (b) Net cash flow.

$$B = \sum_{n=0}^{N} \frac{b_n}{(1 + i)^n}$$ (6.1)

Assume that the cash expenses (including the initial outlay associated with the project) at the end of each period are c_n. The present value expression of cash expenses, C, is

$$C = \sum_{n=0}^{N} \frac{c_n}{(1 + i)^n}$$ (6.2)

Then the PV of the project [denoted by $PV(i)$] is defined by the difference between B and C; that is,

$$PV(i) = \sum_{n=0}^{N} \frac{b_n - c_n}{(1 + i)^n} = \sum_{n=0}^{N} \frac{F_n}{(1 + i)^n}$$ (6.3a)

The F_n will be positive if the corresponding period has a net cash inflow and negative if there is a net cash outflow. The foregoing computation of the PV is based on a rate of interest that remains constant over time. The PV could be computed with different rates of interest over time, in which case we would label the nth period's rate of interest as i_n. The PV expression is then

$$PV(i_n, n) = F_0 + \frac{F_1}{1 + i_1} + \frac{F_2}{(1 + i_1)(1 + i_2)} + \cdots$$ (6.3b)

For simplicity, we assume here a single rate of interest in computing the *PV*. We further assume compounding at discrete points in time. A continuous compounding process or continuous cash flows can be handled according to the procedures outlined in Chapter 2.

A positive *PV* for a project represents a positive surplus, and we should accept the project if sufficient funds are available for it. A project with a negative *PV* should be rejected, because we could do better by investing in other projects at the opportunity rate or outside the market. The decision rule expressed simply is

> If $PV(i) > 0$, accept.
> If $PV(i) = 0$, remain indifferent.
> If $PV(i) < 0$, reject.

Future Value Criterion. As a variation of the *PV* criterion, the future value (*FV*) criterion measures the economic value of a project at the end of the project's life, *N*. Converting the project cash flows into a single payment concentrated at period *N* produces a cash flow equal to *FV*.

$$
FV(i) = \sum_{n=0}^{N} F_n (1 + i)^{N-n}
$$

$$
= PV(i)(1 + i)^N \qquad (6.4)
$$

From another view, if we borrowed and lent at *i*, operated the project, and left all extra funds to accumulate at *i*, we would have a value equal to *FV(i)* at the end of period *N*. If this value is positive, the project is acceptable. If it is negative, the project should be rejected. As expected, the decision rule for the *FV* criterion is the same as that for the *PV* criterion.

> If $FV(i) > 0$, accept.
> If $FV(i) = 0$, remain indifferent.
> If $FV(i) < 0$, reject.

Annual Equivalent Criterion. The annual equivalent (*AE*) criterion is another basis for measuring investment worth that has characteristics similar to those of the *PV* criterion. This similarity is evident when we consider that any cash flow can be converted into a series of equal annual payments by first finding the *PV* for the original series and then multiplying the *PV* by the capital recovery factor.

$$
AE(i) = PV(i)\left[\frac{i(1 + i)^N}{(1 + i)^N - 1} \right] = PV(i)(A/P, i, N) \qquad (6.5)
$$

Because the factor $(A/P, i, N)$ is positive for $-1 < i < \infty$, the AE criterion should provide a consistent basis for evaluating an investment project as the previous criteria have done.

> If $AE(i) > 0$, accept.
>
> If $AE(i) = 0$, remain indifferent.
>
> If $AE(i) < 0$, reject.

Example 6.1

This example will serve to illustrate the use of the PV criterion. Consider a project that requires a $1,000 initial investment with the following patterns of cash flow.

Cash Flow	End of Period n					
	0	1	2	3	4	5
Receipt (b_n)	$0	500	500	500	500	500
Expense (c_n)	$1,000	100	140	180	220	260
Net Flow (F_n)	$-$1,000	400	360	320	280	240

The cash flow diagram is shown in Figure 6.2. Assume the firm's $MARR$ is 10%. Substituting F_n values into Eq. 6.3 and varying i values ($0 \le i \le 40\%$), we obtain Table 6.1 and Figure 6.3. We then find that the project's PV decreases monoto-

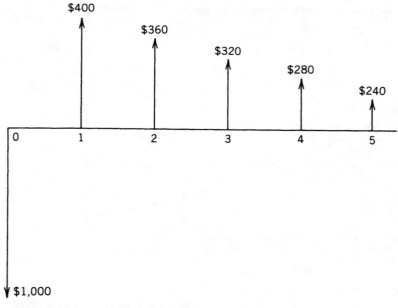

FIGURE 6.2. Cash flow diagram for Example 6.1.

Table 6.1 *Net Present Values PV(i)*
at Varying Interest Rate i, Example 6.1

i (%)	PV(i)	i (%)	PV(i)
0	$600.00	21%	−$19.5
1	556.96	22	−38.84
2	515.77	23	−57.30
3	476.33	24	−75.15
4	438.54	25	−92.43
5	402.31	26	−109.15
6	367.56	27	−125.34
7	334.21	28	−141.03
8	302.19	29	−156.23
9	271.42	30	−170.96
10	241.84	31	−185.25
11	213.40	32	−199.11
12	186.03	33	−212.56
13	159.68	34	−225.61
14	134.31	35	−238.29
15	109.86	36	−250.60
16	86.29	37	−262.56
17	63.55	38	−274.19
18	41.62	39	−285.49
19	20.45	40	−296.48
20	0		

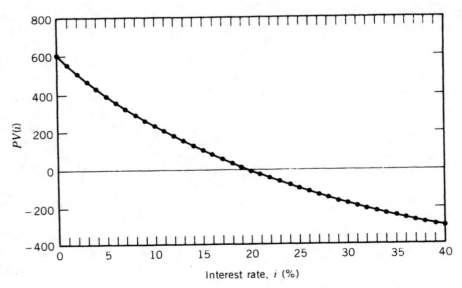

FIGURE 6.3. Plot of *PV(i)* as a function of *i*, Example 6.1.

nically with the firm's i. The project has a positive PV if the firm's interest rate ($MARR$) is below 20% and a negative PV if the $MARR$ is above 20%. At $i = 10\%$, the PV (the equivalent present value to the firm of the total surplus) is $241.84. ·

Using Eqs. 6.4 and 6.5, we find

$$FV(10\%) = \$241.84(F/P,\ 10\%,\ 5) = \$389.49$$
$$AE(10\%) = \$241.84(A/P,\ 10\%,\ 5) = \$58.0$$

Since both $FV(10\%)$ and $AE(10\%)$ are positive, the project is considered viable under these criteria.   □

6.2.2 Economic Interpretation Through Project Balance

An alternative way to interpret the economic significance of these criteria is through the project balance concept. In this section we define the project balance concept and then explain how these criteria are related to the terminal project balance.

Project Balance Concept.   The *project balance* describes the net equivalent amount of dollars tied up in or committed to the project at each point in time over the life of the project. We will use $PB(i)_n$ to denote the project balance at the end of period n computed at the opportunity cost rate ($MARR$) of i. We will assume that the cost of having money tied up in the project is not incurred unless it is committed for the entire period. To show how the $PB(i)_n$ are computed, we consider the project described in Example 6.1. (See Figure 6.2.)

The project balance at the present time ($n = 0$) is just the investment itself.

$$PB(10\%)_0 = -\$1,000$$

At $n = 1$, the firm has an accumulated commitment of $1,100, which consists of the initial investment and the associated cost of having the initial investment tied up in the project for one period. However, the project returns $400 at $n = 1$. This reduces the firm's investment commitment to $700, so the project balance at $n = 1$ is

$$PB(10\%)_1 = -\$1,000(1 + 0.1) + \$400 = -\$700$$

This amount becomes the net amount committed to that project at the beginning of period 2. The project balance at the end of period 2 is

$$PB(10\%)_2 = -\$700(1 + 0.1) + \$360 = -\$410$$

This represents the cost of having $700 committed at the beginning of the second year along with the receipt of $360 at the end of that year.

We compute the remaining project balances similarly.

$$PB(10\%)_3 = -\$410(1.1) + \$320 = -\$131.00$$
$$PB(10\%)_4 = -\$131(1.1) + \$280 = \$135.90$$
$$PB(10\%)_5 = \$135.90(1.1) + \$240 = \$389.49$$

Notice that the firm fully recovers its initial investment and opportunity cost at the end of period 4 and has a profit of \$135.90. Assuming that the firm can reinvest this amount at the same interest rate ($i = 10\%$) in other projects or outside the market, the project balance grows to \$389.49 with the receipt of \$240 at the end of period 5. The project is then terminated with a net profit of \$389.49.

If we compute the present value equivalent of this net profit at time 0, we obtain

$$PV(10\%) = \$389.49(P/F, 10\%, 5) = \$241.84$$

The result is the same as that obtained when we directly compute the present value of the project at $i = 10\%$. Table 6.2 summarizes these computational results.

Mathematical Derivation. Defining the project balance mathematically based on the previous example yields the recursive relationship

$$PB(i)_n = (1 + i)PB(i)_{n-1} + F_n \tag{6.6}$$

where $PB(i)_0 = F_0$ and $n = 0, 1, 2, \ldots, N$.

We can develop an alternative expression for the project balance from Eq. 6.6 by making substitutions as follows.

$$PB(i)_0 = F_0$$
$$PB(i)_1 = (1 + i)F_0 + F_1$$
$$PB(i)_2 = (1 + i)[(1 + i)F_0 + F_1] + F_2$$
$$= F_0(1 + i)^2 + F_1(1 + i) + F_2$$

so that at any period n

$$PB(i)_n = F_0(1 + i)^n + F_1(1 + i)^{n-1} + \cdots + F_n \tag{6.7}$$

The terminal project balance is then expressed by

$$PB(i)_N = F_0(1 + i)^N + F_1(1 + i)^{N-1} + \cdots + F_N$$
$$= \sum_{n=0}^{N} F_n(1 + i)^{N-n}$$
$$= FV(i) \tag{6.8}$$

Note that $PB(i)_N$ is the future value of the project.

Table 6.2 *Project Balance Computations for the Project in Example 6.1*

Item	n: 0	1	2	3	4	5
Beginning project balance, $PB(i)_{n-1}$	\$0	−1,000	−700	−410	−131	+135.90
Interest owed, $i[PB(i)_{n-1}]$	\$0	−100	−70	−41	−13.10	13.59
Cash receipt, F_n	−1,000	400	360	320	280	240
Ending project balance, $PB(i)_n$	−\$1,000	−\$700	−\$410	−\$131	\$135.90	\$389.49 $PB(i)_N$

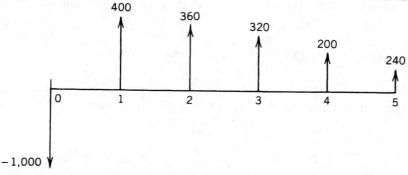

$$PV(10\%) = PB(10\%)_5(1 + 0.1)^{-5} = \$389.49(P/F, 10\%, 5) = \$241.84$$

$$PV(10\%) = -\$1,000 + 400(1.1)^{-1} + 360(1.1)^{-2} + 320(1.1)^{-3}$$
$$+ 280(1.1)^{-4} + 240(1.1)^{-5} = \$241.84$$

Economic Interpretation. If $PB(i)_N > 0$, we can say that the firm recovers the initial investment plus any interest owed, with a profit at the end of the project. If $PB(i)_N = 0$, the firm recovers only the initial investment plus interest owed and breaks even. If $PB(i)_N < 0$, the firm ends up with a loss by not being able to recover even the initial investment and interest owed. Naturally, the firm should accept a project only if $PB(i)_N > 0$. The present equivalent amount of this terminal profit is

$$PV(i) = \frac{PB(i)_N}{(1 + i)^N}$$

$$= \frac{FV(i)_N}{(1 + i)^N} \tag{6.9}$$

The factor $1/(1 + i)^N$ is always positive for $-1 < i < \infty$. This implies that the $PV(i)$ will be positive if and only if $PB(i)_N > 0$ [14].

Now the meaning of the PV criterion should be clear; accepting a project with $PV(i) > 0$ is equivalent to accepting a project with $PB(i)_N > 0$. Because the PV and the future value are measures of equivalence that differ only in the times at which they are stated, they should provide identical results. The analysis and discussion should also make clear why we consider PV as the baseline, or correct, criterion to use in a stable, perfect capital market with complete certainty.

6.3 INTERNAL RATE-OF-RETURN CRITERION

6.3.1 Definition of IRR

Mathematical Definition. The internal rate of return (*IRR*) is another time-discounted measure of investment worth similar to the *PV* criterion. The *IRR* of a project is defined as the rate of interest that equates the *PV* of the entire series of cash flows to zero. The project's *IRR*, i^*, is defined mathematically by

$$PV(i^*) = \sum_{n=0}^{N} \frac{F_n}{(1 + i^*)^n} = 0 \qquad (6.10)$$

Multiplying both sides of Eq. 6.10 by $(1 + i^*)^N$, we obtain

$$PV(i^*)(1 + i^*)^N = \sum_{n=0}^{N} F_n(1 + i^*)^{N-n}$$
$$= FV(i^*) = 0 \qquad (6.11)$$

The left-hand side of Eq. 6.11 is, by definition, the future value (terminal project balance) of the project.

If we multiply both sides of Eq. 6.10 by the capital recovery factor, we obtain the relationship $AE(i^*) = 0$ (see Eq. 6.9). Alternatively, the *IRR* of a project may be defined as the rate of interest that equates the future value, terminal project balance, and annual equivalent value of the entire series of cash flows to zero.

$$PV(i^*) = FV(i^*) = PB(i^*)_N = AE(i^*) = 0 \qquad (6.12)$$

Computational Methods. Note that Eq. 6.11 is a polynomial function of i^*. A direct solution for such a function is not generally possible except for projects with a life of four periods or fewer. Instead, two approximation techniques are in general use, one using iterative procedures (a trial-and-error approach) and the other using Newton's approximation to the solution of a polynomial.

An iterative procedure requires an initial guess. To approximate the *IRR*, we calculate the *PV* for a certain interest rate (initial guess). If this *PV* is not zero, another interest rate is tried. A negative *PV* usually indicates that the choice is too high. We continue approximating until we reach the two bounds that contain the answer. We then interpolate to find the closest approximation to the *IRR(s)*.

The Newton approximation to a polynomial $f(X) = 0$ is made by starting with an arbitrary approximation of X and forming successive approximations by the formula

$$X_{j+1} = X_j - \frac{f(X_j)}{f'(X_j)} \qquad (6.13)$$

where $f'(X_j)$ is the first derivative of the polynomial evaluated at X_j. *The process is continued until we observe $X_j \cong X_{j-1}$.*

Example 6.2

Consider a project with cash flows $-\$100$, 50, and 84 at the end of periods 0, 1, and 2, respectively. The present value expression for this project is

$$PV(i) = -\$100 + \frac{50}{1+i} + \frac{84}{(1+i)^2}$$

Let $X = 1/(1+i)$. Our polynomial, the present value function, is then

$$f(X) = -100 + 50X + 84X^2$$

The derivative of this polynomial is

$$f'(X) = 50 + 168X$$

Suppose the first approximation we make is

$$X_1 = 0.8696 \qquad (i = 0.15)$$

The second approximation is

$$X_2 = 0.8696 - \frac{-100 + 50(0.8696) + 84(0.8696)^2}{50 + 168(0.8696)}$$

$$= 0.8339$$

The third approximation is

$$X_3 = 0.8339 - \frac{-100 + 50(0.8339) + 84(0.8339)^2}{50 + 168(0.8339)}$$

$$= 0.8333$$

Further iterations indicate that $X = 0.8333$ or $i^* = 20\%$. (With any approximation we are limited by rounding, so when we get the same answer twice in the sequence of approximations, we stop. □

Although the calculations in Newton's method are relatively simple, they are time-consuming if many iterations are required. The use of a computer is eventually necessary. (When we program the computer, it is wise to set tolerance limits on the degree of accuracy required to avoid unnecessary iterations.)

Uniqueness of i*.   The existence of a unique *IRR* is of special interest in applying the *IRR* investment worth criterion. Consider a project with cash flows of −\$10, \$47, −\$72, and \$36 at the end of periods 0, 1, 2, and 3, respectively. Applying Eq. 6.10 and solving for *i* gives us three roots: 20%, 50%, and 100%. This really should not surprise us, since Eq. 6.10 is a third-degree polynomial for the project. Here the plot of *PV* as a function of interest rate crosses the *i* axis several times, as illustrated in Figure 6.4. As we will see in later sections, multiple *IRR*s hinder the application of the *IRR* criterion, and we do not recommend the *IRR* criterion in such cases. In this section we will focus on the problem of whether a unique *IRR* for a project can be predicted by the cash flow stream.

One way to predict an upper limit on the number of positive roots of a polynomial is to apply Descartes' rule of signs.

Descartes' Rule. The number of real positive roots of an *n*th-degree polynominal with real coefficients is never greater than the number of sign changes in the sequence of the coefficients.

Letting $X = 1/(1 + i)$, we can write Eq. 6.10 as

$$F_0 + F_1 X + F_2 X^2 + \cdots + F_N X^N = 0 \qquad (6.14)$$

Thus, we need examine only the sign changes in F_n to apply the rule. For example, if the project has outflows followed by inflows, there is only one sign change and hence at most one real positive root.

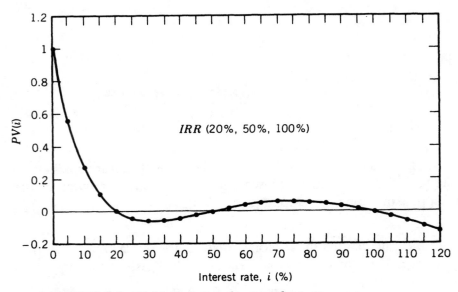

FIGURE 6.4. Multiple internal rates of return.

The Norstrom criterion [5] provides a more discriminating condition for the uniqueness of the root in the interval $(0 < i^* < \infty)$.

Norstrom Criterion. Consider a cash flow series $F_0, F_1, F_2, ..., F_N$. Form the auxiliary series $S_n = \sum_{j=0}^{n} F_j$, $n = 0, 1, ..., N$. If the series S_n starts negative and changes sign only once, there exists a unique positive real root. (6.15)

Additional criteria for the uniqueness of roots do exist, but they are rather tedious to apply and will not be discussed here. Bernhard [5] discusses these additional criteria and provides another general method for detecting the uniqueness of *IRR*.

Example 6.3

To illustrate the use of both Descartes' rule and the Norstrom criterion, consider the following pattern of cash flows.

n	0	1	2
F_n	$-\$100$	$\$140$	$-\$10$

Descartes' rule implies that the maximum number of positive real roots is less than or equal to two, which indicates that there may be multiple roots. There are two sign changes in $F_n(-, +, -)$.

To apply the Norstrom criterion, we first compute the cumulative cash flow stream, S_n.

$$S_0 = F_0 = -\$100$$

$$S_1 = F_0 + F_1 = -\$100 + \$140 = \$40$$

$$S_2 = F_0 + F_1 + F_2 = \$40 - \$10 = \$30$$

The criterion indicates a unique positive, real root for the problem because there is only one sign change in the S_n series $(-, +, +)$. In fact, the project has a unique *IRR* at $i^* = 32.45\%$. $\square$

6.3.2 Classification of Investment Projects

In discussing the *IRR* criterion, we need to distinguish between simple and nonsimple investments. Investment projects are further classified as pure or mixed investments.

Simple versus Nonsimple. A *simple* investment is defined as one in which there is only one sign change in the net cash flow (F_n). A *nonsimple* investment is one whose net cash outflows are not restricted to the initial period but are interspersed with net cash inflows throughout the life of the project. In other

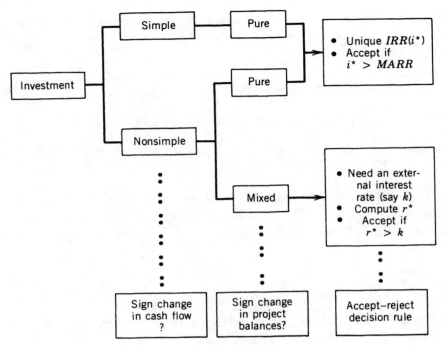

FIGURE 6.5. Classification of investment projects.

words, when there is more than one sign change in the net cash flow, the project is called a nonsimple project.

Pure versus Mixed. A *pure* investment is defined as an investment whose project balances computed at the project's *IRR*, $PB(i^*)_n$, are either zero or negative throughout the life of the project (with $F_0 < 0$). The implication of nonpositivity of $PB(i^*)_n$ for all values of n is that the firm has committed (or "lent") funds in the amount of $PB(i^*)_n$ dollars to the project for time n to time $n + 1$. In other words, the firm does not "borrow" from the project at any time during the life of the project.

A *mixed* investment, in contrast, is defined as any investment for which $PB(i^*)_n > 0$ for some values of n and $PB(i^*)_n \leq 0$ for the remaining values of n. These sign changes in $PB(i^*)_n$ indicate that at some times during the project's life $[PB(i^*)_n < 0]$ the firm acts as an "investor" in the project and at other times $[PB(i^*)_n > 0]$ the firm acts as a "borrower" from the project.

Classification by i_{min}. An alternative way of distinguishing between pure and mixed investments is to compute the value of i_{min}, the smallest interest rate that makes $PB(i)_n \leq 0$ for $n = 0, 1, 2, \ldots, N - 1$. Then we evaluate the sign of $PB(i_{min})_N$, the terminal project balance. If $PB(i_{min})_N \geq 0$, the project is a pure investment. If $PB(i_{min})_N < 0$, the project is a mixed investment.

If $PB(i_{min})_N > 0$, we can find some *IRR*, $i^* > i_{min}$, that will set $PB(i^*)_N$ to zero. Then use of a higher interest rate will simply magnify the negativity of $PB(i)_n$. Thus, the condition of $i^* \geq i_{min}$ will ensure the nonpositivity of $PB(i^*)_n$ for $0 \leq n \leq N - 1$. This is the definition of a pure investment.

If $PB(i_{min})_N < 0$, we can expect that $i^* < i_{min}$, which will set $PB(i^*)_N$ to zero. Because i_{min} is the minimum rate at which the nonpositivity condition $[PB(i_{min}) \le 0]$ satisfies $0 \le n \le N - 1$, we know that $PB(i^*)_n$ is not always zero or negative for $0 \le n \le N - 1$. This implies that the project is a mixed investment.

Figure 6.5 illustrates the final classification scheme that provides the basis for the analysis of investments under the *IRR* criterion. Note that simple investments are always classified as pure investments. (See the proof in Bussey [6].) As we will see, the phenomenon of multiple *IRR*s occurs only in the situation of a mixed investment. Although a simple investment is always a pure investment, a pure investment is not necessarily a simple investment, as we will see in Example 6.4.

Example 6.4

We will illustrate the distinction between pure and mixed investments with numerical examples. Consider the following four projects with known i^* values.

End of Period	Project			
n	A	B	C	D
0	$-\$100$	$-\$100$	$-\$100$	$-\$100$
1	-100	140	50	470
2	200	-10	-50	-720
3	200		200	360
IRR	$i^* = 41.42\%$	$i^* = 32.45\%$	$i^* = 29.95\%$	$i^* = 20\%, 50\%, 100\%$

Table 6.3 summarizes the project balances from these projects at their respective *IRR*s. Project A is the only simple project; the rest are nonsimple. Projects A and C are pure investments, whereas projects B and D are mixed investments. As seen in project B, the existence of a unique *IRR* is a necessary but not a sufficient condition for a pure investment.

Table 6.3 *Project Balances, Example 6.4*

Project	IRR		End of Period n			
			0	1	2	3
A	41.42%	F_n	$-\$100$	-100	200	200
		$PB(i^*)_n$	$-\$100$	-241.42	-141.42	0
B	32.45%	F_n	$-\$100$	140	-10	
		$PB(i^*)_n$	$-\$100$	7.55	0	
C	29.95%	F_n	$-\$100$	50	-50	200
		$PB(i^*)_n$	$-\$100$	-79.95	-153.90	0
		F_n	$-\$100$	470	-720	360
	20%	$PB(20\%)$	$-\$100$	350	-300	0
	50%	$PB(50\%)$	$-\$100$	320	-240	0
D	100%	$PB(100\%)$	$-\$100$	270	-180	0

In distinguishing pure and mixed investments, we could use the $i_{\min}$ test. We will show how this is done for project D. Since $N = 3$, we need to consider $PB(i)_0$, $PB(i)_1$, and $PB(i)_2$.

$$PB(i)_0 = -100$$
$$PB(i)_1 = PB(i)_0(1 + i) + 470 = -100i + 370$$
$$PB(i)_2 = PB(i)_1(1 + i) - 720 = -100i^2 + 270i - 350$$

Since $PB(i)_0 < 0$, we find the smallest value of i that makes both $PB(i)_1$ and $PB(i)_2$ nonpositive. The minimum value is 370%. Now we evaluate $PB(i_{\min})_3$ to find

$$PB(370\%)_3 = -720(4.70) + 360 = -\$3024 < 0$$

Since $PB(i_{\min})_3 < 0$, project D is a mixed investment. □

6.3.3 IRR and Pure Investments

According to the *IRR* criterion, a pure investment should be accepted if its *IRR* is above the *MARR* (or cost of capital) to the firm. We will show why this decision rule can produce an accept–reject decision consistent with the *PV* criterion.

Recall that pure investments have the following characteristics.

1. Net investment throughout the life of the project.

2. Existence of unique i^*.

3. $PB(i^*)_n \leq 0$ for $0 \leq n \leq N - 1$, and $PB(i^*)_N = 0$.

4. $PB(i)_N \left[\dfrac{1}{(1 + i)^N} \right] = PV(i)$

and if $i = i^*$,

$$PB(i)_N = 0 \rightarrow PV(i) = 0$$

We will first consider computing $PB(i)_N$ with $i > i^*$. Here i is the *MARR* (or cost of capital) to the firm. Since $PB(i^*)_n \leq 0$ for $0 \leq n \leq N - 1$ and $PB(i^*)_N = 0$, the effect of a higher compounding rate is to magnify the negativity of these project balances. This implies that $PB(i)_N < PB(i^*)_N = 0$. From Eq. 6.9, this also implies that $PV(i) < 0$. If $i = i^*$, then $PB(i)_N = PB(i^*)_N = 0$ so that $PV(i) = 0$. If $i < i^*$, then $PB(i)_N > 0$, indicating that $PV(i) > 0$. Hence we accept the investment. This proves the equivalence of the *PV* and *IRR* criteria for accept–reject decisions concerning simple investments. These relationships are illustrated in Figure 6.6.

> If $i < i^*$, accept.
> If $i = i^*$, remain indifferent.
> If $i > i^*$, reject.

When a firm makes a pure investment, it has funds committed to the project over the life of the project and at no time takes a loan from the project. Only in such a

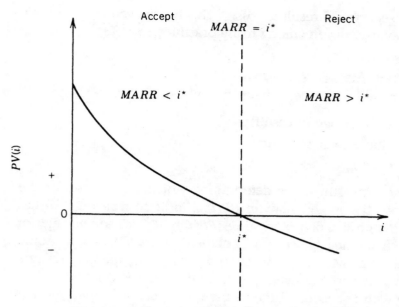

FIGURE 6.6. *PV(i)* of simple investment as a function of *i*.

situation is a rate of return concept *internal* to the project. Then the *IRR* can be viewed as the interest rate *earned* on the committed project balance (unrecovered balance, or negative project balance) of an investment, *not* the interest earned on the initial investment. The reader should keep this in mind, since it is a point not generally understood by many practitioners.

Example 6.5

Consider the project described in Example 6.1. (Note that the project is a simple and pure investment.) The project was acceptable at $i = 10\%$ by the *PV* criterion. We find that the *IRR* of this project is 20% by solving for i^* in Eq. 6.10.

$$PV(i^*) = -\$1,000 + \frac{\$400}{1 + i^*} + \frac{\$360}{(1 + i^*)^2} + \frac{\$320}{(1 + i^*)^3}$$

$$+ \frac{\$280}{(1 + i^*)^4} + \frac{\$240}{(1 + i^*)^5} = 0$$

Since $i^* > 10\%$, the project should be acceptable. The economic interpretation of the 20% is that the investment under consideration brings in enough cash to pay for itself in 5 years and also to provide the firm with a return of 20% on its invested capital over the project life.

Expressed another way, suppose that a firm obtains all its capital by borrowing from a bank at the interest rate of exactly 20%. If the firm invests in the project and uses the cash flow generated by the investment to pay off the principal and interest on the bank loan, the firm should come out exactly even on the transaction. If the firm can borrow the funds at a rate lower than 20%, the project should be profitable. If the borrowing interest rate is greater than 20%, acceptance of the project would result in losses. This break-even characteristic makes the *IRR* a popular criterion among many practitioners. □

6.3.4 IRR and Mixed Investments
Recall that the mixed investments have the following characteristics.

1. More than one sign change in cash flow.
2. Possibility of multiple rates of return.
3. Mixed signs in $PB(i^*)_n$.

The difficulty in mixed investments is determining which rate to use for the acceptance test, if any. The mixed signs in $PB(i^*)_n$ indicate that the firm has funds committed to the project part of the time $[PB(i^*)_n < 0$ for some values of $n]$ and takes a "loan" from the project the rest of the time $[PB(i^*)_n > 0$ for some value of $n]$. Because of this lending and borrowing activity, there is no rate of return concept internal to the project. The return on such mixed investments tends to vary with the external interest rate (i.e., cost of capital) to the firm.

To circumvent this conceptual difficulty, we may modify the procedure for computation by compounding positive project balances at the cost of borrowing capital, k, and negative project balances at the return on invested capital (RIC), r. (We use the symbol r because the return on invested capital of a mixed project is generally not equal to the *IRR*, i^*, of the project.) Since the firm is never indebted to the project for pure investment, it is clear that k does not enter into the compounding process; hence this RIC is independent of k, the cost of capital to the firm. Two approaches may be used in computing r: the trial-and-error approach and the analytical approach.

Trial-and-Error Approach.   The trial-and-error approach is similar to finding a project's internal rate of return. For a given cost of capital, k, we first compute the project balances from an investment with a somewhat arbitrarily selected r value. Since it is hoped that projects will promise a return of at least the cost of capital, a value of r close to k is a good starting point for most problems. For a given pair of (k, r), we calculate the last project balance and see whether it is positive, negative, or zero. Suppose the last project balance $PB(r, k)_N$ is negative—what do we do then? A nonzero terminal project balance indicates that the guessed r value is not the true r value. We must lower the r value and go through the process again. Conversely, if the $PB(r, k)_N > 0$, we raise the r value and repeat the process.

Example 6.6

To illustrate the method described, consider the following cash flow of a project.

n	0	1	2
F_n	−$1,000	2,900	−2,080

Suppose that the cost of capital, k, is known to be 15%. For $k = 15\%$, we must compute r^* by trial and error.

For $k = 15\%$ and trial $r = 16\%$,

$PB(16, 15)_0 = -1,000 \qquad\qquad = -\$1,000$

$PB(16, 15)_1 = -1,000(1 + 0.16) + 2,900 = \quad \$1,300 \quad$ [use r, since $PB(16, 15)_0 < 0$]

$PB(16, 15)_2 = \quad 1,300(1 + 0.15) - 2,080 = \quad -\$585 \quad$ [use k, since $PB(16, 15)_1 > 0$]

The terminal project balance is not zero, indicating that r^* is not equal to our 16% trial r. The next trial value should be smaller than 16% because the terminal balance is negative (-585). After several trials, we conclude that for $k = 15\%$, r^* is approximately at 9.13%. To verify the results,

$PB(9.13, 15)_0 = -1,000 \qquad\qquad\qquad = -\$1,000$

$PB(9.13, 15)_1 = -1,000(1 + 0.0913) + 2,900 = \quad \$1,808.70$

$PB(9.13, 15)_2 = \quad 1,808.70(1 + 0.15) - 2,080 = \quad 0$

Since $r^* < k$, the investment is not profitable. Note that the project would also be rejected under the PV analysis at $MARR = i = k = 15\%$.

$$PV(15\%) = -1,000 + 2,900(P/F, 15\%, 1) - 2,080(P/F, 15\%, 2)$$
$$= -\$51.04 < 0 \quad \square$$

Analytical Approach. The most direct procedure for determining the functional relationship between r and k of a mixed investment is to write out the expression for the future value of the project. Since the project balance of a mixed investment is compounded at either r or k, depending on the sign of the project balance, the terminal (future) balance of the project, denoted by $PB(r, k)_N$, is a function of two variables. The following steps can be used to determine the *RIC*, r.

Step 1: Find $i_{\min}$ by solving for the smallest real rate for which all $PB(i_{\min})_n \leq 0$, for $n = 1, \ldots, N - 1$. This is usually done by a trial-and-error method.

Step 2: Find $PB(i_{\min})_N$.
  a. If $PB(i_{\min})_N \geq 0$, the project is a pure investment.
    (1) Find the *IRR*, i^*, for which $PB(i^*)_N = 0$; $i^* = r^*$ for a pure investment.
    (2) Apply the decision rules given in step 5.
  b. If $PB(i_{\min})_N < 0$, the project is a mixed investment and it is necessary to proceed with step 3.

Step 3: Calculate $PB(r, k)_n$ according to the following.

$PB(r, k)_0 = F_0$

$PB(r, k)_1 = \quad PB(r, k)_0(1 + r) + F_1 \qquad$ if $PB(r, k)_0 \leq 0$

$\qquad\qquad\qquad PB(r, k)_0(1 + k) + F_1 \qquad$ if $PB(r, k)_0 > 0$

$\vdots$

$PB(r, k)_n = \quad PB(r, k)_{n-1}(1 + r) + F_n \qquad$ if $PB(r, k)_{n-1} \leq 0$

$\qquad\qquad\qquad PB(r, k)_{n-1}(1 + k) + F_n \qquad$ if $PB(r, k)_{n-1} > 0$

To determine the positivity or negativity of $PB(r, k)_n$ at each period, set $r = i_{min}$, knowing that $r \le i_{min}$. (See Problem 6.10.)

Step 4: Determine the value of r^* by solving the equation $PB(r, k)_N = 0$.

Step 5: Apply the following set of decision rules to accept or reject the project.

> If $r^* > k$, accept.
> If $r^* = k$, remain indifferent.
> If $r^* < k$, reject.

Example 6.7

Consider the project cash flows given in Example 6.6.

End of Period n	0	1	2
Cash Flow F_n	$-\$1,000$	2,900	$-2,080$

There are two sign changes in the ordered sequence of cash flows $(-, +, -)$. The project has two *IRRs*, corresponding to $i^*_1 = 30\%$ and $i^*_2 = 60\%$. To derive the functional relationship between the return on invested capital, r, and the cost of capital, k, we apply the algorithm described in the preceding section.

Step 1: Find the i_{min} that satisfies the following two equations ($N = 2, N - 1 = 1$).

$$PB(i)_0 = -1,000 < 0$$

$$PB(i)_1 = -1,000(1 + i) + 2,900$$

$$= -1,000i + 1,900 \le 0$$

Since $PB(i)_0 < 0$, we need only find the smallest i that satisfies $PB(i)_1 \le 0$. The value of i_{min} is 190%.

Step 2: Calculate $PB(i_{min})_N$.

$$PB(i_{min})_2 = (-1,000i_{min} + 1900)(1 + i_{min}) - 2,080$$

$$= -2,080$$

Since $PB(i_{min})_2 < 0$, the project is a mixed investment.

Step 3: Calculate $PB(r, k)_n$.

$$PB(r, k)_0 = -1,000$$

Since $PB(r, k)_0 < 0$, we use r.

$$PB(r, k)_1 = -1,000(1 + r) + 2,900$$

$$= -1,000r + 1,900$$

Since r cannot exceed i_{min}, $PB(r, k)_1 \geq 0$. Then we use k.

$$PB(r, k)_2 = (-1,000r + 1,900)(1 + k) - 2,080$$

Step 4: Find the solution of $PB(r, k)_2 = 0$.

$$r = 1.9 - \frac{2.08}{1 + k} \qquad (6.16)$$

The graph of Eq. 6.16 is shown in Figure 6.7. We observe the following characteristics.

1. First, since $\dfrac{dr}{dk} = \dfrac{2.08}{(1 + k)^2} > 0$, r is a monotonically increasing function of k. This means that the higher the cost that the firm places on borrowing funds from the project, the higher the return it will require on the invested capital.

2. Second, if we set $r = k$ in Eq. 6.16, we have $r = k = i^*$. Equation 6.16 intersects the 45° line $r = k$ twice, once at $k = 30\%$ and again at $k = 60\%$. With $r = k = i^*$, the terminal project balance $PB(r, k)_2$ decreases to $PB(i^*)_2 = 0$. Solving $PB(i^*)_2 = 0$ for i^* yields the *IRR* of the project. In other words, this mixed investment has multiple rates of return ($i_1^* = 30\%$, $i_2^* = 60\%$). Therefore, the roots i^* for mixed investment are the values of the return on invested capital, r, when the cost of borrowed money, k, is assumed to be equal to r.

3. Third, applying the decision rule, we have

> If $30\% < k < 60\% \rightarrow r^* > k$,   accept the project.
> If $k = 30\%$ or $k = 60\% \rightarrow r^* = k$,   remain indifferent.
> If $k < 30\%$ or $k > 60\% \rightarrow r^* < k$,   reject the project.

4. Fourth, the decision we make will be consistent with the decision derived from applying the *PV* criterion when $i = MARR = k$. The *PV* of the project at an interest rate of k can be expressed as

$$PV(k) = -\$1,000 + \frac{\$2,900}{1 + k} - \frac{\$2,080}{(1 + k)^2} \qquad (6.17)$$

which is also depicted in Figure 6.7.

The following comments about the *PV* function are in order. First, the *IRR* is by definition the solution to the equation $PV(k) = 0$. Therefore, we observe that $PV(k)$ intersects the horizontal axis at $k = 30\%$ and at $k = 60\%$. Second, since $PV(k)$ is positive only in the range $30\% < k < 60\%$, the *PV* criterion gives the same accept–reject signal as the *IRR* criterion. □

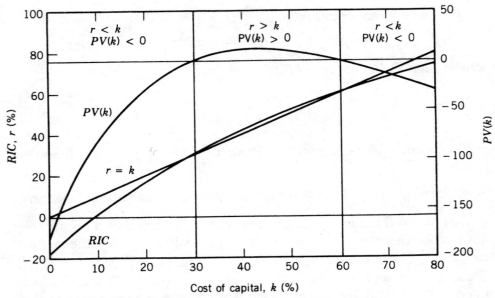

FIGURE 6.7. *RIC* and *PV* as functions of *k*, Example 6.7.

6.3.5 *Modified Rate of Return*

An alternative way of approaching mixed investments is to modify the procedure for computing the rate of return by making explicit and consistent assumptions about the interest rate at which intermediate receipts from projects may be reinvested. This reinvestment could be either in other projects or in the outside market. This procedure is similar to the previous use of two different rates (*r, k*) in the computation of the *project balance*. This section reviews some of the methods for applying the procedure.

Solomon's Average Rate of Return (ARR).   A different way of looking at a project is to ask the following question. Suppose we take the net revenues $F_n(F_n > 0)$ and reinvest them each year at i, letting them accumulate until time N. What rate of interest does investment C_0 have to earn to reach the same accumulated value in N periods [15]?

Mathematically, we wish to find s to solve the equation

$$\underbrace{C_0(1 + s)^N}_{\substack{\text{alternative}\\\text{investment}}} = \underbrace{\sum_{n=1}^{N} F_n(1 + i)^{N-n}}_{\text{current investment}} \qquad (6.18)$$

With known s, the acceptance rule is

> If $s > i = MARR$, accept.
>
> If $s = i$, remain indifferent.
>
> If $s < i$, reject.

We can easily show that the *ARR* criterion is completely consistent with the *PV* criterion [2]. Recall that for a given project with $F_0 < 0$ but $F_n > 0$ for $1 \leq n \leq N$, the *PV* acceptance rule is

$$\sum_{n=0}^{N} F_n(1 + i)^{-n} > 0 \tag{6.19}$$

Substituting C_0 for F_0 (note that $F_0 = -C_0$) gives us

$$C_0 < \sum_{n=1}^{N} F_n(1 + i)^{-n} \tag{6.20}$$

Multiplying both sides of Eq. 6.18 by $(1 + i)^{-N}$ yields

$$C_0(1 + s)^N(1 + i)^{-N} = \sum_{n=1}^{N} F_n(1 + i)^{-n} \tag{6.21}$$

By comparing Eqs. 6.20 and 6.21, we can deduce that

$$C_0(1 + s)^N(1 + i)^{-N} > C_0$$

or

$$(1 + s)^N > (1 + i)^N \tag{6.22}$$

This implies that $s > i$, which is the *ARR* acceptance condition.

Example 6.8

Consider the cash flows shown in Figure 6.2, where $C_0 = \$1,000$, $F_1 = \$400$, $F_2 = \$360$, $F_3 = \$320$, $F_4 = \$280$, and $F_5 = \$240$. Substituting these values into Eq. 6.18, we obtain

$$1,000(1 + s)^5 = 400(1.1)^4 + 360(1.1)^3 + 320(1.1)^2 + 280(1.1) + 240$$

$$= \$2,000$$

Solving for s yields 15%. This tells us that we can invest \$1,000 in the project, reinvest the proceeds at our opportunity rate (*MARR*) of 10%, and have \$2,000 at time 5. If we do not wish to invest in the project but still wish to earn \$2,000, the original \$1,000 would have to earn 15% per period. Since the *MARR* is 10%, we are clearly better off accepting the project. If s had been less than $i = 10\%$, we would have rejected the project. □

Modified Internal Rate of Return (MIRR). As a variation of the *ARR* procedure, we may make explicit the expected reinvestment rate of intermediate incomes

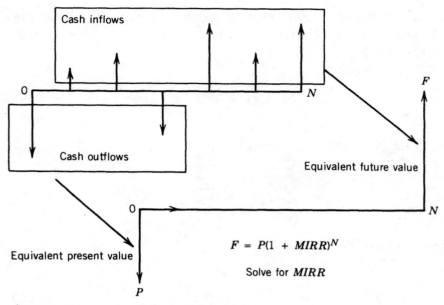

FIGURE 6.8. Illustration of the *MIRR* concept.

and costs and reduce them to an equivalent initial cost and a terminal project balance, a procedure known as the modified internal rate of return (*MIRR*) [12] or the external rate of return. In this way a unique *IRR* can be computed. This *MIRR* is defined by

$$\frac{\text{Future value of net cash inflow}}{\text{Present value of net cash outflow}}$$

$$= \frac{\displaystyle\sum_{n=0}^{N} \max(F_n, 0)(1 + i)^{N-n}}{-\displaystyle\sum_{n=0}^{N} \min(F_n, 0)(1 + i)^{-n}} = (1 + MIRR)^N \tag{6.23}$$

where $\max(F_n, 0) = F_n$ if $F_n > 0$, otherwise $F_n = 0$; $\min(F_n, 0) = F_n$ if $F_n < 0$, otherwise $F_n = 0$; and i is the *MARR* to the firm. The meaning of the *MIRR* is illustrated in Figure 6.8.

By rearranging terms in Eq. 6.23, we can rewrite it as

$$\sum_{n=0}^{N} \max(F_n, 0)(1 + i)^{N-n} = \left[-\sum_{n=0}^{N} \min(F_n, 0)(1 + i)^{-n} \right](1 + MIRR)^N$$

$$\tag{6.24}$$

If the cash outflow is restricted to the first period, $n = 0$, the *MIRR* is exactly the same as the *ARR*, *s*. The acceptance rule is then

> If *MIRR* > *i*, accept.
> If *MIRR* = *i*, remain indifferent.
> If *MIRR* < *i*, reject.

The *MIRR* will always give a unique solution and is also consistent with the *PV* criterion. The *MIRR* will always exceed the alternative rate whenever the investment sequence has a positive *PV* at *i*. This can be visualized from the following equations.

The project acceptance condition by the *PV* criterion is

$$\sum_{n=0}^{N} \max(F_n, 0)(1 + i)^{-n} \quad > \quad -\sum_{n=0}^{N} \min(F_n, 0)(1 + i)^{-n} \qquad (6.25)$$

$$\begin{array}{ccc} \text{Present value of} & > & \text{Present value of} \\ \text{net cash inflow} & & \text{net cash outflow} \end{array}$$

Multiplying both sides of Eq. 6.24 by $(1 + i)^{-N}$ yields

$$\sum_{n=0}^{N} \max(F_n, 0)(1 + i)^{-n}$$

$$= \left[-\sum_{n=0}^{N} \min(F_n, 0)(1 + i)^{-n} \right](1 + MIRR)^N(1 + i)^{-N} \qquad (6.26)$$

From the relation given in Eq. 6.25, we can say

$$\left[-\sum_{n=0}^{N} \min(F_n, 0)(1 + i)^{-n} \right](1 + MIRR)^N(1 + i)^{-N}$$

$$> -\sum_{n=0}^{N} \min(F_n, 0)(1 + i)^{-n} \qquad (6.27)$$

Simplifying the terms above gives

$$(1 + MIRR)^N > (1 + i)^N \qquad (6.28)$$

which indicates that *MIRR* > *i*.

There are three other variations of the *MIRR* [4], but these indices (including *ARR* and *MIRR*) have numerical values distinctly different from one another, and without additional information provided, these rates are considerably more complex to use than the simple *PV* criterion.

Example 6.9

Using an example from [4], we will illustrate the method of computing the *MIRR*. Assume that $i = 6\%$, and the cash flow components are

Cash Flow	n: 0	1	2	3
b_n	$0	3	2	25
c_n	$10	1	5	2
F_n	$-10	2	-3	23

Present value of net cash outflow $= +10 + 3(1 + 0.06)^{-2} = \$12.67$

Future value of net cash inflow $= 2(1 + 0.06)^2 + 23 = \$25.25$

Using Eq. 6.24, we find

$$25.25 = 12.67(1 + MIRR)^3$$

$$MIRR = 25.84\%$$

Since $MIRR > 6\%$, the project should be acceptable. Note that $PV(6\%) = \$8.53 > 0$, so the *MIRR* result is consistent with the *PV* criterion. □

6.4 BENEFIT–COST RATIOS

Another way to express the worthiness of a project is to compare the inflows with the investment. This leads to three types of benefit–cost ratios: the aggregate benefit–cost ratio (Eckstein *B/C*), the netted benefit–cost ratio (simple *B/C*), and the Lorie–Savage ratio.

Let *B* and *C* be the present values of cash inflows and outflows defined by Eqs. 6.1 and 6.2. We will split the equivalent cost *C* into two components, the initial capital expenditure and the annual costs accrued in each successive period. Assuming that an initial investment is required during the first *m* periods, while annual costs accrue in each period following, the components are defined as

$$I = \sum_{n=0}^{m} c_n(1 + i)^{-n} \tag{6.29}$$

$$C' = \sum_{n=m+1}^{N} c_n(1 + i)^{-n} \tag{6.30}$$

and $C = I + C'$.

The following example will be used to demonstrate the application of different B/C ratio criteria.

Cash Flow	n: 0	1	2	3	4	5
b_n	$0	0	10	10	20	20
c_n	$10	5	5	5	5	10
F_n	$-$10	-5	5	5	15	10

With $i = 10\%$, we define

$$N = 5$$

$$m = 1$$

$$B = 10(1.1)^{-2} + 10(1.1)^{-3} + 20(1.1)^{-4} + 20(1.1)^{-5} = \$41.86$$

$$C = 10 + 5(1.1)^{-1} + 5(1.1)^{-2} + 5(1.1)^{-3} + 5(1.1)^{-4}$$
$$+ 10(1.1)^{-5} = \$32.06$$

$$I = 10 + 5(1.1)^{-1} = \$14.55$$

$$C' = 5(1.1)^{-2} + 5(1.1)^{-3} + 5(1.1)^{-4} + 10(1.1)^{-5} = \$17.51$$

$$PV(10\%) = B - C = \$9.80$$

6.4.1 Benefit–Cost Ratios Defined

Aggregate B/C Ratio. The aggregate B/C ratio introduced by Eckstein [7] is defined as

$$R_A = \frac{B}{C} = \frac{B}{I + C'}, \qquad I + C' > 0 \tag{6.31}$$

To accept a project, the R_A must be greater than 1. Historically, this ratio was developed in the 1930s in response to the fact that in public projects the user is generally not the same as the sponsor. To have a better perspective on the user's benefits, we need to separate them from the sponsor's costs. If we assume that for a project b_n represents the user's benefits and c_n the sponsor's costs, the ratio is

$$R_A = \frac{41.86}{14.55 + 17.51} = 1.306$$

The ratio exceeds 1, which implies that the user's benefits exceed the sponsor's costs. Public projects usually also have benefits that are difficult to measure, whereas costs are more easily quantified. In this respect, the Eckstein B/C ratio lends itself readily to sensitivity analysis with respect to the value of benefits. We will discuss this measure in greater detail in Chapter 14.

Netted B/C Ratio. As an alternative expression in defining their terms, some analysts consider only the initial capital expenditure as a cash outlay, and equivalent benefits become net benefits (i.e., revenues minus annual outlays). This alternative measure is referred to as the *netted benefit–cost ratio, R_N,* and is expressed by

$$R_N = \frac{B - C'}{I}, \qquad I > 0 \tag{6.32}$$

The advantage of having the benefit–cost ratio defined in this manner is that it provides an index indicating the net benefit expected per dollar invested, sometimes called a *profitability index.* Again, for a project to remain under consideration, the ratio must be greater than 1. For our example, the R_N is

$$R_N = \frac{41.86 - 17.51}{14.55} = 1.674$$

Note that this is just a comparison of the present value of net revenues (F_n) with the present value of investment. Since $R_N > 1$, there is a surplus at time 0 and the project is favorable. The use of this criterion also had its origin in the evaluation of public projects in the 1930s.

Lorie–Savage Ratio. As a variation on R_N, the Lorie–Savage (*L–S*) ratio is defined as

$$L\!-\!S = \frac{B - C}{I} = \frac{B - C'}{I} - 1 = R_N - 1 > 0 \tag{6.33}$$

Here the comparison is between the surplus at time 0 and the investment itself. If the ratio is greater than 0, the project is favorable. Clearly, the R_N *B/C* and the *L–S B/C* ratios will always yield the same decision for a project, since both the ratios and their respective cutoff points differ by 1.0. For our example, *L–S* = $1.674 - 1 = 0.674 > 0$. Thus the *L–S* ratio also indicates acceptance of the project.

6.4.2 Equivalence of B/C Ratios and PV

Using the notation in Section 6.4.1, we can state the *PV* criterion for project acceptance as

$$PV(i) = B - C$$
$$= B - (I + C') > 0. \tag{6.34}$$

By transposing the term $(I + C')$ to the right-hand side and dividing both sides by $(I + C')$, we have

$$\frac{B}{I + C'} > 1 \qquad (I + C' > 0)$$

which is exactly the decision rule for accepting a project with the R_A criterion. On the other hand, by transposing the term I to the right-hand side and dividing both sides of the equation by I, we obtain

$$\frac{B - C'}{I} > 1 \qquad (I > 0)$$

which is exactly the decision rule for accepting a project with the R_N criterion. In other words, use of R_A or use of R_N will lead to the same conclusion about the initial acceptability of a single project, as long as $I > 0$ and $I + C' > 0$. Notice that these B/C ratios will always agree with each other for an individual project, since I and C' are nonnegative.

$$\frac{B}{I + C'} > 1 \longleftrightarrow B > I + C' \longleftrightarrow B - C' > I$$

$$\updownarrow \qquad\qquad\qquad \updownarrow$$

$$PV(i) = B - (I + C') > 0 \qquad\qquad \frac{B - C'}{I} > 1$$

$$\updownarrow$$

$$\frac{B - C'}{I} - 1 > 0$$

Although *ARR* does not appear to be related to the benefit–cost ratios, it does, in fact, yield the same decisions for a project. From Eq. 6.18 we have

$$C_0(1 + s)^N = \sum_{n=1}^{N} F_n(1 + i)^{N-n}$$

Expressed differently,

$$I(1 + s)^N(1 + i)^{-N} = \sum_{n=1}^{N} F_n(1 + i)^{-n}$$

$$= B - C'$$

$$\frac{B - C'}{I} = \left(\frac{1 + s}{1 + i}\right)^N \tag{6.35}$$

We require $s > i$ for project acceptance, so we must have

$$\frac{B - C'}{I} > 1$$

6.5 PAYBACK PERIOD

A popular rule-of-thumb method for evaluating projects is to determine the number of periods needed to recover the original investment. In this section we present two procedures for assessing the payback period of an investment.

6.5.1 Payback Period Defined

Conventional Payback Period.   The payback period (*PP*) is defined as the number of periods it will take to recover the initial investment outlay. Mathematically, the payback period is computed as the smallest value of n that satisfies the equation

$$\sum_{n=0}^{n_p} F_n \geqslant 0 \qquad\qquad (6.36)$$

This payback period (n_p) is then compared with the maximum acceptable payback period (n_{max}) to determine whether the project should be accepted. If $n_{max} > n_p$, the proposed project will be accepted. Otherwise, the project will be rejected.

Obviously the most serious deficiencies of the payback period are that it fails to consider the time value of money and that it fails to consider the consequences of the investment after the payback period.

Discounted Payback Period.   As a modification of the conventional payback period, one may incorporate the time value of money. The method is to determine the length of time required for the project's equivalent receipts to exceed the equivalent capital outlays.

Mathematically, the discounted payback period Q is the smallest n that satisfies the expression

$$\sum_{n=0}^{Q} F_n(1 + i)^{-n} \geqslant 0 \qquad\qquad (6.37)$$

where i is the *MARR*.

If we multiply both sides of Eq. 6.37 by $(1 + i)^Q$, we should obtain

$$\sum_{n=0}^{Q} F_n(1 + i)^{Q-n} \geqslant 0 \qquad\qquad (6.38)$$

Notice that Eq. 6.38 is the definition of project balance $PB(i)_n$. Thus, the discounted payback period is alternatively defined as the smallest n that makes $PB(i)_n \geqslant 0$.

6.5.2 *Popularity of the Payback Period*

Clearly, the payback period analysis is simple to apply and, in some cases, may give answers approximately equivalent to those provided by more sophisticated methods. A number of authors have tried to show an equivalence between the payback period and other criteria, such as *IRR*, under special circumstances [11]. For example, Gordon [8] interpreted the payback period as an indirect, though quick, measure of return. With a uniform stream of receipts, the reciprocal of the payback period is the *IRR* for a project of infinite life and is a good approximation to this rate for a long-lived project.

Weingartner [19] analyzed the basic reasons why the payback period measure is so popular in business. One reason is that the payback period can function like many other rules of thumb to shortcut the process of generating information and then evaluating it. Payback reduces the information search by focusing on the time when the firm expects to "be made whole again." Hence, it allows the decision maker to judge whether the life of the project past the breakeven (bench mark) point is sufficient to make the undertaking worthwhile.

In summary, the payback period gives some measure of the rate at which a project will recover its initial outlay. This piece of information is not available from either the *PV* or the *IRR*. The payback period may not be used as a direct figure of merit, but it may be used as a constraint: no project may be accepted unless its payback period is shorter than some specified period of time.

Example 6.10

Suppose that a firm is considering a project costing $10,000, the life of the project is 5 years, and the expected net annual cash flows at the end of the year are as follows (assume *MARR* = 10%).

Cash Flow	n: 0	1	2	3	4	5
F_n	−$10,000	$3,000	$3,000	$4,000	$3,000	$3,000
Cumulative F_n	−$10,000	−7,000	−4,000	0	3,000	6,000
$PV(10\%)$	−$10,000	2,727	2,479	3,005	2,049	1,862
Cumulative present value	−$10,000	−7,273	−4,794	−1,789	260	2,122

The conventional payback period is 3 years, whereas the discounted payback period is 3.87 years. This example demonstrates how consideration of the time value of money in payback analysis can produce different results. Clearly, this discounted measure is conceptually better than the conventional one, but both measures fail to indicate the overall profitability of the project. □

6.6 TIME-DEPENDENT MEASURE OF INVESTMENT WORTH

The project balance, which measures the equivalent loss or profit of an investment project as a function of time, is a recent development that provides additional insight into investment decisions. In Section 6.2.2 we defined the project balance and demonstrated its calculation both mathematically and through examples. This section presents particular characteristics of project balance profiles and their economic interpretation. We also discuss some possible measures of investment desirability based on these profiles. (The material presented in this section is based on the analysis given by Park and Thuesen [14].)

6.6.1 Areas of Negative and Positive Balances

Recall that the project balance is defined by

$$PB(i)_n = \sum_{j=0}^{n} F_j(1 + i)^{n-j}, \qquad n = 0, 1, 2, \ldots, N$$

By plotting $PB(i)_n$ as a function of time n, we can trace the time path of project balance as shown in Figure 6.9. This time path is referred to as the *project balance pattern,* and it provides the basic information about the attractiveness of a particular investment proposal as a function of its life. The shaded area represents the period of time during which the project balance has negative values, that is, the time during which the initial investment plus interest is not fully recovered. This area is referred to as the *area of negative balance* (*ANB*). Mathematically, the area is represented by

$$ANB = \sum_{n=0}^{Q-1} PB(i)_n \qquad (6.39)$$

where Q is the discounted payback period [the first period in which $PB(i)_n \geq 0$]. Since the value $PB(i)_n$ for $n < Q$ represents the magnitude of negative balance

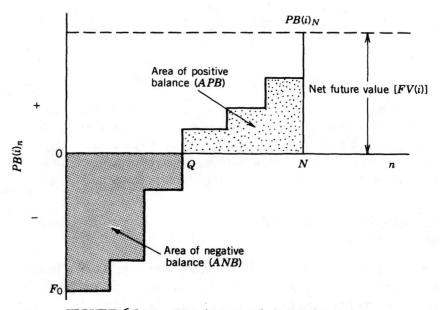

FIGURE 6.9. A general project balance diagram.

of the project at the end of period n, it is equivalent to the amount of possible loss if the project is terminated at this time. With certainty, the *ANB* can be interpreted as the total amount of dollars to be tied up for the particular investment option. The smaller the *ANB*, the more flexible the firm's future investment options. Therefore, the smaller the *ANB* for a project, the more attractive the project is considered, assuming that the expected terminal profits for other projects are the same.

Point Q on the horizontal axis in Figure 6.9 represents the discounted payback period, which indicates how long it will be before the project breaks even. Therefore, the smaller the Q for a project, the more desirable the project is considered, if other things are equal. (See the mathematical definition in Eq. 6.38.)

The stippled area in Figure 6.9 represents the period of time during which the $PB(i)_n$ maintains a positive project balance. This area is referred to as the *area of positive balance* (*APB*). The initial investment of the project has been fully recovered, so receipts during this time period contribute directly to the final profitability of the project. Symbolically, the area is represented by

$$APB = \sum_{n=Q}^{N-1} PB(i)_n \tag{6.40}$$

The project balance diagram during these periods can be interpreted as the rate at which the project is expected to accumulate profits. This is certainly an important parameter which affects project desirability when decisions are made about the retirement of projects. Since the values $PB(i)_n$ for $n > Q$ represent the magnitude of positive project balance, there is no possible loss even though the project is terminated in a period before the end of its life or no additional receipts are received. Thus, $PB(i)_n$ becomes the net equivalent dollars earned.

Finally, the last project balance $PB(i)_N$ represents the net future value of the project (or terminal profit) at the end of its life. The *PV* of the project can be found easily by a simple transformation, shown in Eq. 6.9.

6.6.2. Investment Flexibility

To illustrate the basic concept of investment flexibility and its discriminating ability compared with the traditional measures of investment worth (e.g., *PV*), we consider the hypothetical investment situation shown in Figure 6.10a. Projects 1 and 2 have single-payment and uniform-series cash flows, respectively. Projects 3 and 4 are gradient series, one being an increasing gradient series and the other a decreasing gradient series. All the projects require the same initial investment and have a service life of 3 years. All the projects would have an equivalent future value of $63.40 at a *MARR* of 10% [or PV(10%) = $47.63]. This implies that no project is preferable to the others when they are compared on the basis of present value.

Plotting the project balance pattern for each project provides additional information that is not revealed by computing only present value equivalents

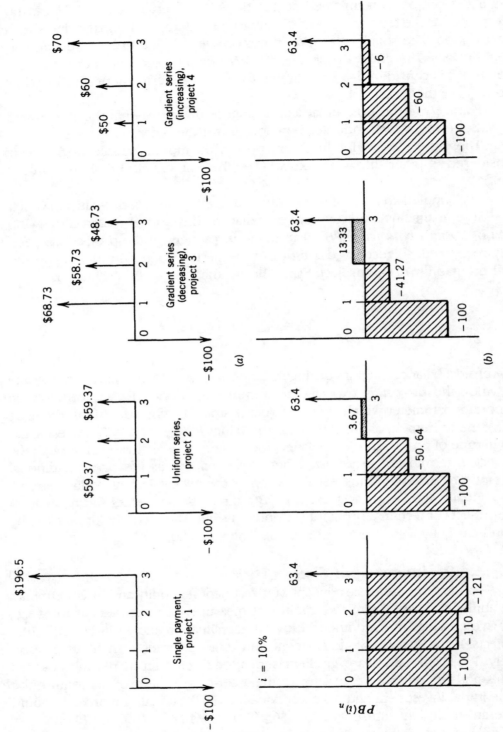

FIGURE 6.10. Project balance for four cash flow patterns.

Table 6.4 *Statistics of Project Balance Patterns for Projects 1, 2, 3, and 4*

Project Number	Cash Flow Pattern	Future Value FV(10%)	ANB	APB	Q
1	Single payment	$63.4	331.00	0	3
2	Uniform series	$63.4	150.63	3.67	2
3	Gradient series (decreasing)	$63.4	141.27	13.33	2
4	Gradient series (increasing)	$63.4	166.00	0	3

(see Figure 6.10*b*). For example, a comparison of project 1 with project 3 in terms of the shape of the project balance pattern shows that project 3 recovers its initial investment within 2 years, whereas project 1 takes 3 years to recover the same initial investment. This, in turn, indicates that project 3 would provide more flexibility in future investment activity to the firm than project 1. By selecting project 3, the investor can be sure of being restored to his or her initial position within a short span of time. Similar one-to-one comparisons can be made among all four projects. Table 6.4 summarizes the statistics obtained from the balance patterns for each project shown in Figure 6.10*b*.

Table 6.4 shows that project 3 appears to be most desirable, even though its terminal profitability is equal to those of the other projects, because its *ANB* is the smallest and its *APB* is the largest among the projects. As discussed in Section 6.6.1, the small value of *ANB* implies more flexibility in the firm's future investment activity. In other words, an early resolution of the negative project balance would make funds available for attractive investment opportunities that become

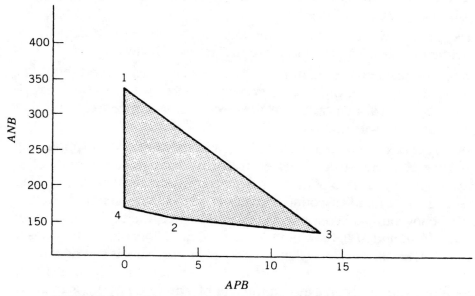

FIGURE 6.11. Plot of *APB* against *ANB* for different cash flow patterns.

available in the subsequent decision periods. One-to-one comparisons of the projects in terms of *ANB* and *APB* can be depicted graphically (see Figure 6.11). From Figure 6.9, it becomes evident that the project balance parameters such as *ANB* and *APB* reflect the changes in the cash flow patterns over time. Since project 3 represents the highest *APB* with the smallest *ANB*, project 3 appears to be the most desirable. Of course, the environment in which the decision is made and individual preferences will dictate which of these parameters should be used so that the economic implications of an investment project are fully understood.

6.7 SUMMARY

In this chapter we showed the following.

1. The *PV, FV,* and *AE* will always yield the same decision for a project. We consider *PV* as the baseline, or "correct," criterion to use in a stable, perfect capital market with complete certainty about investment outcomes.

2. The distinction between pure and mixed investments is needed to determine whether the return on invested capital is independent of the cost of capital.

3. Only for a pure investment is there a rate of return concept internal to the project. For pure investments, the *IRR* and *PV* criteria result in identical acceptance and rejection decisions.

4. The return on invested capital for a mixed project varies directly with the cost of capital. The phenomenon of multiple *IRR*s, which occurs only in the situation of a mixed investment, is actually a manifestation of the existence of this basic functional relationship. The *RIC* is consistent with the *PV* criterion.

5. *ARR* and *MIRR* will also always yield the same decision for a project, consistent with the *PV* criterion.

6. R_A, R_N, and *L–S* ratios will give the same accept–reject decisions for an individual project. The *PV* and these *B/C* ratios will always agree.

7. Neither the payback period nor the discounted payback period should be considered as a criterion, since they may not agree with *PV*. They may be used as additional constraints in the decision-making process, but they should be used with caution.

8. The project balance diagram provides quantitative information about four important characteristics associated with the economic desirability of an investment project. Two of these characteristics, net future value (terminal project balance) and discounted payback period, have generally been a part of conventional economic analyses. However, the other two characteristics, *ANB* and *APB*, have not been considered. Possible applications of the project balance indicate that a variety of measurements can be devised that reflect particular characteristics of the investment project under consideration. The project balance at the end of a project, $PB(i)_N$, is identical to the *FV* criterion.

In conclusion, we can say that the *PV* criterion is superior among the traditional measures of investment worth because of its ease of use, robustness, and consistency.

REFERENCES

1. BALDWIN, R. H., "How to Assess Investment Proposals," *Harvard Business Review,* Vol. 27, No. 3, pp. 98–104, May–June 1959.

2. BERNHARD, R. H., "Discount Methods for Expenditure Evaluation—A Clarification of Their Assumptions," *Journal of Industrial Engineering,* Vol. 18, No. 1, pp. 19–27, January–February 1962.

3. BERNHARD, R. H., "A Comprehensive Comparison and Critique of Discounting Indices Proposed for Capital Investment Evaluation," *The Engineering Economist,* Vol. 16, No. 3, pp. 157–186, Spring 1971.

4. BERNHARD, R. H., "Modified Rates of Return for Investment Project Evaluation—A Comparison and Critique," *The Engineering Economist,* Vol. 24, No. 3, pp. 161–167, Spring 1979.

5. BERNHARD, R. H., "Unrecovered Investment, Uniqueness of the Internal Rate and the Question of Project Acceptability," *Journal of Financial and Quantitative Analysis,* Vol. 12, No. 1, pp. 33–38, March 1977.

6. BUSSEY, L. E., *The Economic Analysis of Industrial Projects,* Prentice–Hall, Englewood Cliffs, N.J., 1978.

7. ECKSTEIN, O., *Water Resource Development: The Economics of Project Evaluation,* Harvard University Press, Cambridge, Mass., 1958.

8. GORDON, M., "The Payoff Period and the Rate of Profit," *Journal of Business,* Vol. 28, No. 4, pp. 253–260, October 1955.

9. KAPLAN, S., "A Note on a Method for Precisely Determining the Uniqueness or Nonuniqueness of the Internal Rate of Return for a Proposed Investment," *Journal of Industrial Engineering,* Vol. 26, No. 1, pp. 70–71, January–February 1965.

10. KAPLAN, S., "Computer Algorithms for Finding Exact Rates of Return," *Journal of Business,* Vol. 40, No. 4, pp. 389–392, October 1967.

11. LEVY, H., and M. SARNAT, *Capital Investment and Financial Decisions,* 2nd edition, Prentice–Hall, Englewood Cliffs, N.J., 1983.

12. LIN, S., "The Modified Internal Rate of Return and Investment Criterion," *The Engineering Economist,* Vol. 21, No. 4, pp. 237–248, Summer 1976.

13. MAO, J. C. T., *Quantitative Analysis of Financial Decisions,* Macmillan, Toronto, 1969.

14. PARK, C. S., and G. J. THUESEN, "Combining Concepts of Uncertainty Resolution and Project Balance for Capital Allocation Decisions," *The Engineering Economist,* Vol. 24, No. 2, pp. 109–127, Winter 1979.

15. SOLOMON, E., "The Arithmetic of Capital-Budgeting Decision," *Journal of Business,* Vol. 29, No. 2, pp. 124–129, April 1956.

16. TEICHROEW, D., A. A. ROBICHEK, and M. MONTALBANO, "Mathematical Analysis of Rates of Return under Certainty," *Management Science,* Vol. 11, No. 3, pp. 395–403, January 1965.

17. TEICHROEW, D., A. A. ROBICHEK, and M. MONTALBANO, "An Analysis of Criteria for Investment and Financing Decisions under Certainty," *Management Science,* Vol. 12, No. 3, pp. 151–179, November 1965.

18. WEINGARTNER, H. M., "The Excess Present Value Index: A Theoretical Basis and Critique," *Journal of Accounting Research,* Vol. 1, No. 2, pp. 213–224, Autumn 1963.

19. WEINGARTNER, H. M., "Some New Views on the Payback Period and Capital Budgeting Decision," *Management Science,* Vol. 15, No. 12, pp. B594–B607, August 1969.

PROBLEMS

All cash flows given in this problem set represent the cash flows after taxes, unless otherwise mentioned.

6.1. Consider the following sets of investment projects.

Project	After-Tax Cash Flows			
	n: 0	1	2	3
A	−$10,000	0	0	19,650
B	−$10,000	5,937	5,937	5,937
C	−$10,000	6,873	5,873	4,873
D	−$10,000	5,000	6,000	7,000

a. Compute the net present value of each project at $i = 10\%$.
b. Compute the project balance of each project as a function of the project year.
c. Compute the future value of each project at $i = 10\%$.
d. Compute the annual equivalent of each project at $i = 10\%$.

6.2. In Problem 6.1
a. Graph the net present value of each project as a function of i.
b. Graph the project balances (at $i = 10\%$) of each project as a function of n.
c. From the graphical results in part b of Problem 6.1, which project appears to be the safest to undertake if there is some possibility of premature termination of the projects at the end of year 2?

6.3. Consider the following set of independent investment projects.

Project	F_n						
	n: 0	1	2	3	4	5	6–20
1	−100	50	50	50	50	−750	100
2	−100	30	30	30	10	10	
3	−16	92	−170	100			

Assume $MARR(i) = 10\%$ for the following questions.
a. Compute the present value for each project and determine the acceptability of each project.
b. Compute the future value of each project at the end of each project period and determine its acceptability.
c. Compute the annual equivalent of each project and determine the acceptability of each project.
d. Compute the project value of each project at the end of 20 years with variable *MARR*s: 10% for $n = 0$ to $n = 10$ and 15% for $n = 11$ to $n = 20$.
e. Compute the project balance as a function of n for project 2.
f. Compute Solomon's average rate of return (*ARR*) for project 2, and determine the acceptability of the project.

g. Compute the modified internal rate of return (*MIRR*) for project 3 and determine the project's acceptability.

6.4. Consider the following project balance profiles for proposed investment projects.

Project	i	$PB(i)_0$	$PB(i)_1$	$PB(i)_2$	$PB(i)_3$	$PB(i)_4$	$PB(i)_5$
				Project Balance (End of Year)			
A	10%	−$1,000	−1,000	−900	−690	−359	105
B	0	−$1,000	−800	−600	−400	−200	0
C	15	−$1,000	−650	−348	−100	85	198
D	18	−$1,000	−680	−302	−57	233	575
E	20	−$1,000	−1,200	−1,440	−1,328	−1,194	−1,000
F	12.9	−$1,000	−530	−99	−211	−89	0

Project balance figures are rounded to dollars.
a. Compute the present value of each investment.
b. Determine the cash flows for each project.
c. Identify the future value of each project.
d. What would the internal rates of return be for projects B and F?

6.5. Consider the following sequence of cash flows.

Project	n: 0	1	2	3
A	−10	5	−5	20
B	100	−216	116	

a. Descartes' rule of sign indicates _____ possible rates of return for project A, but the Norstrom rule indicates _____ real root(s) because there are _____ sign change(s) in the S_n series. The rates of return is are _____.
b. For project B, determine the range of *MARR* for which the project would be acceptable.
c. Compute the *MIRR* for both projects. ($i = 6\%$)
d. Compute i_{min} for both projects and compute the return on invested capital at $k = 6\%$.

6.6. Consider the following set of investment projects.

Project	n: 0	1	2	3	4	5
			After-Tax Cash Flow			
1	−$10	60	−120	80		
2	−$225	100	100	100	100	
3		100	50	0	−230	
4	−$100	50	50	50	−100	600
5	−$100	300	−100	500		

a. Classify each project as either simple or nonsimple.
b. Compute the internal rate(s) of return for each project.
c. Classify each project as either a pure or a mixed investment.
d. Assuming that *MARR* = i = k = 10%, determine the acceptability of each project based on the rate-of-return principle.
e. For all mixed projects, compute the *MIRR*s.

6.7. Consider the following set of investment projects.

	After-Tax Cash Flow					
Project	n: 0	1	2	3	4	5
1	−60	70	−20	240		
2	−100	50	100			
3	−800	400	−100	400	400	−100
4	−160	920	−1,700	1,000		
5	−450	−200	700	−60	2,000	−500

a. Compute the PV for each project. ($i = 12\%$).
b. Classify each project as either simple or nonsimple.
c. Compute the internal rate(s) of return for each project.
d. Classify each project as either a pure or a mixed investment.
e. Assuming that $MARR = i = k = 12\%$, determine the acceptability of each project based on the rate-of-return principle.

6.8. Consider the following set of investment projects.

	After-Tax Cash Flow				
Project	n: 0	1	2	3	4
1	−$10	−30	80	−30	
2	−$70	50	23	11	
3	−$50	25	102	−100	392
4	−$100	500	−600		
5	−$110	10	100	50	
6	−$10	60	−110	60	

a. Classify each project as either simple or nonsimple.
b. Compute the internal rate(s) of return for each project.
c. Classify each project as either a pure or a mixed investment.
d. Assuming that $MARR = i = k = 10\%$, determine the acceptability of each project based on the rate-of-return principle.

6.9. Consider the following series of cash flows for an investment project.

n	0	1	2	3
F_n	−$500	1,000	3,000	−4,000

a. Find i_{min} for this investment.
b. Determine whether this is a mixed investment.
c. If this is a mixed investment, derive the functional relationship between the RIC, r^*, and the cost of capital, k.
d. Assume $k = 10\%$. Determine the value of r^* and the acceptability of this investment.

6.10. Prove that $r \leq i_{min}$, in relation to the project balance.

6.11. Consider the following set of investment projects.

	After-Tax Cash Flow		
Project	n: 0	1	2
1	−$1,000	500	840
2	−$2,000	1,560	944
3	−$1,000	1,400	−100

Assume $MARR = i = 12\%$ in the following questions.

    a. Compute the internal rate of return for each project. If there is more than one rate of return, identify all the rates.

    b. Determine the acceptability of each project based on the rate-of-return principle.

6.12. Consider the projects described in Problem 6.3.

    a. Compute the rate of return (internal rate of return) for each project.

    b. Plot the present value as a function of interest rate (i) for each project.

    c. Classify each project as either simple or nonsimple. Then reclassify each project as either a pure or a mixed investment.

    d. Now determine the acceptability of each project by using the rate-of-return principle. Use $MARR(i) = 10\%$.

6.13. Consider the following investment project at $MARR = 10\%$.

Cash Flow	n: 0	1	2	3	4	5	6	7	8	9	10
b_n				100	100	200	300	300	200	100	50
c_n	$200	100	50	20	20	100	100	100	50	50	30
F_n	−$200	−100	−50	80	80	100	200	200	150	50	20

    a. Identify the values of N, m, B, C, I, and C'.

    b. Compute R_A, R_N, and the L–S ratio.

    c. Compute the $PV(10\%)$.

6.14. Consider the investment situation in which an investment of P dollars at $n = 0$ is followed by a series of equal annual positive payments A over N periods. If it is assumed that A dollars are recovered each year, with A being a percentage of P, the number of years required for payback can be found as a function of the rate of return of the investment. That is, knowing the relationship $A = P(A/P, i^*, N)$, or

$$A = P\left[\frac{i^*(1 + i^*)^N}{(1 + i^*)^N - 1} \right]$$

we can rewrite the relationship as

$$i^* = \frac{A}{P} - \frac{A}{P}\left(\frac{1}{1 + i^*} \right)^N$$

Note that A/P is the payback reciprocal, $R_p = 1/n_p$. Rearranging terms yields

$$R_p = \frac{i^*}{1 - (1 + i^*)^{-N}}$$

This relationship provides a convenient equation for carrying out a numerical analysis of the general relation between the payback reciprocal and the internal rate of return.

    a. Develop a chart that estimates the internal rate of return of a project as a function of payback reciprocal.

    b. Consider a project that requires an initial investment of $1,000 and has annual receipts of $500 for 5 years. This project has a payback period of 2 years, giving $R_p = 0.5$. Verify that the project has the internal rate of return of 41.04% from the chart developed in part a.

6.15. Johnson Chemical Company is considering investing in a new composite material processing project after a 3-year period of research and process development.

R&D cost: $3 million over a 3-year period, with an annual R&D growth rate of 50%/year ($0.63 million at the beginning of year 1, $0.95 million at the beginning of year 2, and $1.42 million at the beginning of year 3). These R&D expenditures will be expensed rather than amortized for tax purposes.

Capital investment: $5 million at the beginning of year 4, depreciated over a 7-year period using MACRS percentages.

Process life: 10 years.

Salvage value: 10% of initial capital investment at the end of year 10.

Total sales: $100 million (at the end of year 4) with a sales growth rate of 10%/year (compound growth) during the first 6 years and −10% (negative compound growth)/year for the remaining process life.

Out-of-pocket expenditures: 80% of annual sales.

Working capital: 10% of annual sales (considered as an investment at the beginning of each year and recovered fully at the end of year 10)

Marginal tax rate: 40%.

Minimum attractive rate of return (MARR): 18%.

a. Compute the net present value of this investment and determine whether the project should be pursued.
b. Compute the rate of return on this investment.
c. Compute the benefit–cost ratio for this investment.
d. Compute the annual equivalent for this project.

7

Decision Rules for Selecting among Multiple Alternatives

7.1. INTRODUCTION

In the previous chapter we presented ten different criteria for measuring the investment worth of an individual project. For an individual project all ten criteria yield consistent answers for the accept–reject decision. Which one to use is therefore a question of convenience and habit. When we *compare* projects, however, the situation is quite different. Naive or improper application of various criteria can lead to conflicting results. Fortunately, the *proper use of any of the ten criteria will always result in decisions consistent with PV analysis, which we consider the baseline, or "correct," criterion.*

In Section 7.2 we present some preliminary steps that must be taken before analysis can begin: formulating mutually exclusive alternatives and ordering them. Section 7.3 is the main part of the chapter, and here we present the criteria and decision rules for comparing alternatives. In Section 7.4 we examine some of the more detailed aspects of the "assumptions" behind the decision criteria and consider other writings on the subject. Section 7.5 treats the subject of unequal lives, which becomes important in service projects; benefits of service projects are unknown or not measured. Finally, there is a brief discussion of investment timing in Section 7.6.

As in Chapter 6, we assume that the *MARR* is known and that we operate in a stable, perfect capital market with complete certainty about the outcome of investments. The firm can therefore borrow funds at the *MARR* and invest any excess funds at the same rate. The firm's ability to borrow may be *limited,* however, which differs from the situation assumed in Chapter 6.

7.2. FORMULATING MUTUALLY EXCLUSIVE ALTERNATIVES

We need to distinguish between projects that are independent of one another and those that are dependent. We say that two or more projects are *independent* if the accept–reject decision of one has no influence, except for a possible budgetary reason, on the accept–reject decision of any of the others. We call this a *set of independent projects*. Typical examples are projects that derive revenues from different markets and require different technical resources.

Two or more projects are *mutually exclusive* if the acceptance of any one precludes the acceptance of any of the others. We call this a *set of mutually exclusive projects*. An example is a set of projects, each of which requires full-time use of a single, special-purpose machine. If we select a particular project, the machine becomes unavailable for any other use.

Two projects are *dependent* if the acceptance of one requires the acceptance of another. For example, the decision to add container ship dock facilities in an existing harbor may require a decision to increase the depth of the harbor channel. The container ship dock project is dependent on the channel project. Notice that the channel project does *not* depend on the dock project, however, since an increase in channel depth can benefit the conventional docks. If the channel project also depended on the container dock project, we would combine the two into one project.

Before applying any investment criterion to selecting among projects, we follow this procedure.

1. Reject any individual project that fails to meet the criterion acceptance test, *unless* some other project that passes the test depends on it. This step is not absolutely necessary, but it speeds later computations.

2. Form all possible, feasible *combinations* with the remaining projects. We call this step formulating mutually exclusive alternatives.

3. *Order* the alternatives formed in step 2, usually, but not always, by the investment required at time 0, c_0. If there is an overall budget limit, we may at this step eliminate any alternatives that exceed the limit.

Example 7.1

A chemical company is considering the manufacture of two products, A and B. The market demand for each of these products is independent of the demand for the other. Product A may be produced by either process x or process y, and product B by either process y or process z. It is inefficient to use more than one process to manufacture a particular product, and no process may be used to manufacture more than one product. *Formulate* all mutually exclusive investment alternatives. Table 7.1 presents the eight alternatives. The first one is the *do-nothing* alternative, which should always be included. We then list all alternatives that consist of a single product for manufacture, followed by all feasible combinations of two products. Since Ay and By are inherently mutually exclusive, we do not consider the combination. Nor do we consider combinations such as Ax, Ay, since they are mutually exclusive according to the problem statement. □

Table 7.1 *Mutually Exclusive Investment Alternatives, Example 7.1*

Alternative	Product–Process Combinations Included
1	None
2	Ax
3	Ay
4	By
5	Bz
6	Ax, By
7	Ax, Bz
8	Ay, Bz

Example 7.2

A marketing manager is evaluating strategies for three market areas, A, B, and C. The strategy selected in any one area is independent of that in any other area. Only one strategy is to be selected for each area. There are two strategies for A, 1 and 2; three for B, 1, 2, and 3; and three for C, 1, 2, and 3. Strategy 1 for any area is a do-nothing strategy. *Formulate* all mutually exclusive investment alternatives. Table 7.2 presents the $(2)(3)(3) = 18$ alternatives. □

After formulating all possible, feasible combinations, we *treat* them as a set of mutually exclusive alternatives. The cash flow for any alternative is simply the sum of the cash flows of the included projects. Since we consider all possible, feasible combinations, we must obtain the optimal combination. The reason for defining mutually exclusive alternatives is related to the properties of an invest-

Table 7.2 *Mutually Exclusive Investment Alternatives, Example 7.2*

Alternative	Strategy Selected for Each Market Area			Alternative	Strategy Selected for Each Market Area		
	A	B	C		A	B	C
1	1	1	1	10	2	1	1
2	1	1	2	11	2	1	2
3	1	1	3	12	2	1	3
4	1	2	1	13	2	2	1
5	1	2	2	14	2	2	2
6	1	2	3	15	2	2	3
7	1	3	1	16	2	3	1
8	1	3	2	17	2	3	2
9	1	3	3	18	2	3	3

ment worth criterion. If we are considering the projects as wholly or partially independent, can we be sure our criterion will always lead to the best combination, no matter which project we examine first? With mutually exclusive alternatives we avoid this type of problem, because we have specific rules for ordering the alternatives before applying the investment worth criterion.

The *ordering* of the alternatives depends on which criterion is to be applied. There are four classifications.

1. Time 0 investment, c_0: order the alternatives by increasing c_0. Applies to *PV, FV, AE, PB*, and *ARR*.
2. *I*, the $PV(i)$ of initial investments $c_0, c_1, ..., c_m$: order by increasing *I*. Here *i* is the *MARR*. Applies to R_N and *L–S*.
3. *C*, the $PV(i)$ of all expenditures, consisting of initial investment plus annual expenses: order by increasing *C*. Again, *i* is the *MARR*. Applies to R_A and *MIRR*.
4. $PV(0\%)$ of all cash flows: order by increasing $PV(0\%)$. When there are ties, order by increasing first derivative of $PV(0\%)$. Applies to *IRR* and *RIC*.

These ordering rules are designed to facilitate the application of the criteria, as shown in the next section. They are not the only rules. For example, *any* ordering rule will work with *PV, FV, AE,* and *PB*. In addition, we can sometimes use ordering rule 1, based on c_0, with the other criteria, provided we modify the decision rules. These modifications often result in cumbersome variations and thus are usually avoided.

7.3 APPLICATION OF INVESTMENT WORTH CRITERIA

7.3.1 Total Investment Approach

This approach applies the investment criterion separately to each mutually exclusive alternative. Example 7.3 illustrates the approach.

Example 7.3

Two mutually exclusive alternatives, *j* and *k*, are being considered as shown in Table 7.3. Apply the various criteria to each alternative, using *MARR* = 10%. The results are shown in the lower part of Table 7.3. (The derivation of the results in the table is left as an exercise; see Problem 7.3.) □

Opposite Ranking Phenomenon.   Four of the criteria seem to indicate that alternative *k* is the better choice, whereas the other six give numerically higher ratings for *j*. We have here an example of the *opposite ranking phenomenon*. The cause of the discrepancy is that some of the criteria are *relative* measures of investment worth and others are *absolute* measures. The resolution of this conflict, for the situation of perfect capital markets and complete certainty, is given by the *incremental approach* in Section 7.3.2.

Table 7.3 *Total Investment Approach, Example 7.3*

Time	Alternative j			Alternative k		
	Outflow	Inflow	Net Flow	Outflow	Inflow	Net Flow
0	$1,000	0	−$1,000	$2,000	0	−$2,000
1	2,000	2,475	475	5,000	5,915	915
2	1,000	1,475	475	6,000	6,915	915
3	500	975	475	7,000	7,915	915

Criterion*	Value for j	Value for k	Alternative with Larger Value
PV	$181	$275	k
FV	$241	$367	k
AE	$ 73	$111	k
PB_N	$242	$367	k
IRR	20%	18%	j
ARR	16%	15%	j
MIRR	12%	11%	j
R_A	1.045	1.016	j
R_N	1.182	1.138	j
L−S	0.182	0.138	j

*$i = 10\%$ for all criteria.

At this point, we argue that *when we apply the total investment approach,* the *PV, FV, AE,* and *PB_N* give the *correct answer.* This is so because maximizing these criteria maximizes the future wealth of the firm. This point is proved in detail in Section 7.4.1. Before we resolve the discrepancies between *PV* and the other criteria, some special cases are considered.

Consistency Within Groups. The consistency within groups of the criteria is not coincidence but rather a fundamental characteristic. If the lifetimes of all alternatives are the same and −100% < *i*, it is easy to show that the following groups will always show internal consistency in ranking mutually exclusive alternatives.

PV, FV, AE and PB_N. The four criteria, *PV, FV, AE,* and *PB,* will always agree among themselves.
If

$$PV(i)_j < PV(i)_k$$

then

$$(F/P, i, N)PV(i)_j < (F/P, i, N)PV(i)_k$$

and

$$FV(i)_j < FV(i)_k$$

In addition,

$$(A/P, \ i, \ N)PV(i)_j < (A/P, \ i, \ N)PV(i)_k$$

and

$$AE(i)_j < AE(i)_k \tag{7.1}$$

The $PB_N(i)$ is the same as $FV(i)$, so we complete the proof.

These criteria measure the surplus in an investment alternative over and above investment of $i = MARR$. It does not matter when we measure the surplus in comparing alternatives—at time 0, at time N, or spread equally over the life of the alternative. If one alternative has a greater time 0 surplus than another, its time N surplus will also be greater, and so forth. The surplus is measured in dollars (or other currency unit), and hence these criteria are *absolute* measures of investment worth. This argument again reinforces the *correctness of using PV, FV, AE, and PB$_N$ with the total investment approach.*

For example, the addition of alternative m to j, where $PV(10\%)_m$ equals 0, does not change the PV measure of j:

Net Cash Flow	n: 0	1	2	3	$PV(10\%)$
Alternative m	$-\$5,000$	0	0	6,655	0
Alternative j	$-\$1,000$	475	475	475	181
Alternative $j + m$	$-\$6,000$	475	475	7,130	181

R_N, *L–S, and ARR.* The Lorrie–Savage ratio $L–S$ is simply the netted benefit–cost ratio minus one, or $L–S = R_N - 1$, so we need only compare Solomon's average rate of return, ARR, with R_N. In addition to equal lifetimes and $-100\% < i$, we assume the initial investment occurs only at time 0 (other outlays are annual operating expenses). Then $I = c_0$, and $R_N = (B - C')/c_0$.
Assume

$$R_{Nj} > R_{Nk}$$

Then

$$\frac{B_j - C'_j}{c_{0j}} > \frac{B_k - C'_k}{c_{0k}}$$

or

$$\sum_{n=1}^{N} \frac{F_{nj}(1 + i)^{-n}}{c_{0j}} > \sum_{n=1}^{N} \frac{F_{nj}(1 + i)^{-n}}{c_{0k}}$$

where F_{nj} is the net cash flow for alternative j at the end of period n. In addition,

$$\sum_{n=1}^{N} \frac{F_{nj}(1 + i)^{N-n}}{c_{0j}} > \sum_{n=1}^{N} \frac{F_{nk}(1 + i)^{N-n}}{c_{0k}}$$

Substituting from Eq. 6.18, we have

$$(1 + s_j)^N > (1 + s_k)^N$$

and

$$s_j > s_k \tag{7.2}$$

If the initial investment extends beyond time 0, the result need not hold (see Problem 7.16 at the end of the chapter).

R_A, *MIRR*. The aggregate benefit–cost ratio, R_A, and the modified internal rate of return as defined by Eq. 6.23, *MIRR*, will always agree. Assume

$$R_{Aj} > R_{Ak}$$

or

$$\frac{B_j}{I_j + C_j'} > \frac{B_k}{I_k + C_k'}$$

From the definitions of B, I, and C', Eqs. 6.1, 6.29, and 6.30, we substitute and obtain

$$\frac{\sum\limits_{n=0}^{N} b_{nj}(1 + i)^{-n}}{\sum\limits_{n=0}^{N} c_{nj}(1 + i)^{-n}} > \frac{\sum\limits_{n=0}^{N} b_{nk}(1 + i)^{-n}}{\sum\limits_{n=0}^{N} c_{nk}(1 + i)^{-n}}$$

Then

$$\frac{\sum\limits_{n=0}^{N} b_{nj}(1 + i)^{N-n}}{\sum\limits_{n=0}^{N} c_{nj}(1 + i)^{N-n}} > \frac{\sum\limits_{n=0}^{N} b_{nk}(1 + i)^{N-n}}{\sum\limits_{n=0}^{N} c_{nk}(1 + i)^{N-n}}$$

Using Eq. 6.23, we obtain

$$(1 + MIRR_j)^N > (1 + MIRR_k)^N$$

$$MIRR_j > MIRR_k \tag{7.3}$$

IRR. The internal rate of return, *IRR*, or return on invested capital, *RIC*, for mixed investments does not necessarily agree with any of the other criteria.

Special Cases. In some special cases there will be agreement across some of the groups [2]. If each alternative has the same initial investment, the PV and R_N groups will give consistent rankings. If each alternative has a constant net cash flow during its lifetime, *IRR* (or *RIC*) will agree with the R_N group.

Modification of Criteria To Include Unspent Budget Amounts. Some authors advocate a modification of the investment criteria to include the effects of left-over funds [8,12]. Applying this concept to alternatives j and k with *IRR*, we would add to alternative j an additional investment of \$1,000 earning interest at *MARR* = 10% and returning $1,000(A/P, 10\%, 3) = \$402$ each year. The argument is that we have \$2,000 to invest at time 0; otherwise we would not consider alternative k. The augmented cash flow, designated by some as a *total cash flow*, becomes for alternative j

Time	Original Net Flow, Alternative j	Unspent 1,000 Earning 10%	Total Flow
0	−\$1,000	−\$1,000	−\$2,000
1	475	402	877
2	475	402	877
3	475	402	877

The *IRR* for the total flow is 15%, which is less than the 18% for k. Thus, *IRR*, applied to the total cash flow, agrees with *PV*. Notice that this agreement between the criteria can be derived from the special cases just mentioned.

A similar approach has been proposed for benefit–cost ratios [8]. The extent to which the total cash flow approach ensures consistent ranking by the various criteria does not appear to have been fully examined. (See Problem 7.20 at the end of the chapter.) The following example illustrates opposite ranking with the same initial investment.

Example 7.4

Relevant summary data for alternatives p and q are given below. Evaluate the alternatives by using R_A and R_N. Here I is assumed to be c_0.

Item	Alternative p	Alternative q
Time 0 investment, c_0	\$100	\$100
PV of annual expenses, C'	10	0
PV of annual receipts, B	220	205

Computing R_A and R_N, we have

Ratio	Alternative p	Alternative q
R_A	2.00	2.05
R_N	2.10	2.05

□

In Example 7.4 alternative p has a smaller R_A value but a larger R_N value. Since the classification of a cash flow element as a user benefit or a sponsor cost is often arbitrary, the use of a total cash flow approach is questionable.

7.3.2 Incremental Analysis

Investment alternatives can have opposite ranking because some criteria are *relative* measures of investment worth. The resolution of the discrepancy requires incremental analysis. The general approach is as follows.

1. *Order* the investment alternatives by the ordering rule specified for the criterion in Section 7.2.
2. Apply the criterion to the cash flow of the first alternative.
3. a. If the criterion value is favorable, go to step 4.
   b. If the criterion value is unfavorable, select the next alternative in order. Continue until an alternative with a favorable criterion value is obtained. (If none is obtained, reject all alternatives.) Go to step 4.
4. Apply the criterion to the cash flow *difference* between the next alternative in order and the one most recently evaluated favorably.
5. Repeat step 4 until no more alternatives exist. Accept the last alternative for which the cash flow difference was evaluated favorably.

See Example 7.6 at the end of Section 7.3 for a comprehensive application of these rules.

Irrelevance of Ordering for PV, FV, AE, and PB$_N$. The ordering rule for criteria *PV*, *FV*, *AE*, and *PB$_N$* is by increasing time 0 investment, c_0. This rule is based on convention but is not required. For these four *absolute* measures of investment worth, the *ordering is irrelevant; furthermore, the incremental analysis always agrees with the total investment approach, which is optimal for perfect capital markets and complete certainty.*

If

$$PV(i)_j < PV(i)_k$$

then

$$PV(i)_{k-j} > 0 \tag{7.4}$$

by the definition of *PV* and the distributive rule of multiplication. In addition,

$$PV(i)_{k-j} = -PV(i)_{j-k} \tag{7.5}$$

and since the other three criteria always agree with *PV*, the ordering of alternatives is irrelevant for this group.

Applying these rules to Example 7.3, we obtain the ordering based on c_0: j, k. We have $PV(10\%)_j = \$181$, which is favorable.

We than examine the cash flow difference between k and j.

n	Net Flow		
	Alt. j	Alt. k	$k - j$
0	$-\$1,000$	$-\$2,000$	$-\$1,000$
1	475	915	440
2	475	915	440
3	475	915	440

We have

$$PV(10\%)_{k-j} = -1,000 + 440 \overset{P/A,\ 10\%,\ 3}{(2.4869)} = \$94$$

There are no more alternatives, and we accept k, the last one for which the cash flow difference was evaluated favorably.

If we had started with the larger time 0 investment, we would have evaluated k and found it favorable with a PV of $275. The cash flow difference between j and k is

n	0	1	2	3
$j - k$, Cash Flow	$1,000	-440	-440	-440

The $PV(10\%)_{j-k} = -\$94$, and we again accept k.

Agreement on Increments Between PV and Other Criteria. Let us compare with PV any *one* of the other criteria, from the set *IRR* (or *RIC*), *ARR*, *MIRR*, R_A, R_N, *L–S*. We will use the ordering rule for the other criterion, since we just showed that for *PV* the ordering is irrelevant. The ordering rules are designed so that each increment appears to be an investment when evaluated by the criterion, as

Table 7.4 *Incremental Analysis, Example 7.3*

Criterion	Value for j	Favorable?	Next Increment	Value for Increment	Favorable?	Final Choice
PV	$181	Yes	$k-j$	$94	Yes	k
FV	$241	Yes	$k-j$	$125*	Yes	k
AE	$73	Yes	$k-j$	$38	Yes	k
PB_N	$242	Yes	$k-j$	$125	Yes	k
IRR	20%	Yes	$k-j$	15%	Yes	k
ARR	16%	Yes	$k-j$	14%	Yes	k
MIRR	12%	Yes	$k-j$	10.3%	Yes	k
R_A	1.045	Yes	$k-j$	1.007	Yes	k
R_N	1.182	Yes	$k-j$	1.093	Yes	k
L–S	0.182	Yes	$k-j$	0.093	Yes	k

*Values do not add to 367 because of rounding.

opposed to a loan, for example. Examining each increment by both criteria will yield the *identical sequence of accept–reject decisions*, because the other criterion *always agrees with PV for an individual project, or cash flow*, as shown in Chapter 6. Therefore, using *incremental analysis with any of the ten criteria will result in optimal decisions*. Some of the ordering rules may give different *sequences* of increments, but since each criterion agrees step by step with *PV*, and since *PV* is indifferent to ordering, the *final decisions will be the same*.

Table 7.4 contains the relevant data for all ten criteria as applied to Example 7.3. For each the ordering is *j, k*. Again, the derivation of table entries is left as an exercise; see Problem 7.4.

Alternative Derivations. In this section we provide some alternative algebraic derivations to show the correctness of incremental analysis. Space limits prevent us from presenting all of them, and some are left as chapter problems. These proofs also illustrate the logic behind the ordering rules.

R_N. If

$$R_{N,k-j} > 1$$

then

$$(B_{k-j} - C'_{k-j})/I_{k-j} > 1$$

and

$$B_{k-j} - C'_{k-j} > I_{k-j}$$

Since

$$I_{k-j} > 0 \quad \text{by the ordering rule,}$$
$$B_k - C'_k - I_k > B_j - C'_j - I_j$$

or

$$PV_k > PV_j \tag{7.6}$$

We can also reverse the step sequence. Thus, the netted benefit–cost ratio, when used with incremental analysis, always agrees with *PV*.

R_A. If

$$R_{A,\,k-j} > 1$$

then

$$B_{k-j}/C_{k-j} > 1$$

and

$$B_{k-j} > C_{k-j}$$

Since

$$C_{k-j} > 0 \quad \text{by the ordering rule}$$

$$B_k - C_k > B_j - C_j$$

or

$$PV_k > PV_j \tag{7.7}$$

Detailed Rules for IRR. Many practitioners apply *IRR* by using incremental analysis and ordering based on time 0 investment, c_0. Most of the time this presents no difficulties. Figure 7.1 shows the *PV* functions of the two alternatives j and k in Example 7.3. The ordering of alternatives by c_0 is first j, then k. If *MARR* $= i_1$, then $i_j^* > MARR$, so alternative j is favorable. The difference cash flow $(k - j)$ has an *IRR* of $i_F > MARR$, so we accept k. (We call the *IRR* i_F for Fisher's intersection, described in Section 7.4.) From the graph in Figure 7.1, it is clear that $PV(i_1)_k > PV(i_1)_j$, so we are consistent with *PV*. If *MARR* $= i_2$, then again $i_j^* > MARR$. But the *IRR* for $(k - j)$ is less than *MARR*, so our final choice is alternative j. Again, we have consistency with *PV*, since $PV(i_2)_k < PV(i_2)_j$.

But what if the ordering is first k, then j, and the *PV* functions are similar to those in Figure 7.1? The next example illustrates this situation.

Example 7.5

Compare the following two alternatives by using *IRR* with incremental analysis based on ordering by c_0, with *MARR* = 10%.

		Net Flow	
n	Alt. w	Alt. j	$j - w$
0	$-\$900$	$-\$1,000$	$-\$100$
1	-350	475	825
2	915	475	-440
3	915	475	-440

The ordering by c_0 is first w, then j.

Examining w, we have $i_w^* = 19\% > 10\%$, so it is favorable. The difference cash flow has multiple sign changes, so multiple roots are possible. However, in the range 0 to 100% there is only one *IRR*: 16%. This value exceeds *MARR*, so we would accept j. However, $PV(10\%)_j = 181$, which is *less* than $PV(10\%)_w = 225$!

The explanation is that the cash flow difference $(j - w)$ represents a borrowing activity, despite the negative time 0 flow. The *PV* function for $(j - w)$ begins negative (which is characteristic of borrowing activities), crosses the horizontal axis near 16%, and then continues upward. The other root is at $i = 660\%$. (Applying *RIC*, we obtain $r_{j-w}^* = -38.64\%$ at $k = i = 10\%$, so we accept w.)

i	0	10	16	20	50	100	200	500	660	700
$PV(i)_{j-w}$	-155	-44	2	27	124	148	110	23	0	-5

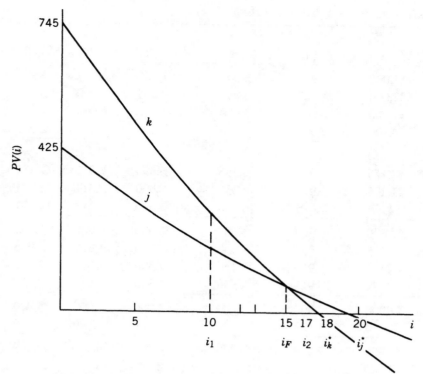

FIGURE 7.1. *IRR* for cash flow difference (*k - j*), Example 7.3.

From this example, it is clear that *ordering by* c_0 for *IRR* can lead to *incorrect* results.

Various other circumstances can cause problems for the practitioner accustomed to ordering by c_0. These include the situations in which the time 0 investment is the same for two alternatives. To remedy these difficulties, Wohl has recently developed a set of strict rules for applying *IRR* with incremental analysis [1, 13]. These rules result in complete consistency with *PV*.

For many applications the ordering rule based on *PV*(0%) clears up any inconsistencies between *IRR* and *PV*. When there are multiple roots, the *IRR* criterion can be replaced by return on invested capital, *RIC*. Multiple roots inevitably cause more computational work, whether we use *RIC*, the strict rules for *IRR* that require obtaining all roots, or plotting of the *PV* function. Plotting the *PV* function need be neither difficult nor time-consuming, and the plot contains at least as much information as is obtained by the other methods. In essence, we have argued for use of the *PV* criterion.

Example 7.6

We end this section with a comprehensive example that demonstrates the incremental analysis technique for several of the criteria. Three independent projects, A, B, and C, are to be evaluated by using *PV*, R_N, R_A, and *IRR*, with *MARR* = 10%. (Note that each of the four groups is represented.) There is a time 0 expenditure budget of $4,000. The cash flows for the three projects are given in the upper left portion of Table 7.5. Select the best project or projects.

Table 7.5 *Preliminary Data for Example 7.6*

Alternative:	1	2	3	4	5	6
Project:	A	B	C	A + B	A + C	B + C
Outflows, $n = 0$	$1,000	900	3,000	1,900	4,000	3,900
1	$2,000	1,265	5,000	3,265	7,000	6,265
2	$1,000	6,000	5,000	7,000	6,000	11,000
3	$500	7,000	5,000	7,500	5,500	12,000
Inflows, $n = 0$	$0	0	0	0	0	0
1	$2,475	915	6,336	3,390	8,811	7,251
2	$1,475	6,915	6,336	8,390	7,811	13,251
3	$975	7,915	6,336	8,890	7,311	14,251
Net flows, $n = 0$	−$1,000	−900	−3,000	−1,900	−4,000	−3,900
1	$475	−350	1,336	125	1,811	986
2	$475	915	1,336	1,390	1,811	2,251
3	$475	915	1,336	1,390	1,811	2,251
c_0	$1,000	900	3,000	1,900	4,000	3,900
m	0	2	0	0,2	0	2,0
$I(10\%)$	$1,000	7,009	3,000	8,009	4,000	10,009
$C'(10\%)$	$3,020	5,259	12,434	8,279	15,455	17,693
$C(10\%)$	$4,020	12,268	15,434	16,288	19,455	27,702
$PV(0\%)$	$425	580	1,008	1,005	1,433	1,588
$B(10\%)$	$4,202	12,493	15,757	16,695	19,958	28,250
$PV(10\%)$	$181	225	322	407	504	548
R_N	1.182	1.032	1.108	NA	NA	NA
R_A	1.045	1.018	1.021	NA	NA	NA
IRR, %	20.0	18.8	16.0	NA	NA	NA

NOTE: m is the period of the initial investments $c_0, c_1, ..., c_m$.

Preliminary screening. The lower left portion of Table 7.5 shows the relevant data for screening the projects individually. Each of the three projects, A, B, and C, is acceptable by each of the four criteria, PV, R_N, R_A, and IRR, using $MARR = 10\%$. (We expected the agreement on the individual projects by the criteria.)

Form investment alternatives. Since we know that the budget is $4,000 and that A, B, and C are independent, we can form three combinations: (A + B), (A + C), and (B + C). We thus have six investment alternatives (in addition to the do-nothing alternative). For the three alternatives composed of combinations of projects, the cash flows are shown in the upper right portion of Table 7.5, and the data needed for applying the criteria are shown in the lower right.

Order the alternatives. Here we apply the ordering rules specified in Section 7.2.

For PV, order by c_0:   alternatives 2, 1, 4, 3, 6, 5.
For R_N, order by I: alternatives 1, 3, 5, 2, 4, 6.

For R_A, order by C: alternatives 1, 2, 3, 4, 5, 6.
For *IRR*, order by $PV(0\%)$: alternatives 1, 2, 4, 3, 5, 6.

We are now ready to apply the incremental method with the four criteria.

PV(10%)

Alt. 2 vs. do nothing, or B vs. do nothing: $PV(10\%)_{2-0} = \$225 > 0$, so alt. 2 is *favorable*.

Alt. 1 vs. alt. 2, or A vs. B: $PV(10\%)_{1-2} = -\$44 < 0$, so alt. 1 is *not* favored over alt. 2. Note that we are using the relation $PV(i)_{x-y} = PV(i)_x - PV(i)_y$ to save ourselves some work. The cash flow difference $(1 - 2)$ is the same as $(A - B)$.

Alt. 4 vs. alt. 2, or $(A + B)$ vs. A: $PV(10\%)_{4-2} = \$182 > 0$, so alt. 4 is *favored* over alt. 2. Note that the difference $(4 - 2)$ is just the cash flow for A.

Alt. 3 vs. alt. 4, or C vs. $(A + B)$: $PV(10\%)_{3-4} = -\$85 < 0$, so alt. 3 is *not* favored over 4.

Alt. 6 vs. alt. 4, or $(B + C)$ vs. $(A + B)$: $PV(10\%)_{6-4} = \$141 > 0$, so alt. 6 is *favored* over alt. 4. The difference $(6 - 4)$ is the same as $(C - B)$.

Alt. 5 vs. alt. 6, or $(A + C)$ vs. $(B + C)$: $PV(10\%)_{5-6} = -\$44 < 0$, so alt. 5 is *not* favored over alt. 6. The difference $(5 - 6)$ is the same as $(A - B)$, which was evaluated earlier.

The last alternative favorably evaluated is 6, so we accept projects B and C with a total *PV* of $548.

R_N, the netted benefit–cost ratio

Alt. 1 vs. do nothing, or A vs. do nothing: $R_{N,1-0} = 1.182 > 1$, so alt. 1 is *favorable*.

Alt. 3 vs. alt. 1, or C vs. A:

$$R_{N,3-1} = \frac{(\$15{,}757 - 4{,}202) - (\$12{,}434 - 3{,}020)}{\$3{,}000 - 1{,}000} = 1.071 > 1$$

so alt. 3 is *favored* over alt. 1.

Alt. 5 vs. alt. 3, or $(A + C)$ vs. C: The difference $(5 - 3)$ is the same as the cash flow for A. So $R_{N,5-3} = 1.182 > 1$, and alt. 5 is *favored* over alt. 3.

Alt. 2 vs. alt. 5, or B vs. $(A + C)$:

$$R_{N,2-5} = \frac{(\$12{,}493 - 19{,}958) - (\$5{,}259 - 15{,}455)}{\$7{,}009 - 4{,}000} = 0.908 < 1$$

so alt. 2 is *not* favored over alt. 5.

Alt. 4 vs. alt. 5, or $(A + B)$ vs. $(A + C)$:

$$R_{N,4-5} = \frac{(\$16{,}695 - 19{,}958) - (\$8{,}279 - 15{,}455)}{\$8{,}009 - 4{,}000} = 0.976 < 1$$

so alt. 4 is *not* favored over 5. The difference $(4 - 5)$ is the same as $(B - C)$.

Alt. 6 vs. alt. 5, or $(B + C)$ vs. $(A + C)$:

$$R_{N, 6-5} = \frac{(\$28,250 - 19,958) - (\$17,693 - 15,455)}{\$10,009 - 4,000} = 1.007 > 1$$

so alt. 6 is *favored* over alt. 5. The difference $(6 - 5)$ is the same as $(B - A)$.

We accept projects B and C, which constitute alternative 6, the last one favorably accepted. This decision agrees with *PV* analysis, as expected.

R_A, The aggregate benefit–cost ratio

Alt. 1 vs. do nothing, or A vs. do nothing: $R_{A, 1-0} = 1.045 > 1$, so alt. 1 is *favorable*.

Alt. 2 vs. alt. 1, or B vs. A:

$$R_{A, 2-1} = \frac{\$12,493 - 4,202}{\$12,268 - 4,020} = 1.005 > 1$$

so alt. 2 is *favored* over alt. 1.

Alt. 3 vs. alt. 2, or C vs. B:

$$R_{A, 3-2} = \frac{\$15,757 - 12,493}{\$15,434 - 12,268} = 1.031 > 1$$

so alt. 3 is *favored* over alt. 2.

Alt. 4 vs. alt. 3, or $(A + B)$ vs. C:

$$R_{A, 4-3} = \frac{\$16,695 - 15,757}{\$16,288 - 15,434} = 1.098 > 1$$

so alt. 4 is *favored* over alt. 3.

Alt. 5 vs. alt. 4, or $(A + C)$ vs. $(A + B)$: The difference $(5 - 4)$ is the same as $(C - B)$, which was evaluated in the comparison of alt. 3 vs. alt. 2. So $R_{A, 5-4} = 1.031 > 1$, and alt. 5 is *favored* over alt. 4.

Alt. 6 vs. alt. 5, or $(B + C)$ vs. $(A + C)$: The difference $(6 - 5)$ is the same as $(B - A)$, which was evaluated in the comparison of alt. 2 vs. alt. 1. So $R_{A, 6-5} = 1.005 > 1$, and alt. 6 is *favored* over alt. 5.

Again, our final selection is alternative 6, or projects B and C.

IRR, internal rate of return, and *RIC*, return on invested capital

Alt. 1 vs. do nothing, or A vs. do nothing: $i^*_{1-0} = 20.0\% > 10\%$, so alt. 1 is *favorable*.

Alt. 2 vs. alt. 1, or B vs. A: The difference cash flow is $+\$100, -825, +440, +440$. The multiple sign changes suggest two roots, and if we refer to

Example 7.5, we see that the roots are 16% and 660%. Applying *RIC*, we obtain $r^* = 15.03\%$, so alt. 2 is *favored* over alt. 1.

As an alternative, consider a more fundamental approach to the analysis of the cash flow for alt. 2 vs. alt. 1. In Example 7.5 the opposite cash flow, that is, $-\$100, +825, -440, -440$, was determined to be a borrowing activity. The cash flow $+100, -825, +440, +440$ is an investment activity, despite the initial inflow.

i	0	10	16	20	50	100
$PV(i)_{2-1}$	\$155	44	−2	−27	−124	−148

Notice that our decision here to accept the cash flow $+\$100, -825, +440, +440$ using $i = 10\%$ is consistent with the decision in Example 7.5 to reject the opposite cash flow using $i = 10\%$. With i_{2-1}^* near 16% > 10%, alt. 2 is *favored* over alt. 1.

Alt. 4 vs. alt. 2, or (A + B) vs. B: The difference cash flow is just that for A. So $i_{2-1}^* = 20.0\% > 10\%$, and alt. 4 is *favored* over alt. 2.

Alt. 3 vs. alt. 4, or C vs. (A + B): The difference cash flow is $-\$1,100, +1,211, -54, -54$. Again, we have multiple sign changes, but Norstrom's auxiliary series S_n is $-\$1,100, +111, +57, +3$. This guarantees a unique, positive, real root (see Section 6.3.1). With $i_{3-4}^* = 0.3\% < 10\%$, alt. 3 is *not* favored over alt. 4.

Alt. 5 vs. alt. 4, or (A + C) vs. (A + B): The difference cash flow is the same as (C − B), or $-\$2,100, +1,686, +421, +421$. This is a pure investment with a unique root of $i_{5-4}^* = 13.5\% > 10\%$, so alt. 5 is *favored* over alt. 4.

Alt. 6 vs. alt. 5, or (B + C) vs. (A + C): We have a repeat of the cash flow for alt. 2 vs. alt. 1, and $i_{6-5}^* = 16\% > 10\%$, so alt. 6 is *favored over alt. 5*.

Again, but after considerable work, our final selection is alternative 6, or projects B and C.

We thus arrive at the same final selection by using incremental analysis with each of the four criteria. ☐

Several conclusions are drawn from Example 7.6.

1. Correct ordering for evaluation is essential for all criteria except *PV* and the related *FV, AE,* and *PB$_N$*.

2. Although the ordering is different for each of the criteria used here, the final results are consistent with the fundamental criterion of *PV*.

3. The *IRR* criterion is particularly troublesome to apply, especially when we take differences between combination alternatives. The *RIC* concept is difficult to apply, and sometimes it is easier to obtain the *PV(i)* function.

4. *PV with the total investment approach is by far the easiest method* to apply. In this example we need to compute the *PV* of each of the three projects, add the appropriate *PV*s to obtain the *PV* of each combination alternative, and simply select the alternative with the largest *PV*.

7.4 REINVESTMENT ISSUES

We will begin this section with a simple example that puzzles most students when they encounter it for the first time.

Example 7.7.

Given projects A and B, which is preferred, project A with $MARR = 5\%$ or project B with $MARR = 10\%$?

	Cash Flows			
Project	n: 0	1	2	3
A	−$1,000	600	500	300
B	−$1,000	300	200	1,000

If we compute PVs, we obtain $PV(5\%)_A = \$284$, $PV(10\%)_B = \$189$. Most students (and practitioners, too) select project A because of its higher PV.

But how can we compare a PV computed at 5% with one computed at 10%? The interest rate used for discounting certainly implies something about reinvestment opportunities, as discussed in Chapter 5. Trying to compare the two projects as stated in the example is tantamount to trying to compare projects in different economic environments. Projects A and B might represent investment opportunities in two different countries, with different reinvestment rates and restrictions on repatriating cash flows. Or perhaps projects A and B occur in different regulatory environments, and the decision maker assumes that after project selection the firm will reinvest its cash flows in the chosen environment.

If we are eventually to recover the reinvested cash, by repatriating it in the one situation or by returning it to the firm's treasury in the second, it does not make sense to compare A and B by using PV. PV measures the surplus of funds a project generates over and above a minimum rate, and in this example the minimum rates differ. Instead, let's compute the total cash available at time 3 for each option.

Direct computation

Project A: $600(1.05)^2 + 500(1.05)^1 + 300 = \$1,487$

Project B: $300(1.1)^2 + 200(1.1)^1 + 1,000 = \$1,583$

Computation from PV

Project A: $(284 + 1,000)(1.05)^3 = \$1,486 \approx \$1,487$

Project B: $(189 + 1,000)(1.1)^3 = \$1,583$

We see that project B produces more cash at time 3, which is a direct result of the higher reinvestment rate, 10% for project B versus 5% for project A. It is clear that the reinvestment rate plays a crucial role in the analysis. □

7.4.1 Net Present Value

Virtually all writers on engineering economics agree that the PV criterion is based on the assumption of reinvestment at the interest rate used for calculating *PV*. In Section 6.2 we assumed that positive cash flows would be reinvested at the outside, or market, interest rate, the same rate used for obtaining *PV*. In Chapter 5 we explained that the equity interest rate is the outside rate from the view of the equity holder. Whichever assumptions we make, we represent the rate by i.

In a perfect capital market we can borrow and lend unlimited amounts at the market interest rate. In this chapter we have modified that assumption to reflect a limited borrowing ability. But we still assume that we can *lend unlimited amounts* by investing at a market interest rate. This is the same as assuming reinvestment at the market interest rate. In this situation, maximizing *PV* is the same as maximizing the future cash of the firm.

Assume that we have two mutually exclusive alternatives, j and k, with cash flows F_{nj}, $n = 0, ..., N_j$, and F_{nk}, $n = 0, ..., N_k$. Further, assume that outlays occur only at time 0 and that we have a budget of M, which is greater than either time 0 outlay. The *MARR* = i. Select a horizon time N as the greater of N_j and N_k.

We have by definition

$$PV(i)_j = \sum_{n=0}^{N_j} F_{nj}(1 + i)^{-n}, \qquad PV(i)_k = \sum_{n=0}^{N_k} F_{nk}(1 + i)^{-n} \qquad (7.8)$$

Now let's obtain the future cash at time N for the three possible decisions. Say $N = N_j$, for example.

Decision 1, do nothing

$$\text{Future cash at time } N = M(1 + i)^N \qquad (7.9)$$

Unspent amounts are invested at i, which is consistent with the reinvestment assumption.

Decision 2, select j

Future cash at time N

$$= (M + F_{0j})(1 + i)^N + \sum_{n=1}^{N} F_{nj}(1 + i)^{N-n}$$

$$= M(1 + i)^N + \sum_{n=0}^{N} F_{nj}(1 + i)^{N-n}$$

$$= M(1 + i)^N + (1 + i)^N \sum_{n=0}^{N} F_{nj}(1 + i)^{-n}$$

$$= M(1 + i)^N + PV(i)_j(1 + i)^N \qquad (7.10)$$

The future cash is the same as for do nothing plus the $PV(i)_j$ shifted to time N. For j the $N_j = N$, so the shifted *PV* is the *FV*.

Decision 3, select k

Future cash at time N

$$= (M + F_{0k})(1 + i)^N + \sum_{n=1}^{N_k} F_{nk}(1 + i)^{N_k - n}(1 + i)^{N - N_k}$$

$$= M(1 + i)^N + \sum_{n=0}^{N} F_{nk}(1 + i)^{N-n}$$

$$= M(1 + i)^N + PV(i)_k(1 + i)^N \tag{7.11}$$

At the end of the project life the accumulated cash from reinvesting project inflows is left to earn interest until time N.

The *PV* of the do-nothing alternative is zero. In each case the future cash at time N is equal to the initial amount M times $(F/P, i, N)$ plus $PV(i)(F/P, i, N)$. Thus, by selecting the alternative with maximum $PV(i)$, we maximize future cash, assuming reinvestment at i.

Let us return to Example 7.7 and evaluate A and B with $i = 5\%$.

$$PV(5\%)_A = \$284, \qquad PV(5\%)_B = \$331$$

Here project B is preferred. Computing future cash amounts, we have

Project A: $(1,000 + 284)(1.05)^3 = \$1,486$

Project B: $(1,000 + 331)(1.05)^3 = \$1,541$

Again, project B is preferred, in agreement with our theoretical analysis.

7.4.2 *Internal Rate of Return*

Some authors have argued that implicit in the use of the *IRR* is an assumption of reinvestment at the project *IRR* [1, 3, 4]. It is difficult to prove or disprove what someone had in mind in stating the *IRR* criterion or using it. Instead, we show in this section the results of selecting alternatives with *IRR* under some special circumstances.

Let us first compute *IRR* for the projects in Example 7.7.

$$\text{Project A:} \quad -\$1,000 + \frac{600}{1 + i} + \frac{500}{(1 + i)^2} + \frac{300}{(1 + i)^3} = 0$$

$$i_A^* = 21.48\%$$

$$\text{Project B:} \quad -\$1,000 + \frac{300}{1 + i} + \frac{200}{(1 + i)^2} + \frac{1,000}{(1 + i)^3} = 0$$

$$i_B^* = 18.33\%$$

If we simply select A over B on the basis of its higher *IRR*, we would be in conflict with the *PV*s calculated at 5%: $1,486 for A and $1,541 for B.

We might ask whether there is a value i for which *PV* favors project A. The

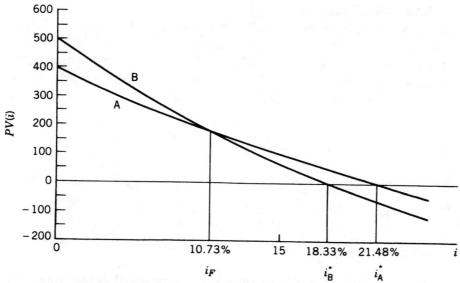

FIGURE 7.2. Fisher's intersection, Example 7.7.

PV curves for A and B are similar to those in Figure 7.1, with B starting higher than A but crossing the horizontal axis sooner. Figure 7.2 shows the curves for A and B. Clearly, *PV*(21.48%) is greater for A than for B. The point of intersection is at 10.73%. This point is also called *Fisher's intersection* or the *rate of return over cost* [5]. For any value of *i* equal to or greater than 10.73%, the *PV* criterion prefers project A. Fisher's intersection is also the *IRR* of the difference cash flow between A and B: $0, 300, 300, −700.

If we are uncertain about the reinvestment rate in selecting one of two alternatives, calculating Fisher's intersection can be useful. In our example any reinvestment rate greater than 10.73% would lead us to prefer A over B, and B would be favored at rates lower than 10.73%. This approach becomes cumbersome when more than two alternatives are compared.

Let us now examine the consequences of *assuming reinvestment at IRR*. If each investment alternative has its excess cash reinvested at its *IRR*, we could select among alternatives by choosing the one with the highest *IRR*. Say that alternative *j* has the highest *IRR*, i_j^*. Then for all others $PV(i_j^*)$ must be less than zero. (If we also have borrowing alternatives with upward-sloping *PV* curves, we must modify the acceptance rules.)

But how sensible is the assumption of reinvestment at *IRR*? Not very sensible at all. Do different *IRR*s imply different reinvestment rates? We don't think so. And with what should we compare the *IRR* if reinvestment is at that rate? The entire discussion is rather fruitless and provides little help for decision making.

The *IRR*, along with *RIC*, is a useful criterion when it is used with correct ordering and the incremental method. Capital that remains invested in a project grows at the *IRR* of the project, and cash released would be invested to grow at the *MARR* (or the cost of capital when this rate is used in *PV* calculation) [9]. When two alternatives are compared, Fisher's intersection is useful if the reinvestment rate is not known with certainty.

DECISION RULES FOR SELECTING AMONG MULTIPLE ALTERNATIVES

7.4.3 Benefit–Cost Ratio

A similar argument can be presented for the aggregate B/C ratio in relation to Fisher's intersection when we are comparing two alternatives [3]. We can demonstrate the logic by applying it to Example 7.7. We assume for simplicity that all investment and operating expenditures occur at time 0 and that the flows from time 1 to time 3 are benefits. Thus, we have

$$B_A = \frac{\$600}{1 + i} + \frac{500}{(1 + i)^2} + \frac{300}{(1 + i)^3}$$

$$I_A + C'_A = 1,000$$

$$B_B = \frac{\$300}{1 + i} + \frac{200}{(1 + i)^2} + \frac{1,000}{(1 + i)^3}$$

$$I_B + C'_B = 1,000$$

The i value for which the $B/(I + C')$ ratios are equal must satisfy the following expression.

$$\frac{\dfrac{\$600}{1 + i} + \dfrac{500}{(1 + i)^2} + \dfrac{300}{(1 + i)^3}}{1,000} = \frac{\dfrac{\$300}{1 + i} + \dfrac{200}{(1 + i)^2} + \dfrac{1,000}{(1 + i)^3}}{1,000}$$

or

$$\frac{\$300}{1 + i} + \frac{300}{(1 + i)^2} - \frac{700}{(1 + i)^3} = 0$$

But this last expression simply yields the *IRR* of the difference cash flow between A and B.

We conclude this section on reinvestment issues by observing that much has been written on the subject, but not all is of use in decision making. The reinvestment rate assumed is critical for alternative selection, and the assumed value should be based on the concepts in Chapter 5. Use of the *PV* criterion implies reinvestment at the rate used for *PV* calculations. Fisher's intersection is useful when comparing two alternatives, but it becomes cumbersome with more than two.

In the real world the reinvestment rates may depend on the time period and on which investments have been accepted. In Chapter 8 we present some mathematical programming approaches that can be used to model such problems.

7.5 COMPARISON OF PROJECTS WITH UNEQUAL LIVES

Comparing projects with unequal lives can be particularly troublesome, for a number of different situations must be considered. Furthermore, many of the methods presented in textbooks have underlying assumptions that are not always clearly stated. Unfortunately, competing projects often have unequal lives, especially in engineering studies for which only costs (not benefits) are known. Problems in this class are more difficult than those for which all benefits are known, and they require more assumptions to be made. Another aspect of the unequal-lives situation is that of repeatability. Decisions involving projects that are likely to be repeated can often be made conveniently by easier methods.

We thus have the following classifications of cases:

1. *Service projects,* for which no revenues or benefits are estimated, or the revenues or benefits do not depend on the project. Here we must select a *study period* common to all alternatives. There are two general cases.
   a. Repeatability is likely.
   b. Repeatability is unlikely.
2. *Revenue projects,* for which all benefits and costs are known. Here the *study period* may be different for each alternative, provided we have a well-specified reinvestment rate.
   a. Repeatability is likely.
   b. Repeatability is unlikely.

These four cases will lead to (and in some instances force us into making) various assumptions concerning reinvestment, salvage values, and characteristics of the repeated projects.

Notice that in this section we are not trying to determine the best life of any individual project that is likely to be repeated. This type of decision is covered in detail in Chapter 16. We now present some of the more common ways of treating unequal lives.

7.5.1 Common Service Period Approach

If the benefit from a project is needed for a much longer period than the individual life of the project, it may be convenient to assume repeatability of identical projects.

Example 7.8.

The Historical Society of New England must repaint its showcase headquarters building. The choice is between a latex paint that costs $12.00/gallon and an oil paint that costs $26.00/gallon. Each gallon would cover 500 square feet; labor is the same for both, 1 hour per 100 square feet at $18.00/hour. The latex paint has an estimated life of 5 years, compared with 8 years for the oil paint. With $i = 8\%$, which paint should be selected?

Let us assume that after either the 5- or the 8-year period the building would be repainted repeatedly with the same paint and that the same costs would apply, as shown in Figure 7.3. The lowest common multiple of 5 and 8 is 40, so we will use 40 as the *common service period.* This becomes the *study period.*

For latex paint, we have the initial painting and seven repaintings.

$$PV(8\%) = \left(\frac{\$12.00}{500} + \frac{\$18.00}{100}\right)[1 + (P/F, 8\%, 5) + (P/F, 8\%, 10)$$

$$+ \cdots + (P/F, 8\%, 35)]$$

$$= (\$0.204)[1 + \overset{P/A,\ 46.9\%,\ 7}{(1.9866)}] = \$0.609 \text{ per square foot}$$

Note: $1.469 = (1.08)^5$.

For oil paint, there are four repaintings plus the initial painting.

$$PV(8\%) = \left(\frac{\$26.00}{500} + \frac{\$18.00}{100}\right)[1 + (P/F, 8\%, 8) + (P/F, 8\%, 16)$$

$$+ \cdots + (P/F, 8\%, 32)]$$

$$= (\$0.232)[1 + \overset{P/A,\ 85.1\%,\ 4}{(1.0751)}] = \$0.481 \text{ per square foot}$$

Note: $1.851 = (1.08)^8$.

The *PV* of the oil paint per square foot is considerably less, so the oil paint should be the choice.   □

In Example 7.8 a service period of 40 years seem reasonable. The number of repaintings needed with each type of paint will depend on the technology of paint, so we may or may not need exactly seven (latex) or four (oil) repaintings. The validity of the analysis also depends on the costs of paint and labor remaining constant. If we assume constant-dollar prices, this may be a reasonable assumption. But then our interest rate of 8% must represent an inflation-free rate i'. Thus, many assumptions are necessary to make the approach valid.

An easier way to solve Example 7.8 is to use annual equivalents. The *AE* of each 40-year cash flow is the same as that of the corresponding 5- or 8-year cash flow.

For latex paint, computing from a 5-year life, we have

$$AE(8\%) = \left(\frac{\$12.00}{500} + \frac{\$18.00}{100}\right)\overset{A/P,\ 8\%,\ 5}{(0.2505)} = \$0.0511 \text{ per square foot}$$

Computing from a 40-year period, we have

$$AE(8\%) = \$0.609\overset{A/P,\ 8\%,\ 40}{(0.0839)} = \$0.0511 \text{ per square foot}$$

For oil paint, computing from an 8-year life, we have

$$AE(8\%) = \left(\frac{\$26.00}{500} + \frac{\$18.00}{100}\right)\overset{A/P,\ 8\%,\ 8}{(0.1740)} = \$0.0403 \text{ per square foot}$$

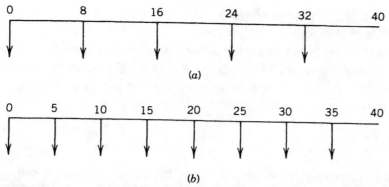

FIGURE 7.3. Common service period approach, Example 7.8: (*a*) oil, five paintings, (*b*) latex, eight paintings.

Computing from a 40-year period, we have

$$AE(8\%) = \overset{A/P,\ 8\%,\ 40}{\$0.481\,(0.0839)} = \$0.0403 \text{ per square foot}$$

With annual equivalents there is another possible interpretation regarding a common service period. We could assume that after the initial period, either 5 or 8 years, the building would be repainted with the type of paint that has the lower *AE* cost. Thus, if oil paint had the lower *AE* cost, the sequences would be

Latex paint (0 → 5), oil paint (5 →)

Oil paint (0 → 8), oil paint (8 →)

After time 5 the *AE* costs are the same. If latex paint had the lower *AE* cost, the sequences would be

Latex paint (0 → 5), latex paint (5 →)

Oil paint (0 → 8), latex paint (8 →)

After time 8 the *AE* costs are the same.

What circumstances would allow us to ignore the costs beyond time 5 when oil paint has the lower *AE* cost or time 8 when latex had the lower *AE* cost? An infinite service period with unchanging costs! Then we could simply look at the first 8 years; thereafter, costs would be identical. Actually, we do not need all these assumptions for reasonable accuracy in decision making. A long service period, say 30 years, and gradual changes in costs and technology will usually lead to the same decision about the initial choice of paint. Thus, we can minimize the *PV* of a long service period by selecting the alternative with the lower *AE* cost for an initial life.

The common service period approach is often used for analyzing *service projects,* for which no revenues or benefits are estimated or whose revenues or benefits are independent. The approach also can be applied to *revenue projects,* whose costs *and* benefits are known. In this situation we must be even more careful about our assumptions, especially regarding benefits.

7.5.2 Estimating Salvage Value of Longer-Lived Projects

If repeatability of projects is not likely for service projects, we must assume something about the salvage value of the longer-lived project. The next example shows how we can *explicitly* incorporate salvage values for assets with value remaining beyond the *required service period*.

Example 7.9

A highway contractor requires a ripper–bulldozer for breaking loose rock without the use of explosives, for a period of 3 years at about 2,000 hours/year. The smaller model, A, costs $300,000, has a life of 8,000 hours, and costs $40,000/year to operate. The larger model, B, costs $450,000, has a life of 12,000 hours, and costs $50,000/year to operate. Model B will perform adequately under all circumstances, whereas for model A some extra drilling is expected at an annual cost of $35,000. With a marginal tax rate of 40%, units of production depreciation, and $i = 15\%$, which model should be purchased?

Since either model's lifetime exceeds the required service period (also the *study period*) of 3 years, we must assume something about the used equipment at that time. Let us assume that after 3 years model A would be sold for $60,000 and model B for $190,000. The after-tax cash flows for each alternative are given in Table 7.6 and shown in Figure 7.4. Model A has the lower *PV* of costs and would be preferred.   □

Table 7.6 *Explicit Salvage Values, Example 7.9*

	After-Tax Cash Flows (thousands)			
Model	n: 0	1	2	3
Model A				
Investment	−$300			
Depreciation, (300/8,000) (2,000) (0.4)		+$30	+30	+30
Operating costs, (40) (0.6)		−$24	−24	−24
Drilling costs, (35) (0.6)		−$21	−21	−21
Salvage value				+60
Tax credit on salvage, (75 − 60) (0.4)				+6
Totals	−$300	−15	−15	+51
Model B				
Investment	−$450			
Depreciation, (450/12,000) (2,000) (0.4)		+30	+30	+30
Operating costs, (50) (0.6)		−30	−30	−30
Salvage value				+190
Tax credit on salvage, (225 − 190) (0.4)				+14
Totals	−$450	0	0	+$204

$PV(15\%)_A = -\$291,$ $PV(15)_B = -\$316$

The outcome of Example 7.9 depends very much on the salvage values received for the used equipment. We estimated these values by using 1 − (hours used/lifetime in hours)$^{0.8}$. What effect would higher salvage values have, say with an exponent of 1.5 instead of 0.8?

Model A:

$$[1 − (0.75)^{1.5}](300,000) = \$105,000 \text{ salvage value}$$

$$\text{Change in cash flow} = (105,000 − 60,000)(0.6) = +\$27,000$$

$$\text{New } PV = −291,000 + 27,000/(1.15)^3 = −\$273,000$$

Model B:

$$[1 − (0.5)^{1.5}](450,000) = \$291,000 \text{ salvage value}$$

$$\text{Change in cash flow} = (291,000 − 190,000)(0.6) = +\$61,000$$

$$\text{New } PV = −316,000 + 61,000/(1.15)^3 = −\$276,000$$

The numbers have changed to the point that intangible factors are likely to determine the selection.

What would happen if we evaluate models A and B by using *AE*s for their respective lives? First, we need some terminal salvage values; assume 10%, which gives $30,000 and $45,000, respectively. Second, we need to make some assumption about the extra drilling costs for model A; assume they would continue during the fourth year. The annual cash flows would be, as in Table 7.6, −$15,000 for model A and and $0 for model B. The positive salvage values

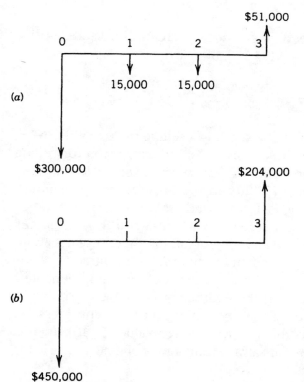

FIGURE 7.4. After-tax cash flows using explicit salvage value estimates, Example 7.9: (*a*) model A, (*b*) model B.

would result in depreciation recapture, so the net salvage proceeds would be $(30,000)(0.6) = \$18,000$ for model A and $(45,000)(0.6) = \$27,000$ for model B. Thus

$$AE(15\%)_A = -300,000\overset{A/P,\ 15\%,\ 4}{(0.3503)} - 15,000 + 18,000\overset{A/F,\ 15\%,\ 4}{(0.2003)}$$

$$= -\$116,485$$

$$AE(15\%)_B = -450,000\overset{A/P,\ 15\%,\ 6}{(0.2642)} + 0 + 27,000\overset{A/F,\ 15\%,\ 6}{(0.1142)}$$

$$= -\$115,807$$

The question at this point is not whether the foregoing analysis is valid, for the problem statement in Example 7.9 implies that it is not. (Many analysts use this method, nevertheless). Rather, we pose this question: Are there 3-year salvage values for models A and B that, when used in a 3-year analysis, yield these AE costs?

The answer is yes, and we can calculate the values as follows [7].

$$AE(15\%)_A = -300,000(A/P,\ 15\%,\ 3) - 15,000 + F_A(A/F,\ 15\%,\ 3)$$
$$= -116,485$$

or

$$AE(15\%)_A = -(300,000 - F_A)(0.4380) - 15,000 - F_A(0.15)$$
$$= -116,485$$

This gives $F_A = \$103,872$, net proceeds after taxes, which implies a selling price of $[103,872 - (0.4)(75,000)]/(0.6) = \underline{\$123,120}$. Similarly,

$$AE(15\%)_B = -(450,000 - F_B)\overset{A/P,\ 15\%,\ 3}{(0.4380)} - F_B(0.15) = -\$115,807$$

and $F_B = \$282,267$, net proceeds after taxes, giving a selling price of $[282,267 - (0.4)(225,000)]/(0.6) = \underline{\$320,445}$. (The derivation of the expression for selling price before depreciation recapture is left as an exercise; see Problem 7.24.)

These 3-year salvage values of \$123,120 and \$320,445 for models A and B, respectively, will result in AE costs of $-\$116,485$ and $-\$115,807$. From another point of view, if we make the selection decision between A and B by using AEs over 4 and 6 years, respectively, we are *implicitly* assuming these 3-year salvage values. Figure 7.5 shows these conversions. In Example 7.9 the contractor needs the equipment for only 3 years and will either sell the selected equipment after the 3-year period or use it elsewhere. If the equipment is sold, the contractor will receive a salvage value. If it is used elsewhere, the contractor considers the *unused value* to be equivalent to the implied salvage value [7, 10]. In this example we might be skeptical of 3-year salvage value ratios of 41% and 71% for bulldozer models A and B, respectively.

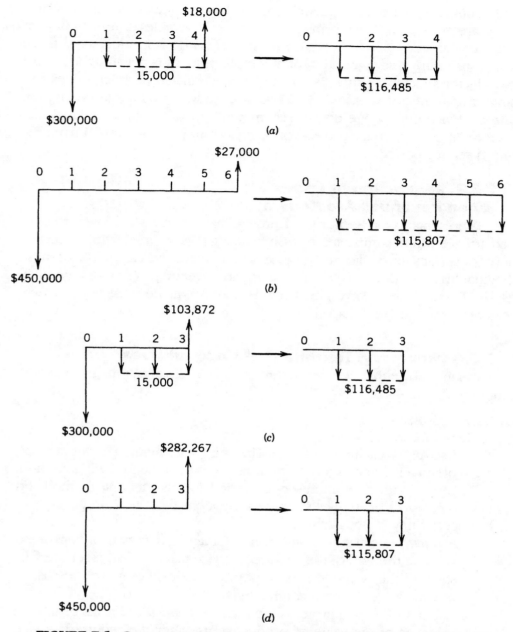

FIGURE 7.5. Conversions to annual equivalents, Example 7.9: (*a*) model A, original life; (*b*) model B, original life; (*c*) model A, 3-year life with implied salvage value; (*d*) model B, 3-year life with implied salvage value.

Sometimes one or more of the projects will have a life shorter than the required service period. One way to analyze such a situation is to *assume explicitly* how the requirement would be satisfied, for instance, by leasing an asset or by subcontracting. The *study period* then coincides with the *required service period,* which is desirable. If we use *AE* over the short life, we are *assuming explicitly* that we can lease an asset or subcontract for the remainder of the required service period at an annual cost equal to the *AE.*

In summary, when using *AE*s over the original, unequal lifetimes of projects, we are making *implicit* assumptions about salvage values or leasing costs at the end of the study period. Because most analysts do not understand these assumptions clearly and calculation of the implied values is not straightforward (especially for an after-tax analysis), we recommend that any salvage values and leasing costs used be *estimated explicitly*. The study period should equal the required service period. We do not recommend using *AE*s over unequal lifetimes for comparing service projects or using a study period different from the required service period.

7.5.3 Reinvestment Issues When Revenues Are Known

The presentation in Section 7.4.1 proved that, when cash inflows are reinvested at *i*, we will maximize future cash by using *PV*(*i*) as a selection criterion. That proof applies for comparing projects with unequal lives as well as of those with equal lives. We thus have a way to compare revenue projects with unequal lives: use *PV*(*i*). (If the reinvestment rate is not known, we must use the techniques presented in later chapters.)

7.5.4 Summary, Treatment of Unequal Lives

We summarize this section in terms of the classification given at the beginning.

1. Service projects
   a. Repeatability is likely.
      i. Use *AE* for each project's life. This is the easy method and is applicable in a greater variety of circumstances than the following method.
      ii. Use *PV* with a common service period. This is a tedious method and it requires or implies stricter assumptions than those in part i.
   b. Repeatability is not likely.
      i. *Explicitly* estimate salvage values for any assets with a remaining value at the end of the required service period. If an asset life falls short of the required service period, explicitly estimate the cost of leasing an asset or subcontracting.
      ii. Using *AE* for each project's life involves *implicit* estimates of salvage value or of the value of productive use after the required service period or both. This method should be used *only* if these implicit values are calculated and judged realistic.

2. Revenue projects
   a. Repeatability is likely.
      i. Use *AE* for each project's life.
      ii. Alternatively, use *PV* with a common service period.
   b. Repeatability is not likely. Use *PV* for each project's life.

It is particularly important to understand the assumptions underlying each of these methods.

7.6 DECISIONS ON THE TIMING OF INVESTMENTS

Sometimes it is possible to change the implementation timing of an investment. There are various reasons why this could occur, related to technology, marketing, production costs, financing costs, and so forth. We discuss briefly some of these situations and indicate how they can be treated analytically. For each situation it is understood that the same investment project with different implementation times should be treated as a set of mutually exclusive projects (a project would be implemented only once, if at all).

A rapidly *changing technology* may be a good reason to consider a timing change. Computer equipment, electronic instrumentation, aircraft, and the like change fast enough that a delay of one or two years in acquiring assets may result in significant differences in operating costs and performance capabilities. Such situations must be evaluated individually.

When the investment involves producing and marketing a product, the *product life cycle* should be considered [6].

PERIOD	CHARACTERISTICS
Early years	Product still being developed.
	High unit costs.
	Relatively small market.
Middle years	Product design is stable.
	Production economies have been achieved.
	Peak annual sales for product.
Late years	Product is being replaced by new ones.
	Annual sales are declining.

Companies with technological strengths try to be leaders and hope to get a marketing advantage by producing an item during its early years. Companies with production and marketing strengths avoid the high development costs and wait until the product design is stable; they will then attempt to produce and market the product at a lower price. During the late years of the product life cycle, the advantage rests with low-cost producers who have widespread marketing organizations. By evaluating its own capabilities, a company can decide how best to utilize its strengths.

Differential inflation rates for first cost have been used to argue for earlier construction of civil works and power plants. For methods for dealing with inflation, see Chapter 2. In the case of nuclear power plants, a positive differential inflation rate combined with more complex technology (related to safety measures) has brought about the cancellation of many planned facilities. Had they been constructed five or ten years earlier, they might have been successful investments.

Changing financing costs are often cited for delaying planned investments. Here we must be careful to separate the effects of raising more capital, perhaps by borrowing, from those of investment in a project. If the financing is not tied directly to the proposed project, a high borrowing cost should be viewed in the context of the company's overall cost of capital and capital structure; see Chapter 5. Viewed in this way, a high current borrowing cost may or may not raise the weighted-average cost of capital sufficiently to make a project undesirable. When borrowing costs are high, a company with financial strength may gain a significant market advantage by investing in new products and services. Delaying investments because of high rates may be shortsighted. Again, each situation must be evaluated by itself.

When we compare different timing decisions for the same project, a common point in time should be selected for the comparison. For example, *PV* at time 0 (a specific date) can be used. Here it is particularly important to have a good estimate of *MARR*, because different lateral time shifts of cash flows for two or more projects may distort the comparison if the *MARR* does not accurately reflect reinvestment opportunities.

7.7 SUMMARY

In this chapter we have shown how the proper use of any of the ten decision criteria presented in Chapter 6 will lead to correct decisions when we select among competing projects. The final selection will be consistent with *PV*, which is the correct, or baseline, criterion to use in a stable, perfect capital market with complete certainty. The necessary steps for proper use of a criterion are

1. Preliminary screening to eliminate unfavorable projects.
2. Forming mutually exclusive alternatives.
3. Ordering the alternatives (not always by the time 0 investment).
4. Applying the incremental procedure.

The total investment approach is guaranteed to work only with *PV, FV, AE,* and *PB*. Moreover, for these four criteria one can use arbitrary ordering with the incremental procedure. Detailed rules apply to *IRR* and make it particularly difficult to use properly.

Use of *PV* implies reinvestment at the rate used for computing *PV*. Since the other criteria, when used properly, give the same project selection, it can be argued that their use also implies reinvestment at the same rate. It is clear that the discount rate, designated *MARR*, must be selected carefully; see Chapter 5. Much has been written about the reinvestment rate implied by use of other criteria, especially *IRR*, but this criterion is of relatively little use for decision making, with the exception of Fisher's intersection.

When comparing projects with unequal lives, one must distinguish between service projects and revenue projects. The likelihood of repeatability affects the analysis techniques to be used. Finally, any salvage value assumptions should be stated clearly and treated explicitly.

This chapter is the last one dealing with "traditional" engineering economic analysis techniques. The next chapter considers more complex decision environments, still assuming certainty. Later chapters deal with variable cash flows and other uncertainties.

REFERENCES

1. Au, T., and T. P. Au, *Engineering Economics for Capital Investment Analysis,* Allyn and Bacon, Boston, 1983.

2. Bernhard, R. H., "A Comprehensive Comparison and Critique of Discounting Indices Proposed for Capital Investment Evaluation," *The Engineering Economist,* Vol. 16, No. 3, pp. 157–186, Spring 1971.

3. Bussey, L. E., *The Economic Analysis of Industrial Projects,* Prentice–Hall, Englewood Cliffs, N.J., 1978 (see Ch. 8).

4. DeGarmo, E. P., W. G. Sullivan, and J. R. Canada, *Engineering Economy,* 7th edition, Macmillan, New York, 1984 (see Chs. 5 and 6).

5. Fisher, I., *The Theory of Interest,* Macmillan, New York, 1930.

6. Kamien, M. I., and N. L. Schwartz, "Timing of Innovations under Rivalry," *Econometrica,* Vol. 40, No. 1, pp. 43–59, 1972.

7. Kulonda, D. J., "Replacement Analysis with Unequal Lives," *The Engineering Economist,* Vol. 23, No. 3, pp. 171–179, Spring 1978.

8. Levy, N. S., "On the Ranking of Economic Alternatives by the Total Opportunity ROR and B/C Ratios—A Note," *The Engineering Economist,* Vol. 26, No. 2, pp. 166–171, Winter 1981.

9. Lohmann, J. R., "The IRR, NPV and the Fallacy of the Reinvestment Rate Assumptions," *The Engineering Economist,* Vol. 33, No. 4, pp. 303–330, Summer 1988.

10. Saxena, U., and A. Garg, "On Comparing Alternatives with Different Lives," *The Engineering Economist,* Vol. 29, No. 1, pp. 59–70, Fall 1983.

11. Theusen, G. J., and W. J. Fabrycky, *Engineering Economy,* 7th edition, Prentice–Hall, Englewood Cliffs, N.J., 1989 (see Ch. 7, Sec. 8.3).

12. White, J. A., M. H. Agee, and K. E. Case, *Principles of Engineering Economic Analysis,* 3rd edition, Wiley, New York, 1989 (see Ch. 5).

13. Wohl, M., "A New Ordering Procedure and Set of Decision Rules for the Internal Rate of Return Method," *The Engineering Economist,* Vol. 30, No. 4, pp. 363–386, Summer 1985.

PROBLEMS

7.1. A company has the capability of manufacturing four products. There are three plants, with product capabilities as follows.

Plant A	Products 1, 2, 4
Plant B	Products 2, 3
Plant C	Products 1, 3, 4

For various reasons, the company does not produce the *same* product in more than *two* plants. In addition, any particular plant is used to produce only *one* product. Form all possible combinations of plants and products that the company should consider.

7.2. If there are four independent investment proposals A, B, C, and D, form all possible investment alternatives with them.

7.3. Apply the ten investment criteria to projects j and k in Example 7.3 to derive the results in Table 7.3.

7.4. Apply the incremental procedure to projects j and k in Example 7.3 to derive the results in Table 7.4.

7.5. Consider the four projects with cash flows as shown.

Project	n: 0	1	2	3
A	−1,000	900	500	100
B	−1,000	600	500	500
C	−2,000	900	900	800
D	+1,000	−402	−402	−402

Before proceeding to the questions, we will need to obtain FV for each project by using $MARR$ = 10%, 20%.

a. Explain why the FV criterion prefers A over B at 20% when it prefers B over A at 10%.

b. With $MARR$ = 10%, how much money would you have at time 3 if you invested $1,000 of your own money in A? In B?

c. Which of the following situations would you prefer?
   i. $MARR$ = 10%; you invest $1000 in B.
   ii. $MARR$ = 20%; you invest $1000 in A.
   Explain your answer.

d. With $MARR$ = 10%, how much money would you have at time 3 if you invested $2,000 of your own money in C?

e. Explain why the FV criterion prefers A over C at 10%, even though in situation d the cash at time 3 is greater than that in situation b (for project A).

f. What is the IRR for D? Would you accept D with $MARR$ = 20%? How would you modify the IRR acceptance rule when examining project D?

g. Suppose A and B are mutually exclusive projects. Which project would you select using $MARR$ of 10% and the IRR criterion?

7.6. Your company is faced with three independent proposals:

Project	n: 0	1	2	3
A	−1,000	500	500	500
B	−1,500	1,000	200	1,000
C	−3,000	1,300	1,300	1,300

a. With a budget of $3,000 at time 0 and $MARR$ = 8%, which project or projects should you choose? Use FV.

b. How much cash would you have at time 3? Answer this part by performing a minimum of computations.

c. Could you use IRR to obtain the answer to part a? Do you foresee any potential difficulties?

7.7. Consider the following three mutually exclusive projects. Each has a lifetime of 20 years and $MARR$ = 15%.

Project	Investment	Annual User Benefits	Annual Sponsor Costs
A	1,000	400	160
B	800	300	110
C	1,500	360	50

a. Select the best project, using the *PV* criterion.

b. Select the best project, using the aggregate benefit–cost ratio.

7.8. Consider the following four mutually exclusive projects. Use the incremental method with *PV* and the aggregate cost–benefit ratio to select the best project. Each has a lifetime of 20 years, and *MARR* = 8%.

Project	Investment	Annual User Benefits	Annual Sponsor Costs
A	978	500	100
B	1,180	492	60
C	1,390	550	120
D	1,600	630	140

7.9. Use *IRR* to select the best of the following three mutually exclusive projects. Each has a lifetime of 10 years, and *MARR* = 15%.

Project	Investment	Annual Net Cash Flow
A	5,000	1,400
B	10,000	2,500
C	8,000	1,900

7.10. Use *IRR* to select the best of the following three independent projects. Each has a lifetime of 5 years, and *MARR* = 8%. The investment budget is $13,000.

Project	Investment	Annual Net Cash Flow
A	5,000	1,319
B	7,000	1,942
C	8,500	2,300

7.11. Use the netted benefit–cost ratio to select the best of the following four mutually exclusive projects. Each has a lifetime of 5 years, and *MARR* = 12%.

Project	Investment	Annual Net Cash Flow
A	10,000	4,438
B	14,000	5,548
C	12,000	5,048
D	5,000	2,774

7.12. Rework Problem 7.11 with the assumption that the projects are independent and the investment budget is $16,000.

7.13. Listed are cash flows for three independent proposals. Use the netted benefit–cost ratio to select the best proposal or proposals with *MARR* = 12% and an investment budget of $34,000.

Project	*n*: 0	1	2	3	4
A	−10,000	4,175	4,175	4,175	4,175
B	−17,500	10,025	3,025	7,025	7,025
C	−15,000	6,025	6,025	6,025	6,025

7.14. Listed are data for three mutually exclusive proposals. Use the aggregate benefit–cost ratio to select the best proposal with $MARR = 10\%$.

	Proposal A		Proposal B		Proposal C	
n	Costs	Benefits	Costs	Benefits	Costs	Benefits
0	10,000	—	14,000	—	17,000	—
1	1,000	5,500	4,000	10,000	1,000	10,000
2	1,000	5,500	4,000	10,000	1,000	3,000
3	1,000	5,500	4,000	10,000	1,000	10,000
4	1,000	5,500	4,000	10,000	1,000	10,000

7.15. Apply *IRR* to the selection in problem 7.14.

7.16. Construct an example in which Solomon's average rate of return yields an answer inconsistent with the netted benefit–cost ratio. Use the total investment approach.

7.17. Prove that if each investment alternative has the same initial investment, then *PV* agrees with the netted benefit–cost ratio. Use the total investment approach.

7.18. Prove that if each investment alternative has a constant net cash flow during its lifetime, then *IRR* agrees with the netted benefit–cost ratio. Use the total investment approach. (Assume a common life).

7.19. What modifications are needed in the accept–reject rules for the aggregate benefit–cost ratio if the ordering for the incremental procedure is by the time 0 investment?

7.20. Prove, or disprove by counterexample, that consistency is obtained across all four groups of investment criteria. Use the total investment approach:

a. When the total invested in each alternative is the same.

b. When the total invested in each alternative is the same, and the lifetimes of all alternatives are the same.

7.21. Prove that incremental analysis with Solomon's average rate of return yields the same answer as *PV* analysis.

7.22. Use the *common service period* approach to compare the following two options. $MARR = 12\%$; ignore taxes.

 i. Initial cost of $1,000, annual costs of $300, salvage value of $100, 10-year lifetime.

 ii. Initial cost of $1,300, annual costs of $270, salvage value of $200, 12-year lifetime.

Is the length of the common service period plausible?

7.23. A manufacturer requires a chemical finishing process for a product produced under contract for a period of 4 years. Three options are available.

 i. Process device A, which costs $100,000, has annual operating and labor costs of $60,000 and an estimated salvage value of $10,000 after 4 years.

 ii. Process device B, which costs $150,000, has annual operating and labor costs of $50,000 and an estimated salvage value of $30,000 after 6 years.

 iii. Subcontracting at $100,000 per year.

a. Which option would you recommend? $MARR = 10\%$.

b. What is the salvage value of process device B after 4 years that would cause the manufacturer to be indifferent in choosing between it and process device A?

c. What options should the manufacturer consider if the required service period is 5 years? 7 years?

7.24. Derive the selling price before depreciation recapture for the assets in Example 7.9.

Outline

Part III: Corporate Finance

- Lecture slides on dividend policy, debt policy, WACC and optimal capital structure

- Chapters 7, 8, 9 and 10 of "Applied Corporate Finance" by Damodaran

Dividend Policy

➢ **The Dividend Controversy**

➢ **The Rightists**

➢ **Taxes and the Radical Left**

➢ **The Middle of the Roaders**

The Dividend Decision

Lintner's "stylized facts" on how dividends are determined)

1. **Companies have long term target dividend payout ratios**

2. **Managers focus more on dividend changes than on absolute dividend levels**

3. **Dividend changes follow shifts in long-run sustainable levels of earnings**

4. **Managers are reluctant to make dividend changes that could be reversed**

Dividend Policy is Irrelevant

Modigliani & Miller

Since investors do not need dividends to convert shares to cash, they will not pay a premium for firms with higher dividend payouts. In other words, dividend policy has no impact on firms' value

Dividends Increase Value

Dividends as Signals

Dividend increases send good news about earnings and cash flows. On the other hand, dividend cuts send bad news

Dividends Decrease Value

Tax Issues

Companies can convert dividends into capital gains by shifting their dividend policies. If dividends are taxed more heavily than capital gains, investors should favor capital gains

Debt Policy

- ➤ **Leverage in a Tax Free Environment**

- ➤ **How Leverage Affects Returns**

- ➤ **The Traditional Position**

Modigliani - Miller

Modigliani & Miller

When there are no taxes and capital markets function well, it makes no difference whether the firm borrows or individual shareholders borrow. Therefore, the market value of a company does not depend on its capital structure

Weighted Average Cost of Capital

Why Do We Use WACC

- **WACC of an asset is the weighed opportunity cost of all investors for putting their money into the asset given the risk of the asset. It therefore reflects:**

  - **The riskiness of the asset, and**

  - **The way the asset is financed**

Weighted Average Cost of Capital

WACC Tree

$$WACC = k_d(1-t)\frac{B}{V} + k_e\frac{S}{V} + k_p\frac{P}{V} + k_l(1-t)\frac{L}{V}$$

- ➤ k_d: cost of debt

- ➤ t: tax rate

- ➤ B: market value of debt

- ➤ V: market value of assets of company

- ➤ k_e: cost of equity

- ➤ S: market value of stocks

- ➤ k_p: cost of preferred stock

- ➤ P: market value of preferred stock

- ➤ k_l: cost of leases

- ➤ L: market value of leases

Weighted Average Cost of Capital

WACC Tree

$$WACC = k_d(1-t)\frac{B}{B+S} + k_e\frac{S}{B+S}$$

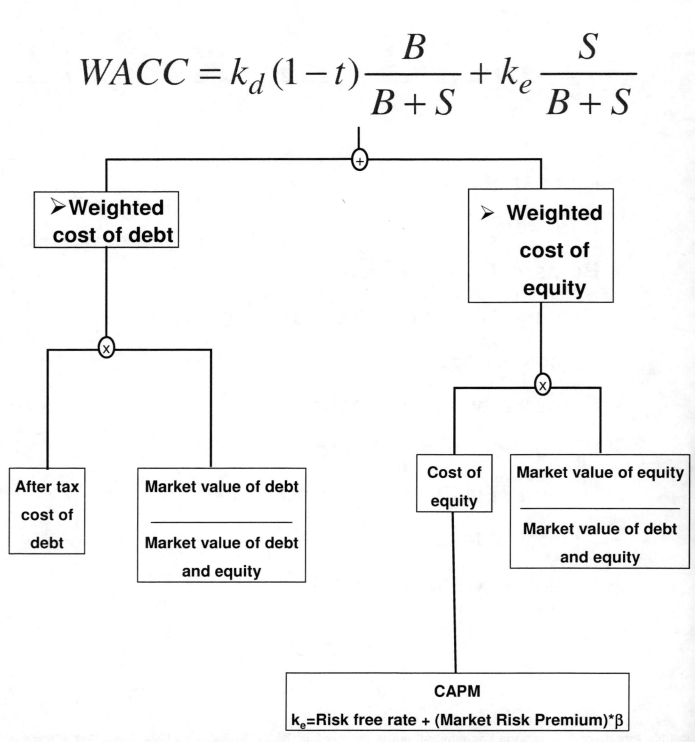

> Weighted cost of debt

> Weighted cost of equity

After tax cost of debt

$$\frac{\text{Market value of debt}}{\text{Market value of debt and equity}}$$

Cost of equity

$$\frac{\text{Market value of equity}}{\text{Market value of debt and equity}}$$

CAPM

k_e=Risk free rate + (Market Risk Premium)*β

Weighted Average Cost of Capital

➢ **For any security (including corporate debt and equity), the nominal rate required by the investors is a function of:**

- **The expected inflation over the life of the security**

- **The expected real rate over the life of the security**

- **The expected interest rate risk premium (if any)**

- **The expected risk premiums**

- **The expected illiquidity premium**

Weighted Average Cost of Capital

Guidelines for Estimating WACC Parameters

➤ **Average rates of return of various securities, 1926-1997**

(%/year)

Inflation	**3.2%**
Treasury Bills (3-month bills)	**3.8%**
Government Bonds	**5.3%**
Corporate Bonds	**5.8%**
Common Stocks (S&P 500)	**11.2%**
Small-firm Common Stocks	**12.9%**

Weighted Average Cost of Capital

Cost of Equity and CAPM

➤ **Cost of equity:**

$$k_e = E[r_e] = r_f + \beta_e \cdot (E[r_m] - r_f)$$

$$\text{where } \beta_e = \frac{Cov(R_e, R_m)}{Var(R_m)}$$

- It takes into account the first four components in our security return decomposition (riskless rate takes into account the first three)

- For the riskless rate, use a long-term government bond rate and for the market risk premium, use the long-term realized risk premium of 3.5-4% (McK)

Weighted Average Cost of Capital (Finer Points)

- **Levering-Unlevering relationship:**

$$\beta_e = \beta_a + [\beta_a - \beta_d](1 - t_c) \cdot \frac{B}{S}$$

This is the crucial formula as now, we can compute a new β_e (and k_e) if we want to use a new capital structure (**B/S**). This is true because:

- ✓ β_{assets} stays the same even if the capital structure changes as long as the projects (=assets) of the company do not change

- ✓ However, we should realize that in dramatic capital structure changes, β_{assets} changes

Cost of Financial Distress

Costs of Financial Distress: Costs arising from bankruptcy or distorted business decisions when close to bankruptcy

Market Value =   *Value if firm is all equity financed*

+ PV tax shield

- PV costs of financial distress

Cost of Financial Distress

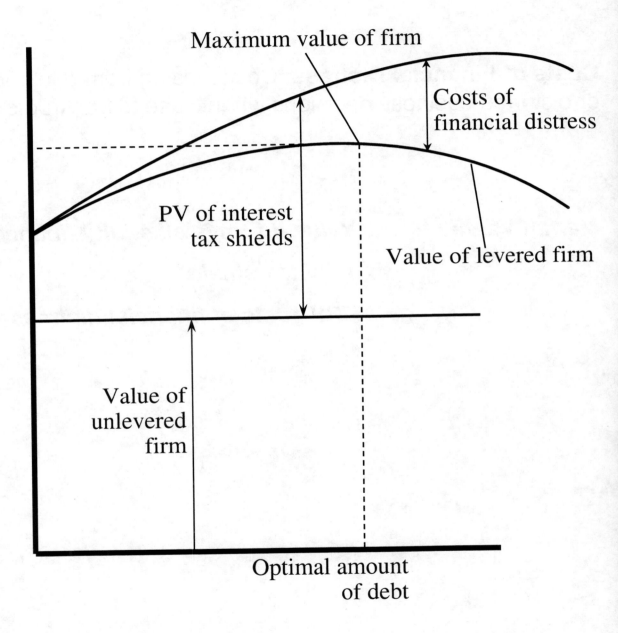

Maximum value of firm

Costs of financial distress

PV of interest tax shields

Value of levered firm

Value of unlevered firm

Optimal amount of debt

Debt

Outline

Part III: Corporate Finance

- Lecture slides on dividend policy, debt policy, WACC and optimal capital structure

- Chapters 7, 8, 9 and 10 of "Applied Corporate Finance" by Damodaran

CHAPTER 7

CAPITAL STRUCTURE: AN OVERVIEW OF THE FINANCING DECISION

In the last few chapters, we have examined the investment principle and argued that projects that earn a return greater than the minimum acceptable hurdle rate are good projects. In coming up with the cost of capital, which we defined to be the minimum acceptable hurdle rate, however, we used the existing financing mix of the firm. In this chapter, we examine the choices that a firm has in terms of financing instruments and the basic trade-off between using debt and equity. In the process, we examine the following questions:

- What are the fundamental characteristics of debt and equity, and what are the different types of debt and equity securities? What are hybrid securities, and why do firms issue them?

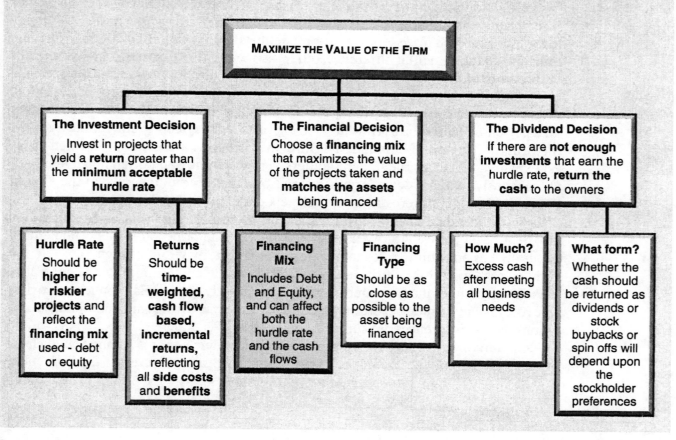

- What is the basic trade-off between debt and equity? Why might more debt be good for some firms and not for others?
- Under what conditions does the financing mix not matter?

THE CHOICES: TYPES OF FINANCING

There are only two ways in which any business can raise money—debt or equity. This may seem simplistic, given the array of choices firms have in terms of financing vehicles. We will begin this section with a discussion of a broad distinction between debt and equity and then look at a range of financing vehicles available within each of these categories. We will then examine securities that share some characteristics with debt and some with equity and are therefore called *hybrid securities*.

Hybrid Security: This refers to any security that shares some of the characteristics of debt and some characteristics of equity.

The Continuum between Debt and Equity

While the distinction between debt and equity is often made in terms of bonds and stocks, its roots lie in the nature of the cash flow claims of each type of financing. The first distinction is that a *debt claim* entitles the holder to a contracted set of cash flows (usually interest and principal payments), whereas an *equity claim* entitles the holder to any residual cash flows left over after meeting all other promised claims. While this remains the fundamental difference, other distinctions have arisen, partly as a result of the tax code and partly as a consequence of legal developments.

The second distinction, which is a logical outgrowth of the nature of cash flow claims (contractual versus residual), is that debt has a prior claim on both cash flows on a period-to-period basis (for interest and principal payments) and on the assets of the firm (in the case of liquidation). Third, the tax laws have generally treated interest expenses, which accrue to debt holders, very differently and often much more advantageously than dividends or other cash flows that accrue to equity. In the United States, for instance, interest expenses are tax deductible, and thus create tax savings, whereas dividend payments have to be made out of after-tax cash flows. Fourth, usually debt has a fixed maturity date, at which point the principal is due, while equity generally has an infinite life. Finally, equity investors, by virtue of their claim on the residual cash flows of the firm, are generally given the bulk of or all of the control of the management of the firm. Debt investors, on the other hand, play a much more passive role in management, exercising, at most, veto power[1] over significant financial decisions. These differences are summarized in Figure 7.1.

To summarize, debt is defined as any financing vehicle that is a contractual claim on the firm (and not a function of its operating performance), creates tax-deductible

---
[1] The veto power is usually exercised through covenants in bond agreements.

470

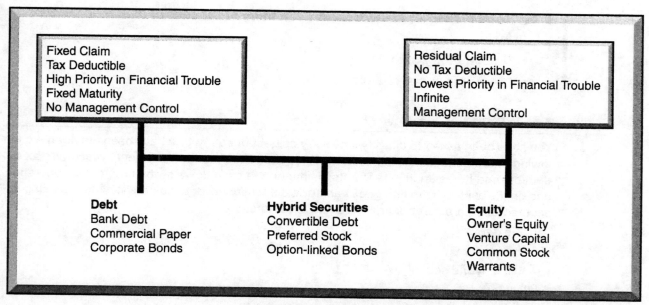

Fixed Claim	Residual Claim
Tax Deductible	No Tax Deductible
High Priority in Financial Trouble	Lowest Priority in Financial Trouble
Fixed Maturity	Infinite
No Management Control	Management Control

Debt
Bank Debt
Commercial Paper
Corporate Bonds

Hybrid Securities
Convertible Debt
Preferred Stock
Option-linked Bonds

Equity
Owner's Equity
Venture Capital
Common Stock
Warrants

Figure 7.1   Debt Versus Equity.

payments, has a fixed life, and has priority claims on cash flows in both operating periods and in bankruptcy. Conversely, equity is defined as any financing vehicle that is a residual claim on the firm, does not create a tax advantage from its payments, has an infinite life, does not have priority in bankruptcy, and provides management control to the owner. Any security that shares characteristics with both is a hybrid security.

IN PRACTICE: A FINANCING CHECKLIST FOR CLASSIFYING SECURITIES

Some new securities, at first sight, are difficult to categorize as either debt or equity. To check where on the spectrum between straight debt and straight equity these securities fall, answer the following questions:

1. *Are the payments on the securities contractual or residual?*
   - If contractual, it is closer to debt.
   - If residual, it is closer to equity.
2. *Are the payments tax deductible?*
   - If yes, it is closer to debt.
   - If no, it is closer to equity.
3. *Do the cash flows on the security have a high priority or a low priority if the firm is in financial trouble?*
   - If it has high priority, it is closer to debt.
   - If it has low priority, it is closer to equity.
4. *Does the security have a fixed life?*
   - If yes, it is closer to debt.
   - If no, it is closer to equity.

5. *Does the owner of the security get a share of the control of management of the firm?*

- If no, it is closer to debt.
- If yes, it is closer to equity.

7.1 IS IT DEBT OR IS IT EQUITY?

You have been asked to classify a security as debt or equity, and have been provided the following characteristics for the security: It requires fixed monthly payments which are tax deductible and it has an infinite life. Its claims on the cash flows of the firm, during operation, and on the assets, if the firm goes bankrupt, come after all debt holders' claims (including unsecured debt) are met but prior to equity investors.

☐ It is debt.

☐ It is equity.

☐ It is a hybrid security.

Explain.

EQUITY

While most people think of equity in terms of common stock, the equity claim can take a variety of forms, depending partly upon whether the firm is privately owned or publicly traded, and partly upon the firm's growth and risk characteristics.

Private firms have fewer choices available than do publicly traded firms, since they cannot issue securities to raise equity. Consequently, they have to depend either upon the owner or a private entity, usually a venture capitalist, to bring in the equity needed to keep the business operating and expanding.

1. Owner's Equity

Most businesses, including the most successful companies of our time, such as Microsoft and Wal-Mart, started off as small businesses with one or a few individuals providing the seed money and plowing back the earnings of the firm into the businesses. These funds, brought in by the owners of the company, are referred to as the *owner's equity,* and provide the basis for the growth and eventual success of the business.

2. Venture Capital

As small businesses succeed and grow, they typically run into a funding constraint, where the funds that they have access to are insufficient to cover their investment and growth needs. A *venture capitalist* provides equity financing to small and often risky businesses in return for a share of the ownership of the firm.

Generally speaking, the capacity to raise funds from alternative sources and/or to go public will increase with the size of the firm and decrease with the uncertainty about its future prospects. Thus, smaller and riskier businesses are more likely to seek venture capital and are also more likely to be asked to give up a disproportionate share of the value of the firm when receiving the venture capital.

Venture Capital: This is usually equity capital provided to a private firm by an investor or investors, in exchange for a share of the ownership of the firm.

7.2 THE EFFECTS OF DIVERSIFICATION ON VENTURE CAPITALISM

You are comparing the required returns of two venture capitalists who are interested in investing in the same software firm. One venture capitalist has all of his capital invested in only software firms, whereas the other venture capitalist has invested her capital in small companies in a variety of businesses. Which of these two will have the higher required rate of return?

☐ The venture capitalist who is invested only in software companies
☐ The venture capitalist who is invested in a variety of businesses
☐ Cannot answer without more information

7.3 REQUIRED RETURN AND PROPORTIONAL OWNERSHIP

If both venture capitalists described above had the same expected cash flow estimates for the business, which one would demand a larger share of the ownership for the same capital investment?

☐ The venture capitalist with the higher required rate of return
☐ The venture capitalist with the lower required rate of return

3. Common Stock

The conventional way for a publicly traded firm to raise equity is to issue common stock at a price the market is willing to pay. For a newly listed company, this price is estimated by the issuing entity (such as an investment banker); for an existing company, it is based upon the current market price. In some cases, the common stock issued by a company is uniform; that is, each share receives a proportional share of both the cash flows (such as dividends) and the voting rights. In other cases, different classes of common stock will provide different cash flows and voting rights.

While existing firms do not use common stock very often to raise new financing for their projects and operations, it remains the most widely used approach to raising equity. Common stock is a simple security, and it is relatively easy to understand and value. In fact, it can be argued that common stock makes feasible all other security choices for a publicly traded firm, since a firm without equity cannot issue debt or hybrid securities. The accounting treatment of common stock follows well-established precedent and can be presented easily within the conventional format of financial statements.

4. Warrants

In recent years, firms have started looking at equity alternatives to common stock. One alternative used successfully by the Japanese companies in the late 1980s involved warrants, where the holders received the right to buy shares in the company at a fixed price in return for paying for the warrants up front. Since their value is derived from the price of the underlying common stock, warrants have to be treated as another form of equity.

Why might a firm use warrants rather than common stock to raise equity? We can think of several reasons. First, warrants are priced based upon the implied volatility assigned to the underlying stock; the greater the volatility, the greater the value. To the degree that the market overestimates the firm's volatility, the firm may gain by using warrants and option-like securities. Second, warrants, by themselves, create no financial obligations at the time of the issue. Consequently, issuing warrants is a good way for a high-growth firm to raise funds, especially when current cash flows are low or nonexistent. Third, for financial officers who are sensitive to the dilution created by issuing common stock, warrants seem to provide the best of both worlds—they do not create any new additional shares currently, while they raise equity investment funds for current use.

Warrants: A warrant is a security issued by a company that provides the holder with the right to buy a share of stock in the company at a fixed price during the life of the warrant.

7.4 STOCK PRICE VARIANCE AND WARRANT USE

Companies with high variance in their stock prices should use warrants more than companies with low variance in their stock prices, because warrant prices increase with variance.

☐ True

☐ False

Explain.

IN PRACTICE: VALUING WARRANTS

Warrants are long-term call options, but standard option pricing models are based upon the assumption that exercising an option does not affect the value of the underlying asset. This may be true for listed options on stocks, but it is not true for warrants, since their exercise increases the number of shares outstanding and brings fresh cash into the firm, both of which will affect the stock price. The expected negative impact (dilution) of exercise will make warrants less valuable than otherwise similar call options. The adjustment for dilution to the stock price in the Black-Scholes model involves three steps:

Step 1: The stock price is adjusted for the expected dilution from warrant exercise:

$$\text{Dilution-adjusted S} = S + \frac{n_w}{n_s} W$$

where

S = Current value of the stock $\qquad$ n_w = Number of warrants outstanding

W = Market value of warrants outstanding $\quad$ n_s = Number of shares outstanding

When the warrants are exercised, the number of shares outstanding will increase, reducing the stock price. The numerator reflects the market value of equity, including both stocks and warrants outstanding.

Step 2: The variance used in the option pricing formula is the variance in the value of the equity in the company (i.e., the value of stocks plus warrants, not just the stocks).

Step 3: Once the call is valued using the option pricing model, the option value is adjusted to reflect dilution:

Dilution-Adjusted Value = Call Value from Model $* \, n_s / (n_w + n_s)$

5. Contingent Value Rights

Contingent value rights provide investors with the right to sell stocks for a fixed price, and thus derive their value from the volatility of the stock and the desire on the part of investors to hedge against losses. *Put options,* which are traded on the option exchanges, give their holders a similar right to sell the underlying stock at a fixed price. There are two primary differences between contingent value rights and puts. First, the proceeds from the contingent value rights sales go to the firm, whereas those from the sale of listed puts go to private parties. Second, contingent value rights tend to be much more long term than typical listed puts.

There are several reasons why a firm may choose to issue contingent value rights. The most obvious is that the firm believes it is significantly undervalued by the market. In such a scenario, the firm may offer contingent value rights to take advantage of its belief and to provide a signal to the market of the undervaluation. Contingent value rights are also useful if the market is overestimating volatility and the put price reflects this misestimated volatility. Finally, the presence of contingent value rights as insurance may attract new investors to the market for the common stock.

 Contingent Value Rights: A contingent value right (CVR) provides the holder with the right to sell a share of stock in the underlying company at a fixed price during the life of the right.

DEBT

The clear alternative to using equity, which is a residual claim, is to borrow money. This option both creates a fixed obligation to make cash flow payments and provides the lender with prior claims if the firm is in financial trouble.

1. Bank Debt

Historically, the primary source of borrowed money for all private firms and many publicly traded firms have been commercial banks with the interest rates on the debt based upon the perceived risk of the borrower. Bank debt provides the borrower with several advantages. First, it can be used for borrowing relatively small amounts of money; in contrast, bond issues thrive on economies of scale, with larger issues having lower costs. Second, if the company is neither well known nor widely followed, bank debt provides a convenient framework to convey information to the lender that will help in both pricing and evaluating the loan. The presence of hundreds of investors in bond issues makes this both costly and infeasible if bonds are issued as the primary vehicle for debt. Finally, in order to issue bonds, firms have to submit to being rated. The added dynamic of dealing with ratings agencies, in addition to the equity investors, may create conflicts between the two, which the manager then has to resolve. In contrast, firms have to deal with only the lending bank when they take on bank debt, which may be simpler to do in some cases,[2] and minimizes the amount of information that they have to make public.

---

[2]This is especially true if the bank is a local bank and knows the firm well. This knowledge may allow the bank to grant more freedom to the borrowing firm.

7.5   CORPORATE BONDS AND BANK DEBT

If a company can issue corporate bonds, it should not use bank debt.

☐   True

☐   False

Explain.

2. Bonds

For larger publicly traded firms, an alternative to bank debt is to issue bonds. Generally speaking, bond issues have several advantages. One is that bonds usually carry more favorable financing terms than equivalent bank debt, largely because risk is shared by a larger number of financial market investors. A second advantage is that bond issues might provide a chance for the issuer to add on special features that could not be added on to bank debt. For instance, bonds can be convertible into common stock or have commodity options attached to them. In borrowing money, firms have to make a variety of choices including:

1.   Whether the debt should be *short term* or *long term*

2.   Whether the interest payments on the debt should be *fixed* for the lifetime of the borrowing or be a function of a market interest rate *(floating rate)*

3.   Whether the debt should be *secured* using specific assets or the general cash flows of the firm

4.   What *currency* the cash flows on the debt should be in

5.   How the debt should be *repaid*

6.   Any *special features* that should be added on to the debt

7.6   DEBT MATURITY AND INTEREST RATES

Assume that you have an upward-sloping yield curve, and that your investment banker advises you to issue short-term debt because it is cheaper than long-term debt. Is this true?

☐   Yes

☐   No

Why or why not?

IN PRACTICE: DEBT INNOVATIONS

The past two decades have seen an explosion in new features added on to bonds. Some, such as floating rates and caps and floors, arose as a consequence of the high inflation and interest rate volatility that characterized the late 1970s. Some of these features take advantage of the better understanding issuers (or their agents) have of how to price options. Table 7.1 summarizes some of the most important innovations, and the rationale for their introduction. While these innovations provide both companies and buyers with more options and the capacity to tailor bonds to their specific needs, they do carry a downside. The special features, especially when combined, become more and more difficult to value and to keep track of over time.

Table 7.1 INNOVATIONS IN BOND MARKET

Innovation	Description	Rationale for Innovation
Floating rate loans	Interest rate varies with index	Volatility in inflation and interest rates
Puttable bonds	Bondholders can put bond back to firm, and get face value, under specified events	Protection of bondholder interests
Convertible/exchangeable floating rate notes	Floating rate note can be converted into equity	Provide flexibility to buyer of bond
Extendable bonds	Life of the bond can be extended at the option of the issuer	Provide more flexibility to the issuer
Caps and floors	Limits interest rate movements on a floating rate loan	Limit risk to issuer and buyer
Swaps	Allows exchange of bonds for bonds with different characteristics (fixed to floating, different currency)	Allow firms to alter their financing mix
Reverse floating rate notes	Interest rate varies inversely with an index; as index rate goes up, rate on bond goes down	Increase duration and price sensitivity of bond
Swaptions	Option on a swap	Allows firms to buy options to do swaps

HYBRID SECURITIES

Summarizing our analysis thus far, equity represents a residual claim on the cash flows and assets of the firm and is generally associated with management control. Debt, on the other hand, represents a fixed claim on the cash flows and assets of the firm and is usually not associated with management control. There are a number of securities that do not fall neatly into either of these two categories; rather, they share some characteristics with equity and some with debt. These securities are called *hybrid securities.*

1. Convertible Debt

A *convertible bond* is a bond that can be converted into a predetermined number of shares, at the discretion of the bondholder. While it generally does not pay to convert at the time of the bond issue, conversion becomes a more attractive option as stock prices increase. Firms generally add conversion options to bonds to lower the interest rate paid on the bonds.

In a typical convertible bond, the bondholder is given the option to convert the bond into a specified number of shares of stock. The *conversion ratio* measures the number of shares of stock for which each bond may be exchanged. Stated differently, the *market conversion value* is the current value of the shares for which the bonds can be exchanged. The *conversion premium* is the excess of the bond value over the conversion value of the bond.

Thus, a convertible bond with a par value of $1,000, which is convertible into 50 shares of stock, has a conversion ratio of 50. The conversion ratio can also be used to compute a conversion price—the par value divided by the conversion ratio— yielding a conversion price of $20. If the current stock price is $25, the market conversion value is $1,250 (50 * $25). If the convertible bond is trading at $1,300, the conversion premium is $50.

Convertible Debt: This is debt that can be converted into equity at a rate that is specified as part of the debt agreement (conversion rate).

IN PRACTICE: A SIMPLE APPROACH TO DECOMPOSING DEBT AND EQUITY

The value of a convertible debt can be decomposed into straight debt and equity components using a simple approach. Since the price of a convertible bond is the sum of the straight debt and the call option components, the value of the straight bond component in conjunction with the market price of the convertible bond should be sufficient to estimate the call option component, which is also the equity component:

Value of Equity Component = Market Price of Convertible Bond − Value of Straight Bond Component

The value of the straight bond component can be estimated using the coupon payments on the convertible bond, the maturity of the bond and the market interest rate the company would have to pay on a straight debt issue. This last input can be estimated directly if the company also has straight bonds in the market place, or it can be based upon the bond rating, if any, assigned to the company.

For instance, assume that you have a 10-year convertible bond, with a 5% coupon rate trading at $1,050, and that the company has a debt rating of BBB (with a market interest rate of 8%). The value of the straight bond and equity components can be estimated as follows:

Straight Bond Component = $50 (PVA, 10 years, 8%) + $1000/1.08^{10}$ = $798.69
Equity Component = $1,050 − $799 = $251

7.7 CONVERTIBLE DEBT AND YIELDS

The yields on convertible bonds are much lower than the yields on straight bonds issued by a company. Therefore, convertible debt is cheaper than straight debt.

☐ True
☐ False
Why or why not?

2. Preferred Stock

Preferred stock is another security that shares some characteristics with debt and some with equity. Like debt, preferred stock has a fixed dollar dividend; if the firm does not have the cash to pay the dividend, it is cumulated and paid in a period when there are sufficient earnings. Like debt, preferred stockholders do not have a share of control in the firm, and their voting privileges are restricted to issues that might affect their claims on the firm's cash flows or assets. Like equity, payments to preferred stockholders are not tax deductible and come out of after-tax cash flow. Also like equity, preferred stock does not have a maturity date when the face value is due. In terms of priority, in the case of bankruptcy, preferred stockholders have to wait until the debtholders' claims have been met before receiving any portion of the assets of the firm.

While accountants and ratings agencies continue to treat preferred stock as equity, it can be argued that the fixed commitments that preferred stock create are like debt obligations and have to be dealt with likewise. The obligations created by preferred stock are generally less onerous than those created by debt, however, since they are cumulated, cannot cause default, and do not have priority over debt claims in the case of bankruptcy.

Unlike convertible debt, which can be decomposed into equity and debt components, preferred stock cannot really be treated as debt because preferred dividends are not tax deductible and certainly cannot be viewed as the equivalent of equity because of the differences in cash flow claims and control. Consequently, preferred stock is treated as a third component of capital, in addition to debt and equity, for purposes of capital structure analysis and for estimating the cost of capital.

Preferred Stock: This is a hybrid security. Like debt, it has a promised payment (the preferred dividend) in each period. Like equity, its cash flows are not tax deductible and it has an infinite life.

7.8 PREFERRED STOCK AND EQUITY

Many ratings agencies and regulators treat preferred stock as equity in computing debt ratios because it does not have a finite maturity and firms cannot be forced into bankruptcy if they fail to pay preferred dividends. Do you agree with this categorization?

☐ Yes
☐ No
Why or why not?

3. Option-Linked Bonds

In recent years, firms have recognized the value of combining options with straight bonds to create bonds that more closely match the firm's specific needs. Consider two examples. In the first, commodity companies issued bonds linking the principal and/or interest payments to the price of the commodity. Thus interest payments would rise if the price of the commodity increased, and would fall if the commodity's price fell. The benefit for the company was that it tailored the cash flows on the bond to the cash flows from its assets and reduced the likelihood of default. These *commodity-linked bonds* can be viewed as a combination of a straight bond and a call option on the underlying commodity. In the second example, consider insurance companies that have recently issued bonds whereby the principal or interest on the bond is reduced in the case of a specified catastrophe, and remains unaffected in its absence. For instance, an insurance firm which has the bulk of its revenues coming from homeowners' insurance in California, might attach a provision that reduces principal and/or interest in the case of a major earthquake. Again, the rationale is to provide the firm with some breathing room when it needs it the most—when a catastrophe creates huge cash outflows for the firm.

Commodity Bonds: Commodity bonds are bonds where the interest and/or the principal payments are linked to the price of the commodity. In most cases, the payments will increase with the price of the commodity and decrease if it drops.

THE BENEFITS OF DEBT

In the broadest terms, debt provides two differential benefits over equity. The first is the *tax benefit:* interest payments on debt are tax deductible, while cash flows on equity are not. The second is the *added discipline imposed on management,* by having to make payments on debt. Both benefits can and should be quantified if firms want to make reasonable judgments on debt capacity.

Debt Has a Tax Advantage

The primary benefit of debt relative to equity is the tax advantage it confers on the borrower. In the United States, interest paid on debt is tax deductible, whereas cash flows on equity (such as dividends) have to be paid out of after-tax cash flows. For the most part, this is true in other countries as well, though some countries try to provide partial protection against the *double taxation* of dividends by providing a tax credit to investors who receive the dividends for the corporate taxes paid (Britain) or by taxing retained earnings at a rate higher than dividends (Germany).

Double Taxation: There is double taxation when the same income gets taxed twice, once at the entity level and once at the individual level. Thus, dividends, which are paid out of after-tax corporate profits, are double taxed when individuals have to pay taxes on them as well.

The tax benefits from debt can be presented in two ways. In the first approach, the present value of tax savings arising from interest payments are computed and added on to firm value. In the second approach, the savings from the tax deduction are shown as the difference between the pre-tax rate of borrowing and the after-tax rate.

The Dollar Tax Savings

Consider a firm that borrows B to finance its operations, on which it faces an interest rate of $r\%$, and assume that it faces a marginal tax rate of t on income. The annual tax savings from the interest tax deduction can be calculated as follows:

Annual Interest Expense Arising from the Debt = r B
Annual Tax Savings Arising from the Interest Payment = t r B

The present value of the annual tax savings can be computed by making three other assumptions. The first is that the debt is perpetual, which also means that the dollar savings are a perpetuity. The second is that the appropriate discount rate for this cash flow is the interest rate on the debt, since it reflects the riskiness of the debt. The third is that the expected tax rate for the firm will remain unchanged over time, and that the firm is in a tax-paying position. With these three assumptions, the present value of the savings can be computed as follows:

Present Value of Tax Savings from Debt $\quad = t\,r\,B\,/\,r = t\,B$
$= \text{Marginal Tax Rate} * \text{Debt}$

While the conventional view is to look at the tax savings as a perpetuity, the approach is general enough to be used to compute the tax savings over a shorter period (say, ten years). Thus, a firm which borrows $100 million at 8% for ten years, and has a tax rate of 40%, can compute the present value of its tax savings as follows:

Present Value of Interest Tax Savings = Annual Tax Savings (PV of Annuity)
$= (.08 * 0.4 * \$100 \text{ million})$ (PV of Annuity, 8%, 10 years) = $ 21.47 million

In addition, the net tax benefit can be computed if dividends also provide a tax benefit, albeit one that is smaller than that conferred by debt. In such a case, the present value of the net tax savings from debt can be written as:

Present Value of Net Tax Savings from Debt
= PV of Tax Savings from Debt − PV of Tax Savings from Dividend Payments

To illustrate, consider the example of a country whose tax rate on cash paid out as dividends (t_{div}) is less than the tax rate on retained earnings (t_{re}). The present value of the tax savings arising from dividends can be written as follows, assuming a growth rate of g in dividends and a cost of equity of k_e:

Present Value of Tax Savings from Dividends = $(t_{re} - t_{div})$ Dividend $(1 + g) / (k_e - g)$

Note that this is the present value of a growing perpetuity.

When asked to analyze the effect of adding debt on value, some analysts use a shortcut and simply add the tax benefit from debt to the value of the firm with no debt:

Value of Levered Firm with Debt B = Value of Unlevered Firm + t B

The limitation of this approach is that it considers only the tax benefit from borrowing and none of the additional costs. It also yields the unrealistic conclusion that firm value increases monotonically with more debt.

Marginal Tax Rate: This is the tax rate that applies on the marginal dollar of income at a firm. In general, it will be higher than the average tax rate.

Pretax and After-Tax Costs

The tax benefit from debt can also be expressed in terms of the difference between the pre-tax and after-tax cost of debt. To illustrate, if r is the interest rate on debt, and t is the marginal tax rate, the after-tax cost of borrowing (k_d) can be written as follows:

$$\text{After-Tax Cost of Debt } (k_d) = r\,(1 - t)$$

This is the familiar formula used for calculating the cost of debt in the cost of capital calculation. In this formula, the after-tax cost of debt is a decreasing function of the tax rate. A firm with a tax rate of 40%, which borrows at 8%, has an after-tax cost of debt of 4.8%. Another firm with a tax rate of 70%, which borrows at 8%, has an after-tax cost of debt of 2.4%. There are two points to be emphasized in this calculation. First, the tax rate to be used is the *marginal rate* and not the average rate, since interest tax deductions are set off against the marginal dollar. Second, this calculation makes sense only if the firm is making money and paying taxes; a firm that has large accumulated losses and no taxable income may not get a tax benefit from debt.

7.9 NET OPERATING LOSS CARRYFORWARDS AND TAX BENEFITS

(?) You have been asked to assess the after-tax cost of debt for a firm which has $2 billion in net operating losses to carry forward and operating income of roughly $2 billion this year. If the company can borrow at 8%, and the marginal corporate tax rate is 40%, the after-tax cost of debt this year is

☐ 8%.

☐ 4.8%.

What would your after-tax cost of debt be next year?

Implications for Optimal Capital Structure

Other things remaining equal, the benefits of debt are much greater when tax rates are higher. Consequently, there are four predictions that can be made about debt ratios across companies and across time.

1. The debt ratios of entities facing higher tax rates should be higher than the debt ratios of comparable entities facing lower tax rates. These differences in tax rates across entities are most commonly seen in U.S. real estate, where operations can be organized as Real Estate Investment Trusts (REITs) or Master Limited Partnerships (MLPs), whereby the income is taxed at the individual investor level rather than the entity level or as corporations where income is

taxed at both levels. We would expect REITs and MLPs to have lower debt ratios than real estate corporations.

2. Firms that have substantial non-debt tax shields, such as depreciation, should be less likely to use debt than firms that do not have these tax shields.

3. If tax rates increase over time, we would expect debt ratios to go up over time as well, reflecting the higher tax benefits of debt.

4. While it is always difficult to compare debt ratios across countries, we would expect debt ratios in countries where debt has a much larger tax benefit or whose tax rates are higher to be higher than debt ratios in countries where debt has a lower tax benefit.

Real Estate Investment Trusts (REITs) A real estate investment trust is an entity that owns real estate and is allowed to pass through its earnings to its investors without being taxed. In return, it is restricted to just real estate investments, and it has to pay 95% of its earnings as dividends.

The Discipline of Debt

In the 1980s, in the midst of the leveraged buyout boom, a group of practitioners and academics, led by Michael Jensen at Harvard, developed and expounded on a new rationale for borrowing, based upon improving firms' efficiency in the utilization of their free cash flows. *Free cash flows* represent cash flows made on operations over which managers have discretionary spending power—they may use them to take projects, pay them out to stockholders, or hold them as idle cash balances. The group argued that managers in firms that have substantial free cash flows and no or low debt have such a large cash cushion against mistakes that they have no incentive to be efficient in either project choice or project management. One way to introduce discipline into the process is to force these firms to borrow money, since borrowing creates the commitment to make interest and principal payments, increasing the risk of default on projects with substandard returns. It is this difference between the forgiving nature of the equity commitment and the inflexibility of the debt commitment that has led some to call equity a cushion and debt a sword.

The underlying assumptions in this argument are that there is a separation of ownership and management, and that managers will not maximize shareholder wealth without a prod (debt). From our discussion in Chapter 2, it is clear that both assumptions are grounded in fact. Most large U.S. corporations employ managers who own only a very small portion of the outstanding stock in the firm; they receive much of their income as managers rather than stockholders. Furthermore, evidence indicates that managers, at least sometimes, put their interests ahead of those of stockholders.

While conceding the need for discipline, we would also add that debt may have a beneficial effect *only up to a certain point*. At some point, the risk added by the leverage may be so great that managers become reluctant to take even the slightest risks, for fear of bankruptcy, and turn down even good projects.

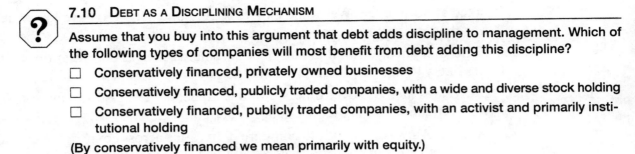

7.10 DEBT AS A DISCIPLINING MECHANISM

Assume that you buy into this argument that debt adds discipline to management. Which of the following types of companies will most benefit from debt adding this discipline?

☐ Conservatively financed, privately owned businesses

☐ Conservatively financed, publicly traded companies, with a wide and diverse stock holding

☐ Conservatively financed, publicly traded companies, with an activist and primarily institutional holding

(By conservatively financed we mean primarily with equity.)

Free Cash Flows (Jensen's): The free cash flows referred to here are the operating cash flows after taxes, but before discretionary capital expenditures.

Management Considerations on Using Debt

The argument that debt adds discipline to the process also provides an interesting insight into management perspectives on debt. Based purely upon managerial incentives, the optimal level of debt may be much lower than that estimated based upon shareholder wealth maximization. Left to themselves, why would managers want to burden themselves with debt, knowing fully well that they will have to become more efficient and pay a larger price for their mistakes?

The corollary to this argument is that the debt ratios of firms in countries in which stockholder power to influence or remove managers is minimal will be much lower than optimal because managers enjoy a more comfortable existence by carrying less debt than they can afford to. Conversely, as stockholders acquire power, they will push these firms to borrow more money and, in the process, increase their stock prices.

There is a data set on the Web that summarizes, by sector, the percentage of stock that is closely held and debt ratios (**indcapst.xls**).

The Empirical Evidence

Do increases in leverage lead to improved efficiency? The answer to this question should provide some insight into whether the argument for added discipline has some basis. A number of studies have attempted to answer this question, though most have done so indirectly.

- Firms that are taken over in hostile takeovers are generally characterized by poor performance in both accounting profitability and stock returns. Bhide (1993), for instance, notes that the return on equity of these firms is 2.2% below their peer group, while the stock returns are 4% below the peer group's returns.

- While the poor performance, by itself, does not constitute support for the free cash flow hypothesis, Palepu (1986) presents evidence that target firms in acquisitions are underleveraged relative to similar firms that are not taken over.

- There is evidence that increases in leverage are followed by improvements in operating efficiency. Palepu (1990) presents evidence of modest improvements in operating efficiency at firms involved in leveraged buyouts. Kaplan (1989) and Smith (1990) also report improvements in operating efficiency at firms following leveraged buyouts. Denis and Denis (1993) present more direct evidence of improvements in operating efficiency after leveraged recapitalizations. In their study of 29 firms, which increased debt substantially, they report a median increase in the return on assets of 21.5%. Much of this gain seems to arise out of cutbacks in unproductive capital investments, since the median reduction in capital expenditures of these firms is 35.5%.

Of course, we must consider that the evidence presented above is consistent with a number of different hypotheses, among them the free cash flow hypothesis. Moreover, acquisitions, which often comprise the sample in most of these studies, are accompanied by a number of changes, in addition to leverage shifts, making it difficult to isolate the impact of leverage on firm performance.

Leveraged Recapitalization: In a leveraged recapitalization, a firm borrows money and either buys back stock or pays a dividend, thus increasing its debt ratio substantially.

THE COSTS OF DEBT

As any borrower will attest, debt certainly has disadvantages. In particular, borrowing money can expose the firm to default and eventual liquidation, increase the agency problems arising from the conflict between the interests of equity investors and lenders, and reduce the flexibility of the firm to take actions now or in the future.

A. Bankruptcy Costs

The primary concern when borrowing money is the increase in expected bankruptcy costs that typically follows. The expected bankruptcy cost can be written as a product of the probability of bankruptcy and the direct and indirect costs of bankruptcy.

The Probability of Bankruptcy

The *probability of bankruptcy* is the likelihood that a firm's cash flows will be insufficient to meet its promised debt obligations (interest and principal). While such a failure does not automatically imply bankruptcy, it does trigger default, with all its negative consequences. Using this definition, we find that the probability of bankruptcy is a function of the following:

1. *Size of operating cash flows relative to size of cash flows on debt obligations:* Other things remaining equal, the larger the operating cash flows relative to the cash flows on debt obligations, the smaller the likelihood of bankruptcy. Accordingly, the probability of bankruptcy increases marginally for all firms, as they borrow more money, irrespective of how large and stable their cash flows might be.

2. *Variance in operating cash flows:* Given the same cash flows on debt, a firm with stable and predictable cash flows has a lower probability of bankruptcy than does another firm with a similar level of operating cash flows, but with far greater variability in these cash flows.

 There is a data set on the Web that summarizes, by sector, variances in operating earnings (**indcapst.xls**).

The Cost of Bankruptcy

The cost of going bankrupt is neither obvious nor easily quantified. It is true that bankruptcy is a disaster for all involved in the firm—lenders often get a fraction of what they are owed, and equity investors get nothing—but the overall cost of bankruptcy includes the indirect costs on operations of being perceived as having high default risk.

1. Direct Costs

The direct, or deadweight, cost of bankruptcy is that which is incurred in terms of cash outflows at the time of bankruptcy. These costs include the legal and administrative costs of a bankruptcy, as well as the present value effects of delays in paying out the cash flows. Warner (1977) estimated the legal and administrative costs of 11 railroads to be, on average, 5.3% of the value of the assets at the time of the bankruptcy. He also estimated that it took, on average, 13 years before the railroads were reorganized and released from the bankruptcy costs. These costs, while certainly not negligible, are not overwhelming, especially in light of two additional factors. First, the direct cost as a percentage of the value of the assets decreases to 1.4% if the asset value is computed five years before the bankruptcy. Second, railroads, in general, are likely to have higher bankruptcy costs than other companies, because of the nature of their assets (real estate and fixed equipment).

2. Indirect Costs

If the only costs of bankruptcy were the direct costs noted above, the low leverage maintained by many firms would be puzzling. There are, however, much larger costs associated with taking on debt and increasing default risk, which arise prior to the bankruptcy, largely as a consequence of the perception that a firm is in financial trouble. The first is the perception on the part of the *customers of the firm* that the firm is in trouble. When this happens, customers may *stop buying the product or service,* because of the fear that the company will go out of business. In 1980, for example, when car buyers believed that Chrysler was on the verge of bankruptcy, they chose to buy from Ford, GM, and other car manufacturers, largely because they were concerned about receiving service and parts for their cars after their purchases. Similarly, in the late 1980s, when Continental Airlines found itself in financial trouble, business travelers switched to other airlines because they were unsure about whether they would be able to accumulate and use their frequent flier miles on the airline. The second indirect cost is the stricter terms *suppliers start demanding* to protect themselves against the possibility of default, leading to an increase in working capital and a decrease in cash flows. The third cost is the difficulty the firm may experience trying *to raise fresh capital* for its projects—both debt and equity investors are reluctant to take the risk, leading to capital rationing constraints, and the rejection of good projects.

Shapiro (1986) points out that the indirect costs of bankruptcy are likely to be higher for the following types of firms:

- *Firms that sell durable products with long lives that require replacement parts and service:* Thus, a personal computer manufacturer would have higher indirect costs associated with bankruptcy than would a grocery store.

- *Firms that provide goods or services for which quality is an important attribute but is difficult to determine in advance:* Since the quality cannot be determined easily in advance, the reputation of the firm plays a significant role in whether the customer will buy the product in the first place. For instance, the perception that an airline is in financial trouble may scare away customers who worry that the planes belonging to the airline will not be maintained in good condition.

- *Firms producing products whose value to customers depends on the services and complementary products supplied by independent companies:* Returning to the example of personal computers, a computer system is valuable only insofar as there is software available to run it. If the firm manufacturing the computers is perceived to be in trouble, it is entirely possible that the independent suppliers that produce the software might stop providing it. Thus, as Apple Computers gets into financial trouble, many software manufacturers might stop producing software for its computers, leading to an erosion in its potential market.

- *Firms that sell products that require continuous service and support from the manufacturer:* A manufacturer of copying machines, for which constant service seems to be a necessary operating characteristic, would be affected more adversely by the perception of default risk than would a furniture manufacturer, for example.

7.11 DEBT AND BANKRUPTCY

Rank the following companies on the magnitude of bankruptcy costs from most to least, taking into account both explicit and implicit costs:

☐ Grocery store

☐ Airplane manufacturer

☐ High-technology company

Explain.

Implications for Optimal Capital Structure

If the expected bankruptcy cost is indeed the product of the probability of bankruptcy and the direct and indirect bankruptcy cost, interesting and testable implications emerge for capital structure decisions:

1. Firms operating in businesses with volatile earnings and cash flows should use debt less than should otherwise similar firms with stable cash flows. For instance, regulated utilities in the United States have high leverage because regulation and the monopolistic nature of their businesses result in stable earnings and cash flows. At the other extreme, toy manufacturing firms such as Mattel can have large shifts in income from one year to another, based upon the commercial success or failure of a single toy.[3] These firms should use leverage far less in meeting their funding needs.

2. If firms can structure their debt in such a way that the cash flows on the debt increase and decrease with their operating cash flows, they can afford to borrow

---

[3]In years past, a single group of toys, such as the Teenage Mutant Ninja Turtles or the Power Rangers, could account for a substantial proportion of a major toy manufacturer's profits.

more. This is because the probability of default is greatest when operating cash flows decrease, and the concurrent reduction in debt cash flows makes the default risk lower. Commodity companies, whose operating cash flows increase and decrease with commodity prices, may be able to use more debt if the debt payments are linked to commodity prices. Similarly, a company whose operating cash flows increase as interest rates (and inflation) go up and decrease when interest rates go down may be able to use more debt if the debt has a floating rate feature.

3. If an external entity provides protection against bankruptcy, by providing either insurance or bailouts, firms will tend to borrow more. To illustrate, the deposit insurance offered by the FSLIC and the FDIC enables savings and loans and banks to maintain higher leverage than they otherwise could. While one can argue for this insurance on the grounds of preserving the integrity of the financial system, undercharging for the insurance will accentuate this tendency and induce high-risk firms to take on too much debt, letting taxpayers bear the cost. Similarly, governments that step in and regularly bail out firms on social grounds (e.g., to save jobs) will encourage all firms to overuse debt.

4. Since the direct bankruptcy costs are higher, when the assets of the firm are not easily divisible and marketable, firms with assets that can be easily divided and sold should be able to borrow more than firms with assets that do not share these features. Thus, a firm, such as Weyerhauser, whose value comes from its real estate holdings should be able to borrow more money than a firm such as Coca Cola, which derives a great deal of its value from its brand name.

5. Firms that produce products that require long-term servicing and support generally should have lower leverage than similar firms whose products do not share this feature.

B. Agency Costs

Equity investors and lenders will not always agree on the best course of action for a firm, largely because they have very different cash flow claims to the firm. Equity investors, who receive a residual claim on the cash flows, tend to favor actions that increase the value of their holdings, even if that means increasing the risk that the bondholders (who have a fixed claim on the cash flows) will not receive their promised payments. Bondholders, on the other hand, want to preserve and increase the security of their claims. Since the equity investors generally control the firm's management and decision making, their interests will dominate bondholder interests, unless bondholders take some protective action. By borrowing money, a firm exposes itself to this conflict and its negative consequences, and pays the price in terms of both real costs and a loss of freedom in decision making.

The Conflict Between Stockholders and Bondholders

The conflict between bondholder and stockholder interests manifests itself in all three aspects of corporate finance: (1) deciding what projects to take (investment decisions), (2) how to finance these projects, and (3) how much to pay out as dividends.

Investment Decisions

Earlier, we emphasized that any project that earns a return that exceeds the hurdle rate, adjusted to reflect the riskiness of the project, is a good project that should increase firm value. It would seem logical that both stockholders and bondholders would be in favor of taking all such projects, but this is not always so. While stockholders may enthusiastically support this proposition, bondholders may find themselves worse off after some of these projects are taken. This is because bondholders lend money to the firm with the expectation that the projects taken will have a certain risk level and set the interest rate on the bonds accordingly. If the firm takes projects that are riskier than expected, however, the bondholder will lose on his or her existing holdings because the price of the holdings will decrease (and the interest rate increase) to reflect the higher risk. The bondholder's loss is the stockholder's gain. While the project may have a positive net present value, the stockholders not only gain the entire present value but they expropriate wealth from the bondholders, as well. This wealth expropriation can sometimes lead to perverse decision making, whereby stockholders take projects that do not earn the hurdle rate (i.e., have negative net present value) but the value of equity actually increases because the wealth transferred from bondholders exceeds the negative net present value.

Bondholders and lenders often attempt to protect themselves against the risk shifting that occurs with investment decisions by writing in covenants in lending agreements constraining the firm from increasing the riskiness of its investments. These constraints may range from mild limits on investments in new businesses to tighter limits, giving bondholders veto power over investment decisions.

Risk Shifting: Risk shifting refers to the tendency of stockholders in firms and their agents (managers) to take on much riskier projects than bondholders expect them to.

Financing Decisions

The conflict between stockholder and bondholder interests also comes to the fore when new projects have to be financed. The equity investors in a firm, left to their own devices, would like to take on new debt, using the assets of the firm as security and providing the new lenders with prior claims over existing lenders, since this reduces the interest rate on the new debt. The existing lenders in a firm obviously do not want to provide new lenders with priority over their claims, since it makes their debt riskier.

Similarly, a firm may adopt a conservative financial policy and borrow money at low rates, with the implicit expectation of keeping its default risk low. Once it has borrowed the money, however, the firm might choose to shift to a strategy of higher leverage and default risk, leaving the original lenders worse off. In 1988, for example, RJR Nabisco rocked the corporate bond markets by announcing its intention to do a leveraged buyout. The company's existing debt, which had enjoyed a high rating dropped dramatically in price upon the announcement, as shown in Figure 7.2.

The decline in the market value of the bonds can be seen as a transfer of wealth from existing bondholders to stockholders.

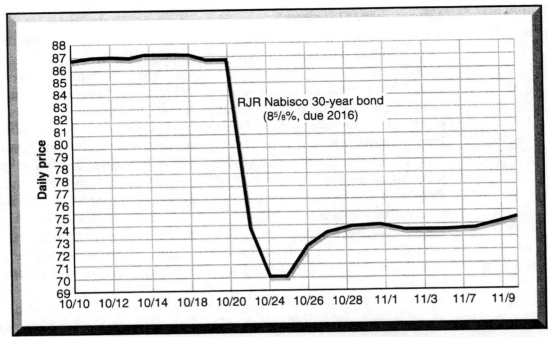

Figure 7.2 RJR Nabisco: Bond prices Around LBO announcement (October 20, 1988).

While bondholders cannot protect themselves against all such eventualities, they can protect themselves at least against a specified set of actions that stockholders might take by inserting a put clause in the bonds, allowing them to sell the bonds back to the firm at face value, if these actions are taken.

Protective Puts (in Bonds): A protective put in a bond allows a bondholder to return the bonds to the issuer before maturity and receive the face value, under a series of conditions which are enumerated in the bond covenants. For instance, the put may be triggered by an increase in the leverage.

Dividend Decisions
Dividend payments and equity repurchases also divide stockholders and bondholders. Consider a firm that has built up a large cash reserve but has very few good projects available. The stockholders in this firm may benefit if the cash is paid out as a dividend or used to repurchase stock. The bondholders, on the other hand, will prefer that the firm retain the cash, since it can be used to make payments on the debt, thereby reducing default risk.

It should come as no surprise that stockholders, if not constrained, will go ahead and pay the dividends or buy back stock, overriding bondholder concerns. In some cases, the payments are large and can increase the default risk of the firm dramatically. In 1989, for example, Colt Industries sold its most liquid assets and used the cash to pay a dividend that was 50% of the stock price. As a result, its bond rating dropped from investment grade to junk bond status.

If increases in dividends are indeed bad news for bondholders, bond prices should react negatively to the announcement of such increases. The empirical evidence supports this hypothesis. As illustrated in Figure 7.3, bond prices decrease following the

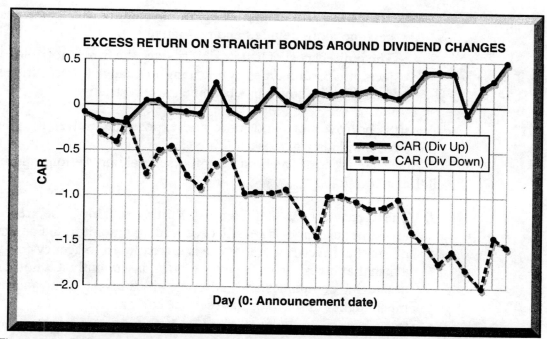

Figure 7.3 Effects of dividend changes on bond prices. CAR: Cululative Abnormal Return on the Stock.

announcement of dividend increases, while they are relatively unaffected by dividend decreases. At the same time, empirical evidence indicates that stock prices increase following the announcement of dividend increases.

Bondholders can protect themselves against such loss by restricting dividends in the bond covenants to a certain percentage of earnings or by limiting dividend increases to a specified amount. Hybrid securities also provide an appealing way of dealing with agency costs. Convertible bonds give bondholders some protection against expropriation by stockholders, for instance, because they can convert their holdings into equity.

7.12 RISK SHIFTING AND BONDHOLDERS

It is often argued that bondholders who plan to hold their bonds until maturity and collect the coupons and the face value are not affected by risk shifting that occurs after they buy the bonds, since the effect is only on market value. Do you agree?

☐ Yes

☐ No

Explain.

Where Does the Agency Cost Show Up?

The agency cost of this disagreement can show up in a couple of ways as real costs:

1. If bondholders believe that there is a significant chance that stockholder actions might make them worse off, they can build this expectation into bond prices by demanding much higher rates on debt.

2. If bondholders can protect themselves against such actions by writing in restrictive covenants, two costs follow:

- The direct cost of monitoring the covenants, which increases as the covenants become more detailed and restrictive.

- The indirect cost of lost flexibility since the firm is not able to take certain projects, use certain types of financing, or change its payout; this cost will also increase as the covenants become more restrictive.

As firms borrow more and more and expose themselves to greater agency costs, these costs will also increase.

Since agency costs can be substantial, several implications relating to optimal capital structure follow:

1. The agency cost arising from risk shifting is likely to be greatest in firms whose investments cannot be easily observed and monitored. For example, a lender to a firm that invests in real estate is less exposed to agency cost than is a lender to a firm that invests in intangible assets. Consequently, it is not surprising that manufacturing companies and railroads, which invest in substantial real assets, have much higher debt ratios than service companies.

2. The agency cost associated with monitoring actions and second-guessing investment decisions is likely to be largest for firms whose projects are long term, follow unpredictable paths, and may take years to come to fruition. Pharmaceutical companies in the United States, for example, which often take on research projects that may take years to yield commercial products, have historically maintained low debt ratios, even though their cash flows would support more debt.

C. Loss of Flexibility

As noted earlier, one of the byproducts of the conflict between stockholders and bondholders is the introduction of strict bond covenants that reduce the flexibility of firms to make investment, financing, or dividend decisions. It can be argued that this is part of a much greater loss of flexibility arising from taking on debt. One of the reasons firms do not use their debt capacity is that they like to preserve it for a rainy day, when they might need the debt to meet funding needs or specific contingencies. Firms that borrow to capacity lose this flexibility and have no fall-back funding if they do get into trouble.

Firms value flexibility for two reasons. First, the value of the firm may be maximized by preserving some flexibility to take on future projects as they arise. Second, flexibility provides managers with more breathing room and more power, and it protects them from the monitoring that comes with debt. Thus, while the argument for maintaining flexibility in the interests of the firm is based upon sound principles, it is sometimes used as camouflage by managers pursuing their own interests. There is also a trade-off between not maintaining enough flexibility (because a firm has too much debt) and having too much flexibility (by not borrowing enough).

Financial Flexibility: Financial flexibility refers to the capacity of firms to meet any unforeseen contingencies that may arise (such as recessions and sales downturns) and take advantage of unanticipated opportunities (such as great projects), using the funds they have on hand and any excess debt capacity that they might have available.

Valuing Flexibility

When making financial decisions, mangers consider the effects such decisions will have on their capacity to take new projects or meet unanticipated contingencies in future periods. Practically, this translates into firms maintaining excess debt capacity or larger cash balances than are warranted by current needs, to meet unexpected future requirements. While maintaining this financing flexibility has value to firms, it also has a cost; the large cash balances earn low returns, and excess debt capacity implies that the firm is giving up some value and has a higher cost of capital.

The value of flexibility can be analyzed using the option pricing framework; a firm maintains large cash balances and excess debt capacity in order to have the option to take projects that might arise in the future. The value of this option will depend upon two key variables:

1. *Quality of the firm's projects:* It is the excess return that the firm earns on its projects that provides the value to flexibility. Other things remaining equal, firms operating in businesses where projects earn substantially higher returns than their hurdle rates should value flexibility more than those that operate in stable businesses where excess returns are small.

2. *Uncertainty about future projects:* If flexibility is viewed as an option, its value will increase when there is greater uncertainty about future projects; thus, firms with predictable capital expenditures should value flexibility less than those with high variability in capital expenditures.

This option framework would imply that firms such as Compaq, which earn large excess returns on their projects and face more uncertainty about future investment needs, can justify holding large cash balances and excess debt capacity, whereas a firm with much smaller excess returns and more predictable investment needs should hold a much smaller cash balance and less excess debt capacity.

IN PRACTICE: Using Option Pricing Model to Value Flexibility

The value of flexibility can be calculated as a percentage of firm value, with the following inputs for the option pricing model:

S = Annual Net Capital Expenditures as % of Firm Value (1 + Excess Return)

K = Annual Net Capital Expenditures as % of Firm Value

t = 1 year

σ^2 = Variance in ln (Net Capital Expenditures)

y = Annual Cost of Holding Cash or Maintaining Excess Debt Capacity as % of Firm Value

To illustrate, assume that a firm which earns 18% on its projects has a cost of capital of 13%, and that net capital expenditures are 10% of firm value; the variance in ln(net capital expenditures) is 0.04. Also assume that the firm could have a cost of capital of 12% if it used its excess debt capacity. The value of flexibility as a percentage of firm value can be estimated as follows:

$S = 10\% \ (1.05) = 10.50\%$ [Excess Return = 18% − 13% = 5%]

$K = 10\%$

$t = 1$ year

$\sigma^2 = 0.04$

$y = 13\% - 12\% = 1\%$

Based on these inputs and a riskless rate of 5%, the value of flexibility is 1.31% of firm value.

7.13 VALUE OF FLEXIBILITY AND FIRM CHARACTERISTICS

Both Chrysler and Microsoft have huge cash balances, and you are a stockholder in both firms. The management of each firm claims to hold the cash because they need the flexibility. Which of the two managements are you more likely to accept this argument from?

☐ Microsoft's management

☐ Chrysler's management

Explain.

Implications for Optimal Capital Structure

The above variables have implications for optimal capital structure:

- Firms that have large and unpredictable demands on their cash flows to take on projects with high excess returns will value flexibility more and borrow less than firms with stable investment requirements and low-return projects. Thus, even the most successful firms in the high-technology arena (which is characterized by high returns and uncertainty about investment requirements), such as Intel and Microsoft, use very little debt in their capital structure.

- As firms and industries mature, the returns on projects drop off and project requirements become more stable. These changes increase the capacity of firms to borrow money. Intel and Microsoft, by this reasoning, will find the value of flexibility decrease over time, increasing their debt capacities.

THE TRADE-OFF IN A BALANCE SHEET FORMAT

Bringing together the benefits and the costs of debt, we can present the trade-off in a balance sheet format:

ADVANTAGES OF BORROWING	DISADVANTAGES OF BORROWING
1. *Tax Benefit:* Higher tax rates → Higher tax benefit	1. *Bankruptcy Cost:* Higher business risk → Higher cost
2. *Added Discipline:* Greater the separation between managers and stockholders → Greater the benefit	2. *Agency Cost:* Greater the separation between stockholders and lenders → Higher the cost
	3. *Loss of Future Financing Flexibility:* Greater the uncertainty about future financing needs → Higher the cost

Table 7.2 FINANCIAL PRINCIPLES DETERMINING CAPITAL STRUCTURE DECISIONS

Planning Principle by Order of Importance	Percentage of Responses Within Each Rank						
	Unimportant	2	3	4	Important	Not Ranked	Mean
1. Maintaining financial flexibility	0.6	0.0	4.5	33.0	61.4	0.6	4.55
2. Ensuring long-term survivability	4.0	1.7	6.8	10.8	76.7	0.0	4.55
3. Maintaining a predictable source of funds	1.7	2.8	20.5	39.2	35.8	0.0	4.05
4. Maximizing security prices	3.4	4.5	19.3	33.5	37.5	1.7	3.99
5. Maintaining financial independence	3.4	4.5	22.2	27.3	40.9	1.7	3.99
6. Maintaining a high debt rating	2.3	9.1	32.4	43.2	13.1	0.0	3.56
7. Maintaining comparability with other firms in the industry	15.9	36.9	33.0	10.8	2.8	0.6	2.47

Overall, if the marginal benefits of borrowing exceed the marginal costs, the firm should borrow money. Otherwise, it should use equity.

Survey Results

What do firms consider when they make capital structure decisions? To answer this question, Pinegar and Wilbricht (1989) surveyed financial managers at 176 firms in the United States. They concluded that the financial principles listed in Table 7.2 determine capital structure decisions, in the order of importance in which they were given.

The foremost principles the survey participants identified were maintaining financial flexibility and ensuring long-term survivability (which can be construed as avoiding bankruptcy). Surprisingly few managers attached much importance to maintaining comparability with other firms in their industries or maintaining a high debt rating.

THERE IS NO OPTIMAL CAPITAL STRUCTURE: THE MILLER-MODIGLIANI THEOREM

In spite of the arguments presented above, there is a large and influential school of thought that argues that capital structure decisions do not really affect the value of the firm. The seeds of this argument were sown in a seminal paper written by Miller & Modigliani containing one of corporate finance's best-known theorems, the *Miller-Modigliani theorem.*

In their initial work, Miller and Modigliani (MM) operated in an environment void of taxes, transactions costs, and the possibility of default. In that environment, they concluded that the value of a firm was unaffected by its leverage and that investment and financing decisions could be separated. Their conclusion can be confirmed in several ways; we present two below.

The Irrelevance of Capital Structure: Balance Sheet Proof

Miller and Modigliani made the following assumptions about the markets in which they were working:

1. There are no taxes.

2. Markets are frictionless and there are no transactions costs.

3. There are no direct or indirect bankruptcy costs (the expected bankruptcy costs are zero).

4. There are no agency costs, either between stockholders and managers and between stockholders and bondholders.

In such an environment, reverting back to the balance sheet format developed earlier, it is quite clear that all of the advantages and disadvantages disappear, leaving debt with no marginal benefits and costs. Accordingly, we can conclude that debt does not affect value.

In a later paper, Miller and Modigliani preserved the environment they introduced above but made one change, allowing for a tax benefit for debt. In this scenario, where debt continues to have no costs, the optimal debt ratio for a firm is 100% debt. In fact, in such an environment the value of the firm increases by the present value of the tax savings for interest payments (See Figure 7.4).

$$\text{Value of Levered Firm} = \text{Value of Unlevered Firm} + t_c B$$

where t_c is the corporate tax rate and B is the dollar borrowing.

An Alternative Proof

Miller and Modigliani presented an alternative proof of the irrelevance of leverage, grounded in the notion that debt does not affect the underlying cash flows of the firm in the absence of taxes. Consider two firms that have the same cash flow (X) from operations. The first firm is an all-equity firm, while the second firm has both equity and debt. The interest rate on debt is r.

	FIRM A	**FIRM B**
Type of firm	All-equity firm: $(V_u = E)$	Has some equity and debt $(V_L = E_L + D_L)$
Actions now	Investor buys a fraction α of the firm: (αV_u)	Investor buys a fraction α of both equity and debt of the firm: $\alpha E_L + \alpha D_L$
Next period	Investor receives a fraction α of the cash flow: (αX)	Investor receives the following: $\alpha(X - rD_L) + \alpha r D_L = \alpha X$

Since the investor receives the same cash flows in both firms, the price he or she will pay for either firm has to be the same. This implies that leverage is irrelevant.

Note that this proof works only if the firm does not receive a tax benefit from debt; a tax benefit would give Firm B a higher cash flow than Firm A.

The Effect of Taxes: The Miller Proof of Irrelevance

It is clear in the Miller-Modigliani model that introducing the tax benefit of debt into the mix undercuts the conclusion that debt is irrelevant. In an address in 1976,

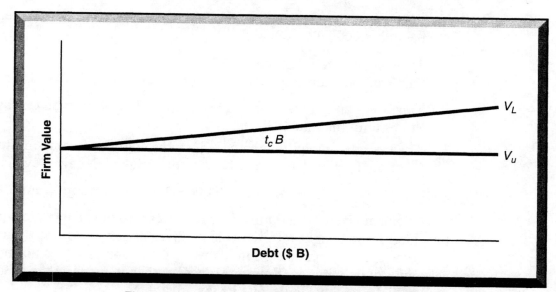

Figure 7.4 Value of Levered Firm: MM with Taxes.

however, Merton Miller argued that the debt irrelevance theorem could be resuscitated even in the presence of corporate taxes if taxes on the dividend and interest income individuals receive from firms were factored into the analysis.

To see the Miller proof of irrelevance, assume that investors face a tax rate of t_d on interest income and a tax rate of t on equity income. Assume also that the firm pays an interest rate of r on debt and faces a corporate tax rate of t_c. The after-tax return to the investor from owning debt can then be written as follows:

$$\text{After-Tax Return from Owning Debt} = r\,(1 - t_d)$$

The after-tax return to the investor from owning equity can be written after the double taxation—once at the corporate level and once at the investor level:

$$\text{After-Tax Return from Owning Equity} = k_e\,(1 - t_c)\,(1 - t_e)$$

The returns to equity can take two forms—dividends or capital gains; the equity tax rate is a blend of the tax rates on both. In such a scenario, Miller noted that the value of the firm, with leverage, could be written as:

$$V_L = V_u + [1 - (1 - t_c)\,(1 - t_e)/(1 - t_d)]B$$

where V_L is the value of the firm with leverage, V_U is the value of the firm without leverage, and B is the dollar debt.

As Miller noted, there are several possible scenarios that can be considered here:

1. *The tax rate on equity is the same as the tax rate on debt:* If this were the case, the result reverts back to the original one—the value of the firm increases monotonically with the debt.

2. *The tax rate on debt is higher than the tax rate on equity:* In such a case, the differences in the tax rates may more than compensate for the double taxation of equity cash flows. To illustrate, assume that the tax rate on ordinary income is 70%, the tax rate on capital gains on stock is 28%, and the tax rate on corporations is 35%. In

497

such a case, the tax liabilities for debt and equity can be calculated for a firm that pays no dividend as follows:

Tax Rate on Debt Income = 70%
Tax Rate on Equity Income = $1 - (1 - 0.35)(1 - .28) = 0.532$ or 53.2%

This is not an implausible scenario, especially considering tax law in the United States until the mid-1980s.

3. The tax rate on equity income is just low enough to compensate for the double taxation: In this case, we are back to the original debt irrelevance theorem.

$$(1 - t_d) = (1 - t_c)(1 - t_e) \quad \text{Debt is irrelevant}$$

Miller's analysis brought investor tax rates into the analysis for the first time and provided some insight into the role of investor tax preferences on a firm's capital structure. As Miller himself notes, however, this analysis does not reestablish the irrelevance of debt under all circumstances; rather, it opens up the possibility that debt could still be irrelevant, despite its tax advantages.

The Consequences of Debt Irrelevance

If the financing decision is irrelevant, as posited by Miller and Modigliani, corporate financial analysis is simplified in a number of ways:

- *The cost of capital, which is the weighted average of the cost of debt and the cost of equity, is unaffected by changes in the proportions of debt and equity.* This might seem unreasonable, especially since the cost of debt is much lower than the cost of equity. In the MM world, however, any benefits incurred by substituting cheaper debt for more expensive equity are offset by increases in both their costs, as shown in Figure 7.5.

- *The value of the firm is unaffected by the amount of leverage it has.* Thus, if the firm is valued as an all-equity entity, its value will remain unchanged even if it is valued with any other debt ratio. (This actually follows from the implication that the cost of capital is unaffected by changes in leverage and from the assumption that the operating cash flows are determined by investment decisions rather than financing decisions.)

- *The investment decision can be made independently of the financing decision.* In other words, if a project is a bad project when evaluated as an all-equity project, it will remain so using any other financing mix.

Some Closing Thoughts

It is unlikely that capital structure is irrelevant in the real world, given tax preferences for debt and default risk. In spite of this, Miller and Modigliani were pioneers in moving capital structure analysis from an environment in which firms picked their debt ratios based upon their peer group and management preferences to one that recognized the trade-offs. They also drew attention to the fact that good investment decisions comprise the core of value creation for firms. To be more precise, a firm that takes bad projects cannot hope to recoup the lost value by making better financing

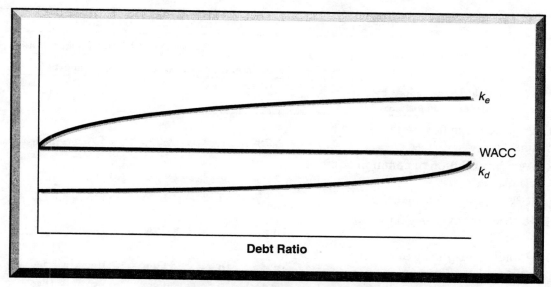

Figure 7.5 Cost of Capital in the MM World.

decisions; a firm that takes good projects will succeed in creating value, even if its capital structure choices are suboptimal. Finally, while the concept of a world with no taxes, default risk, or agency problems may seem a little far-fetched, there are some environments about which the description might hold. Assume, for instance, that the U.S. government decides to encourage small businesses to invest in urban areas by relieving them of their tax burden and providing a backup guarantee on loans (default protection). Firms that respond to these initiatives might find that their capital structure decisions do not affect their value.

Finally, surveys of financial managers indicate that, in practice, they do not attach as much weight to the trade-off mentioned earlier as we do in theory. In a survey by Pinegar and Wilbricht (1989), managers were asked to cite the most important inputs governing their financial decisions. Their responses are ranked in the order of the importance managers attached to them in Table 7.3.

Notice that, while the capital structure trade-off theory would predict that bankruptcy cost and tax-related variables would be the most important variables, this survey suggests that they are not actually given as much weight by financial managers making capital structure decisions as the theory suggests. Instead, financial managers seem to weigh financial flexibility and potential dilution much more heavily in their capital structure decisions.

IN PRACTICE: THE DILUTION BOGEY

The dilution effect refers to the possible decrease in earnings per share from any action that might lead to an increase in the number of shares outstanding. As evidenced in Table 7.3, managers, especially in the United States, weigh these potential dilution effects heavily in decisions on what type of financing to use, and how to fund projects. Consider, for instance, the choice between raising equity using a rights issue, where the stock is issued at a price below the current market price, and a public issue of stock at the market price. The latter is a much more expensive option, from the

Table 7.3 INPUTS INTO CAPITAL STRUCTURE DECISIONS

Inputs/Assumptions by Order of Importance	Percentage of Responses Within Each Rank						
	Least Important ....Most Important					Not Ranked	Mean
	1	2	3	4	5		
1. Projected cash flow from asset to be financed	1.7%	1.1%	9.7%	29.5%	58.0%	0.0%	4.41
2. Avoiding dilution of common equity's claims	2.8%	6.3%	18.2%	39.8%	33.0%	0.0%	3.94
3. Risk of asset to be financed	2.8%	6.3%	20.5%	36.9%	33.0%	0.6%	3.91
4. Restrictive covenants on senior securities	9.1%	9.7%	18.7%	35.2%	27.3%	0.0%	3.62
5. Avoiding mispricing of securities to be issued	3.4%	10.8%	27.3%	39.8%	18.7%	0.0%	3.60
6. Corporate tax rate	4.0%	9.7%	29.5%	42.6%	13.1%	1.1%	3.52
7. Voting control	17.6%	10.8%	21.0%	31.2%	19.3%	0.0%	3.24
8. Depreciation & other tax shields	8.5%	17.6%	40.9%	24.4%	7.4%	1.1%	3.05
9. Correcting mispricing of securities	14.8%	27.8%	36.4%	14.2%	5.1%	1.7%	2.66
10. Personal tax rates of debt and equity holders	31.2%	34.1%	25.6%	8.0%	1.1%	0.0%	2.14
11. Bankruptcy costs	69.3%	13.1%	6.8%	4.0%	4.5%	2.3%	1.58

perspective of investment banking fees and other costs, but is chosen, nevertheless, because it results in fewer shares being issued (to raise the same amount of funds). The fear of dilution is misplaced for the following reasons:

1. Investors measure their returns in terms of total return and not just in terms of stock price. While the stock price will go down more after a rights issue, each investor will be compensated adequately for the price drop (by either receiving more shares or by being able to sell their rights to other investors). In fact, if the transaction costs are considered, stockholders will be better off after a rights issue than after an equivalent public issue of stock.

2. While the earnings per share will almost always drop in the immediate aftermath of a new stock issue, the stock price will not necessarily follow suit. In particular, if the stock issue is used to finance a good project (i.e., a project with a positive net present value), the increase in value should be greater than the increase in the number of shares, leading to a higher stock price.

Ultimately, the measure of whether a company should issue stock to finance a project should depend upon the quality of the investment. Firms that dilute their stockholdings to take good investments are making the right choice for their stockholders.

THERE IS AN OPTIMAL CAPITAL STRUCTURE

The counter to the Miller-Modigliani proposition is that the trade-offs on debt may work in favor of the firm, at least initially, and that borrowing money may lower the cost of capital and increase firm value. We will examine the mechanics of putting this argument into practice in the next chapter; here, we will make a case for the existence of an optimal capital structure, and look at some of the empirical evidence for and against it.

The Case for an Optimal Capital Structure

If the debt decision involves a trade-off between the benefits of debt (tax benefits and added discipline) and the costs of debt (bankruptcy costs, agency costs, and lost flexibility), it can be argued that the marginal benefits will be exactly offset by the marginal costs *only in exceptional cases,* and not always (as argued by Miller and Modigliani). In fact, under most circumstances, the marginal benefits will either exceed the marginal costs (in which case, debt is good and will increase firm value) or fall short of marginal costs (in which case, equity is better). Accordingly, there is an optimal capital structure for most firms at which firm value is maximized.

Of course, it is always possible that managers may be operating under an *illusion* that capital structure decisions matter when the reality might be otherwise. Consequently, we examine some of the empirical evidence to see if it is consistent with the theory of an optimal mix of debt and equity.

Empirical Evidence

The question of whether there is an optimal capital structure can be answered in a number of ways. The first is to see if differences in capital structure across firms can be explained systematically by differences in the variables driving the trade-offs. Other things remaining equal, we would expect to see the relationships listed in Table 7.4.

While this may seem like a relatively simple test to run, keeping all other things equal in the real world is often close to impossible. In spite of this limitation, attempts to see if the direction of the relationship is consistent with the theory have produced mixed results.

Bradley, Jarrell, and Kim (1984) analyzed whether differences in debt ratios can be explained by proxies for the variables involved in the capital structure trade-off. They noted that the debt ratio is:

- *Negatively correlated with the volatility in annual operating earnings,* as predicted by the bankruptcy cost component of the optimal capital structure trade-off.

- *Positively related to the level of non-debt tax shields,* which is counter to the tax hypothesis, which argues that firms with large non-debt tax shields should be less inclined to use debt.

- *Negatively related to advertising and R&D expenses used as a proxy for agency costs;* this is consistent with optimal capital structure theory.

Table 7.4 Debt Ratios and Fundamentals	
Variable	**Effect on Debt Ratios**
Marginal tax rate	As marginal tax rates increase, debt ratios increase.
Separation of ownership and management	The greater the separation of ownership and management, the higher the debt ratio.
Variability in operating cash flows	As operating cash flows become more variable, the bankruptcy risk increases, resulting in lower debt ratios.
Debt holders' difficulty in monitoring firm actions, investments, and performance	The more difficult it is to monitor the actions taken by a firm, the lower the optimal debt ratio.
Need for flexibility	The greater the need for decision-making flexibility in future periods, the lower the optimal debt ratio.

Others who have attempted to examine whether cross-sectional differences in capital structure are consistent with the theory have come to contradictory conclusions.

A second test of whether differences in capital structure can be explained by differences in firm characteristics involves examining differences in debt ratios across industries. Table 7.5 summarizes debt ratios, by industry, on both book value and market value terms at the end of 1994. The table provides relevant information on average tax rates, variability in operating income, and investment needs for each industry.

An alternate test of the optimal capital structure hypothesis is to examine the stock price reaction to actions taken by firms either to increase or decrease leverage. In evaluating the price response, we have to make some assumptions about the motivation of the firms making these changes. If we assume that firms are rational and that they make these changes to get closer to their optimal, both leverage-increasing and -decreasing actions should be accompanied by positive excess returns, at least on average. In a study cited in the previous chapter, Smith (1988) notes that the evidence is *not* consistent with an optimal capital structure hypothesis, however, since leverage-increasing actions seem to be accompanied by positive excess returns while leverage-reducing actions seem to be followed by negative returns. The only way to reconcile this tendency with an optimal capital structure argument is by assuming that managerial incentives (desire for stability and flexibility) keep leverage below the optimal for most firms and that actions by firms to reduce leverage are seen as serving managerial interests rather than stockholder interests.

Industry	Debt Ratio: MV	Debt Ratio: BV	Variances	Insider Holdings	Cap Ex/MV	ROE	FCF/Price
Agricultural Products	35.05%	47.05%	30.86%	30.16%	7.18%	24.35%	11.72%
Mining	26.33%	36.64%	34.50%	14.28%	6.55%	13.86%	6.70%
Petroleum Production & Refining	27.08%	39.88%	28.91%	26.00%	13.05%	16.11%	7.45%
Building Contractors & Related Areas	28.21%	36.16%	42.19%	33.34%	6.51%	15.16%	7.72%
Food Production	22.90%	39.89%	39.27%	28.38%	7.77%	24.12%	5.06%
Beverages	25.07%	40.19%	38.07%	33.20%	7.13%	17.52%	5.36%
Tobacco	31.42%	49.82%	37.59%	4.28%	3.48%	33.16%	6.98%
Textile & Clothing Manufacturers	21.89%	27.23%	46.01%	33.97%	5.98%	14.84%	7.12%
Furniture	16.66%	22.83%	47.80%	42.89%	7.59%	19.69%	7.85%
Paper & Plastic Production	30.41%	46.81%	42.48%	20.64%	8.74%	20.96%	5.96%
Publishing	16.29%	32.38%	42.39%	30.75%	6.92%	26.82%	6.28%
Chemicals	17.30%	31.57%	42.88%	21.66%	7.17%	37.80%	6.19%
Pharmaceuticals	8.52%	24.63%	39.12%	27.62%	10.35%	26.25%	2.76%
Consumer Products	18.62%	39.23%	44.38%	29.05%	6.94%	26.45%	4.36%
Autos & Related	26.91%	38.00%	47.17%	28.23%	6.67%	21.66%	7.71%
Miscellaneous Manufacturing	24.00%	37.75%	47.91%	26.05%	8.71%	21.10%	8.45%
Equipment Manufacturing	19.06%	29.57%	49.32%	25.60%	6.52%	18.45%	6.83%
Computers & Office Equipment	8.44%	17.29%	51.26%	25.84%	7.34%	18.89%	5.50%
Consumer Electronics	9.48%	15.79%	59.81%	23.96%	7.30%	14.22%	4.82%
Other Consumer Durables	15.89%	25.18%	41.72%	39.32%	6.71%	18.71%	5.02%
Transportation	33.57%	44.97%	41.62%	29.22%	8.64%	18.09%	7.26%
Telephone Utilities	19.83%	38.54%	25.24%	19.34%	12.28%	16.21%	3.37%
Entertainment (TV & Movies)	19.60%	39.83%	38.78%	41.59%	7.24%	26.68%	10.80%
Electric & Gas Utilities	43.22%	52.90%	32.25%	19.49%	6.51%	12.31%	5.29%
Wholesalers	19.16%	28.18%	46.94%	33.12%	4.79%	15.22%	6.95%
Retailers	21.65%	30.01%	45.21%	35.39%	9.24%	20.42%	5.49%
Restaurants & Eating Places	20.21%	32.28%	42.94%	29.45%	16.12%	18.19%	7.45%
Banks & Financial Service	17.23%	28.40%	67.01%	30.13%	2.07%	18.99%	11.39%

Table 7.5 **DEBT RATIOS BY INDUSTRY-1995**

	Debt Ratio: MV	Debt Ratio: BV	Variances	Insider Holdings	Cap Ex/MV	ROE	FCF/Price
Industry							
Insurance	14.35%	31.71%	39.84%	34.15%	5.15%	19.11%	5.51%
Real Estate	30.85%	40.97%	39.49%	29.15%	3.08%	19.15%	7.75%
Other Services	20.17%	34.86%	39.92%	36.07%	7.18%	24.67%	6.99%
Computer Software & Services	3.48%	10.10%	43.58%	34.16%	9.28%	19.07%	3.80%
Health Services	17.30%	27.97%	44.72%	30.13%	5.83%	12.30%	6.12%
Average	**21.52%**	**33.90%**	**42.46%**	**28.69%**	**7.46%**	**20.32%**	**6.61%**

Table title: **Table 7.5** CONTINUED

This data set on the web that summarizes average debt ratios, by industry, for firms in the U.S.

HOW FIRMS CHOOSE THEIR CAPITAL STRUCTURES

While the theory suggests that firms should pick the mix of debt and equity that maximizes firm value, the most common approach is to set leverage close to that of the peer group to which the firm belongs. If firms in the peer group are similar on the fundamental characteristics (tax rates and cash flow variability) and tend to be right, at least on average, it can be argued that this approach provides a shortcut to arriving at the optimal. It is likely to fail, however, when firms differ on these characteristics.

A Financing Hierarchy

It can be argued that firms follow a financing hierarchy: retained earnings are the most preferred choice for financing, followed by debt; new equity, common and preferred, is the least preferred choice. The argument is supported as follows. First, managers value *flexibility and control*. To the extent that external financing reduces flexibility for future financing (especially if it is debt) and control (bonds have covenants; new equity attracts new stockholders into the company and may reduce insider holdings as a percentage of total holding), managers prefer retained earnings as a source of capital. Second, while it costs nothing in terms of flotation costs to use retained earnings, *it costs more* to use external debt and even more to use external equity.

Survey Results

There is some evidence to support a financing hierarchy. For instance, in the survey by Pinegar and Wilbricht (Table 7.6), managers were asked to rank six different sources of financing: from most preferred to least preferred, internal equity, external equity, external debt, preferred stock, and hybrids (convertible debt and preferred stock).

Retained earnings (internal equity) emerged as the clear first choice for financing projects. The survey yielded some other interesting conclusions as well:

Table 7.6   SURVEY RESULTS ON PLANNING PRINCIPLES

Ranking	Source	Planning Principle Cited	Score
1	Retained Earnings	None	5.61
2	Straight Debt	Maximize Security Prices	4.88
3	Convertible Debt	Cash Flow & Survivability	3.02
4	External Common Equity	Avoiding Dilution	2.42
5	Straight Preferred Stock	Comparability	2.22
6	Convertible Preferred	None	1.72

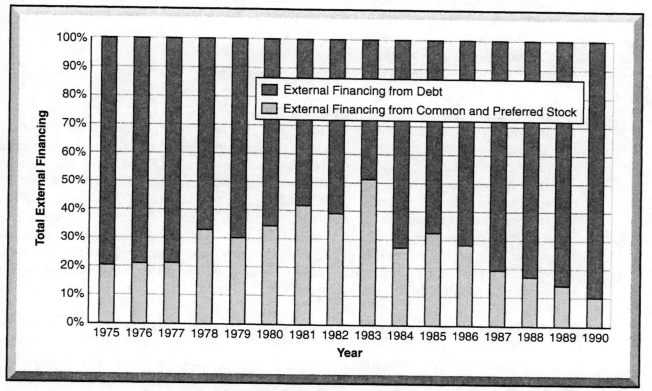

Figure 7.6   Breakdown of financing for U.S. firms: 1975–1990.

- External debt is strongly preferred over external equity as a way of raising funds. The values of external debt and external equity issued between 1975 and 1990 by U.S. corporations are shown in Figure 7.6.

- Given a choice, firms would much rather use straight debt than convertible debt, in spite of the lower interest cost on the latter. Managers perhaps have a much better sense of the value of the conversion option than is recognized, since the conventional wisdom holds that the lure of lower rates will result in more convertibles being issued than justified by theory.

- The primary reason for *not* issuing external equity seems to be the avoidance of dilution, and the main reason *for using* debt is the maximization of stock prices.

- A firm's choices may say a great deal about its financial strength. Thus, the decisions by RJR Nabisco and GM, in 1993, to raise new funds through convertible preferred stock were seen by markets as an admission by these firms of their financial weakness. Not surprisingly, the financial market response to the issue of the securities listed in Table 7.6 mirrors the preferences: the most negative responses are reserved for securities near the bottom of the list, the most positive (or at least the least negative) for those at the top of the list.

7.14 SECURITY CHOICE AND FIRM HEALTH

You are reading the *Wall Street Journal* and notice a tombstone ad for a company, offering to sell convertible preferred stock. What would you hypothesize about the health of the company issuing these securities?

☐ Nothing

☐ Healthier than the average firm

☐ In much more financial trouble than the average firm

Information Asymmetry and Financing Hierarchy

In the discussion of financing choices so far, we have steered away from questions about how firms convey information to financial markets about their future choices and how well the securities that the firms issue are priced. Firms know more about their future prospects than do the financial markets that they deal with; markets may under- or overprice securities issued by firms. Myers and Majluf (1984) note that, in the presence of this asymmetric information, firms which believe that their securities are underpriced, given their future prospects, may be inclined to reject good projects rather than raise external financing. Alternatively, firms which believe that their securities are overpriced are more likely to issue these securities, even if they have no projects available. In this environment, the following implications emerge:

- Managers prefer retained earnings to external financing, since it allows them to consider projects on their merits, rather than depending upon whether markets are pricing their securities correctly. It follows then that firms will be more inclined to retain earnings over and above their current investment requirements to finance future projects.

- When firms issue securities, markets will consider the issue a signal of whether these securities are overvalued. This signal is likely to be more negative for securities, such as stocks, where the asymmetry of information is greater, and smaller for securities, such as straight bonds, where the asymmetry is smaller. This would explain both the rankings in the financial hierarchy and the market reaction to these security issues.

CONCLUSION

In this chapter we have laid the groundwork for analyzing a firm's optimal mix of debt and equity by laying out the benefits and the costs of borrowing money. In particular, we made the following points:

- We differentiated between debt and equity, at a generic level, by pointing out that any financing approach that results in fixed cash flows and has prior claims in the case of default, has fixed maturity, and has no voting rights is debt, while a financing approach that provides for residual cash flows and has low or no priority in claims in the case of default, has infinite life, and has a lion's share of the control is equity.

- The primary benefit of debt is a tax benefit: Interest expenses are tax deductible, while cash flows to equity (dividends) are not. This benefit increases with the tax rate of the entity taking on the debt.

- A secondary benefit of debt is that it forces managers to be more disciplined in their choice of projects by increasing the costs of failure; a series of bad projects may create the possibility of defaulting on interest and principal payments.

- The primary cost of borrowing is an increase in the expected bankruptcy cost—the product of the probability of default and the cost of bankruptcy. The probability of default is greater for firms that have volatile cash flows. The cost of bankruptcy includes both the direct costs of bankruptcy and the indirect costs (lost sales, tighter credit, and less access to capital).

- Borrowing money exposes the firm to the possibility of conflicts between stock- and bondholders over investment, financing, and dividend decisions. The covenants that bondholders write into bond agreements to protect themselves against expropriation cost the firm in both monitoring costs and lost flexibility.

- The loss of flexibility that arises from borrowing money is more likely to be a problem for firms with substantial and unpredictable investment opportunities.

- In the special case where there are no tax benefits, default risk, or agency problems, the financing decision is irrelevant.

- In most cases, however, the trade-off between the benefits and costs of debt will result in an optimal capital structure, whereby the value of the firm is maximized.

PROBLEMS AND QUESTIONS

1. An income bondholder receives interest payments only if the firm makes income. If the firm does not make interest payments in a year, the interest is cumulated and paid in the first year that the firm makes income. A preferred stockholder receives preferred dividends only if the firm makes income. If a firm does not make preferred dividend payments in a year, the dividend is cumulated and paid in the first year that the firm makes income. Are income bonds really preferred stock? What are the differences? For purposes of analyzing debt, how would you differentiate between income bonds and regular bonds?

2. A commodity bond links interest and principal payments to the price of a commodity. Differentiate a commodity bond from a straight bond, and then from equity. How would you factor these differences into your analysis of the debt ratio of a company that has issued exclusively commodity bonds?

3. You are analyzing a new security that has been promoted as equity, with the following features:
   - The dividend on the security is fixed in dollar terms for the life of the security, which is 20 years.
   - The dividend is not tax deductible.

- In the case of default, the holders of this security will receive cash only after all debtholders, secured as well as unsecured, are paid.
- The holders of this security will have no voting rights.

Based on the description of debt and equity in the chapter, how would you classify this security? If you were asked to calculate the debt ratio for this firm, how would you categorize this security?

4. You are analyzing a convertible preferred stock, with the following characteristics for the security:
   - There are 50,000 convertible preferred shares outstanding, with a face value of $100 each and a 6% preferred dividend rate.
   - The firm has straight preferred stock outstanding, with a preferred dividend rate of 9%.
   - The convertible preferred stock is trading at $105.

   Estimate the preferred stock and equity components of this preferred stock.

5. You have been asked to calculate the debt ratio for a firm which has the following components to its financing mix:
   - The firm has 1 million shares outstanding, trading at $50 per share.
   - The firm has $25 million in straight debt, carrying a market interest rate of 8%.
   - The firm has 20,000 10-year convertible bonds outstanding, with a face value of $1,000, a market value of $1,100, and a coupon rate of 5%.

   Estimate the debt ratio for this firm.

6. You have been asked to estimate the debt ratio for a firm, with the following financing details:
   - The firm has two classes of shares outstanding; 50,000 shares of class A stock, with 2 voting rights per share, trading at $100 per share and 100,000 shares of class B stock, with 1/2 voting right per share, trading at $90 per share.
   - The firm has $5 million in bank debt, and the debt was taken on recently.

   Estimate the market debt ratio. Why does it matter when the bank debt was taken on?

7. You are the owner of a small and successful firm with an estimated market value of $50 million.

You are considering going public.
   a. What are the considerations you would have in choosing an investment banker?
   b. You want to raise $20 million in new financing which you plan to reinvest back in the firm. (The estimated market value of $50 million is based on the assumption that this $20 million is reinvested.) What proportion of the firm would you have to sell in the initial public offering to raise $20 million?
   c. How would your answer to (b) change if the investment banker plans to underprice your offering by 10%?
   d. If you wanted your stock to trade in the $20 to $25 range, how many shares would you have to create? How many shares would you have to issue?

8. U.S. firms are heavily dependent on debt for external financing, and they are overleveraged. Comment.

9. Convertible bonds are often issued by small, high-growth companies to raise debt. Why?

10. A manager of NoZone Inc., a company in urgent need of financing, is debating whether to issue straight debt at 11% or convertible debt at 7%. He is leaning toward the convertible debt because it is cheaper. Is it? How would you check this proposition?

11. Complex Inc. is trying to estimate its debt ratio. It has 1 million shares outstanding, trading at $50 per share, and had $250 million in straight debt outstanding (with a market interest rate of 9%). It also has two other securities outstanding:
   a. It has 200,000 warrants outstanding, conferring on its holders the right to buy stock in the Complex Inc., at $65 per share. These warrants are trading at $12 each.
   b. It also has 10,000 20-year convertible bonds outstanding, with a coupon rate of 6% and 10 years to maturity (Face value is $1,000), trading at par.

   Estimate the debt ratio in market value terms.

12. Venture capitalists take advantage of small businesses by demanding a disproportionate share of the ownership of the company for their investment. Comment.

13. Firms generally can borrow money by using bank debt or by issuing bonds. Why might a firm choose one method over the other?

14. Preferred stock is often considered as equity, when analysts calculate debt ratios. Is this appropriate? Under what conditions would you consider it to be more like debt?

15. Debt will always be cheaper than preferred stock, because of the tax advantage that it confers on the firm. What is the source of the tax advantage? Is this statement true?

16. MVP Inc., a manufacturing firm with no debt outstanding and a market value of $100 million, is considering borrowing $40 million and buying back stock. Assuming that the interest rate on the debt is 9% and that the firm faces a tax rate of 35%, answer the following questions:
  a. Estimate the annual interest tax savings each year from the debt.
  b. Estimate the present value of interest tax savings, assuming that the debt change is permanent.
  c. Estimate the present value of interest tax savings, assuming that the debt will be taken on for 10 years only.
  d. What will happen to the present value of interest tax savings if interest rates drop tomorrow to 7% but the debt itself is a fixed rate debt?

17. A business in the 45% tax bracket is considering borrowing money at 10%.
  a. What is the after-tax interest rate on the debt?
  b. What is the after-tax interest rate if only half of the interest expense is allowed as a tax deduction?
  c. Will your answer change if the firm is losing money now and does not expect to have taxable income for the next three years?

18. WestingHome Inc. is a manufacturing company that has accumulated a net operating loss of $2 billion over time. It is considering borrowing $5 billion to acquire another company.
  a. Based on the corporate tax rate of 36%, estimate the present value of the tax savings that could accrue to the company.
  b. Does the existence of a net operating loss carryforward affect your analysis? (Will the tax benefits be diminished as a consequence?)

19. Answer true or false to the following questions relating to the free cash-flow hypothesis.
  a. Companies with high operating earnings have high free cash flows.
  b. Companies with large capital expenditures, relative to earnings, have low free cash flows.
  c. Companies that are committed to paying a large portion of their free cash flow as dividends do not need debt to add discipline.
  d. The free cash-flow hypothesis for borrowing money makes more sense for firms in which there is a separation of ownership and management.
  e. Firms with high free cash flows are run inefficiently.

20. Assess the likelihood that the following firms will be taken over, based on your understanding of the free cash-flow hypothesis.
  a. A firm with high growth prospects, good projects, low leverage, and high earnings.
  b. A firm with low growth prospects, poor projects, low leverage, and poor earnings.
  c. A firm with high growth prospects, good projects, high leverage, and low earnings.
  d. A firm with low growth prospects, poor projects, high leverage, and good earnings.
  e. A firm with low growth prospects, poor projects, low leverage, and good earnings.

You can assume that earnings and free cash flows are highly correlated.

21. Nadir, Inc., an unlevered firm, has expected earnings before interest and taxes of $2 million per year. Nadir's tax rate is 40%, and the market value is $V = E = $12 million. The stock has a beta of 1, and the risk-free rate is 9%. (Assume that $E(R_m) - R_f = 6\%$.) Management is considering the use of debt; debt would be issued and used to buy back stock, and the size of the firm would remain constant. The default-free interest rate on debt is 12%. Because interest expense is tax deductible, the value of the firm would tend to increase as debt is added to the capital structure, but there would be an offset in the form of the rising cost of bankruptcy. The firm's analysts have estimated that the present value of any bankruptcy cost is $8 million and that the probability of bankruptcy will increase with leverage according to the following schedule:

Value of Debt	Probability of Failure (%)
$2,500,000	0.0
5,000,000	8.0
7,500,000	20.5
8,000,000	30.0
9,000,000	45.0
10,000,000	52.5
12,500,000	70.0

a. What is the cost of equity and cost of capital at this time?

b. What is the optimal capital structure when bankruptcy costs are considered?

c. What will the value of the firm be at this optimal capital structure?

22. Agency costs arise from the conflict between stockholders and bondholders, but they do not impose any real costs on firms. Comment.

23. Two firms are considering borrowing. One firm has excellent prospects in terms of future projects and is in a business in which cash flows are volatile and future needs are difficult to assess. The other firm has more stable cash flows and fewer project opportunities and predicts its future needs with more precision. Other things remaining equal, which of these two firms should borrow more?

24. How would you respond to a claim by a firm that maintaining flexibility is always good for stockholders, although they might not recognize it in the short term?

25. A firm that has no debt has a market value of $100 million and a cost of equity of 11%. In the Miller-Modigliani world:
a. What happens to the value of the firm as the leverage is changed (assume no taxes)?
b. What happens to the cost of capital as the leverage is changed (assume no taxes)?
c. How would your answers to (a) and (b) change if there were taxes?

26. XYZ Pharma Inc. is a pharmaceutical company that traditionally has not used debt to finance its projects. Over the last 10 years, it has also reported high returns on its projects and growth rates, and has incurred substantial research and development expenses over the time period. The health-care business overall is growing much slower now, and the projects the firm is considering have lower expected returns.
a. How would you justify the firm's past policy of not using debt?
b. Do you think the policy should be changed now? Why or why not?

27. Stockholders can expropriate wealth from bondholders through their investment, financing, and dividend decisions. Explain.

28. Bondholders can always protect themselves against stockholder expropriation by writing bond covenants. Therefore, no agency cost is associated with the conflict between stockholders and bondholders. Do you agree?

29. Unitrode Inc., which makes analog/linear integrated circuits for power management, has not used debt in the financing of its projects. The managers of the firm contend that they do not borrow money because they want to maintain financial flexibility.
a. How does not borrowing money increase financial flexibility?
b. What is the trade-off you will be making if you have excess debt capacity and you choose not to use it because you want financial flexibility?

30. Consolidated Power is a regulated electric utility that has equity with a market value of $1.5 billion and debt outstanding of $3 billion. A consultant notes that this is a high debt ratio relative to the average across all firms, which is 27%, and suggests that the firm is overlevered.
a. Why would you expect an electric utility to be able to maintain a higher debt ratio than the average company?
b. Does the fact that the company is a regulated monopoly affect its capacity to carry debt?

31. Assume that legislators are considering a tax reform plan that will lower the corporate tax rate from 36% to 17%, while preserving the tax deductibility of internal expenses. What effect would this tax reform plan have on the optimal debt ratios of companies? Why? What if the tax deductibility of debt were removed?

32. Governments often step in to protect large companies that get into financial trouble and bail them out. If this is an accepted practice, what effect would you expect it to have on the debt ratios of firms? Why?

33. The Miller-Modigliani theorem proposes that debt is irrelevant. Under what conditions is this true? If debt is irrelevant, what is the effect of changing the debt ratio on the cost of capital?

34. Based on the financing hierarchy described in this chapter, what types of securities would you expect financially strong firms to issue? What about financially weak firms? Why?

35. In general, private firms tend to take on much less debt than publicly traded firms. Based on the discussion in this chapter, how would you explain this phenomenon?

36. There is a significant cost to bankruptcy because the stock price essentially goes to zero. Comment.

37. Studies indicate that the direct cost of bankruptcy is small. What are the direct costs? What are the indirect costs of bankruptcy? What types of firms are most exposed to these indirect costs?

38. When stockholders have little power over incumbent managers, firms are likely to be underlevered. Comment.

39. Debt is always cheaper than equity. Therefore, the optimal debt ratio is all debt. How would you respond to this statement?

LIVE CASE STUDY

V. CAPITAL STRUCTURE CHOICES

Objective: To examine the current financing choices of the firm, and analyze, from a qualitative standpoint, whether the firm is under or over leveraged.

Key
Questions

- What are the different kinds or types of financing that this company has used to raise funds? Where do they fall in the continuum between debt and equity?
- How large, in qualitative or quantitative terms, are the advantages to this company from using debt?
- How large, in qualitative or quantitative terms, are the disadvantages to this company from using debt?
- From the qualitative trade-off, does this firm look like it has too much or too little debt?

Framework
for Analysis

1. Benefits of Debt
- What marginal tax rate does this firm face and how does this measure up to the marginal tax rates of other firms? Are there other tax deductions that this company has (like depreciation) to reduce the tax bite?
- Does this company have high free cash flows (e.g., EBITDA/Firm Value)? Has it taken and does it continue to have good investment projects? How responsive are managers to stockholders? (Will there be an advantage to using debt in this firm as a way of keeping managers in line or do other (cheaper) mechanisms exist?)

2. Costs of Debt
- How high are the current cash flows of the firm (to service the debt) and how stable are these cash flows? (Look at the variability in the operating income over time.)
- How easy is it for bondholders to observe what equity investors are doing? Are the assets tangible or intangible? If not, what are the costs in terms of monitoring stockholders or in terms of bond covenants?
- How well can this firm forecast its future investment opportunities and needs? How much does it value flexibility?

Getting Information on Capital Structure Choices

To find out the breakdown on the types of securities and financing that your company has outstanding, check the footnotes on the 10-K report (**www.sec.gov/edgarhp.htm**). To get the other inputs needed for the analysis, you should check the historical financials on the firm. To get industry average numbers for these inputs, check the data set on my web page for capital structure variables (**indcapst.xls**).

CHAPTER 8

CAPITAL STRUCTURE: MODELS AND APPLICATIONS

In the last chapter, we examined the costs and benefits of borrowing, and noted that the trade-off favors debt for some firms and equity for others. In this chapter, we move beyond generalities to practical tools for analyzing the capital structure and choosing an optimal debt level for a firm. We explore two ways of doing so. The first approach is to choose the debt ratio that minimizes the cost of capital. Here, we revisit the cost of capital, explain its role in analysis and valuation, and discuss its relationship to the optimal debt ratio. The second approach also attempts to maximize firm value, but does so by adding the value of the unlevered firm to the present value of tax benefits, and then netting out the expected bankruptcy costs.

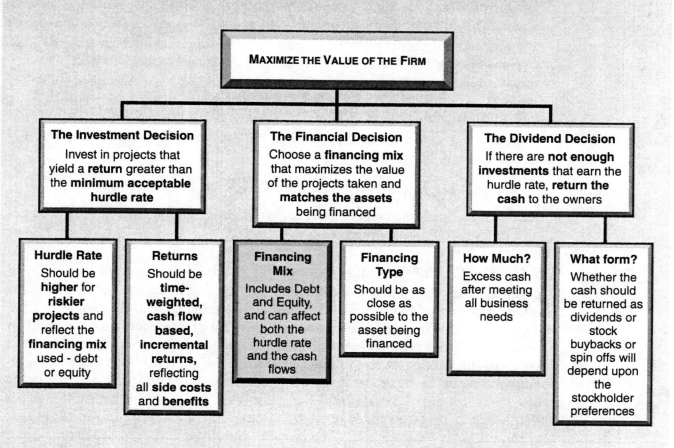

COST OF CAPITAL APPROACH

In Chapters 3 and 4, we estimated the minimum acceptable hurdle rates for equity investors (the cost of equity), and for all investors in the firm (the cost of capital). We defined the *cost of capital* to be the weighted average of the costs of the different components of financing—including debt, equity, and hybrid securities—used by a firm to fund its financial requirements. By altering the weights of the different components, firms might be able to change their cost of capital.[1]

Definition of the Weighted Average Cost of Capital (WACC)

The *weighted average cost of capital* is defined as the weighted average of the costs of the different components of financing used by a firm:

$$\text{WACC} = k_e\,(E/(D + E + PS)) + k_d\,(D/(D + E + PS)) + k_{ps}\,(PS/(D + E + PS))$$

where WACC is the weighted average cost of capital, k_e, k_d, and k_{ps} are the costs of equity, debt, and preferred stock, and E, D, and PS are their respective market values.

The estimation of the costs of the individual components—equity, debt, and preferred stock—and of the weights in the cost of capital formulation are explored in detail in Chapter 4. To summarize:

- The cost of equity should reflect the riskiness of an equity investment in the company. The standard models for risk and return—the capital asset pricing model and the arbitrage pricing model—measure risk in terms of non-diversifiable risk, and convert the risk measure into an expected return.

- The cost of debt should reflect the default risk of the firm (the higher the default risk, the greater the cost of debt) and the tax advantage associated with debt (interest is tax deductible):

$$\text{Cost of Debt} = \text{Pretax Interest Rate on Borrowing}\,(1 - \text{tax rate})$$

- The cost of preferred stock should reflect the preferred dividend and the absence of tax deductibility:

$$\text{Cost of Preferred Stock} = \text{Preferred Dividend}\,/\,\text{Preferred Stock Price}$$

- The weights used for the individual components should be market value weights rather than book value weights.

The Role of Cost of Capital in Investment Analysis and Valuation

In order to understand the relationship between the cost of capital and optimal capital structure, we first have to establish the relationship between firm value and the cost of capital. In Chapter 5, we noted that the value of a project to a firm could be computed by discounting the expected cash flows on it at a rate that reflected the riskiness of the cash flows, and that the analysis could be done either from the viewpoint of equity investors alone or from the viewpoint of the entire firm. In the latter

---

[1]If capital structure is irrelevant, the cost of capital will be unchanged as the capital structure is altered.

approach, we discounted the cash flows to the firm on the project (i.e., the project cash flows prior to debt payments but after taxes) at the project's cost of capital. Extending this principle, the value of the entire firm can be estimated by discounting the expected cash flows over time at the firm's cost of capital. The firm's aggregate cash flows can be estimated as cash flows after operating expenses, taxes, and any capital investments needed to create future growth in both fixed assets and working capital:

Free Cash Flow to Firm (FCFF) = EBIT $(1 - t)$ − (Capital Expenditures − Depreciation) − Change in Non-cash Working Capital

The value of the firm can then be written as:

$$\text{Value of Firm} = \sum_{t=1}^{t=n} \frac{\text{CF to Firm}_t}{(1 + \text{WACC})^t}$$

The value of a firm is therefore a function of its cash flows and its cost of capital. In the specific case where the cash flows to the firm are unaffected by the debt/equity mix, and the cost of capital is reduced, the value of the firm will increase. If the objective in choosing the financing mix for the firm is the maximization of firm value, this can be accomplished, in this case, by *minimizing the cost of capital.* In the more general case where the cash flows to the firm are a function of the debt/equity mix, the optimal financing mix is the one *that maximizes firm value.*[2]

The optimal financing mix for a firm is simple to compute if one is provided with a schedule that relates the costs of equity and debt to the leverage of the firm.

WACC, Firm Value, and Leverage

Assume that you are given the costs of equity and debt at different debt levels for Jershey's, a leading manufacturer of chocolates and other candies, and that the cash flows to this firm are currently $200 million. Jershey's is in a relatively stable market, and these cash flows are expected to grow at 6% forever, and are unaffected by the debt ratio of the firm. The WACC schedule is provided in Table 8.1, along with the value of the firm at each level of debt. Note that the value of the firm = Cash flows to firm * $(1 + g)/(\text{WACC} - g)$ = $200 * 1.06 / (\text{WACC} - .06)$.

The value of the firm increases (decreases) as the WACC decreases (increases), as illustrated in Figure 8.1.

While this illustration makes the choice of an optimal financing mix seem trivial, it obscures some real problems that may arise in its applications. First, an analyst typically does not have the benefit of having the entire schedule of costs of financing prior to an analysis. In most cases, the only level of debt about which there is any certainty about the cost of financing is the current level. Second, the analysis assumes implicitly that the level of cash flows to the firm is unaffected by the financing mix of the firm and, consequently, by the default risk (or bond rating) for the firm. While this may be reasonable in some cases, it might not in others. For instance, a firm that manufactures consumer durables (cars, televisions, etc.) might find that its sales drop if its default risk increases because consumers are reluctant to buy its products.

---

[2]In other words, the value of the firm might not be maximized at the point that cost of capital is minimized, if firm cash flows are much lower at that level.

Table 8.1 WACC, Firm Value, and Debt Ratios				
D/(D + E)	Cost of Equity	Cost of Debt	WACC	Firm Value
0	10.50%	4.80%	10.50%	$4,711
10%	11.00%	5.10%	10.41%	$4,807
20%	11.60%	5.40%	10.36%	$4,862
30%	12.30%	5.52%	10.27%	$4,970
40%	13.10%	5.70%	10.14%	$5,121
50%	14.00%	6.30%	10.15%	$5,108
60%	15.00%	7.20%	10.32%	$4,907
70%	16.10%	8.10%	10.50%	$4,711
80%	17.20%	9.00%	10.64%	$4,569
90%	18.40%	10.20%	11.02%	$4,223
100%	19.70%	11.40%	11.40%	$3,926

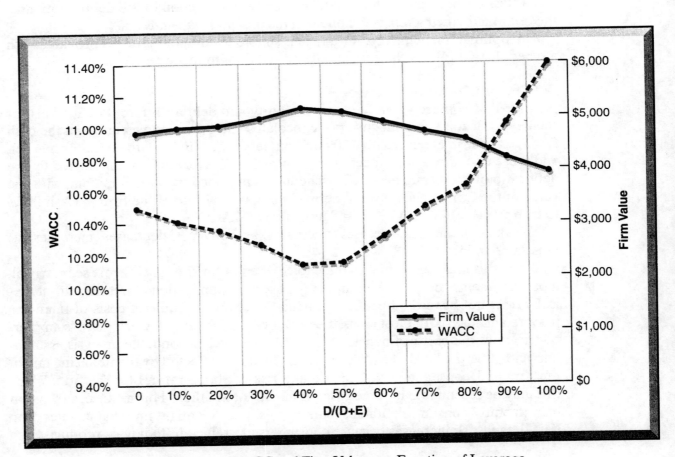

Figure 8.1   WACC and Firm Value as a Function of Leverage.

A lower cost of capital will lead to a higher firm value only if

☐ the operating income does not change as the cost of capital declines.

☐ the operating income goes up as the cost of capital goes down.

☐ any decline in operating income is offset by the lower cost of capital.

A PRACTICAL FRAMEWORK FOR ANALYZING CAPITAL STRUCTURE

As noted above, there are compromises that have to be made in order to apply the cost of capital approach to real-world problems. A general framework for analyzing these problems is provided in this section.

Cost of Equity

The primary task here is to estimate the cost of equity at different levels of debt. The approach described below applies if the CAPM is used to estimate cost of equity; the approach can be modified if the APM or a multi-factor model is used to estimate the cost of equity, instead.

Step 1: Obtain a current estimate of the equity beta and the debt/equity ratio. The current beta estimate can be estimated either with top-down (with a regression) approaches, or bottom-up (with sector betas) approaches.

Step 2: Estimate the unlevered beta (i.e., the beta that the firm would have had if it had no debt at all). If one uses the relationship between beta and leverage developed in Chapter 4, the unlevered beta can be written as:

$$\beta_u = \beta_{current}/[1 + (1 - t)D/E]$$

where β_u is the unlevered beta of the firm, $\beta_{current}$ is the current equity beta of the firm, t is the tax rate for the firm, and D/E is the average debt/equity ratio during the period of the regression.

Step 3: Reestimate the levered betas for different levels of debt:

$$\beta_{levered} = \beta_u [1 + (1 - t)D/E]$$

where $\beta_{levered}$ is the equity beta given new leverage and D/E is the new debt/equity ratio. At each level of leverage, measured using the debt/equity ratio, the equity beta is reestimated.

Step 4: Estimate the costs of equity using this levered beta:

$$k_e = R_f + \beta_{levered} [E(R_m) - R_f]$$

where k_e is the cost of equity, $E(R_m)$ is the expected return on the market index, and R_f is the current risk-free rate.

The definition of levered beta used in this table is based upon the assumption that all market risk is borne by the equity investors; this is unrealistic especially at higher levels of debt. An alternative estimate of levered betas apportions some of the market risk to the debt:

$$\beta_{levered} = \beta_u\,[1 + (1 - t)D/E] \; - \; \beta_{debt}\,(1 - t)\,D/E$$

The beta of debt is based upon the rating of the bond, and is estimated by regressing past returns on each rating class against returns on a market index. The levered betas estimated using this approach will generally be lower than those estimated with the conventional model.

8.2 BETAS OF DEBT, EQUITY, AND OPTIMAL DEBT RATIOS

When we assign a beta for debt, we are assuming that debt holders bear some market risk (as opposed to the assumption that equity investors will bear all the market risk). This assumption

☐ will increase the optimal debt ratio for a firm (relative to that calculated assuming that the beta of debt is 0).

☐ will decrease the optimal debt ratio for a firm.

☐ should not really affect the optimal debt ratio for a firm.

Explain.

Costs of Debt

Once again, the task is to estimate the cost of debt of the firm at different levels of debt. As background to estimating the cost of debt, two schedules have to be developed. The first lays out the relationship between default risk and a firm's underlying characteristics. For instance, if bond ratings are used to measure default risk, this schedule will describe the relationship between ratings and financial ratios, using either general information or information pertaining to a particular industry. The other schedule includes current market interest rates on corporate bonds in each ratings class. These default premiums will change over time and will have to be updated on a regular basis.

Given this background, the cost of debt for a firm can be estimated at different levels of debt by first estimating the bond rating for the firm at each debt level and then using the interest rate that corresponds to that rating:

Step 1: Prepare the latest income statement showing the current operating income and relevant financial ratios.

Step 2: Compute the current market value of the firm:

Market Value of Firm = Market Value of Equity + Market Value of Debt

Step 3: As the debt ratio is changed, compute the dollar value of debt:

Dollar Value of Debt = [Debt/(Debt + Equity)] * Current Market Value of Firm

Step 4: Compute the amount that will be paid as interest (Interest Rate * Dollar Value of Debt) and the financial ratios at each new debt ratio.

Step 5: Using the schedule relating bond ratings to financial ratios, estimate what the firm's rating will be at each new debt ratio and the market interest rate that would correspond to that rating; this is the before-tax cost of debt.

Step 6:   The after-tax cost of debt can then be computed using the firm's tax rate:

$$k_d = \text{After-Tax Cost of Debt} = \text{Before-Tax Cost of Debt} * (1 - \text{Tax Rate})$$

Cost of Capital

The costs of capital for different levels of debt can be estimated using the costs of equity and debt at each level. The debt ratio at which the cost of capital is minimized is the optimal debt ratio.

General Assumptions

The approach described above for estimating the cost of capital at different levels of debt rests on several assumptions. First, the effect on firm value of changing the capital structure is isolated by keeping the asset side fixed and changing the liability side. In practical terms, this implies that the debt ratio is increased (decreased) by issuing debt (equity) and repurchasing equity (debt). You may wonder if the optimal debt ratio obtained by doing this can be generalized to cases where the firm plans to invest the new funds in projects rather than in buying back securities. The answer is yes, on one condition: as long as the firm continues to make investments in the same line of business[3] in which it has operated in the past, the optimal debt ratio obtained from the above analysis can continue to be used. If the firm is planning to invest in new businesses, with different risk profiles, however, the optimal debt ratio calculated, keeping the asset side fixed, may no longer be appropriate.

The pretax operating income is assumed to be unaffected by the firm's financing mix and, by extension, its bond rating. If the operating income is a function of the firm's default risk, the basic framework will not change. Minimizing the cost of capital may not be the optimal course of action, however, since the value of the firm is determined by both the cash flows and the cost of capital. The value of the firm will have to be computed at each debt level, and the optimal debt ratio will be that which maximizes firm value.

ILLUSTRATION **8.1**   Analyzing the Capital Structure for Disney—June 1997

The general framework can be used to find the optimal capital structure for a firm, as we did for Disney in June 1997. In 1997, Disney had debt outstanding of $12.342 billion, much of it as a consequence of financing the acquisition of Capital Cities in the previous year. This debt is estimated[4] to have a market value of $11.18 billion. In June 1997, there were 675.13 million shares outstanding trading at $75.38 per share. In Chapter 4, we used these inputs in conjunction with an estimated beta of 1.25 and a tax rate of 36% for Disney as a firm to arrive at a cost of capital of 12.22%:

Value of Equity = 675.13 million Shares * $ 75.38 = $ 50,888 million
Value of Debt = $ 11,180 million
Value of Disney as a Firm = $ 50,888 m + $ 11,180 m = $ 62,068 million
Cost of Equity = 7% + 1.25 (5.5%) = 13.85%

---

[3]The implicit assumption is that projects in the same business line have similar cash flow generating potential.

[4]This market value is estimated using an average maturity of three years for the debt, an interest expense of $478 million, and a pretax cost of debt, based upon Disney's current borrowing rate of 7.5%. The present value of the interest expenses and the book value are estimated using this borrowing rate.

After-Tax Cost of Debt = 7.50% (1 − .36) = 4.80%
Cost of Capital = (50,888/62,068)(13.85%) + 4.80% (11,180/62,068) = 12.22%

8.3 MARKET VALUE, BOOK VALUE, AND COST OF CAPITAL

Disney had a book value of equity of approximately $16.5 billion. Using the book value of debt of $12.342 billion, estimate the cost of capital for Disney using book value weights.

Disney's Cost of Equity and Leverage

In Chapter 4, we laid the groundwork for estimating cost of equity as leverage changes, by stating the beta as a function of the leverage. We estimated[5] Disney's unlevered beta by taking the weighted average of the unlevered betas of the businesses it was involved in to be 1.09. Using the equation for the levered beta,

Levered Beta = Unlevered Beta * [1 + (1 − tax rate) (Debt/ Equity)]

a long-term bond rate of 7%, and the historical premium of 5.5%, we estimate the cost of equity at different debt ratios for Disney in Table 8.2.

To examine how sensitive our assumptions are to this definition of levered betas, we also estimated the betas, apportioning some of the market risk to debt:

$$\beta_{levered} = \beta_u [1 + (1 − t)D/E] − \beta_{debt} (1 − t) D/E$$

The beta of debt is based upon the rating of the bond and is estimated by regressing past returns on each rating class against returns on a market index.

This spreadsheet allows you to estimate the betas and costs of equity for a firm as the leverage changes (**unlev.xls**).

Disney's Cost of Debt and Leverage

A number of financial ratios are correlated with bond ratings, and ideally we would build a sophisticated model to predict ratings. For purposes of this illustration, however, we use a much simpler version: We assume that bond ratings are determined solely by the interest coverage ratio, which is defined as follows:

Interest Coverage Ratio = Earnings Before Interest & Taxes / Interest Expense

Interest Coverage Ratio: The interest coverage ratio is the earnings before interest and taxes divided by the interest expense. It is a measure of the firm's capacity to service its interest payments, with higher coverage ratios representing more safety.

We chose the interest coverage ratio for three reasons. First, it is a key ratio that is used by both Standard and Poor's and Moody's to determine ratings. Second, there is significant correlation not only between the interest coverage ratio and bond ratings, but

---

[5]The alternative approach would be to unlever the beta from the regression of Disney returns against market returns of 1.40 using the average debt/equity ratio of 14% for Disney during the regression period, which was 1992 to 1996.

Unlevered Beta = Current Beta / (1 + (1 − t) Average Debt/Equity)
= 1.40 / (1 + (1 − 0.36) (0.14)) = 1.28

Table 8.2 LEVERAGE, BETAS, AND THE COST OF EQUITY

Debt Ratio	D/E Ratio	Beta	Cost of Equity
0%	0%	1.09	13.00%
10%	11%	1.17	13.43%
20%	25%	1.27	13.96%
30%	43%	1.39	14.65%
40%	67%	1.56	15.56%
50%	100%	1.79	16.85%
60%	150%	2.14	18.77%
70%	233%	2.72	21.97%
80%	400%	3.99	28.95%
90%	900%	8.21	52.14%

also between the interest coverage ratio and other ratios used in analysis, such as the debt coverage ratio and the funds flow ratios. Third, the interest coverage ratio changes as a firm changes its financing mix and decreases as the debt ratio increases.

The data in Table 8.3 was obtained based upon an analysis of the financial ratios of large manufacturing firms in different ratings classes. Using this table as a guideline, then, a firm with an interest coverage ratio of 2.55 would have a rating of BBB for its bonds.

The relationship between bond ratings and interest rates in June 1997 was obtained by looking at yields to maturity of long-term bonds in each ratings class and averaging these yields. Table 8.4 summarizes the interest rates/rating relationship and reports the spread for these bonds over treasury bonds (the treasury bond rate in June 1997 was 7%).

Table 8.5 summarizes Disney's projected operating income statement for the financial year 1996–97. It shows that Disney had earnings before interest and taxes of $5,559 million and paid out interest of only $479 million. The financial ratios provide evidence of the capacity of Disney to meet its debt obligations.

Default Spreads: This is the difference between the rate at which a firm with a specified default risk can borrow and the government bond rate on a bond of equivalent maturity.

Disney's actual earnings before interest and taxes were much lower than $5,559 million, because of the amortization charge that Disney took in 1996 to reflect its acquisition of Capital Cities. Since our intention is to measure "normalized operating income," and Disney has already paid[6] for this acquisition, we will not consider it in our analysis. Note that the interest coverage ratio is 11.61, but Disney's current rating is AA. Referring to Table 8.3, based upon the coverage ratio alone, Disney should command a AAA rating. Part of the reason for this is that Disney's interest expenses

[6]In contrast, the depreciation charges on existing assets will have to be reinvested back in these assets as capital maintenance expenditure to maintain the earning capacity of the assets.

Table 8.3 BOND RATINGS AND INTEREST COVERAGE RATIOS

Bond Rating	Interest Coverage Ratio	
	Low	High
AAA	8.50	∞
AA	6.50	8.50
A+	5.50	6.50
A	4.25	5.50
A−	3.00	4.25
BBB	2.50	3.00
BB	2.00	2.50
B+	1.75	2.00
B	1.50	1.75
B−	1.25	1.50
CCC	0.80	1.25
CC	0.65	0.80
C	0.20	0.65
D	−∞	0.20

Table 8.4 BOND RATINGS AND MARKET INTEREST RATES

Rating	Interest Rate	Spread Over Long Bond Rate
AAA	7.20%	0.20%
AA	7.50%	0.50%
A+	7.80%	0.80%
A	8.00%	1.00%
A−	8.25%	1.25%
BBB	8.50%	1.50%
BB	9.00%	2.00%
B+	9.50%	2.50%
B	10.25%	3.25%
B−	11.25%	4.25%
CCC	12.00%	5.00%
CC	13.00%	6.00%
C	14.50%	7.50%
D	17.00%	10.00%

for 1996 do not reflect the annualized interest expenses that the company is likely to face next year on its total book debt of slightly more than $12 billion.

Finally, to compute Disney's ratings at different debt levels, we redo the operating income statement at each level of debt, compute the interest coverage ratio at that level of debt, and find the rating that corresponds to that level of debt. For example, Table 8.6 provides operating income statements showing the debt ratio in-

Table 8.5 DISNEY'S INCOME STATEMENT IN 1996

Revenues	18,739
−Operating expenses	12,046
EBITDA	6,693
−Depreciation	1,134
EBIT	5,559
−Interest expense	479
Income before taxes	5,080
−Taxes	847
Income after taxes	4,233
Interest coverage ratio = 5,559/479 = 11.61	

Table 8.6 EFFECT OF MOVING TO HIGHER DEBT RATIOS

D/(D + E)	0.00%	10.00%
D/E	0.00%	11.11%
$ Debt	$0	$6,207
EBITDA	$6,693	$6,693
Depreciation	$1,134	$1,134
EBIT	$5,559	$5,559
Interest Expense	$0	$447
Taxable Income	$5,559	$5,112
Pretax Int. cov.	∞	12.44
Likely Rating	AAA	AAA
Interest Rate	7.20%	7.20%
Eff. Tax Rate	36.00%	36.00%
After-Tax Cost of Debt	4.61%	4.61%

creased to 10% of the overall value of the firm. The first step in the process is to estimate the dollar debt at 10%, which can be calculated as 10% of the value of Disney as a firm:

$$\text{Value of Disney} = \text{Market Value of Equity} + \text{Market Value of Debt}$$
$$= \$50,888 \text{ million} + \$11,180 \text{ million} = \$62,068 \text{ million}$$
$$\text{Dollar Debt at } 10\% = 10\% \text{ of } \$62,068 \text{ million} = \$6207 \text{ million}$$

Note that there is an element of circular reasoning involved here. The interest rate is needed to calculate the interest coverage ratio, and the coverage ratio is necessary to compute the interest rate. To get around the problem, we do a series of iterations until there is consistency between the rate used to calculate the interest expense and the rate that is obtained from the coverage ratio. (We start with a AAA rate).

This process is repeated for each level of debt from 20% to 90%, and the after-tax costs of debt are obtained at each level of debt, and reported in Table 8.7.

			Table 8.7	COSTS OF DEBT AT DIFFERENT DEBT RATIOS		
Debt Ratio	$ Debt	Interest Exp.	Interest Coverage Ratio	Bond Rating	Interest Rate	AT Cost of Debt
0%	$0	$0	∞	AAA	7.20%	4.61%
10%	$6,207	$447	12.44	AAA	7.20%	4.61%
20%	$12,414	$968	5.74	A+	7.80%	4.99%
30%	$18,621	$1,536	3.62	A−	8.25%	5.28%
40%	$24,827	$2,234	2.49	BB	9.00%	5.76%
50%	$31,034	$3,181	1.75	B	10.25%	6.56%
60%	$37,241	$4,469	1.24	CCC	12.00%	7.68%
70%	$43,448	$5,214	1.07	CCC	12.00%	7.68%
80%	$49,655	$5,959	0.93	CCC	12.00%	7.97%
90%	$55,862	$7,262	0.77	CC	13.00%	9.42%

Interest Coverage Ratio = EBIT/Interest Expense; EBIT for Disney = $ 5,559 million

8.4 MARKET VALUE, BOOK VALUE, AND COST OF CAPITAL

Using the framework developed in Table 8.6, estimate the bond rating and cost of debt for Disney at a 20% debt ratio.

D/(D+E)	0.00%	10.00%	20.00%
D/E	0.00%	11.11%	
$ Debt	$0	$6,207	
EBITDA	$6,693	$6,693	
Depreciation	$1,134	$1,134	
EBIT	$5,559	$5,559	
Interest Expense	$0	$447	
Taxable Income	$5,559	$5,112	
Pretax Int. cov.	∞	12.44	
Likely Rating	AAA	AAA	
Interest Rate	7.20%	7.20%	
Eff. Tax Rate	36.00%	36.00%	
After-tax Cost of Debt	4.61%	4.61%	

There is a dataset on the Web that summarizes bond ratings, interest coverage ratios, and spreads for U.S. firms (**ratings.xls**).

Disney: Effects of Leverage on Cost of Capital

Now that we have estimated the cost of equity and the cost of debt at each debt level, we are in a position to compute Disney's cost of capital. This is done for each debt level in Exhibit 8.1. The cost of capital, which is 13.00% when the firm is unlevered,

Exhibit 8.1   Cost of Capital Worksheet for Disney

D/(D+E)	0.00%	10.00%	20.00%	30.00%	40.00%	50.00%	60.00%	70.00%	80.00%	90.00%
D/E	0.00%	11.11%	25.00%	42.86%	66.67%	100.00%	150.00%	233.33%	400.00%	900.00%
$ Debt	$0	$6,207	$12,414	$18,621	$24,827	$31,034	$37,241	$43,448	$49,655	$55,862
Beta	1.09	1.17	1.27	1.39	1.56	1.79	2.14	2.72	3.99	8.21
Cost of Equity	13.00%	13.43%	13.96%	14.65%	15.56%	16.85%	18.77%	21.97%	28.95%	52.14%
Operating Inc.	$6,693	$6,693	$6,693	$6,693	$6,693	$6,693	$6,693	$6,693	$6,693	$6,693
Depreciation	$1,134	$1,134	$1,134	$1,134	$1,134	$1,134	$1,134	$1,134	$1,134	$1,134
Interest	$0	$447	$968	$1,536	$2,234	$3,181	$4,469	$5,214	$5,959	$7,262
Taxable Income	$5,559	$5,112	$4,591	$4,023	$3,325	$2,378	$1,090	$345	($400)	($1,703)
Tax	$2,001	$1,840	$1,653	$1,448	$1,197	$856	$392	$124	($144)	($613)
Net Income	$3,558	$3,272	$2,938	$2,575	$2,128	$1,522	$698	$221	($256)	($1,090)
(+)Deprec'n	$1,134	$1,134	$1,134	$1,134	$1,134	$1,134	$1,134	$1,134	$1,134	$1,134
Funds from Op.	$4,692	$4,406	$4,072	$3,709	$3,262	$2,656	$1,832	$1,355	$878	$44
Pre-tax Int. Cov	∞	12.44	5.74	3.62	2.49	1.75	1.24	1.07	0.93	0.77
Funds Int. Cov	∞	9.86	4.21	2.41	1.46	0.83	0.41	0.26	0.15	0.01
Funds/Debt	∞	0.71	0.33	0.20	0.13	0.09	0.05	0.03	0.02	0.00
Likely Rating	AAA	AAA	A+	A−	BB	B	CCC	CCC	CCC	CC
Interest Rate	7.20%	7.20%	7.80%	8.25%	9.00%	10.25%	12.00%	12.00%	12.00%	13.00%
Eff Tax Rate	36.00%	36.00%	36.00%	36.00%	36.00%	36.00%	36.00%	36.00%	33.59%	27.56%

Cost of Capital Calculations

D/(D+E)	0.00%	10.00%	20.00%	30.00%	40.00%	50.00%	60.00%	70.00%	80.00%	90.00%
D/E	0.00%	11.11%	25.00%	42.86%	66.67%	100.00%	150.00%	233.33%	400.00%	900.00%
$ Debt	$0	$6,207	$12,414	$18,621	$24,827	$31,034	$37,241	$43,448	$49,655	$55,862
Cost of Equity	13.00%	13.43%	13.96%	14.65%	15.56%	16.85%	18.77%	21.97%	28.95%	52.14%
Cost of Debt	4.61%	4.61%	4.99%	5.28%	5.76%	6.56%	7.68%	7.68%	7.97%	9.42%
WACC	13.00%	12.55%	12.17%	11.84%	11.64%	11.70%	12.11%	11.97%	12.17%	13.69%
Firm Value (C)	$58,319	$60,435	$62,314	$64,054	$65,133	$64,800	$62,597	$63,372	$62,332	$55,393
Firm Value (G)	$53,172	$58,014	$62,705	$67,419	$70,542	$69,560	$63,445	$65,524	$62,751	$47,140

decreases as the firm initially adds debt, reaches a minimum of 11.64% at 40% debt, and then starts to increase again. This is illustrated in Table 8.8. The same information is presented in Figure 8.2.

To illustrate the robustness of this solution to alternative measures of levered betas, the costs of debt, equity, and capital were reestimated under the assumption that debt bears some market risk. If the debt holders bear some market risk, the cost of equity is lower at each level of debt and Disney's optimal debt ratio remains at 40%.

Table 8.8	COSTS OF DEBT, EQUITY, AND CAPITAL—DISNEY		
Debt Ratio	**Cost of Equity**	**AT Cost of Debt**	**Cost of Capital**
0.00%	13.00%	4.61%	13.00%
10.00%	13.43%	4.61%	12.55%
20.00%	13.96%	4.99%	12.17%
30.00%	14.65%	5.28%	11.84%
40.00%	15.56%	5.76%	11.64%
50.00%	16.85%	6.56%	11.70%
60.00%	18.77%	7.68%	12.11%
70.00%	21.97%	7.68%	11.97%
80.00%	28.95%	7.97%	12.17%
90.00%	52.14%	9.42%	13.69%

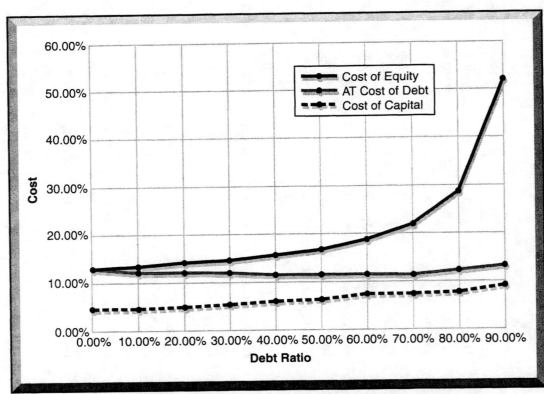

Figure 8.2   Disney: Cost of Debt, Equity, and Capital.

Firm Value and Cost of Capital

The rationale for minimizing the cost of capital is that it maximizes the value of the firm. To illustrate the effects of moving to the optimal on Disney's firm value, we start off with a simple formula:

$$\text{Firm Value} = \text{CF to Firm} (1 + g) / (\text{WACC} - g)$$

where

$$g = \text{Growth rate in the cash flow to the firm (steady state)}$$

The current value of the firm is $62,068 million and the current weighted average cost of capital is 12.22%. The current cash flow to the firm is:

$$\text{Cash Flow to Firm} = \text{EBIT} (1 - \text{tax rate}) + \text{Depreciation} - \text{Capital Spending}$$
$$= 5,559 (1 - 0.36) + 1,134 - 1745 - = \$ 2,947 \text{ million}$$

(Working capital was ignored)
Solving for the implied growth rate:

$$\text{Growth Rate} = (\text{Firm Value} * \text{WACC} - \text{CF to Firm})/(\text{Firm Value} + \text{CF to Firm})$$
$$= (62,068 * .1222 - 2947)/(62,068 + 2,947) = .0713 \text{ or } 7.13\%$$

Now assume that Disney moves to 40% debt and a WACC of 11.64%. By moving to the lower cost of capital, the firm will save the following amount in annual financing costs:

$$\text{Annual Financing Costs with Existing WACC} = \$62,068m (.1222) = \$7,583$$
$$\text{Annual Financing Costs with New WACC} = \$62,068 (.1164) = \$7,227$$
$$\text{Savings in Annual Financing Costs} = \$7,583 - \$7,227 = \$356 \text{ m}$$

(Differences in dollar values are due to rounding)
The present value of these savings, assuming it grows at the same rate as the cash flows to the firm, is:

$$\text{Present Value of Savings} = (\$356 * 1.0713)/(.1164 - .0713) = \$8,474 \text{ million}$$

The value of the firm[7] will increase by $8,474 million by moving to the optimal debt ratio. With 675.13 million shares outstanding, assuming that stockholders can rationally evaluate the effect of this refinancing, the increase in the stock price can be calculated:

$$\text{Increase in Stock Price} = \text{Increase in Firm Value} / \text{Number of Shares Outstanding}$$
$$= 8474 / 675.13 = \$12.55$$

Since the current stock price is $75.38, the stock price can be expected to increase to $87.93, which translates into a 16.65% increase in the price. Since the asset side of the balance sheet is kept fixed and changes in capital structure are made by borrowing funds and repurchasing stock, this implies that the stock price would increase to

---

[7] An alternative approach is to value the entire firm using the new cost of capital:

Cash Flow to Firm = $2,947 million
WACC = 11.64%
Growth Rate in Cash Flows to Firm = 7.13%
Firm Value = $2,947 * 1.0713 / (.1164 - .0713) = $70,056 million

The difference between this value ($72,888) and the value estimated in the text can be attributed to the fact that we kept firm value fixed at $62,068 while estimating the annual financing savings.

Table 8.9 COSTS OF CAPITAL AND FIRM VALUE: DISNEY		
Debt Ratio	Cost of Capital	Firm Value
0.00%	13.00%	$53,172
10.00%	12.55%	$58,014
20.00%	12.17%	$62,705
30.00%	11.84%	$67,419
40.00%	11.64%	$70,542
50.00%	11.70%	$69,560
60.00%	12.11%	$63,445
70.00%	11.97%	$65,524
80.00%	12.17%	$62,751
90.00%	13.69%	$47,140

$87.93 on the announcement of the repurchase. The firm value and cost of capital at different debt ratios are summarized in Table 8.9.

8.5 RATIONALITY AND STOCK PRICE EFFECTS

This analysis assumes that the stock will be bought back at the higher estimated price of $87.93. Estimate the effect on the stock price of the capital structure change if you were able to buy stock back at the old price of $75.38.

IN PRACTICE: EFFECTIVE TAX RATES, INCOME, AND INTEREST EXPENSES

While it is conventional to leave the marginal tax rate unchanged as the debt ratio is increased, we adjust the tax rate to reflect the potential loss of the tax benefits of debt at higher debt ratios, where the interest expenses exceed the earnings before interest and taxes. To illustrate this point, note that the earnings before interest and taxes at Disney are $5,559 million. As long as interest expenses are less than $5,559 million, interest expenses remain fully tax deductible and earn the 36% tax benefit. For instance in Exhibit 8.1, even at a 70% debt ratio, the interest expenses are $5,214 million and the tax benefit is, therefore, 36% of this amount.

At an 80% debt ratio, however, the interest expenses balloon to $5,959 million, which is greater than the earnings before interest and taxes of $5,559 million. We consider the tax benefit on the interest expenses up to this amount:

Tax Benefit = $5,559 million * .36 = $ 2,001 million

As a proportion of the total interest expenses, the tax benefit is now less than 36%:

Effective Tax Rate = $2,001/$5.959 = 33.59%

This, in turn, raises the after-tax cost of debt. This is a conservative approach, since losses can be carried forward. Given that this is a permanent shift in leverage, it does make sense to be conservative.

This spreadsheet allows you to compute the optimal debt ratio firm value for any firm, using the same information used for Disney. It has updated interest coverage ratios and default spreads built in (**capstr.xls**).

Caveat Emptor: Some Considerations in Using the Model

There are several considerations that need to be taken into account when using this approach to come up with an optimal debt ratio. First, the bond rating is assumed to be predictable, based upon financial ratios. The ratings agencies would argue, however, that subjective factors, such as the perceived quality of management, are part of the ratings process. One way to build these factors into the analysis would be to modify the ratings obtained from the financial ratio analysis across the board to reflect the ratings agencies' subjective concerns.[8] Second, it is assumed that at every debt level, all existing debt will be refinanced at the "new" interest rate that will prevail after the capital structure change. For instance, Disney's existing debt of approximately $12 billion, which has a AA rating, is assumed to be refinanced at the interest rate corresponding to a BB rating, which is our estimate of Disney's rating at the optimal debt level of 40%. This is done for two reasons. The first is that existing debt holders might have protective puts that enable them to put their bonds back to the firm and receive face value.[9] The second is that it gives us the value increment without "wealth expropriation" effects—the effects of stockholders expropriating wealth from bondholders, when debt is increased, and vice versa, when debt is reduced—from the value calculations. These wealth-transfer effects can be built in by locking in current rates on existing bonds and recalculating the optimal debt ratio.[10] Third, the assumption that the operating income is unaffected by the bond rating is a key one. If the operating income is adversely affected by the drop in the bond rating, the value of the firm may not be maximized where the weighted average cost of capital is minimized. Again, the analysis can be modified so that the operating income is a function of the bond rating, and by calculating the value of the firm at each debt level.[11] Finally, the unconstrained analysis leaves us with the uncomfortable finding that at its optimal debt ratio, Disney has a bond rating below investment grade. Since most financial managers would be troubled by this sudden increase in default risk and its implications for the long-term survival of the firm, we introduce constraints into the analysis.

Investment Grade Bonds: An investment grade bond is one with a rating greater than BBB. Some institutional investors, such as pension funds, are constrained from holding bonds with lower ratings.

---

[8]For instance, assume that a firm's current rating is AA, but that its financial ratios would result in an A rating. It can then be argued that the ratings agencies are, for subjective reasons, rating the company one notch higher than the rating obtained from a purely financial analysis. The ratings obtained for each debt level can then be increased by one notch across the board to reflect these subjective considerations.

[9]If they do not have protective puts, it is in the best interests of the stockholders not to refinance the debt (as in the leveraged buyout of RJR Nabisco) if debt ratios are increased.

[10]This will have the effect of reducing interest cost, when debt is increased, and thus increasing interest coverage ratios. This will lead to higher ratings, at least in the short term.

[11]For example, we assumed that Disney's operating income would drop 10% if its rating dropped below A− and another 10% if it dropped below BBB. Consequently, the optimal debt ratio is reduced to 20%.

Building Constraints into the Analysis

The simplest solution is a "bond rating constraint," whereby the debt level that has the lowest cost of capital subject to the constraint that the bond rating meets or exceeds a certain level is chosen. For example, in the previous illustration, if Disney insisted on preserving a bond rating of A− or above, the optimal debt ratio would be 30%.

While this approach is simple, it is essentially subjective and is therefore open to manipulation. For instance, the management at Disney could insist that it wants to preserve a AA rating and hence justify the existing debt policy. One way to make managers more accountable in this regard is to measure the cost of a rating constraint:

$$\text{Cost of Rating Constraint} = \text{Maximum Firm Value without Constraints} -$$
$$\text{Maximum Firm Value with Constraints}$$

If Disney insisted on maintaining an A− rating, its constrained optimal debt ratio would be 30%. The cost of preserving the constraint can then be measured as the difference in firm value at 40% and at 30%:

$$
\begin{aligned}
\text{Cost of Rating Constraint for Disney} &= \text{Value at 40\% Debt} - \text{Value at 30\% Debt} \\
&= \quad \$70{,}542 \quad\quad - \quad\quad \$67{,}419 \\
&= \$3{,}123 \text{ million}
\end{aligned}
$$

This does overstate the cost of the rating constraint, since operating income is being held constant as the rating drops from A- to BB. To the degree that operating income moves with ratings, this cost will drop.

The second approach to building in constraints is to analyze the effects of changes in operating income on the optimal debt ratio. In the base case described above, Disney's operating income in 1996 was used to find the optimal leverage. One could argue that Disney's operating income is volatile and could change, however, depending upon the health of the entertainment business (Table 8.10).

There are several ways of using historical data to modify the analysis. One approach is to look at the firm's performance during previous downturns. In Disney's case, the recession in 1991 resulted in a drop in operating income of almost 22% from $1,287 million to $1,004 million. A second approach is to obtain a statistical measure of the volatility in operating income, so that we can be more conservative in choosing debt levels for firms with more volatile earnings. In Disney's case, the standard deviation in percentage changes in operating income is 38.43%. Finally, it has to be noted that Disney's acquisition of Capital Cities has changed its risk exposure and made it more susceptible to the swings in income in the broadcasting business.

To examine the sensitivity of the conclusions to changes in operating income, we lowered EBITDA by 30% and examined the effect on the optimal debt ratio. The optimal debt ratio declines from 40% to 30%. Table 8.11 summarizes the effect on optimal debt ratios of lower earnings.

As you can see, the optimal debt ratio declines as the EBITDA decreases. It is striking to note, however, that Disney can afford to carry a significantly higher amount of debt even with dramatically lower operating income.

Table 8.10	DISNEY'S OPERATING INCOME HISTORY: 1981–1996	
Year	**Operating Income**	**Change in Operating Income**
1981	$119.35	
1982	$141.39	18.46%
1983	$133.87	−5.32%
1984	$142.60	6.5%
1985	$205.60	44.2%
1986	$280.58	36.5%
1987	$707.00	152.0%
1988	$789.00	11.6%
1989	$1,109.00	40.6%
1990	$1,287.00	16.1%
1991	$1,004.00	−22.0%
1992	$1,287.00	28.2%
1993	$1,560.00	21.2%
1994	$1,804.00	15.6%
1995	$2,262.00	25.4%
1996	$3,024.00	33.7%

Table 8.11	EFFECTS OF OPERATING INCOME ON OPTIMAL DEBT RATIO: DISNEY	
% Lower	**$ EBITDA**	**Optimal Debt Ratio**
10%	$6,271.20	40%
20%	$5,574.40	40%
30%	$4,877.60	30%
40%	$4,180.80	20%
50%	$3,484.00	20%
60%	$2,787.20	10%
70%	$2,090.40	10%
80%	$1,393.60	0%
90%	$696.80	0%

8.6 BANKRUPTCY COSTS AND DEBT RATIOS

The optimal debt ratio obtained by minimizing the cost of capital is too high because it does not consider bankruptcy costs.

☐ True

☐ False

Explain.

Determinants of Optimal Debt Ratio

The preceding analysis highlights some of the determinants of the optimal debt ratio.

(a) Firm's Tax Rate

In general, the tax benefits from debt increase as the tax rate goes up. In relative terms, firms with higher tax rates have higher optimal debt ratios than do firms with lower tax rates, other things being equal. It also follows that a firm's optimal debt ratio will increase as its tax rate increases.

(b) Pretax Returns on the Firm (in Cash Flow Terms)[EBITDA/Firm Value]

This is defined as the EBITDA as a percentage of the market value of the firm. It follows that a firm with higher pretax returns can sustain much more debt as a proportion of the market value of the firm, since debt payments can be met much more easily from prevailing cash flows. Disney, for example, has EBITDA which is 10.78% of firm value in the base case, and an optimal debt ratio of 40%. Halving this to pretax return to 5.39% will reduce the optimal debt ratio to 10%.

(c) Variance in Operating Income

The variance in operating income enters the base case analysis in two ways. First, it plays a role in determining the current beta: firms with high (low) variance in operating income will tend to have high (low) betas. Second, the volatility in operating income can be one of the factors determining bond ratings at different levels of debt: ratings drop off much more dramatically for higher-variance firms as debt levels are increased. It follows that firms with higher (lower) variance in operating income will have lower (higher) optimal debt ratios. The variance in operating income also plays a role in the constrained analysis, since higher variance firms are much more likely to register significant drops in operating income. Consequently, the decision to increase debt should be made much more cautiously for these firms.

(d) Default Spreads

The default spreads commanded by different ratings classes tend to increase during recessions and decrease during recoveries. Keeping other things constant, as the spreads increase (decrease) optimal debt ratios decrease (increase), for the simple reason that higher spreads penalize firms which borrow more money and have lower ratings. In fact, the default spreads on corporate bonds have steadily declined since 1992, leading to higher optimal debt ratios for all firms.

8.7 LEVEL OF INTEREST RATES AND OPTIMAL DEBT RATIOS

As interest rates go down, the optimal debt ratios for all firms should go up since debt becomes much cheaper.

☐ True

☐ False

Explain.

Extending the Cost of Capital Approach

The cost of capital approach, which works so well for manufacturing firms that are publicly traded and rated and stay financially healthy, may have to be adapted in other cases, such as for private firms that might not be rated; financial service firms such as banks, and insurance companies; and firms in financial trouble.

Firms That Are Not Rated

There are two advantages to working with a publicly rated company like Disney. First, the current rating for the company provides information that can be used to assess its current default risk and how this risk might change as the debt ratio changes. Second, it provides a rationale for the process of estimating ratings and then using the ratings to estimate the interest rate on the debt. This does not imply that the approach cannot be used for unrated firms; however, there are at least two ways of dealing with this deficit. The first is to estimate a synthetic bond rating for the firm, based upon interest coverage or other financial ratios, and then use this rating to estimate an interest rate on debt. For private firms in the United States, this may provide a useful approximation of default risk. The second is to develop an alternative measure of default risk, which can then be used to estimate an interest rate on the debt. This measure can be based upon credit scoring approaches used by banks to determine default risk and interest rates; it can be as simple as classifying firms on a continuum from "very safe" to "very risky."

ILLUSTRATION 8.2   Applying the Cost of Capital Approach to a Private Firm: Bookscape Books

Bookscape, as a private firm, has neither a market value for its equity nor a rating for its debt. In order to estimate the optimal capital structure for Bookscape, we made the following assumptions:

- The operating income and depreciation estimates were obtained from the most recent income statement for the firm:

Revenues	$ 20,000,000
Operating Expenses	
Labor	$ 4,000,000
Material	$ 12,000,000
Lease Expenses	$ 500,000
Other Supplies	$ 1,000,000
Depreciation & Amortization	$ 500,000
EBIT	$ 2,000,000
Interest Expenses	$ 0
Taxable Income	$ 2,000,000
Taxes	$ 840,000
Net Income	$ 1,160,000

Since we consider the present value of operating lease expenses to be debt, we add back the lease expenses to the earnings before interest and taxes to arrive at an adjusted earnings before interest and taxes. For the rest of the analysis, operating lease expenses will be viewed as the equivalent of interest expenses:

$$\text{Adjusted EBIT} = \text{EBIT} + \text{Operating Lease Expenses}$$
$$= \$\,2,000,000 + \$\,500,000 = \$\,2,500,000$$

- While Bookscape has no debt outstanding, the present value of the operating lease expenses (see Chapter 4) of \$ 3.36 million is considered as debt.

- To estimate the market value of equity, we use a multiple of 22.41 times net income. This multiple is the average multiple at which comparable firms which are publicly traded are valued:

$$\text{Estimated Market Value of Equity} = \text{Net Income} * \text{Average Multiple}$$
$$= 1,160,000 * 22.41 = 26,000,000$$

- The interest rates at different levels of debt will be estimated based upon a "synthetic" bond rating. This rating will be assessed using the following table, which summarizes ratings and default spreads over the long-term bond rate as a function of interest coverage ratios for small firms which are rated by S&P as of June 1997.

Interest Coverage Ratio	Rating	Spread over T Bond Rate
>12.5	AAA	0.20%
9.50–12.50	AA	0.50%
7.5–9.5	A+	0.80%
6.0–7.5	A	1.00%
4.5–6.0	A−	1.25%
3.5–4.5	BBB	1.50%
3.0–3.5	BB	2.00%
2.5–3.0	B+	2.50%
2.0–2.5	B	3.25%
1.5–2.0	B−	4.25%
1.25–1.5	CCC	5.00%
0.8–1.25	CC	6.00%
0.5–0.8	C	7.50%
< 0.5	D	10.00%

Note that smaller firms need higher coverage ratios than the larger firms to get the same rating. Based upon this table and Bookscape's current income statement, we can estimate a synthetic rating for it:

$$\text{Current Interest Coverage Ratio} = \text{Adjusted EBIT}/ \text{Interest Expense (Lease Expense)}$$
$$= 2,500,000/500,000 = 5.00$$

Table 8.12 COSTS OF CAPITAL AND FIRM VALUE FOR BOOKSCAPE

Debt Ratio	Beta	Cost of Equity	Interest Coverage Ratio	Bond Rating	Interest Rate	AT Cost of Debt	Cost of Capital	Firm Value
0%	1.03	12.65%	∞	A+	7.80%	4.52%	12.65%	$26,781
10%	1.09	13.01%	8.79	A+	7.80%	4.52%	12.16%	$29,025
20%	1.18	13.47%	4.03	BBB	8.50%	4.93%	11.76%	$31,182
30%	1.28	14.05%	2.23	B	10.25%	5.95%	11.62%	$32,000
40%	1.42	14.83%	1.52	B−	11.25%	6.53%	11.51%	$32,679
50%	1.62	15.93%	1.05	CC	13.00%	7.54%	11.73%	$31,341
60%	2.00	18.00%	0.88	CC	13.00%	8.20%	12.12%	$29,250
70%	2.74	22.09%	0.68	C	14.50%	10.39%	13.90%	$22,267
80%	4.12	29.64%	0.59	C	14.50%	10.90%	14.65%	$20,184
90%	8.23	52.28%	0.53	C	14.50%	11.30%	15.40%	$18,434

This coverage ratio suggests that Bookscape will have a bond rating of A− and a pretax cost of debt of 8.25% at its current debt ratio. Note that this is close to the cost of debt of 8% that we used in Chapter 4 as Bookscape's cost of debt.

- The tax rate used in the analysis is 42%. The long-term bond rate at the time of this analysis was 7%.

Based upon this information and using the same approach that we used for Disney, the cost of capital and firm value were estimated for Bookscape at different debt ratios. The information is summarized in Table 8.12.

The firm value is maximized (and the cost of capital is minimized) at a debt ratio of 40%, though the firm value is relatively flat between 20% and 50%.

IN PRACTICE: OPTIMAL DEBT RATIOS FOR PRIVATE FIRMS

While the trade-off between the costs and benefits of borrowing remain the same for private and publicly traded firms, there are differences between the two that may result in private firms borrowing less money. A comparison of the costs and benefits of debt for private and public firms yields the following conclusions:

- Taking on debt increases default risk and expected bankruptcy cost much more substantially for small private firms than for larger publicly traded firms, partly because the owners of the former are exposed more frequently to unlimited (personal) liability, and partly because the perception of financial trouble can be much more damaging to small, private firms. This is partially reflected in the use of different interest coverage ratios to get ratings.

- Taking on debt yields a smaller advantage in terms of disciplining decision makers in the case of privately run firms, since there is no separation of ownership and management.

- Taking on debt generally exposes small private firms to more restrictive bond covenants and higher agency costs than it does large publicly traded firms. .
- The loss of flexibility associated with using excess debt capacity is likely to weigh more heavily on small, private firms than large, publicly traded firms, due to the former's lack of access to public markets.

Barring the scenario in which the individual tax rate is substantially higher than the corporate tax rate and the tax benefits of debt are therefore substantially larger for small, private firms, all of the factors mentioned above would lead us to observe much lower debt ratios at small private firms.

Banks and Insurance Companies

There are several problems in applying the cost of capital approach to financial service firms, such as banks and insurance companies. The first is that the interest coverage ratio spreads, which are critical in determining the bond ratings, have to be estimated separately for financial service firms; applying manufacturing company spreads will result in absurdly low ratings for even the safest banks, and very low optimal debt ratios. The second is a measurement problem that arises partly from the difficulty in estimating the debt on a financial service company's balance sheet. Given the mix of deposits, repurchase agreements, short-term financing, and other liabilities that may show up on the balance sheet, one solution may be to focus only on long-term debt, defined tightly, and to use interest coverage ratios defined consistently. The third problem is that financial service firms may find their operating income affected by their bond rating; as the rating drops, the operating income might drop too. The final and most critical problem is that financial service firms operate under significant regulatory constraints on book capital that may restrict their capacity to change leverage.

ILLUSTRATION 8.3   Applying the Cost of Capital Approach to Deutsche Bank
We analyze the optimal capital structure for Deutsche Bank, using data from 1996. To begin, we make the following assumptions:

- The earnings before long-term interest expenses and taxes amounted to 23,209 million DM.
- Deutsche Bank was ranked AAA and paid 7.70% on its long-term debt in 1994. It had 110,111 DM in long-term debt outstanding at the end of the year.
- Deutsche Bank had 526.847 million shares outstanding, trading at 119.2 DM per share, and had a beta of 0.94 (the German long bond rate at that time was 7.50%).
- The interest coverage ratios used to estimate the bond ratings were adjusted downward, based upon the ratings of banks.[12]
- The operating income for Deutsche Bank is assumed to drop if its rating drops. Table 8.13 summarizes the interest coverage ratios and estimated operating income drops for different ratings classes.

---

[12]U.S. banks were used to estimate the numbers in the table. Since there are no "junk bond" status banks in our sample, we extrapolated the table below BBB.

Table 8.13 INTEREST COVERAGE RATIOS, RATINGS, AND OPERATING INCOME DECLINES

Interest Coverage Ratio	Rating is	Spread is	Operating Income Decline
<0.05	D	10.00%	−50.00%
0.05–0.10	C	7.50%	−40.00%
0.10–0.20	CC	6.00%	−40.00%
0.20–0.30	CCC	5.00%	−40.00%
0.30–0.40	B−	4.25%	−25.00%
0.40–0.50	B	3.25%	−20.00%
0.50–0.60	B+	2.50%	−20.00%
0.60–0.80	BB	2.00%	−20.00%
0.80–1.00	BBB	1.50%	−20.00%
1.00–1.50	A−	1.25%	−17.50%
1.50–2.00	A	1.00%	−15.00%
2.00–2.50	A+	0.80%	−10.00%
2.50–3.00	AA	0.50%	−5.00%
> 3.00	AAA	0.20%	0.00%

Table 8.14 DEBT RATIOS, WACC, AND FIRM VALUE: DEUTSCHE BANK

Debt Ratio	Cost of Equity	Cost of Debt	WACC	Firm Value
0%	10.13%	4.24%	10.13%	DM 124,288.85
10%	10.29%	4.24%	9.69%	DM 132,558.74
20%	10.49%	4.24%	9.24%	DM 142,007.59
30%	10.75%	4.24%	8.80%	DM 152,906.88
40%	11.10%	4.24%	8.35%	DM 165,618.31
50%	11.58%	4.24%	7.91%	DM 165,750.19
60%	12.30%	4.40%	7.56%	DM 162,307.44
70%	13.51%	4.57%	7.25%	DM 157,070.00
80%	15.92%	4.68%	6.92%	DM 151,422.87
90%	25.69%	6.24%	8.19%	DM 30,083.27

Thus, we assume that the operating income will drop 5% if Deutsche Bank's rating drops to AA and 20% if it drops to BBB.

Based upon these assumptions, the optimal long-term debt ratio for Deutsche Bank is estimated to be 50%, lower than the current debt ratio of 60%. Table 8.14 summarizes the cost of capital and firm values at different debt ratios for the firm. The actual long-term debt ratio for Deutsche Bank of 60% is slightly higher than the optimal. Going to the optimal will increase firm value by roughly 3.4 billion DM or 2%.

IN PRACTICE: Building in Regulatory, Self-Imposed, and Lender Constraints

In most analyses of optimal capital structure, an analyst will be faced with a series of constraints, some of which come from regulatory requirements, some of which are self-imposed, and some of which are imposed by existing lenders to the firm. One very common constraint imposed by all three is a constraint that the book value debt ratio not exceed a specified number. Since the analysis we have done so far has focused on market value debt ratios, there is the risk that the book value constraint may be violated. There are two solutions:

1. The first is to do the entire analysis using book value of debt and equity, looking for the optimal debt ratio. Since the approach we have described is driven by cash flows, the optimal dollar debt that is computed should not be affected significantly by doing this.

2. The second and more general approach (since it can be used to analyze any kind of constraint) is to keep track of the book value debt ratio in the traditional analysis, and view the optimal capital structure as the one that minimizes the cost of capital subject to the book value debt ratio being lesser than the specified constraint.

Firms in Trouble

As we discussed earlier, a key input that drives the optimal capital structure is the current operating income. If this income is depressed, either because the firm is a cyclical one or due to firm-specific factors that are expected to be temporary, the optimal debt ratio that will emerge from the analysis will be much lower than the firm's true optimal. For example, automobile manufacturing firms would have had very low debt ratios if the optimal debt ratios had been computed based upon the operating income in 1991 and 1992, which were recession years. If the drop in operating income is permanent, however, this lower optimal debt ratio is, in fact, the correct estimate.

When faced with a firm with depressed current operating income, the first issue to address is whether the drop in income is temporary or permanent. If the drop is temporary, we must determine the normalized operating income for the firm. The *normalized operating income* is an estimate of how much the firm can be expected to earn in a normal year, that is, a year without the specific characteristics that depressed earnings this year. The optimal debt ratio arrived at using the normalized operating income has to be approached cautiously, since the analysis is based upon the assumption that earnings will recover to this level.

Normalized Income: This is a measure of the income that a firm can make in a normal year, where there are no extraordinary gains or losses either from firm-specific factors (such as write offs and onetime sales) or macroeconomic factors (such as the economic cycle).

■▲
▼● ᴵˡˡᵁˢᵀᴿᴬᵀᴵᴼᴺ **8.4   Applying the Cost of Capital Approach to Aracruz Cellulose**
Aracruz Cellulose, the Brazilian pulp and paper manufacturing firm, reported depressed revenues and earnings in 1996. We estimated the optimal debt ratio for Aracruz, based upon the following facts:

- In 1996, Aracruz had earnings before interest and taxes of only 15 million BR, and claimed depreciation of 190 million BR. Capital expenditures amounted to 250 million BR.

- Aracruz had gross debt outstanding of 1520 million BR. While the nominal rate on this debt, especially the portion that is in Brazilian Real, is high, we will continue to do the analysis in real terms, and use a current real cost of debt of 5.5%, which is based upon a real risk-free rate of 5% and a default spread of 0.5%.

- The corporate tax rate in Brazil is estimated to be 32%.

- Aracruz had 976.10 million shares outstanding, trading 2.05 BR per share. The beta of the stock is estimated, using comparable firms, to be 0.71.

In Chapter 4, we estimated Aracruz's current real cost of capital to be 7.48%:

Current Cost of Equity = 5% + 0.71 (7.5%) = 10.33%
Market Value of Equity = 2.05 BR * 976.1 = 2,001 million BR
Current Cost of Capital
= 10.33% (2001/(2001+1520)) + 5.5% (1−.32) (1520/(2001+1520)) = 7.48%

Based upon 1996 operating income, the optimal debt ratio for Aracruz is 0%. It is worth noting, however, that 1996 was a poor year for Aracruz, both in terms of revenues and operating income. In 1995, Aracruz had earnings before interest and taxes of 271 million BR. In Table 8.15, the cost of capital and the firm value are estimated under this operating income for different debt ratios.

Table 8.15   Aʀᴀᴄʀᴜᴢ Cᴇʟʟᴜʟᴏsᴇ: Cᴏsᴛ ᴏғ Cᴀᴘɪᴛᴀʟ, Fɪʀᴍ Vᴀʟᴜᴇ, ᴀɴᴅ Dᴇʙᴛ Rᴀᴛɪᴏs

Debt Ratio	Beta	Cost of Equity	Rating	Cost of Debt	AT Cost of Debt	Cost of Capital	Firm Value
0.00%	0.47	8.51%	AAA	5.20%	3.54%	8.51%	2,720 BR
10.00%	0.50	8.78%	AAA	5.20%	3.54%	8.25%	2,886 BR
20.00%	0.55	9.11%	AA	5.50%	3.74%	8.03%	3,042 BR
30.00%	0.60	9.53%	A	6.00%	4.08%	7.90%	3,148 BR
40.00%	0.68	10.10%	A−	6.25%	4.25%	7.76%	3,262 BR
50.00%	0.79	10.90%	BB	7.00%	4.76%	7.83%	3,205 BR
60.00%	0.95	12.09%	B−	9.25%	6.29%	8.61%	2,660 BR
70.00%	1.21	14.08%	CCC	10.00%	6.80%	8.98%	2,458 BR
80.00%	1.76	18.23%	CCC	10.00%	6.92%	9.18%	2,362 BR
90.00%	3.53	31.46%	CCC	10.00%	7.26%	9.68%	2,149 BR

Table 8.16	OPTIMAL DEBT RATIO AND OPERATING INCOME
EBIT	**Optimal Debt Ratio**
$15 (1996 level)	0%
$100	10%
$150	20%
$200	30%
$271 (1995 level)	40%

The optimal debt ratio, with gross debt, is 40%. It is not clear whether Aracruz can earn as much as it did in 1995 in a normal year. Table 8.16 summarizes the optimal debt ratios for intermediate levels of operating income between 1995 and 1996 levels.

Using the normalized operating income, we find that the optimal debt ratio is lower than the existing debt ratio of 43.17%, suggesting that Aracruz is overlevered, especially at existing levels of earnings.

IN PRACTICE: NORMALIZING OPERATING INCOME

In estimating optimal debt ratios, it is always more advisable to use normalized operating income rather than current operating income. Most analysts normalize earnings by taking the average earnings over a period of time (usually five years). Since this holds the scale of the firm fixed, it may not be appropriate for firms which have changed in size over time. The right way to normalize income will vary across firms:

1. For cyclical firms, whose current operating income may be overstated (if the economy is booming) or understated (if the economy is in recession), the operating income can be estimated using the average operating margin over an entire economic cycle (usually 5 to 10 years):

    Normalized EBIT = Average Operating Margin (Cycle) * Current Sales

2. For firms which have had a bad year in terms of operating income, due to firm-specific factors (such as the loss of a contract), the operating margin for the industry in which the firm operates can be used to calculate the normalized operating income:

    Normalized EBIT = Average Operating Margin (Industry) * Current Sales

The normalized operating income can also be estimated using returns on capital across an economic cycle (for cyclical firms) or an industry (for firms with firm-specific problems), but returns on capital are much more likely to be skewed by mismeasurement of capital and accounting differences across firms.

 There is a dataset on the Web that summarizes operating margins by industry group in the United States for the most recent quarter (**margin.xls**).

ADJUSTED PRESENT VALUE

In the adjusted present value approach, the firm value and leverage are connected using the value of the firm without debt as the starting point and adding the positive and negative value effects of leverage to it. In particular, when the primary benefit of borrowing is a tax benefit and the most significant cost of borrowing is the risk of bankruptcy, the value of a levered firm can be written as follows:

Value of Levered Firm = Value of Unlevered Firm + Present Value of
Tax Benefits of Debt − Present Value of Expected Bankruptcy Costs

The value of the levered firm can then be estimated at different levels of the debt, and the debt level that maximizes firm value is the optimal debt ratio.

Value of Unlevered Firm

The first step in this approach is the estimation of the value of the unlevered firm. This can be accomplished by valuing the firm as if it had no debt (i.e., by discounting the expected after-tax operating cash flows at the unlevered cost of equity). In the special case where cash flows grow at a constant rate in perpetuity,

$$\text{Value of Unlevered Firm} = \text{FCFF}_0 (1 + g)/(\rho_u - g)$$

where FCFF_0 is the current after-tax operating cash flow to the firm, ρ_u is the unlevered cost of equity, and g is the expected growth rate.

The inputs needed for this valuation are the expected cash flows, growth rates, and the unlevered cost of equity. To estimate the latter, we can draw on our earlier analysis and compute the unlevered beta of the firm:

$$\beta_{unlevered} = \beta_{current}/[1 + (1 - t)D/E]$$

where $\beta_{unlevered}$ is the unlevered beta of the firm, $\beta_{current}$ is the current equity beta of the firm, t is the tax rate for the firm, and D/E is the average debt/equity ratio during the regression. This unlevered beta can then be used to arrive at the unlevered cost of equity.

Expected Tax Benefit from Borrowing

The second step in this approach is the calculation of the expected tax benefit from taking on a given level of debt. This tax benefit is a function of the tax rate of the firm, and is discounted back at the cost of debt to reflect the riskiness of this cash flow. If the tax savings are viewed as a perpetuity, we have the following:

$$\begin{aligned}\text{Value of Tax Benefits} &= [\text{Tax Rate} * \text{Cost of Debt} * \text{Debt}] / \text{Cost of Debt} \\ &= \text{Tax Rate} * \text{Debt} \\ &= t_c D\end{aligned}$$

The tax rate referred to here is the firm's marginal tax rate, and the approach is general enough to allow it to change over time.

Estimating Expected Bankruptcy Costs

The third step is to evaluate the effect of the given level of debt on the default risk of the firm and on expected bankruptcy costs. In theory, at least, this requires the estimation of the probability of default with the additional debt and the direct and indirect cost of bankruptcy. If π_a is the probability of default after the additional debt and BC is the present value of the bankruptcy cost, the present value of expected bankruptcy cost can be estimated as follows:

$$\text{PV of Expected Bankruptcy Cost} = \text{Probability of Bankruptcy} * \text{PV of Bankruptcy Cost}$$
$$= \pi_a \, BC$$

This component of the adjusted present value approach poses the most significant estimation problem, since neither the probability of bankruptcy nor the bankruptcy cost can be estimated directly.

There are two basic ways in which the probability of bankruptcy can be indirectly estimated. One is to estimate a bond rating, as we did in the cost of capital approach, at each level of debt and use the empirical estimates of default probabilities for each rating. For instance, Table 8.17, based upon a study by Altman and Kishore, summarizes the probability of default over ten years by bond rating class.[13]

The other approach is to use a statistical approach, such as a *probit,* to estimate the probability of default based upon the firm's observable characteristics at each level of debt.

The bankruptcy cost can be estimated, albeit with considerable noise, from studies that have looked at the magnitude of this cost in actual bankruptcies. Combining the results of Warner (1977) on direct bankruptcy cost and shapiro (1989a) on indirect bankruptcy cost may provide a measure of the total bankruptcy costs faced by firms.

Table 8.17   DEFAULT RATES BY BOND RATING CLASSES

Rating	Default Probability
AAA	0.01%
AA	0.28%
A+	0.40%
A	0.53%
A−	1.41%
BBB	2.30%
BB	12.20%
B+	19.28%
B	26.36%
B−	32.50%
CCC	50.00%
CC	65.00%
C	80.00%
D	100.00%

---

[13]This study estimated default rates over ten years only for some of the ratings classes. We extrapolated the rest of the ratings.

■ **Probit:** This is a statistical technique that allows the probability of an event to be estimated as a function of the observable characteristics.

■ **Bankruptcy Cost:** This is the cost associated with going bankrupt. It includes both direct costs (from a firm going bankrupt) and indirect costs (arising from the perception that a firm may go bankrupt).

IN PRACTICE: USING PROBITS TO ESTIMATE THE PROBABILITY OF BANKRUPTCY

It is possible to estimate the probability of default using statistical techniques, when there is sufficient data available. For instance, if we have a dataset that lists all firms that went bankrupt during a period of time, as well as firms that did not go bankrupt during the same period, together with descriptive characteristics on these firms, a probit analysis can be used to estimate the likelihood of bankruptcy as a function of these characteristics. The steps involved in a probit analysis are as follows:

1. Identify the event of interest: Probits work best when the event either occurs or it does not. For bankruptcy, the event might be the filing for bankruptcy protection under the law.

2. Over a specified time period, collect information on all the firms that were exposed to the event. In the bankruptcy case, this would imply collecting information on which firms that filed for bankruptcy over a certain period (say, 5 years).

3. Based upon your knowledge of the event, and other research on it, specify measurable and observable variables that are likely to be good predictors of that event. In the case of bankruptcy, these might include excessive debt ratios, declining income, poor project returns and small market capitalization.

4. Collect information on these variables for the firms that filed for bankruptcy, at the time of the filing. Collect the same information for all other firms that were in existence at the same time, and which have data available on these variables. (If this is too data intensive, a random sampling of the firms that were not exposed to the event can be used.) In the bankruptcy analysis, this would imply collecting information on debt ratios, income trends, project returns and market capitalization for the firms that filed for bankruptcy at the time of the filing, and for all other firms across the period.

5. In a probit, the dependent variable is the occurrence of the specified event (1 if it occurs, 0 if it does not) and the independent variables are the variables specified in step 3. The output from the probit looks very much like the output from a multiple regression, with statistical significance attached to each of the independent variables.

Once the probit has been done, the probability of a firm defaulting can be estimated by plugging in that firm's values for the independent variables into the probit. The predicted value that emerges from the probit is the probability of default.

The Net Effect

The net effect of adding debt can be calculated by aggregating the costs and the benefits at each level of debt:

$$\text{Value of Levered Firm} = \text{FCFF}_0\,(1 + g)/(\rho_u - g) + t_c\,D - \pi_a\,BC$$

The debt level that maximizes firm value is the optimal debt ratio.

Benefits and Limitations of This Approach

The advantage of this approach is that it separates out the effects of debt into different components and allows the analyst to use different discount rates for each component. It does not make the assumption that the debt ratio stays unchanged forever, which is an implicit assumption in the cost of capital approach. Instead, it allows the analyst the flexibility to keep the dollar value of debt fixed, and calculate the benefits and costs of the fixed dollar debt.

These advantages have to be weighed off against the difficulty of estimating probabilities of default and the cost of bankruptcy. In fact, many analysts that use the adjusted present value approach ignore the expected bankruptcy costs, leading them to the conclusion that firm value increases monotonically with leverage.

 ILLUSTRATION 8.5 Using the Adjusted Present Value Approach to Calculate Optimal Debt Ratio for Disney in 1997

This approach can be applied to estimate the optimal capital structure for Disney. The first step is to estimate the value of the unlevered firm. To make this estimate, we start with the value of Disney as a firm in 1997 and net the effect of the tax savings and bankruptcy costs arising from the existing debt.

Value of Disney as a Firm in 1997: (Value of Equity + Value of Debt)	$50,888 + $11,180 = $62,068
−PV of Tax Savings from Existing Debt: (Existing Debt * Tax Rate)	$11,180 * 0.36 = $4,025
+ PV of Expected Bankruptcy Cost (Probability of Bankruptcy * Cost)	$62,068 * .25 * .0028 = $41
= Value of Disney as Unlevered Firm	$62,068 − $4,025 + $41 = $58,084

The probability of bankruptcy is estimated using the bond rating for Disney in 1997, which was AA, and the default probabilities in Table 8.17. The bankruptcy cost is assumed to be 25% of the firm value, prior to the tax savings.[14]

The next step in the process is to estimate the tax savings at different levels of debt (Table 8.18). While we use the standard approach of assuming that the present value is calculated over a perpetuity, we reduce the tax rate used in the calculation, if interest expenses exceed the earnings before interest and taxes. The adjustment to the tax rate is described more fully in the preceding section on the cost of capital.

---

[14]This estimate is based upon the Warner study, which estimates bankruptcy costs for large companies to be 10% of the value, and upon the qualitative analysis of indirect bankruptcy costs in Cornell and Shapiro.

Table 8.18   TAX SAVINGS FROM DEBT (T_cD)

Debt Ratio	$ Debt	Tax Rate	Tax Benefits
0%	$0	36.00%	$0
10%	$6,207	36.00%	$2,234
20%	$12,414	36.00%	$4,469
30%	$18,621	36.00%	$6,703
40%	$24,827	36.00%	$8,938
50%	$31,034	36.00%	$11,172
60%	$37,241	36.00%	$13,407
70%	$43,448	35.43%	$15,394
80%	$49,655	31.00%	$15,394
90%	$55,862	24.71%	$15,394

Table 8.19   EXPECTED BANKRUPTCY COST

Debt Ratio	Bond Rating	Probability of Default	Expected Bankruptcy Cost
0%	AAA	0.01%	$2
10%	AAA	0.01%	$2
20%	A+	0.40%	$62
30%	A−	1.41%	$219
40%	BB	12.20%	$1,893
50%	B	26.36%	$4,090
60%	CCC	50.00%	$7,759
70%	CC	65.00%	$10,086
80%	CC	65.00%	$10,086
90%	C	80.00%	$12,414

Note that the tax benefits of debt are capped at the level of current earnings before interest and taxes, which is $5,559 million. Beyond the 60% debt level, the interest expenses exceed the earnings before interest and taxes. The final step in the process is to estimate the expected bankruptcy cost, based upon the bond ratings, probabilities of default, and the assumption that the bankruptcy cost is 25% of firm value. Table 8.19 summarizes these probabilities.

The value of the levered firm is estimated in Table 8.20 by aggregating the effects of the tax savings and the expected bankruptcy costs.

The firm value is optimized at between 40% and 50% debt, which is consistent with the findings from the other approach. These findings are, however, very sensitive to both the estimate of bankruptcy cost, as a percent of firm value, and the probabilities of default.

This spreadsheet allows you to compute the value of a firm, with leverage, using the adjusted present value approach (**apv.xls**).

	Table 8.20	VALUE OF DISNEY WITH LEVERAGE		
Debt Ratio	**Unlevered Firm Value**	**Tax Benefits**	**Expected Bankruptcy Cost**	**Value of Levered Firm**
0%	$58,084	$0	$2	$58,083
10%	$58,084	$2,234	$2	$60,317
20%	$58,084	$4,469	$62	$62,491
30%	$58,084	$6,703	$219	$64,569
40%	$58,084	$8,938	$1,893	$65,129
50%	$58,084	$11,172	$4,090	$65,166
60%	$58,084	$13,407	$7,759	$63,732
70%	$58,084	$15,394	$10,086	$63,392
80%	$58,084	$15,394	$10,086	$63,392
90%	$58,084	$15,394	$12,414	$61,065

COMPARATIVE ANALYSIS

The most common approach to analyzing the debt ratio of a firm is to compare its leverage to that of "similar" firms. A simple way of doing this analysis is to compare a firm's debt ratio to the average debt ratio for the industry in which the firm operates. The underlying assumptions here are that firms within the same industry are comparable, and that, on average, these firms are operating at or close to their optimal. Both assumptions can be contested, however. Firms within the same industry can have different product mixes, different amount of operating risk, different tax rates, and different project returns; in fact, most do. For instance, Disney is considered part of the entertainment industry, but its mix of business is very different from that of Time Warner or Viacom. Furthermore, Disney's size and risk characteristics are very different from those of King World, which is also considered part of the same industry group. There is also anecdotal evidence that since firms try to mimic the industry average, the average debt ratio across an industry might not be at or even close to its optimal.

There is a dataset on the Web that summarizes market value and book value debt ratios, by industry, in addition to other relevant characteristics (**indcapst.xls**).

ILLUSTRATION 8.6 **Estimating Debt Ratio Based upon Comparable Firms**
In the following table, we report the debt ratios and financial characteristics of the firms that were considered by Value Line to be part of the entertainment group in July 1997.

Based upon the average debt ratios, Disney can be considered to be slightly underlevered in market value terms, since its debt ratio at 18.17% is lower than the average of 23.79%. This comparison, however, would not factor in the significant differences in both market capitalization and other characteristics across firms in this sample.

COMPANY NAME	MARKET DEBT RATIO	BOOK DEBT RATIO	TAX RATE	EBITDA/ VALUE	STANDARD DEVIATION IN OPER. INCOME
Disney (Walt)	18.19%	43.41%	43.58%	8.37%	22.57%
Time Warner	29.39%	68.34%	40.00%	6.80%	24.46%
Westinghouse Electric	26.98%	51.97%	36.00%	4.93%	30.92%
Viacom Inc. "A"	48.14%	46.54%	61.50%	14.55%	33.22%
Clear Channel	11.95%	58.60%	39.89%	3.14%	33.70%
BHC Communic. "A"	0.00%	0.00%	36.00%	5.04%	13.02%
Gaylord Entertainm. "A"	13.92%	41.47%	36.00%	8.71%	29.70%
Belo (A.H.) "A" Corp.	23.34%	63.04%	39.25%	10.93%	21.89%
Evergreen Media "A"	16.77%	39.45%	36.00%	9.62%	0.00%
Tele-Communications Intl Inc.	23.28%	34.60%	36.00%	4.29%	0.00%
King World Productions	0.00%	0.00%	36.00%	12.72%	21.73%
Jacor Communications	30.91%	57.91%	47.53%	3.97%	62.07%
LIN Television	19.48%	71.66%	36.30%	9.78%	0.00%
Regal Cinemas	4.53%	15.24%	39.43%	7.38%	0.00%
Westwood One	11.40%	60.03%	36.00%	4.53%	76.55%
United Television	4.51%	15.11%	39.72%	6.91%	15.48%
Amer Radio Sys "A"	26.27%	45.49%	48.49%	4.98%	0.00%
Cox Radio "A" Inc.	0.00%	0.00%	39.49%	6.44%	0.00%
Le Groupe Videotron Ltee	74.97%	88.69%	36.00%	14.36%	25.24%
Spelling Entmt Group	33.76%	49.63%	64.05%	22.03%	30.28%
Western Int'l Communications	27.94%	44.66%	63.38%	9.74%	23.00%
Cinar Films Inc.	0.61%	2.08%	36.00%	3.11%	0.00%
SFX Broadcasting "A"	55.61%	83.59%	36.00%	7.07%	0.00%
Baton Broadcasting Inc.	36.50%	63.40%	70.56%	9.46%	32.97%
EMMIS Broad. "A"	24.35%	76.99%	40.48%	10.57%	0.00%
Scandinavian Broadcasting Sys.	34.17%	83.93%	36.00%	−8.11%	0.00%
Carmike Cinemas	43.44%	60.12%	36.00%	17.94%	29.50%
GC Companies Inc.	1.16%	2.10%	41.00%	18.10%	0.00%
Cineplex Odeon	54.38%	60.96%	36.00%	15.05%	59.60%
Quintel Entmt Inc	0.00%	0.00%	36.00%	5.40%	0.00%
Moffat Communications Ltd.	10.88%	24.77%	40.39%	16.41%	24.82%
Sinclair Broadcast Group	85.77%	85.53%	86.00%	21.64%	0.00%
Seattle FilmWorks	0.00%	0.00%	36.00%	7.46%	34.41%
Tele-Metropole	23.71%	38.53%	47.50%	18.54%	34.47%
Telemundo Group	49.26%	81.23%	80.33%	14.84%	0.00%
Silicon Gaming	0.59%	2.75%	36.00%	0.46%	0.00%
Boston Celtics LP	31.99%	79.82%	36.00%	8.11%	19.08%
AMC Entertainment	57.58%	76.15%	41.35%	47.87%	41.16%
Jones Intercable Inv LP	19.37%	68.07%	36.00%	13.31%	24.22%

COMPANY NAME	MARKET DEBT RATIO	BOOK DEBT RATIO	TAX RATE	EBITDA/ VALUE	STANDARD DEVIATION IN OPER. INCOME
All Amer Communications	58.34%	67.05%	41.98%	16.61%	44.26%
Clark (Dick) Prods.	0.00%	0.00%	38.26%	8.93%	43.57%
Granite Broadcasting	77.89%	100.90%	36.00%	15.56%	0.00%
CHUM Ltd.	0.00%	0.00%	48.45%	40.09%	20.05%
Boston Acoustics	0.00%	0.00%	36.00%	11.53%	28.26%
Price Communications	0.00%	0.00%	36.00%	−1.59%	118.47%
Image Entertainment	0.54%	1.58%	36.00%	19.09%	36.96%
Rentrak Corp	9.07%	30.73%	38.61%	19.99%	42.06%
Box Worldwide	0.00%	0.00%	36.00%	−5.37%	116.72%
Cinergi Pictures Entmt	21.72%	13.48%	36.00%	−14.93%	0.00%
Lancit Media Prods.	0.00%	0.00%	36.00%	−1.56%	51.29%
Electrohome Ltd.	70.87%	42.50%	50.42%	45.15%	36.55%
Average	23.79%	40.04%	42.51%	10.98%	25.53%

One way of controlling for these differences is to regress debt ratios against the variables that we showed to affect optimal debt ratios—tax rates, the standard deviation in operating income, and the cash flow generating capacity (EBITDA/Firm Value):

Debt Ratio = −0.1067 + 0.69 Tax Rate + 0.61 EBITDA/Value − 0.07 Std Dev in OI
 (0.90) (2.58)   (2.21)   (0.60)

The R-squared of the regression is 27.16%. This regression can be used to arrive at a predicted value for Disney of:

Predicted Debt Ratio = -0.1067 + 0.69 (.4358) + 0.61 (.0837) − 0.07 (.2257) = .2314

Based upon the capital structure of other firms in the entertainment industry, Disney should have a market value debt ratio of 23.14%.

Extending to the Market

To ensure comparability on debt ratios, a firm with similar tax rates, pretax returns as a fraction of the market value of the firm, and variance in operating income has to be identified. Note, though, that the firm need not be in the same industry nor produce the same product. The difficulty of finding such a firm gives rise to a second approach, whereby differences on these variables are controlled for when debt ratios are compared across firms. The simplest way to control for these differences, while using the maximum information available in the cross-section of firms, is to run a cross-sectional regression, regressing debt ratios against these variables:

Debt Ratio = α_0 + α_1 Tax Rate + α_2 Pretax Returns + α_3 Variance in Operating Income

There are several advantages to this approach. Once the regression has been run and the basic relationship established (i.e., the intercept and coefficients have been estimated), the predicted debt ratio for any firm can be computed quickly using the measures of the independent variables for this firm. If a task involves calculating the optimal debt ratio for a large number of firms in a short time period, this may be the only practical way of approaching the problem, since using the cost of capital approach is time intensive.[15]

There are also limitations to this approach. The coefficients tend to be unstable and shift over time. Besides some standard statistical problems and errors in measuring the variables, these regressions also tend to explain only a small portion of the differences in debt ratios between firms.[16] However, they provide significantly more information than does a naive comparison of a firm's debt ratio to the industry average.

There is a dataset on the Web that summarizes the latest debt ratio regression across the entire market (**Regress.xls**).

Illustration 8.7 An Illustration of the Cross-sectional Approach

A cross-sectional regression of debt ratios against a number of relevant variables uses 1996 data for 2929 firms listed on the NYSE, AMEX, and NASDAQ databases. The regression provides the following results:

$$\text{DFR} = 0.1906 - 0.0552\text{ PRVAR} - .1340\text{ CLSH} - 0.3105\text{ CPXFR} + 0.1447\text{ FCP}$$
$$(37.97^a)\quad(2.20^a)\qquad\qquad(6.58^a)\qquad\quad(8.52^a)\qquad\qquad(12.53^a)$$

where

DFR = Book Value of Debt / (Book Value of Debt + Market Value of Equity)
PRVAR = Variance in firm value
CLSH = Closely held shares as a percent of outstanding shares
CPXFR = Capital Expenditures / (Book Value of Debt + Book Value of Equity)
FCP = Free Cash Flow to Firm / Market Value of Equity

While the coefficients all have the right sign and are statistically significant, the regression itself has an R-squared of only 9.38%.

SIC: This is a four-digit industry code used by most services in the United States to classify firms. For a broader aggregation, the classification is often done using the first two digits of the code.

---

[15]There are some who have hypothesized that underleveraged firms are much more likely to be taken over than firms that are overleveraged or correctly leveraged. If an analyst wants to find the 100 firms on the New York Stock Exchange that are most underleveraged, the cross-sectional regression and the predicted debt ratios that come out of this regression can be used to find this group.

[16]The independent variables are correlated with each other. This multicollinearity makes the coefficients unreliable and they often have signs that go counter to intuition.

One way to improve the predictive power of the regression is to aggregate the data first and then do the regression. To illustrate using 1996 data, the firms are aggregated into two-digit SIC codes, and the same regression is rerun:

$$DFR = 0.2370 - 0.1854 \text{ PRVAR} + .1407 \text{ CLSH} + 1.3959 \text{ CPXFR} - .6483 \text{ FCP}$$
$$\qquad (6.06^a) \quad (1.96^b) \qquad\qquad (1.05) \qquad\quad (5.73^a) \qquad\qquad (3.89^a)$$

Note that the size of the coefficients has changed and the R-squared of the regression has increased to 42.47%.

The other way to improve the regression is to transform the variables to conform more closely to the regression ideal, which is that the variables should be normally distributed.

8.8   OPTIMAL DEBT RATIOS BASED UPON COMPARABLE FIRMS

The predicted debt ratio from the regression shown above will generally yield

☐   a debt ratio similar to the optimal debt ratio from the cost of capital approach.

☐   a debt ratio higher than the optimal debt ratio from the cost of capital approach.

☐   a debt ratio lower than the optimal debt ratio from the cost of capital approach.

☐   any of the above, depending upon . . .

Explain.

CONCLUSION

This chapter has provided background on three tools that can be used to analyze capital structure.

• The first approach uses the cost of capital—the weighted average of the costs of equity, debt, and preferred stock—where the weights are market value weights and the costs of financing are current costs. The objective is to minimize the cost of capital, which also maximizes the value of the firm. A general framework is developed to use this model in real-world applications and applied to find the optimal financing mix for Disney. We find that Disney, which had almost $12 billion in debt in 1996, would minimize its cost of capital at a debt level of 40%, leading to an increase in market value of the firm of about $8.5 billion. Even allowing for a much-diminished operating income, we find that Disney has excess debt capacity.

• The second approach estimates the value of the firm at different levels of debt by adding the present value of the tax benefits from debt to the unlevered firm's value, and then subtracting out the present value of expected bankruptcy costs. The optimal debt ratio is the one that maximizes firm value.

• The final approach is to compare a firm's debt ratio to "similar" firms. While comparisons of firm debt ratios to an industry average are commonly made, they are generally not very useful in the presence of large differences among firms within the same industry. A cross-sectional regression of debt ratios against underlying financial variables brings in more information from the general population of firms and can be used to predict debt ratios for a large number of firms.

PROBLEMS AND QUESTIONS

1. Rubbermaid Corporation, a manufacturer of consumer plastic products, is evaluating its capital structure. The balance sheet of the company is as follows (in millions):

Assets		Liabilities	
Fixed Assets	4000	Debt	2500
Current Assets	1000	Equity	2500

In addition, you are provided with the following information:

   a. The debt is in the form of long term-bonds, with a coupon rate of 10%. The bonds are currently rated AA and are selling at a yield of 12%. (The market value of the bonds is 80% of the face value).
   b. The firm currently has 50 million shares outstanding, and the current market price is $80 per share. The firm pays a dividend of $4 per share and has a price/earnings ratio of 10.
   c. The stock currently has a beta of 1.2. The six-month Treasury bill rate is 8%.
   d. The tax rate for this firm is 40%.
   (1) What is the debt/equity ratio for this firm in book value terms? in market value terms?
   (2) What is the debt/(debt+equity) ratio for this firm in book value terms? in market value terms?
   (3) What is the firm's after-tax cost of debt?
   (4) What is the firm's cost of equity?
   (5) What is the firm's current cost of capital?

2. Now assume that Rubbermaid Corporation has a project that requires an initial investment of $100 million and has the following projected income statement:

EBIT	$20 million
−Interest	$4 million
EBT	$16 million
Taxes	$6.40 million
Net Income	$9.60 million

(Depreciation for the project is expected to be $5 million a year forever.)

This project is going to be financed at the same debt/equity ratio as the overall firm and is expected to last forever. Assume that there are no principal repayments on the debt (it too is perpetual).

   (1) Evaluate this project from the equity investors' standpoint. Does it make sense?
   (2) Evaluate this project from the firm's standpoint. Does it make sense?
   (3) In general, when would you use the cost of equity as your discount rate/benchmark?
   (4) In general, when would you use the cost of capital as your hurdle rate?
   (5) Assume, for economies of scale, that this project is going to be financed *entirely* with debt. What would you use as your cost of capital for evaluating this project?

3. Rubbermaid is considering a major change in its capital structure. It has three options:

Option 1: Issue $1 billion in new stock and repurchase half of its outstanding debt. This will make it a AAA rated firm. (AAA rated debt is yielding 11% in the marketplace.)

Option 2: Issue $1 billion in new debt and buy back stock. This will drop its rating to A−. (A− rated debt is yielding 13% in the marketplace.)

Option 3: Issue $3 billion in new debt and buy back stock. This will drop its rating to CCC. (CCC rated debt is yielding 18% in the marketplace.)

   (1) What is the cost of equity under each option?
   (2) What is the after-tax cost of debt under each option?
   (3) What is the cost of capital under each option?
   (4) What would happen to (a) the value of the firm; (b) the value of debt and equity; and (c) the stock price under each option, if you assume rational stockholders?
   (5) From a cost of capital standpoint, which of the three options would you pick, or would you stay at your current capital structure?
   (6) What role (if any) would the variability in Rubbermaid's income play in your decision?

(7) How would your analysis change (if at all) if the money under the three options listed above were used to make new investments (instead of repurchasing debt or equity)?

(8) What other considerations (besides minimizing the cost of capital) would you bring to bear on your decision?

(9) Intuitively, why doesn't the higher rating in option 1 translate into a lower cost of capital?

4. Rubbermaid Corporation is interested in how it compares with its competitors in the same industry.

	Rubbermaid Corporation	Other Competitors
Debt/Equity Ratio	50%	25%
Variance in EBITDA	20%	40%
EBITDA/MV of firm	25%	15%
Tax rate	40%	30%
R&D/sales	2%	5%

a. Considering each of these variables, explain at an intuitive level whether you would expect Rubbermaid to have more or less debt than its competitors and why.

b. You have also run a regression of debt/equity ratios against these variables for all the firms on the New York Stock Exchange and have come up with the following regression equation:

$$D/E = .10 - .5 \text{ (Variance in EBITDA)} + 2.0 \text{ (EBITDA/MV)} + .4 \text{ (Tax rate)} + 2.5 \text{ (R&D/sales)}$$

(All inputs to the regression were in decimals; that is, 20% was input as .20 ....)

Given this cross-sectional relationship, what would you expect Rubbermaid's debt/equity ratio to be?

5. As CEO of a major corporation, you have to make a decision on how much you can afford to borrow. You currently have 10 million shares outstanding, and the market price per share is $50. You also currently have about $200 million in debt outstanding (market value). You are rated as a BBB corporation now.

a. Your stock has a beta of 1.5 and the Treasury bond rate is 8%.

b. Your marginal tax rate is 46%.

c. You estimate that your rating will change to a B if you borrow $100 million. The BBB rate now is 11%. The B rate is 12.5%.

(1) Given the marginal costs and benefits of borrowing the $100 million, should you go ahead with it?

(2) What is your best estimate of the weighted average cost of capital with and without the $100 million in borrowing?

(3) If you do borrow the $100 million, what will the price per share be after the borrowing?

(4) Assume that you have a project that requires an investment of $100 million. It has expected before-tax revenues of $50 million and costs of $30 million a year in perpetuity. Is this a desirable project by your criteria? Why or why not?

(5) Does it make a difference in your decision if you are told that the cash flows from the project in (4) are certain?

6. You have been hired as a management consultant by AD Corporation to evaluate whether it has an appropriate amount of debt. (The company is worried about a leveraged buyout.) You have collected the following information on AD's current position:

a. There are 100,000 shares outstanding, at $20 a share. The stock has a beta of 1.15.

b. The company has $500,000 in long-term debt outstanding and is currently rated as a "BBB." The current market interest rate is 10% on BBB bonds and 6% on Treasury bills.

c. The company's marginal tax rate is 40%.

You proceed to collect the data on what increasing debt will do to the company's ratings:

Additional Debt*	New Rating	Interest Rate
$500,000	BB	10.5
$1,000,000	B	11.5
$1,500,000	B−	13.5
$2,000,000	C	15

*In addition to the existing debt of $500,000:

(1) How much additional debt should the company take on?

(2) What will the price per share be after the company takes on new debt?

(3) What is the weighted average cost of capital before and after the additional debt?

(4) Assume that you are considering a project that has the following earnings in perpetuity, and is of comparable risk to existing projects.

Revenues/year	$1,000,000
Cost of goods sold	$400,000 (includes depreciation of $100,000)
EBIT	$600,000
Debt payments	$100,000 (all interest payments)
Taxable income	$500,000
Tax	$200,000
After-tax profit	$300,000

If this project requires an investment of $3 million, what is its NPV?

7. UB Inc. is examining its capital structure with the intent of arriving at an optimal debt ratio. It currently has no debt and has a beta of 1.5. The riskless interest rate is 9%. Your research indicates that the debt rating will be as follows at different debt levels.

D/(D+E)	Rating	Interest Rate
0%	AAA	10%
10%	AA	10.5%
20%	A	11%
30%	BBB	12%
40%	BB	13%
50%	B	14%
60%	CCC	16%
70%	CC	18%
80%	C	20%
90%	D	25%

The firm currently has 1 million shares outstanding at $20 per share (tax rate = 40%).

a. What is the firm's optimal debt ratio?

b. Assuming that the firm restructures by repurchasing stock with debt, what will the value of the stock be after the restructuring?

8. GenCorp, an automotive parts manufacturer, currently has $25 million in outstanding debt and has 10 million shares outstanding. The book value per share is $10, while the market value is $25. The company is currently rated A, and its bonds have a yield to maturity of 10%, and the current beta of the stock is 1.06. The six-month Treasury bond rate is 8% now, and the company's tax is 40%.

a. What is the company's current weighted average cost of capital?

b. The company is considering a repurchase of 4 million shares at $25 per share with new debt. It is estimated that this will push the company's rating down to a B (with a yield to maturity of 13%). What will the company's weighted average cost of capital be after the stock repurchase?

9. You have been called in as a consultant for Herbert's Inc., a sporting goods retail firm, which is examining its debt policy. The firm currently has a balance sheet that looks as follows:

Liability		Assets	
LT bonds	$100	Fixed Assets	300
Equity	$300	Current assets	100
Total	$400	Total	400

The firm's income statement is as follows:

Revenues	250
COGS	175
Depreciation	25
EBIT	50
LT interest	10
EBT	40
Taxes	16
Net income	24

The firm currently has 100 shares outstanding, selling at a market price of $5 per share, and the bonds are selling at par. The firm's current beta is 1.12, and the Treasury bond rate is 7%.

a. What is the firm's current cost of equity?

b. What is the firm's current cost of debt?

c. What is the firm's current weighted average cost of capital?

Assume that management of Herbert's Inc. is considering doing a debt equity swap (i.e., borrowing enough money to buy back 70 shares of stock at $5 per share). It is believed that this swap will lower the firm's rating to C and raise the interest rate on the company's debt to 15%.

d. What is the firm's new cost of equity?
e. What is the effective tax rate (for calculating the after-tax cost of debt) after the swap?
f. What is the firm's new cost of capital?

10. Terck Inc., a leading pharmaceutical company, currently has a balance sheet as follows:

Liability		Assets	
LT Bonds	$1000	Fixed assets	1700
Equity	$1000	Current assets	300
Total	$1000	Total	1000

The firm's income statement looks as follows:

Revenues	1000
COGS	400
Depreciation	100
EBIT	500
LT interest	100
EBT	400
Taxes	200
Net income	200

The firm's bonds are all 20-year bonds with a coupon rate of 10% and are selling at 90% of face value. (The yield to maturity on these bonds is 11%.) The stocks are selling at a PE ratio of 9 and have a beta of 1.25. The Treasury bond rate is 6%. [Cost of debt = 10%; tax rate = 40%]

a. What is the firm's current cost of equity?
b. What is the firm's current after-tax cost of debt?
c. What is the firm's current weighted average cost of capital?

Assume that management of Terck Inc., which is very conservative, is considering doing an equity-for-debt swap (i.e., issuing $200 more of equity to retire $200 of debt). This action is expected to lower the firm's interest rate by 1%.

d. What is the firm's new cost of equity?
e. What is the new WACC?
f. What will the value of the firm be after the swap?

11. You have been asked to analyze the capital structure of DASA Inc., an environmental waste disposal firm, and to make recommendations on a future course of action. DASA Inc. has 40 million shares outstanding, selling at $20 per share, and a debt equity ratio (in market value terms) of 0.25. The beta of the stock is 1.15 and the firm currently has a AA rating, with a corresponding market interest rate of 10%. The firm's income statement is as follows:

EBIT	$150 million
Interest exp.	$20 million
Taxable income	$130 million
Taxes	$52 million
Net income	$78 million

The current Treasury bond rate is 8%. Tax rate = 40%.

a. What is the firm's current weighted average cost of capital?
b. The firm is proposing borrowing an additional $200 million in debt and repurchasing stock. If it does so, its rating will decline to A, with a market interest rate of 11%. What will the weighted average cost of capital be if the firm makes this move?
c. What will the new stock price be if the firm borrows $200 million and repurchases stock (assuming rational investors)?

12. You have been asked by JJ Corporation, a California-based firm that manufactures and services digital satellite television systems, to evaluate its capital structure. They currently have 70 million shares outstanding trading at $10 per share. In addition, it has 500,000 ten-year convertible bonds, with a coupon rate of 8%, trading at $1000 per bond. JJ Corporation is rated BBB, and the interest rate on BBB straight bonds is currently 10%. The beta for the company is 1.2, and the current risk-free rate is 6%. The tax rate is 40%.

a. What is the firm's current debt/equity ratio?

b. What is the firm's current weighted average cost of capital?

JJ Corporation is proposing to borrow $250 million to use for the following purposes:

> Buy back $100 million worth of stock.
>
> Pay $100 million in dividends.
>
> Invest $50 million in a project with a NPV of $25 million.

The effect of this additional borrowing will be a drop in the bond rating to B, which currently carries an interest rate of 11%.

c. What will the firm's cost of equity be after this additional borrowing?

d. What will the firm's weighted average cost of capital be after this additional borrowing?

e. What will the value of the firm be after this additional borrowing?

13. Pfizer, one of the largest pharmaceutical companies in the United States, is considering its debt capacity. In March 1995, Pfizer had an outstanding market value of equity of $24.27 billion, debt of $2.8 billion, and a AAA rating. Its beta was 1.47, and it faced a marginal corporate tax rate of 40%. The Treasury bond rate at the time of the analysis was 6.50%, and AAA bonds trade at a spread of 0.30% over the Treasury rate.

a. Estimate the current cost of capital for Pfizer.

b. It is estimated that Pfizer will have a BBB rating if it moves to a 30% debt ratio and that BBB bonds have a spread of 2% over the Treasury rate. Estimate the cost of capital if Pfizer moves a 30% debt ratio.

c. Assuming a constant growth rate of 6% in the firm value, how much will firm value change if Pfizer moves its optimal? What will the effect be on the stock price?

d. Pfizer has considerable research and development expenses. Will this fact affect whether Pfizer takes on the additional debt?

14. Upjohn, another major pharmaceutical company, is also considering whether it should borrow more. It has $664 million in book value of debt outstanding and 173 million shares outstanding at $30.75 per share. The company has a beta of 1.17 and faces a tax rate of 36%. The Treasury bond rate is 6.50%.

a. If the interest expense on the debt is $55 million, the debt has an average maturity of 10 years, and the company is currently rated AA− (with a market interest rate of 7.50%), estimate the market value of the debt.

b. Estimate the current cost of capital.

c. It is estimated that if Upjohn moves to its optimal debt ratio, and no growth in firm value is assumed, the value per share will increase by $1.25. Estimate the cost of capital at the optimal debt ratio.

15. Bethlehem Steel, one of the oldest and largest steel companies in the United States, is considering the question of whether it has any excess debt capacity. The firm has $527 million in market value of debt outstanding and $1.76 billion in market value of equity. The firm has earnings before interest and taxes of $131 million, and faces a corporate tax rate of 36%. The company's bonds are rated BBB, and the cost of debt is 8%. At this rating, the firm has a probability of default of 2.30%, and the cost of bankruptcy is expected to be 30% of firm value. The T. Bond rate is 6.5%.

a. Estimate the unlevered value of the firm.

b. Estimate the levered value of the firm, using the adjusted present value approach, at a debt ratio of 50%. At that debt ratio, the firm's bond rating will be CCC, and the probability of default will increase to 46.61%.

16. Kansas City Southern, a railroad company, had debt outstanding of $985 million and 40 million shares trading at $46.25 per share in March 1995. It earned $203 million in earnings before interest and taxes and faced a marginal tax rate of 36.56%. The firm was interested in estimating its optimal leverage using the adjusted present value approach. The following table summarizes the estimated bond ratings and probabilities of default at each level of debt from 0% to 90%.

Debt Ratio (%)	Bond Rating	Probability of Default (%)
0	AAA	0.28
10	AAA	0.28
20	A−	1.41
30	BB	12.20
40	B−	32.50
50	CCC	46.61
60	CC	65.00
70	C	80.00
80	C	80.00
90	D	100.00

(Assume marginal tax rate does not change)
The direct and indirect bankruptcy cost is estimated to be 25% of the firm value. Estimate the optimal debt ratio of the firm, based on levered firm value. The T. Bond rate is 7%.

17. In 1995, an analysis of the capital structure of Reebok provided the following results on the weighted average cost of capital and firm value.

	Actual	Optimal	Change
Debt ratio	4.42%	60.00%	55.58%
Beta for the stock	1.95	3.69	1.74
Cost of equity	18.61%	28.16%	9.56%
Bond rating	A−	B+	
After-tax cost of debt	5.92%	6.87%	0.95%
WACC	18.04%	15.38%	−2.66%
Firm value (with no growth)	$3,343 mil	$3,921 mil	$578 mil
Stock price	$39.50	$46.64	$7.14

This analysis was based on the 1995 earnings before interest and taxes of $420 million and a tax rate of 36.90%.

a. Why is the optimal debt ratio for Reebok so high?
b. What might be some of your concerns in moving to this optimal?

18. Timberland Inc., a manufacturer and retailer of footwear and sportswear, is considering its highly levered status. In 1995, the firm had $237 million in market value of debt outstanding and 11 mil-

lion shares outstanding at $19.88 per share. The firm had earnings before interest and taxes of $44 million, a book value of capital of $250 million, and a tax rate of 37%. The Treasury bond rate is 7.88%, and the stock has a beta of 1.26. The following table summarizes the estimated bond ratings and interest rates at different levels of debt for Timberland:

Debt Ratio (%)	Bond Rating	Interest Rate on Debt (%)
0	AAA	8.18
10	AAA	8.18
20	A+	8.88
30	A	9.13
40	A−	9.38
50	BB	10.38
60	BB	10.38
70	B	11.88
80	B−	12.88
90	CCC	13.88

a. Estimate the optimal debt ratio, using the cost of capital approach.

19. You are trying to evaluate whether United Airlines has any excess debt capacity. In 1995, UAL had 12.2 million shares outstanding at $210 per share and debt outstanding of approximately $3 billion (book as well as market value). The debt had a rating of B and carried a market interest rate of 10.12%. In addition, the firm had leases outstanding, with annual lease payments anticipated to be $150 million. The beta of the stock is 1.26, and the firm faces a tax rate of 35%. The Treasury bond rate is 6.12%.

a. Estimate the current debt ratio for UAL.
b. Estimate the current cost of capital.
c. Based on 1995 operating income, the optimal debt ratio is computed to be 30%, at which point the rating will be BBB, and the market interest rate is 8.12%. Estimate the cost of capital and firm value at the optimal.
d. Would the fact that 1995 operating income for airlines was depressed alter your analysis in any way? Explain why.

20. Intel has earnings before interest and taxes of $3.4 billion and faces a marginal tax rate of 36.50%. It currently has $1.5 billion in debt outstanding and a market value of equity of $51 billion. The beta for the stock is 1.35, and the pretax cost of debt is 6.80%. The Treasury bond rate is 6%. Assume that the firm is considering a massive increase in leverage to a 70% debt ratio, at which level the bond rating will be C (with a pretax interest rate of 16%).

   a. Estimate the current cost of capital.

   b. Assuming that all debt is refinanced at the new market interest rate, what would your interest expenses be at 70% debt? Would you be able to get the entire tax benefit? Why or why not?

   c. Estimate the beta of the stock at 70% debt, using the conventional levered beta calculation. Reestimate the beta, on the assumption that C rated debt has a beta of 0.60. Which one would you use in your cost of capital calculation?

   d. Estimate the cost of capital at 70% debt.

   e. What will happen to firm value if Intel moves to a 70% debt ratio?

   f. What general lessons on capital structure would you draw for other growth firms?

21. NYNEX, the phone utility for the New York Area, has approached you for advice on its capital structure. In 1995, NYNEX had debt outstanding of $12.14 billion and equity outstanding of $20.55 billion. The firm had earnings before interest and taxes of $1.7 billion, and faced a corporate tax rate of 36%. The beta for the stock is 0.84, and the bonds are rated A− (with a market interest rate of 7.5%). The probability of default for A− rated bonds is 1.41%, and the bankruptcy cost is estimated to be 30% of firm value. The T. Bond rate is 6.5%.

   a. Estimate the unlevered value of the firm.

   b. Value the firm if it increases its leverage to 50%. At that debt ratio, its bond rating would be BBB, and the probability of default would be 2.30%.

   c. Assume now that NYNEX is considering a move into entertainment, which is likely to be both more profitable and riskier than

the phone business. What changes would you expect in the optimal leverage?

22. A small, private firm has approached you for advice on its capital structure decision. It is in the specialty retailing business, and it had earnings before interest and taxes last year of $500,000.

   - The book value of equity is $1.5 million, but the estimated market value is $6 million.

   - The firm has $1 million in 5-year debt outstanding and paid an interest expense of $80,000 on the debt last year. (Based on the interest coverage ratio, the firm would be rated AA and would be facing an interest rate of 8.25%.)

   - The equity is not traded, but the average beta for comparable traded firms is 1.05, and their average debt/equity ratio is 25%. The T. Bond rate is 7%.

   a. Estimate the current cost of capital for this firm.

   b. Assume now that this firm doubles its debt from $1 million to $2 million, and that the interest rate at which it can borrow increases to 9%. Estimate the new cost of capital, and the effect on firm value.

   c. You also have a regression that you have run of debt ratios of publicly traded firms against firm characteristics:

$$\text{DBTFR} = 0.15 + 1.05 \ (\text{EBIT/FIRM VALUE}) - 0.10 \ (\text{BETA})$$

Estimate the debt ratio for the private firm, based on this regression.

   d. What are some of the concerns you might have in extending the approaches used by large publicly traded firms to estimate optimal leverage to smaller firms?

23. XCV Inc., which manufactures automobile parts for assembly, is considering the costs and the benefits of leverage. The CFO notes that the return on equity of the firm, which is only 12.75% now, based on the current policy of no leverage, could be increased substantially by borrowing money. Is this true? Does it follow that the value of the firm will increase with leverage? Why or why not?

24. You have been provided the information on the after-tax cost of debt and cost of capital that a company will have at a 10% debt ratio, and asked to estimate the after-tax cost of debt and cost of capital at 20%. The long term treasury bond rate is 7%.

Debt Ratio	10%	20%	Extra Column
$ Debt	$1,500		
EBIT	$1,000		
Interest Expenses	$120		
Interest Coverage Ratio	8.33		
Bond Rating	AA		
Interest Rate	8.00%		
After-tax Cost of Debt	4.80%		
Beta	1.06		
Cost of Equity	12.83%		
Cost of Capital	12.03%		

The interest coverage ratios, ratings and spreads are as follows:

Coverage Ratio	Rating	Spread over Treasury
> 10	AAA	0.30%
7–10	AA	1.00%
5–7	A	1.50%
3–5	BBB	2.00%
2–3	BB	2.50%
1.25–2	B	3.00%
0.75–1.25	CCC	5.00%
0.50–0.75	CC	6.50%
0.25–0.50	C	8.00%
< 0.25	D	10.00%

25. CSL Corporation is a mid-sized transportation firm with 10 million shares outstanding, trading at $25 per share and debt outstanding of $50 million. It is estimated that the cost of capital, which is currently 11%, will drop to 10%, if the firm borrows $100 million and buys back stock. Estimate the expected change in the stock price if the expected growth rate in operating earnings over time is 5%.

26. You have run a regression of changes in firm value against changes in long term bond rates and arrived at the following regression:

Change in Firm Value = 0.16 − 5.00 Change in Long Term Bond Rate

The firm has $100 million in zero-coupon two-year notes outstanding, and plans to borrow another $150 million using zero-coupon securities. If your objective is to match the duration of the financing to those of the assets, what should the maturity of these zero-coupon notes be?

27. You have been asked to assess analyze the financial mix for ServiStar, a privately owned chain of hardware stores, and have been provided with the following information on the firm:

a. The firm has $4.5 million in bank debt outstanding on its books, and it had interest payments of $300,000 in the most recent year. The book value of equity was $2 million.

b. The firm had a return on equity of 21% in the most recent year, and the average PE ratio of publicly traded hardware firms is 20.

c. The firm faces a tax rate of 40%, and was able to claim $250,000 in depreciation in the most recent year.

Estimate the following inputs for this firm:
Estimated Market Value of Firm =
Estimated EBITDA =
Current Market Value Debt Ratio =

VI. OPTIMAL CAPITAL STRUCTURE

Objective: To estimate the optimal mix of debt and equity for this firm, based upon its characteristics and constraint.

Key Questions

- Based upon the cost of capital approach, what is the optimal debt ratio for your firm?
- Bringing in reasonable constraints into the decision process, what would your recommended debt ratio be for this firm?
- Does your firm have too much or too little debt relative to the sector? relative to the market?

Framework for Analysis

1. Cost of Capital Approach

- What is the current cost of capital for the firm?
- What happens to the cost of capital as the debt ratio is changed?
- At what debt ratio is the cost of capital minimized and firm value maximized? (If they are different, explain)
- What will happen to the firm value if the firm moves to its optimal?
- What will happen to the stock price if the firm moves to the optimal, and stockholders are rational?

2. Building Constraints into the Process

- What rating does the company have at the optimal debt ratio? If you were to impose a rating constraint, what would it be? Why? What is the optimal debt ratio with this rating constraint?
- How volatile is the operating income? What is the "normalized" operating income of this firm and what is the optimal debt ratio of the firm at this level of income?

3. Relative Analysis

- Relative to the sector to which this firm belongs, does it have too much or too little in debt? (Do a regression, if necessary)
- Relative to the rest of the firms in the market, does it have too much or too little in debt? (Use the market regression, if necessary)

Getting Information on Optimal Capital Structure

To get the inputs needed to estimate the optimal capital structure, examine the 10-K report (**www.sec.gov/edgarhp.htm**) or the annual report. The ratings, interest coverage ratios and default spreads come from the ratings table on my web site (**ratings.xls**).

The market regression for debt ratios is available on my web site (**regress.xls**). You can download information on other firms in the sector individually or look at the Value Line pages corresponding to each of these firms. You can get a list of the comparable firms on the web site (**www.dailystocks.com**—enter a symbol and pick the industry comparison).

To estimate the optimal capital structure for your firm, you can use the excel spreadsheet on my web site titled **capstr.xls,** and enter the inputs for your firm. The ratings and coverage ratios are built into the spreadsheet.

CHAPTER 9

CAPITAL STRUCTURE—
THE FINANCING DETAILS

In this chapter, we complete our analysis of the financing decision by building on the discussion of optimal capital structure initiated in the previous chapter. In particular, we examine the following questions:

- When the actual and optimal debt ratios differ, what is the best path for moving from the actual to the optimal?
- When and how should firms increase or decrease leverage *quickly?*
- When and how should firms increase or decrease leverage *gradually?*
- What is the appropriate financing mix for a firm? In particular, how should firms decide on the maturity, currency mix, and special features for their debt issues?
- How do tax, agency cost, and information asymmetry affect the financing mix?

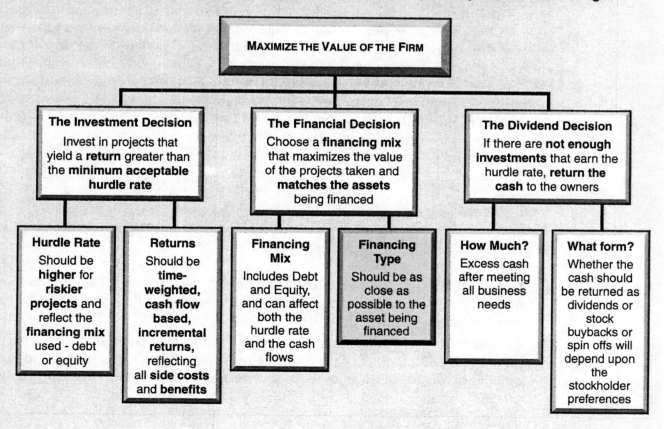

A FRAMEWORK FOR CAPITAL STRUCTURE CHANGES

A firm whose actual debt ratio is very different from its optimal has several choices to make. First, it has to decide *whether to move toward the optimal or preserve the status quo.* Second, once it decides to move toward the optimal, the firm has to choose *between changing its leverage quickly or moving more deliberately.* This decision may also be governed by pressure from external sources, such as impatient stockholders or bond ratings agency concerns. Third, if the firm decides to move gradually to the optimal, it has to decide whether to use new financing *to take new projects, or to shift its financing mix on existing projects.*

In the previous chapter, we presented the rationale for moving toward the optimal in terms of the value that could be gained for stockholders by doing so. Conversely, the cost of preserving the status quo is the loss of this potential value increment. While managers make this decision, they will often find themselves under some pressure from stockholders, if they are underlevered, or under threat of bankruptcy, if they are overlevered, to move toward their optimal debt ratios.

IMMEDIATE OR GRADUAL CHANGE

When firms are significantly underlevered or overlevered, they have to decide whether to adjust their leverage quickly or gradually over time. The advantage of a prompt movement to the optimal is that the firm immediately receives the benefits of the optimal leverage, which include a lower cost of capital and a higher value. The disadvantage of a sudden change in leverage is that it changes both the way and the environment in which managers make decisions within the firm. If the optimal debt ratio has been misestimated, a sudden change may also increase the risk that the firm may have to backtrack and reverse its financing decisions. To illustrate, assume that a firm's optimal debt ratio has been calculated to be 40% and that the firm moves to this optimal from its current debt ratio of 10%. A few months later, the firm discovers that its optimal debt ratio is really 30%. It will then have to repay some of the debt that it has taken on to get back to the optimal leverage.

Underlevered Firms

For underlevered firms, the decision to increase the debt ratio to the optimal quickly or gradually is determined by a number of factors:

1. *Degree of Confidence in the Optimal Leverage Estimate:* The greater the noise in the estimate of optimal leverage, the more likely the firm will choose to move gradually to the optimal.

2. *Comparability to Peer Group:* When the optimal debt ratio for a firm is very different from that of its peer group, the firm is much less likely to move to the optimal quickly because analysts and ratings agencies might not look favorably on the change.

3. *Likelihood of a Takeover:* Empirical studies of the characteristics of target firms in acquisitions have noted that underleveraged firms are much more likely to be acquired than are overlevered firms.[1] Often, the acquisition is financed at least partially by the target firm's unused debt capacity. Consequently, firms with excess debt capacity which delay increasing debt run the risk of being taken over; the greater this risk, the more likely the firm will choose to take on additional debt quickly.

A number of factors may determine the likelihood of a takeover. One is the prevalence of antitakeover laws (at the state level) and amendments (at the firm level) designed specifically to prevent the possibility of hostile acquisitions. Another is the size of the firm; the larger the firm, the more protected it may feel from hostile takeovers. The third is the extent of holdings by insiders and managers in the company; insiders and managers with substantial stakes may be able to preempt hostile acquisitions.

4. *Need for Financing Slack:* On occasion, firms may require financial slack to meet unanticipated needs for funds, either to keep existing projects going, or to take on new ones. Firms that need and value financial slack will be less likely to move quickly to their optimal debt ratios and use up their excess debt capacity.

Financing Slack: The financing slack is the difference between the debt that a firm chooses to carry and the optimal debt that it could carry, when the former is less than the latter.

■▲ ILLUSTRATION 9.1 **Debt Capacity and Takeovers**
▼● The Disney acquisition of Capital Cities, while a friendly acquisition, illustrates some of the advantages to the acquiring firm of acquiring an underlevered firm. Capital Cities at the time of the acquisition had $657 million in outstanding debt, and 154.06 million shares outstanding trading at $100 per share; its market value debt ratio was only 4.07%. With a beta of 0.95, a borrowing rate of 7.70%, and a corporate tax rate of 43.50%, this yielded a cost of capital of 11.90%. (The Treasury bond rate at the time of the analysis was 7%.)

$$\text{Cost of Capital} = 12.23\% \ (15{,}406/(15{,}406 + 657)) + 7.70\% \ (1 - .435) \ (657/(15{,}406 + 657))$$
$$= 11.90\%$$

The following table summarizes the costs of equity, debt, and capital, as well as the estimated firm values and stock prices at different debt ratios for Capital Cities:

Debt Ratio	Beta	Cost of Equity	Interest Coverage Ratio	Bond Rating	Interest Rate	Cost of Debt	Cost of Capital	Firm Value	Stock Price
0.00%	0.93	12.10%	∞	AAA	7.30%	4.12%	12.10%	$15,507	$96.41
10.00%	0.99	12.42%	10.73	AAA	7.30%	4.12%	11.59%	$17,007	$106.15

[1] Palepu (1986) notes that one of the variables that seems to predict a takeover is a low debt ratio, in conjunction with poor operating performance.

Debt Ratio	Beta	Cost of Equity	Interest Coverage Ratio	Bond Rating	Interest Rate	Cost of Debt	Cost of Capital	Firm Value	Stock Price
20.00%	1.06	12.82%	4.75	A	8.25%	4.66%	11.19%	$18,399	$115.19
30.00%	1.15	13.34%	2.90	BBB	9.00%	5.09%	10.86%	$19,708	$123.69
40.00%	1.28	14.02%	1.78	B	11.00%	6.22%	10.90%	$19,546	$122.63
50.00%	1.45	14.99%	1.21	CCC	13.00%	7.35%	11.17%	$18,496	$115.81
60.00%	1.71	16.43%	1.00	CCC	13.00%	7.35%	10.98%	$19,228	$120.57
70.00%	2.37	20.01%	0.77	CC	14.50%	9.63%	12.74%	$13,939	$86.23
80.00%	3.65	27.08%	0.61	C	16.00%	11.74%	14.81%	$10,449	$63.58
90.00%	7.30	47.16%	0.54	C	16.00%	12.21%	15.71%	$9,391	$56.71

Note that the firm value is maximized at a debt ratio of 30%, leading to an increase in the stock price of $23.69.

While debt capacity was never stated as a rationale for Disney's acquisition of Capital Cities, it is worth noting that Disney borrowed about $10 billion for this acquisition and paid $125 per share. Capital Cities stockholders could well have achieved the same premium, if management at the company had borrowed the money and repurchased stock. While in this case it can be argued that Capital Cities stockholders did not lose as a result of the acquisition, they would have (at least based on our numbers) if Disney had paid a smaller premium on the acquisition.

Overlevered Firms

Similar considerations apply to overlevered firms that are considering how quickly they should lower their debt ratio. As in the case of underlevered firms, the precision of the estimate of the optimal leverage will play a role, with more precise estimates leading to quicker adjustments. The other factor, in the case of overlevered firms, is *the possibility of default*—the primary risk of having too much debt. Too much debt results in higher interest rates and lower ratings on the debt. Thus, the greater the chance of bankruptcy, the more likely the firm is to move quickly to reduce debt and move to its optimal.

9.1 INDIRECT BANKRUPTCY COSTS AND LEVERAGE

In Chapter 7, we talked about indirect bankruptcy costs, where the perception of default risk affected sales and profits. Assume that a firm with substantial indirect bankruptcy costs has too much debt. Is the urgency to get back to an optimal debt ratio for this firm greater or lesser than it is for a firm without such costs?

☐ Greater

☐ Lesser

Explain.

THE PROCESS OF CHANGE

The process by which firms adjust their leverage will depend upon two factors: (1) the speed with which they want to change their financing mix, and (2) the availability of new projects that can be financed with the new debt or equity.

Increasing Leverage Quickly

When underlevered firms need to increase leverage quickly, they can do so in a number of ways: borrowing money and buying back stock; replacing equity with debt of equal market value; or selling assets and repurchasing stock.

- *Borrowing money and buying back stock (or paying a special dividend)* increases leverage because the borrowing increases the debt, while the equity repurchase or dividend payment concurrently reduces the equity. A number of companies have used this approach to increase leverage quickly, largely in response to takeover attempts. For example, in 1985, to stave off a hostile takeover, Atlantic Richfield borrowed $4 billion and repurchased stock to increase its leverage from 12% to 34%.

- In a *debt-for-equity swap,* a firm replaces equity with debt of equivalent market value by swapping the two securities. Here, again, the simultaneous increase in debt and the decrease in equity causes the debt ratio to increase substantially. In many cases, as can be seen in Table 9.1, firms offer equity investors a combination of cash and debt in lieu of equity. In 1986, for example, Owens Corning gave its stockholders $52 in cash and debt with a face value of $35, for each outstanding share, thereby increasing its debt and reducing equity.

- Finally, when firms currently have debt outstanding, and want to change their debt ratio, they can do so by *selling a portion of their assets and using the proceeds to repurchase stock.*

In each of these cases, the firm may be stymied by bond covenants that explicitly prohibit these actions or impose large penalties on the firm. The firm will have to weigh these restrictions against the benefits of the higher leverage and the increased value that flows from it.

In the last few years, several firms have gone through *leveraged recapitalizations,* whereby one or more of the above strategies has been used to increase leverage quickly. Table 9.1 lists some of the firms and the strategies they used.

Note that nearly every one of these restructurings was motivated by a desire to prevent a hostile takeover. Managers seldom initiate large increases in leverage since the leverage puts added pressure on them to perform.

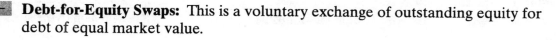

Debt-for-Equity Swaps: This is a voluntary exchange of outstanding equity for debt of equal market value.

9.2 INSIDER HOLDINGS AND LEVERAGE

Closely held firms (where managers and insiders hold a substantial portion of the outstanding stock) are less likely to increase leverage quickly than firms with widely dispersed stockholdings.

☐ True

☐ False

Explain.

ILLUSTRATION 9.2 Changing Leverage Quickly: Nichols Research

In 1994, Nichols Research, a firm that provides technical services to the defense industry, had debt outstanding of $6.8 million and market value of equity of $120

Table 9.1 A SELECTIVE SAMPLE OF LEVERAGED RECAPITALIZATIONS

Company	Date	Trigger for Recap	Strategy Used
CBS Inc.	1985	Hostile takeover bid by Ted Turner	Acquisition of 21% of common stock.
Caeser's World	1987	Hostile bid by Martin Sosnoff	Borrow $1 billion and pay special dividend of $26.25.
Carter Hawley Hale	1986	Hostile bid by The Limited	Spin off division and pay special dividend of $325 mil.
Colt Industries	1986		Borrow $1.5 billion and pay special dividend of $85.
FMC	1986	Potential hostile takeover	Pay special dividend of $80.
GenCorp	1987	Hostile takeover by AFG	Borrow $1.6 billion and buy back stock.
Gillette Corp.	1986	Hostile bid by Revlon	Repurchase 7 million shares in the open market.
Goodyear Tire & Rubber Co.	1986	Hostile bid by James Goldsmith	Sell three units and buy back 20 million shares of stock.
HBO & Co.	1986	Maintain stockholder value	Purchase 26% of the outstanding stock.
Harcourt Brace Jovanovich	1987	Hostile bid by British Painting	Borrow money and pay special dividend.
Holiday Corp.	1986	Hostile takeover bid by Donald Trump	Pay special dividend of $65 per share.
Inco Ltd.	1988	Potential for hostile takeover	Pay $1 billion in special dividends.
Interco Ltd.	1988	Hostile takeover bid by Rales Brothers	Borrow $2.8 billion and pay special dividend of $14 per share.
Kroger	1988	Hostile takeover bid by Haft Brothers	Pay special dividend.
Multimedia	1988	LBO proposal from management	Borrow money and buy back stock.
Newmont Mining	1987	Hostile bid by Ivanhoe Partners	Pay special dividend of $33 per share.
Optical Coating Laboratories	1988		Pay special dividend of $13 per share.
Owens Corning	1986	Hostile bid by Wickes	Debt-for-equity swap + special dividend ($52 + $35 of debt for equity).
Phillips Petroleum	1984	Hostile takeover by Pickens	Double firm's debt and buy back stock.
Quantum Chemical	1988		Pay special dividend of $50 per share.
Santa Fe Southern Pacific	1987	Potential for hostile takeover	Pay $4 billion to the stockholders.
Shoney's	1988		Special dividend + debt-for-equity swap.
Standard Brand Paints	1987	Hostile bid for Entregrowth	Buy back 53% of the outstanding shares.
Swank Inc.	1987	Hostile takeover	Pay special dividend of $17.
UAL	1987	Potential for hostile takeover	Borrow money and repurchase 63% of outstanding shares.
USG Corp.	1988	Potential for hostile bid from Desert Partners	Special dividend + debt-for-equity swap.
Union Carbide	1985	Hostile bid by GAF Inc.	Special dividend + debt-for-equity swap.
Unocal	1985	Hostile bid by T. Boone Pickens	Repurchase 49% of the outstanding shares.

million. Based upon its EBITDA of $12 million, Nichols had an optimal debt ratio of 30%, which would lower the cost of capital to 12.07% (from the current cost of capital of 13%) and increase the firm value to $146 million (from $126.8 million). There are a number of reasons for arguing that Nichols should increase its leverage quickly:

- Its small size, in conjunction with its low leverage and large cash balance ($25.3 million), makes it a prime target for an acquisition.

- While 17.6% of the shares are held by owners and directors, this amount is unlikely to hold off a hostile acquisition, since institutions own 60% of the outstanding stock.

- The firm has been reporting steadily decreasing returns on its projects, due to the shrinkage in the defense budget. In 1994, the return on capital was only 10%, which is much lower than the cost of capital.

If Nichols decides to increase leverage, it can do so in a number of ways:

- It can borrow enough money to get to 30% of its overall firm value ($146 million at the optimal debt ratio) and buy back stock. This would require $37 million in new debt.

- It can borrow $37 million and pay a special dividend of that amount.

- It can use its current cash balance of $25 million to buy back stock or pay dividends, and increase debt to 30% of the remaining firm value (30% of $121 million).[2] This would require approximately $29.5 million in new debt, which can be used to buy back stock.

Decrease Leverage Quickly

Firms that have to decrease leverage quickly face a more difficult problem, since the perception that they might not survive affects their capacity to raise new financing. Optimally, such firms would like to issue equity and use it to pay off some of the outstanding debt, but their equity issues might not be well received in the market. Consequently, they have to consider two options—they can either renegotiate debt agreements or sell their assets to pay off the debt.

- *When firms renegotiate debt agreements,* they try to convince some of the lenders to take an equity stake in the firm in lieu of some or all of their debt in the firm. The best bargaining chip the firm possesses is the possibility of default, since lenders faced with default are more likely to agree to these terms. In the late 1980s, for example, many U.S. banks were forced to trade in their Latin American debt for equity stakes or receive little or nothing on their loans.

- The firm may choose to *sell assets and use the proceeds to retire some of the outstanding debt.* Many firms that had taken on too much debt in the course of leveraged buyouts in the 1980s, and wanted to pay off some of it, adopted this approach.

---

[2]We are assuming that the optimal debt ratio will be unaffected by the paying out of the special dividend. It is entirely possible that the paying out of the cash will make the firm riskier (leading to a higher unlevered beta) and lower the optimal debt ratio.

(?)   **9.3   ASSET SALES TO REDUCE LEVERAGE**

Assume that a firm has decided to sell assets to pay off its debt. In deciding which assets to sell, the firm should

☐   sell its worst-performing assets to raise the cash.

☐   sell its best-performing assets to raise the cash.

☐   sell its most liquid assets to raise the cash.

☐   Other . . .

Explain.

Increasing Leverage Gradually

Firms that have the luxury of increasing their leverage gradually over time begin by analyzing the availability of good projects that can be financed with the debt. If there are good projects available, borrowing the money to take on these projects will provide firms with an added benefit: The firm not only gets the increase in value of moving to the optimal debt ratio, it also gets the additional increment in value from the positive net present value of new projects.

In the earlier chapters on investment analysis, we defined good projects as those that earn a return greater than the hurdle rate. The return can be measured in either cash flow terms (as the internal rate of return) or accounting terms (as the return on equity or the return on capital), and must be compared to an appropriate benchmark (cost of equity for equity returns, and cost of capital for return on capital).

Firms that have excess debt capacity but do not have good projects to choose from will be better off increasing the debt ratio by repurchasing stock and/or increasing dividends over time.

IN PRACTICE: DEBT CAPACITY AND ACQUISITIONS

It is sometimes argued that firms with excess debt capacity use it to acquire other firms. This makes sense only if the acquisition can be justified on a standalone basis, without the benefit of the added value from moving to the optimal debt ratio. To illustrate, assume that a firm is currently underleveraged but could increase its value by $50 million if it moves to its optimal debt ratio by borrowing $200 million. The firm proceeds to borrow $200 million and buy a target firm worth $175 million; it then argues that it is in fact better off overall because it has a net gain in value of $25 million ($50 million in increased value from moving to the optimal reduced by the overpayment of $25 million on the acquisition). This argument does not hold up, however, because the firm could have increased its value by $50 million if it had borrowed the money and bought back stock. Excess debt capacity cannot be used, therefore, to justify bad investment or acquisition decisions.

■▲
▼●   ILLUSTRATION 9.3   Charting a Framework for Changing Leverage: Disney

Reviewing the capital structure analysis done for Disney in Chapter 8, Disney had a debt ratio of approximately 18% in July 1997, with $11.18 billion in debt (estimated market value) and $50.89 billion in equity. Its optimal debt ratio, based upon minimizing cost of capital, was 40%. Table 9.2 summarizes the debt ratios, costs of capital, and firm value at debt ratios ranging from 0% to 90%.

Table 9.2	DEBT RATIO, WACC, AND FIRM VALUE: DISNEY	
Debt Ratio	**Cost of Capital**	**Firm Value**
0.00%	13.00%	$53,172
10.00%	12.55%	$58,014
20.00%	12.17%	$62,705
30.00%	11.84%	$67,419
40.00%	11.64%	$70,542
50.00%	11.70%	$69,560
60.00%	12.11%	$63,445
70.00%	11.97%	$65,524
80.00%	12.17%	$62,751
90.00%	13.69%	$47,140

The optimal debt ratio for Disney is 40%, since the cost of capital is minimized and the firm value is maximized at this debt level. Assuming that Disney operates under an investment grade rating constraint (of BBB), the optimal debt ratio is 30%.

Disney is not under any immediate pressure to increase its leverage, partly because of its size ($62 billion) and partly because it has done well for its stockholders over the previous years.[3] Let us assume, however, that Disney decides to increase its leverage over time toward its optimal for two reasons:

1. It is embarking on international expansion, which will require extensive external financing.

2. Its stockholders are restive due to a series of management missteps[4] and compensation issues, and its stock price has stagnated for the last year.

The question of how to increase leverage over time can be best answered by looking at the quality of the projects that Disney had available to it in 1996. To make this judgment, we estimate the return on capital earned by Disney in 1996:

$$\text{Return on Capital} = \text{EBIT} (1 - \text{tax rate}) / (\text{BV of Debt} + \text{BV of Equity})$$
$$= 5559 (1 - .36)/(7663 + 11368)$$
$$= 18.69\%$$

This is higher than the cost of capital[5] of 12.22% that Disney faced in 1997 and the 11.84% it will face if it moves to the optimal. Assuming that the returns on capital will be higher than the cost of capital in the future, Disney should finance its new pro-

---

[3]See Jensen's alpha calculation in Chapter 4. Over the 1992-96 time period, Disney has earned an excess return of 1.81% a year.

[4]Disney and its chief operating officer, Michael Ovitz, parted company after Mr. Ovitz and Disney's CEO, Mr. Eisner could not get along. The parting was expensive, costing Disney an estimated $90 million.

[5]The correct comparison should be to the cost of capital that Disney will have at its optimal debt ratio. It is, however, even better if the return on capital also exceeds the current cost of capital, since it will take time to get to the optimal.

jects with debt. Over time, we would expect to see an increase in the debt ratio, though the value of equity will itself increase as earnings are reinvested back in the company. To make forecasts of changes in leverage over time, we made the following assumptions:

- Revenues, operating earnings, capital expenditures, and depreciation are expected to grow 10% a year for the next five years (based upon analyst estimates of growth). The current values for each of these is provided in Table 9.3.
- Non-cash working capital is assumed to be 5% of revenues, and to stay at that level through the entire five-year period.
- The interest rate on new debt is expected to be 7.5%.
- The dividend payout ratio is currently 22.32%.
- The current beta for Disney is 1.25.
- The Treasury bond rate is 7%, and the risk premium is assumed to be 5.5%.

The values of debt and equity, over time, are estimated as follows:

$$\text{Equity}_t = \text{Equity}_{t-1}\,(1 + \text{Cost of Equity}_{t-1}) - \text{Dividends}_t$$

The rationale is simple: The cost of equity measures the expected return on the stock, inclusive of price appreciation and the dividend yield, and the payment of dividends reduces the value of equity outstanding at the end of the year.[6] The value of debt is estimated by adding the new debt taken on to the debt outstanding at the end of the previous year.

We begin this analysis by looking at what would happen to the debt ratio if Disney maintains its existing payout ratio of 22.32%, does not buy back stock, and applies excess funds to pay off debt. Table 9.3 uses the expected capital expenditures and non-cash working capital needs over the next five years, in conjunction with external financing needs, to estimate the debt ratio in each year.

Disney produces a cash surplus every year, since internal cash flows (net income + depreciation) are well in excess of capital expenditures and working capital needs. If this is applied to paying off debt, the increase in the market value of equity over time will cause the debt ratio to drop from 18.01% to 9.06% by the end of year 5. If Disney wants to increase its debt ratio to 30%, it will need to do one or a combination of the following:

1. **Increase its dividend payout ratio:** The higher dividend increases the debt ratio in two ways. It increases the need for debt financing in each year, and it reduces the expected price appreciation on the equity. In Table 9.4, for instance, increasing the dividend payout ratio to 50% results in a debt ratio of 11.42% at the end of the fifth year (instead of 9.06%).

   In fact, increasing dividend payout alone is unlikely to increase the debt ratio substantially.

---

[6] The effect of dividends on the market value of equity can best be captured by noting the effect the payment on dividends has on stock prices on the ex-dividend day. Stock prices tend to drop on ex-dividend day by about the same amount as the dividend paid.

Table 9.3   ESTIMATED DEBT RATIO WITH EXISTING PAYOUT RATIOS: DISNEY

	Current Year	1	2	3	4	5
Equity	$50,888	$57,651	$65,251	$73,793	$83,393	$94,183
Debt	$11,180	$10,908	$10,599	$10,246	$9,844	$9,386
Debt/(Debt + Equity)	18.01%	15.91%	13.97%	12.19%	10.56%	9.06%
Revenues	$18,739	$20,613	$22,674	$24,942	$27,436	$30,179
Capital Expenditures	$1,745	$1,920	$2,111	$2,323	$2,555	$2,810
+ Chg in Work. Cap.	$15	$94	$103	$113	$125	$137
− Depreciation	$1,134	$1,247	$1,372	$1,509	$1,660	$1,826
− Net Income	$1,214	$1,335	$1,483	$1,647	$1,830	$2,033
+ Dividends	$271	$298	$331	$368	$408	$454
= New Debt	($317)	($272)	($309)	($353)	($402)	($458)
Beta	1.25	1.23	1.21	1.19	1.18	1.17
Cost of Equity	13.88%	13.76%	13.65%	13.56%	13.48%	13.41%
Growth Rate		10.00%	10.00%	10.00%	10.00%	10.00%
Dividend Payout Ratio	22.32%	22.32%	22.32%	22.32%	22.32%	22.32%

[a]Net Income$_t$ = Net Income$_{t-1}$ (1+ g)-Interest Rate (1-t) * (Debt$_t$-Debt$_{t-1}$)

Table 9.4   ESTIMATED DEBT RATIO WITH HIGHER DIVIDEND PAYOUT RATIO

	Current Year	1	2	3	4	5
Equity	$50,888	$57,281	$64,446	$72,479	$81,486	$91,587
Debt	$11,180	$11,278	$11,389	$11,513	$11,653	$11,810
D/(Debt + Equity)	18.01%	16.45%	15.02%	13.71%	12.51%	11.42%
Revenues	$18,739	$20,613	$22,674	$24,942	$27,436	$30,179
Capital Expenditures	$1,745	$1,920	$2,111	$2,323	$2,555	$2,810
Chg in Work. Cap.	$15	$94	$103	$113	$125	$137
− Depreciation	$1,134	$1,247	$1,372	$1,509	$1,660	$1,826
− Net Income	$1,214	$1,335	$1,464	$1,605	$1,759	$1,927
+ Dividends	$271	$668	$732	$802	$879	$964
= New Debt	($317)	$98	$110	$124	$140	$157
Beta	1.25	1.23	1.22	1.21	1.20	1.19
Cost of Equity	13.88%	13.79%	13.71%	13.64%	13.58%	13.52%
Growth Rate		10.00%	10.00%	10.00%	10.00%	10.00%
Payout Ratio	22.32%	50.00%	50.00%	50.00%	50.00%	50.00%

2. ***Repurchase stock each year:***   This affects the debt ratio in much the same way as does increasing dividends, because it increases debt requirements and reduces equity. For instance, if Disney bought back 5% of the stock outstanding each year, the debt ratio at the end of year 5 would be significantly higher as shown in Table 9.5.

	Current Year	1	2	3	4	5
Table 9.5 ESTIMATED DEBT RATIO WITH EQUITY BUYBACK OF 5% A YEAR						
Equity	$50,888	$54,768	$59,030	$63,717	$68,875	$74,561
Debt	$11,180	$13,791	$16,703	$19,958	$23,604	$27,697
Debt/(Debt + Equity)	18.01%	20.12%	22.06%	23.85%	25.52%	27.09%
Revenues	$18,739	$20,613	$22,674	$24,942	$27,436	$30,179
Capital Expenditures	$1,745	$1,920	$2,111	$2,323	$2,555	$2,810
+ Chg in Work. Cap.	$15	$94	$103	$113	$125	$137
− Depreciation	$1,134	$1,247	$1,372	$1,509	$1,660	$1,826
− Net Income	$1,214	$1,335	$1,335	$1,320	$1,285	$1,227
+ Dividends	$271	$298	$298	$295	$287	$274
+ Stock Buyback		$2,883	$3,107	$3,354	$3,625	$3,924
= New Debt	($317)	$2,611	$2,912	$3,255	$3,646	$4,092
Beta	1.25	1.27	1.29	1.32	1.34	1.36
Cost of Equity	13.88%	14.00%	14.12%	14.24%	14.35%	14.46%
Growth Rate		10.00%	10.00%	10.00%	10.00%	10.00%
Dividend Payout Ratio	22.32%	22.32%	22.32%	22.32%	22.32%	22.32%

Note that the debt ratio increases to 27.09% by the end of year 5.

3. ***Increase capital expenditures each year:*** While the first two approaches increase the debt ratio by shrinking the equity, the third approach increases the scale of the firm. It does so by increasing the capital expenditures, which incidentally includes acquisitions of other firms, and financing these expenditures with debt. Disney could increase its debt ratio fairly significantly by embarking on a series of acquisitions. In Table 9.6, we estimate the debt ratio for Disney if it triples its capital expenditures and meets its external financing needs with debt.

This is the riskiest strategy of the three, since it presupposes the existence of enough good investments (or acquisitions) to cover $35 billion in new investments over the next five years. It may, however, be the strategy that seems most attractive to management that is intent on building a global entertainment empire.

9.4 CASH BALANCES AND CHANGING LEVERAGE

Companies with excess debt capacity often also have large cash balances. Which of the following actions by a company with a large cash balance and debt on its books will increase its debt ratio? (You can pick more than one.)

☐ Using the cash to acquire another company

☐ Paying a large special dividend

☐ Paying off debt

☐ Buying back stock

Explain.

Table 9.6 ESTIMATED DEBT RATIO WITH HIGHER CAP EX

	Current Year	1	2	3	4	5
Equity	$50,888	$57,637	$65,573	$74,725	$85,283	$97,465
Debt	$11,180	$14,445	$18,167	$22,408	$27,243	$32,753
Debt/(Debt + Equity)	18.01%	20.04%	21.69%	23.07%	24.21%	25.15%
Revenues	$18,739	$20,613	$22,674	$24,942	$27,436	$30,179
Capital Expenditures	$1,745	$5,759	$6,334	$6,968	$7,665	$8,431
Chg in Work. Cap.	$15	$94	$103	$113	$125	$137
− Depreciation	$1,409	$1,550	$1,705	$1,875	$2,063	$2,269
− Net Income	$1,214	$1,335	$1,302	$1,241	$1,148	$1,016
+ Dividends	$271	$298	$291	$277	$256	$227
= New Debt	($592)	$3,265	$3,721	$4,241	$4,834	$5,510
Beta	1.25	1.32	1.34	1.36	1.37	1.38
Cost of Equity	13.85%	14.27%	14.38%	14.47%	14.55%	14.62%
Growth Rate		10.00%	10.00%	10.00%	10.00%	10.00%
Dividend Payout Ratio	22.32%	22.32%	22.32%	22.32%	22.32%	22.32%

Decreasing Leverage Gradually

The benefits overlevered firms gain by lowering their debt ratios gradually over time include the residual cash flows that can be used to take on new projects and the increase in equity over time, leading to lower debt ratios. For this to work, however, firms must have access to good projects, which can be financed either with the internal equity or with new stock issues, leading to higher equity and lower debt ratios. If firms do not have access to good projects, the residual cash flows of the firms will have to be utilized to pay off outstanding debt and lower the debt ratio. It goes without saying that firms should desist from paying dividends or repurchasing stock during the course of this adjustment.

Internal Equity: Internal equity usually is that portion of the earnings that gets reinvested back into the company (i.e., the retained earnings).

IN PRACTICE: HYBRID SECURITIES AND CHANGING FINANCING MIX

In some cases, overlevered firms can gain from issuing hybrid securities, such as convertible debt, where the mix of debt and equity changes over time as the stock price changes. As the firm's fortunes improve, the equity component in convertible debt increases as a proportion of the convertible bond's value, leading to lower debt ratios.

ILLUSTRATION 9.4   A Framework for Changing Leverage: Time Warner

In 1994, Time Warner had 379.3 million shares outstanding, trading at $44 per share, and $9.934 billion in outstanding debt, left over from the leveraged acquisition of Time by Warner Communications in 1989. The EBITDA in 1994 was $1.146 billion, and Time Warner had a beta of 1.30. The optimal debt ratio for Time Warner, based upon this operating income, is only 10%. Table 9.7 examines the effect on leverage of cutting dividends to zero and using operating cash flows to take on projects and repay debt.

	Current Year	1	2	3	4	5
			Table 9.7 Estimated Debt Ratios: Time Warner			
Equity	$16,689	$19,051	$21,694	$24,651	$27,960	$31,663
Debt	$9,934	$9,745	$9,527	$9,276	$8,988	$8,655
Debt/(Debt + Equity)	37.31%	33.84%	30.52%	27.34%	24.33%	21.47%
Capital Expenditures	$300	$330	$363	$399	$439	$483
− Depreciation	$437	$481	$529	$582	$640	$704
− Net Income	$35	$39	$52	$68	$88	$112
− Dividends	$67	$0	$0	$0	$0	$0
= New Debt	($105)	($189)	($218)	($251)	($289)	($332)
Beta	1.30	1.25	1.21	1.17	1.14	1.11
Cost of Equity	14.15%	13.87%	13.63%	13.42%	13.24%	13.08%
Growth Rate		10.00%	10.00%	10.00%	10.00%	10.00%
Payout Ratio	11%	0%	0%	0%	0%	0%

Allowing for a growth rate of 10% in operating income, Time Warner repays $189 million of its outstanding debt in the first year. By the end of the fifth year, the growth in equity and the reduction in debt combine to lower the debt ratio to 21.47%.

Figure 9.1 summarizes the framework that we have developed in the last few pages.

This spreadsheet allows you to estimate the effects of changing dividend policy or capital expenditures on debt ratios over time (**chgfin.xls**).

9.5   Investing in Other Business Lines

In the analysis above, we have argued that firms should invest in projects as long as the return on equity is greater than the cost of equity. Assume that a firm is considering acquiring another firm with its debt capacity. In analyzing the return on equity the acquiring firm can make on this investment, we should compare the return on equity to

☐   the cost of equity of the acquiring firm.

☐   the cost of equity of the acquired firm.

☐   a blended cost of equity of the acquired and acquiring firm.

☐   none of the above.

Explain.

Security Innovation and Capital Structure Changes

While the changes in leverage discussed so far in this chapter have been accomplished using traditional securities such as straight debt and equity, firms that have specific objectives on leverage may find certain products that are designed to meet those objectives. Consider a few examples:

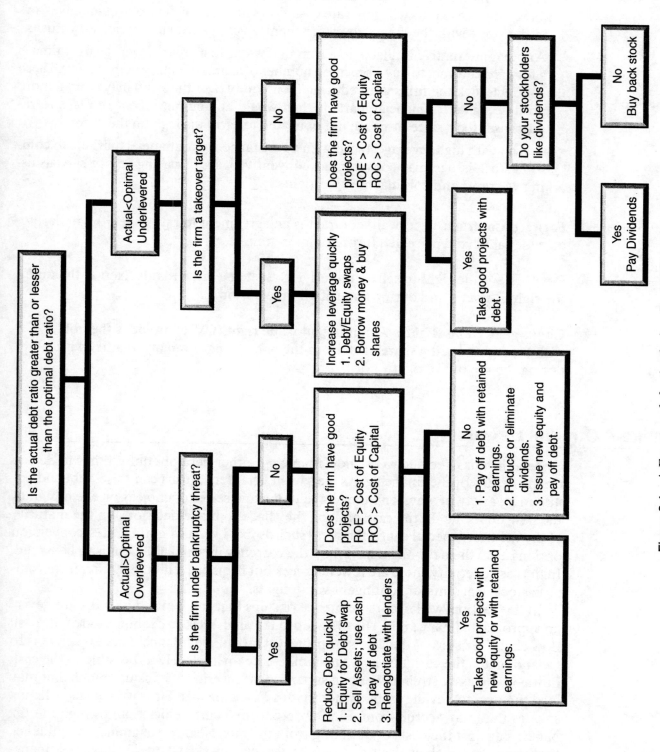

Figure 9.1　A Framework for Analyzing Capital Structure.

- A firm that intends to raise its debt ratio over time may do so by selling *puts* on its equity. These puts will generate cash flows now, and will also provide investors in the stock with the means to insure themselves against stock price downturns.

- Another alternative available to a firm that wants to increase leverage over time is a forward contract to buy a specified number of shares of equity in the future. These contracts lock the firms into reducing their equity over time and may carry a more positive signal to financial markets than would an announcement of plans to repurchase stock, since firms are not obligated to carry through on the latter.

- A firm with high leverage, faced with a resistance from financial markets to common stock issues, may consider more inventive ways of raising equity, such as using warrants and contingent value rights.

Forward Contract: A forward contract is an agreement to buy or sell the underlying asset at a fixed price at a future point in time.

Puts: This is the right to sell an underlying asset at a price that is fixed at the time the right is issued and during a specified time period.

Contingent Value Rights: A contingent value right (CVR) provides the holder with the right to sell a share of stock in the underlying company at a fixed price during the life of the right.

WORKING OUT THE DETAILS

Once a firm has decided to use new financing, either debt or equity, it has to decide on the details of the financing. As we saw in Chapter 7, firms can raise debt and equity in a variety of ways, and they have to make a series of choices on the design of the new financing. In the case of debt, they have to make decisions on the maturity of the debt, any special characteristics (such as fixed versus floating rates, conversion options, etc.) the debt might have, and the currency in which the debt is to be issued. In the case of equity, there are fewer choices, but firms can still raise equity from common stock, warrants, or contingent value rights.

In this section, we lay out a sequence of steps that can be used by a firm to devise an appropriate finance mix. The first step in the analysis is an examination of the cash flow characteristics of the assets or projects that will be financed; the objective is to try and match the cash flows on the liability stream as closely as possible to the cash flows on the asset stream. We then superimpose a series of considerations that may lead the firm to deviate from or modify this financing mix. First, we consider the tax savings that may accrue from using different financing vehicles, and weigh the tax benefits against the costs of deviating from the mix. Next, we examine the influence that equity research analysts and ratings agency views have on the choice of financing vehicle; instruments that are looked on favorably by either or, better still, both groups will clearly be preferred to those that evoke strong negative responses from them. We also factor in the difficulty that some firms might have in conveying information to markets; in the presence of asymmetric information, firms may have to make financing choices that do not reflect their asset mix. Finally, we allow for the possibility that firms may want to structure their financing to reduce agency conflicts between stockholders and bondholders.

Step 1: Examine the Cash Flow Characteristics of Assets

The first and most important factor that a firm has to consider in the design of the securities it will use to raise funds is the *cash flow patterns of the assets* that are to be financed with these securities. We will argue that firms should begin with the premise that the cash flows on their liability streams should match up with the cash flows on the assets that they own.

Why Match Asset Cash Flows to Cash Flows on Liabilities?

To see why firms should match up cash flows on assets to cash flows on liabilities, let us begin by defining firm value as the present value of the cash flows generated by the assets owned by the firm. This firm value will vary over time, not only as a function of firm-specific factors such as project success but also as a function of broader macroeconomic variables—interest rates, inflation rates, economic cycles, and exchange rates. Figure 9.2 provides the time series of predicted firm value for a hypothetical firm, where all of the changes in firm value are assumed to occur as a result of changes in macroeconomic variables.

This firm can choose to finance these assets with any financing mix it wants. The value of equity at any point in time is the difference between the value of the firm and the value of outstanding debt. Assume, for instance, that the firm chooses to

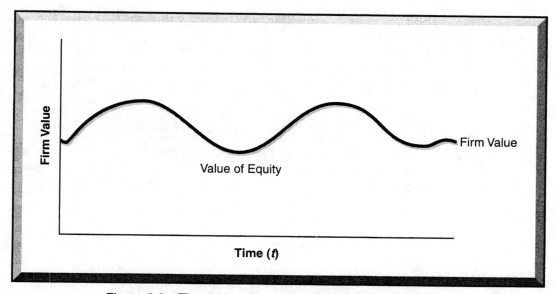

Figure 9.2   Firm Value Over Time with Short-Term Debt.

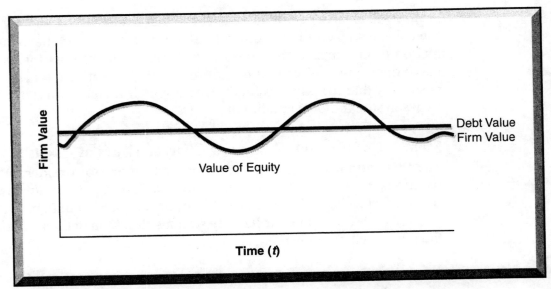

Figure 9.3 Firm Value Over Time with Short-Term Debt.

finance the assets shown in Figure 9.2 using very-short-term debt, and that this debt is unaffected by changes in macroeconomic variables. Figure 9.3 provides the firm value, debt value, and equity value over time for the firm. Note that there are periods when the firm value drops below the debt value, which would suggest that the firm is flirting with bankruptcy in those periods. Firms that weigh this possibility into their financing decision will therefore borrow much less.

Now consider a firm which finances the assets described in Figure 9.2 with debt that matches up exactly to the assets, in terms of cash flows, and also in terms of the sensitivity of debt value to changes in macroeconomic variables. Figure 9.4 provides the firm value, debt value, and equity value for this firm. Since debt value and firm value move together here, the possibility of default is significantly reduced. This, in turn, will allow the firm to carry much more debt, and the added debt should provide tax benefits that make the firm more valuable. Thus, matching liability cash flows to asset cash flows allows firms to have higher optimal debt ratios.

9.6 THE RATIONALE FOR ASSET AND LIABILITY MATCHING

In Chapter 4, we argued that firms should focus on only market risk, since firm-specific risk can be diversified away. By the same token, it should not matter if firms use short-term debt to finance long-term assets, since investors in these firms can diversify away this risk anyway.

☐ True

☐ False

Comment.

Financing Maturity

Notwithstanding the discussion above, it is difficult and expensive to match individual cash flows on assets perfectly with individual cash flows on liabilities. However,

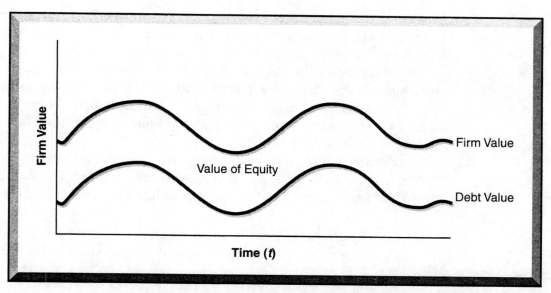

Figure 9.4 Firm Value Over Time with Long-Term Debt.

firms can often obtain a significant portion of the benefits listed in the previous section by matching the duration of their assets to the duration of their liabilities. The *duration of an asset or a liability* is a weighted maturity of all the cash flows on that asset or liability, where the weights are based upon both the timing and the magnitude of the cash flows. In general, larger and earlier cash flows are weighted more than are smaller and later cash flows. By incorporating the magnitude and timing of all the cash flows, duration encompasses all the variables that affect the interest rate sensitivity of an asset or liability. The higher the duration of an asset or liability, the more sensitive it is to changes in interest rates.

Duration of a Firm's Debt

The duration of a straight bond or loan issued by a company can be written in terms of the coupons (interest payments) on the bond (loan) and the face value of the bond, as follows (N is the bond maturity):

$$\text{Duration of Bond} = dP/dr = \frac{\left[\sum_{t=1}^{t=N} \frac{t*\text{Coupon}_t}{(1+r)^t} + \frac{N*\text{Face Value}}{(1+r)^N}\right]}{\left[\sum_{t=1}^{t=N} \frac{\text{Coupon}_t}{(1+r)^t} + \frac{\text{Face Value}}{(1+r)^N}\right]}$$

Where r is the yield to maturity.

Holding other factors constant, the duration of a bond will increase with the maturity of the bond and decrease with the coupon rate on the bond. For example, the duration of a 7%, 30-year coupon bond, when interest rates are 8%, can be written as follows:

$$\text{Duration of Bond} = dP/dr = \frac{\left[\sum_{t=1}^{t=30} \frac{t*\$70}{(1.08)^t} + \frac{30*\$1000}{(1.08)^{30}}\right]}{\left[\sum_{t=1}^{t=30} \frac{\$70}{(1.08)^t} + \frac{\$1000}{(1.08)^N}\right]} = 12.41$$

Note that the duration is lower than the maturity. This will generally be true for coupon-bearing bonds, though special features in the bond may sometimes increase duration.[7] For zero-coupon bonds, the duration is equal to the maturity.

The measure of duration estimated above is called *Macaulay duration,* and it does make some strong assumptions about the yield curve; specifically, the yield curve is assumed to be flat and move in parallel shifts. Other duration measures change these assumptions. For purposes of our analysis, however, a rough measure of duration will suffice.

The duration of the bond will be affected by any changes made to the bond's cash flow characteristics. Table 9.8 summarizes the direct impact of a couple of widely used bond features on duration and the indirect impact on interest rate risk.

Macaulay Duration: This is a specific measure of duration which is estimated on the assumption of a flat term structure and parallel shifts in the yield curve.

Duration of a Firm's Assets

This measure of duration can be extended to any asset with expected cash flows. Thus, the duration of a project or asset can be estimated in terms of its predebt operating cash flows:

$$
\text{Duration of Project/Asset} = dPV/dr = \frac{\left[\sum_{t=1}^{t=N} \frac{t*CF_t}{(1+r)^t} + \frac{N*\text{Terminal Value}}{(1+r)^N} \right]}{\left[\sum_{t=1}^{t=N} \frac{CF_t}{(1+r)^t} + \frac{\text{Terminal Value}}{(1+r)^N} \right]}
$$

where

CF$_t$ = After-tax operating cash flow on the project in year t
Terminal value = Value at the end of the project lifetime
N = Life of the project
r = Discount rate for project (Cost of Equity or Capital)

The duration of any asset provides a measure of the interest rate risk embedded in that asset.

One of the limitations of traditional duration analysis is that it keeps cash flows fixed, while interest rates change. On real projects, however, the cash flows will be adversely affected by the increases in interest rates, and the degree of the effect will vary from business to business—more for cyclical firms (automobiles, housing) and less for noncyclical firms (food processing). Thus the actual duration of most projects will be higher than the estimates obtained by keeping cash flows constant.

---

[7]For instance, in reverse floater bonds, the coupon rate varies inversely with the interest rate, rising when interest rates drop and dropping when interest rates rise. This will increase bond duration.

Table 9.8	EFFECTS OF SPECIAL FEATURES ON DURATION
Special Feature	**Effect on Duration/Interest Rate Risk**
Interest rate is floating instead of fixed	• Duration is lowered. If the floating rate has no caps or floors, the floating rate loan will have the same duration as the rate to which it is pegged (e.g., 6-month LIBOR).
	• The value of the bond is not sensitive to interest rate changes.
Bond is callable	• Duration is lowered. As interest rates go down and the likelihood of a call increases, the duration of these bonds decreases.
	• The value of a callable bond becomes less sensitive to interest rate changes as interest rates go down. It will look more like a non-callable bond as interest rates go up.

One way of estimating duration without depending upon the traditional bond duration measures is to use historical data. If the duration is, in fact, the sensitivity of asset values to interest rate changes, and a time series of data of asset value and interest rate changes is available, a regression of the former on the latter should yield a measure of duration:

$$\Delta \text{ Asset Value}_t = a + b \, \Delta \text{ Interest Rate}_t$$

In this regression, the coefficient b on interest rate changes should be a measure of the duration of the assets. For firms with publicly traded stocks and bonds, the firm value is the sum of the market values of the two over time. For a private company, the regression can be run, using changes in operating income as the dependent variable:

$$\Delta \text{ Operating Income}_t = a + b \, \Delta \text{ Interest Rate}_t$$

Here again, the coefficient b is a measure of the duration of the assets.

9.7 PROJECT LIFE AND DURATION

In investment analyses, analysts often cut off project lives at an arbitrary point and estimate a salvage or a terminal value. If these cash flows are used to estimate project duration, we will tend to

☐ understate duration.

☐ overstate duration.

☐ not affect the duration estimate.

Explain.

IN PRACTICE: Calculating Duration for the Disney Theme Park

In this application, we will calculate duration using the traditional measures for the Disney Theme Park in Thailand. The cash flows for the project are summarized in Table 9.9, together with the present value estimates, calculated using the cost of capital.

Table 9.9	Calculating a Project's Duration		
Year	Total FCFF	PV of FCFF	PV*t
1	($39,078 Bt)	(31,161 Bt)	−31160.969
2	($36,199 Bt)	(23,017 Bt)	−46034.931
3	($11,759 Bt)	(5,962 Bt)	−17886.497
4	16,155 Bt	6,532 Bt	26128.0524
5	21,548 Bt	6,947 Bt	34736.1086
6	33,109 Bt	8,512 Bt	51073.1332
7	46,692 Bt	9,572 Bt	67005.9744
8	58,169 Bt	9,509 Bt	76074.0372
9	902,843 Bt	117,694 Bt	1059242.66
NPV		98,626 Bt	1219177.57

Duration of the Project = 1,219,178 / 98,626 = 12.36 years

This duration is understated, however, because the project is arbitrarily cut off after nine years. Using the true life for the project should yield a higher duration estimate. (In fact, the duration of a perpetuity is $\frac{1+r}{r}$.)

Duration and Financing Choices

Once the duration of the assets is known, the duration of the financing can be set in one of two ways: by matching individual assets and liabilities, or by matching the assets of the firm with its collective liabilities. In the first approach, the cash flows on the financing can be matched up as closely as possible to the individual project being financed. Alternatively, the duration of the financing can be matched up to the duration of the asset it funds. While this approach provides a precise matching of each asset's characteristics to those of the financing used for it, it has several limitations. First, it is expensive to arrange separate financing for each project, given the fixed costs associated with raising funds. Second, this approach ignores interactions and correlations between projects which might make project-specific financing suboptimal for the firm. Consequently, this approach works only for companies that have very large, independent projects.

When it is difficult or costly to pair up financing to the specific projects being financed, the duration of all assets can be estimated in one of two ways:

1. By taking a weighted average of the duration of individual assets

2. By estimating the duration of all assets from the cumulated operating cash flows to the firm or the cumulated firm value.

The duration of liabilities can be estimated collectively as well and matched up as closely as possible to the duration of the assets. This approach saves on transactions costs.

9.8 PROJECT AND FIRM DURATION

Which of the following types of firms should be most likely to use project-specific financing (as opposed to financing the portfolio of projects)?

☐ Firms with a few large homogeneous projects

☐ Firms with a large number of small homogeneous projects

☐ Firms with a few large heterogeneous projects

☐ Firms with a large number of small heterogeneous projects

Explain. (Homogeneous and heterogeneous refer to similarities or differences in cash flow patterns across projects)

The Fixed/Floating Rate Choice

In recent years, firms have been provided far more choices in the design of their debt. One of the most common choices firms have to make is whether to make the coupon rate a fixed rate or a floating rate, pegged to an index rate such as the LIBOR. In making this decision, we once again examine the characteristics of the projects being financed with the debt.

Uncertainty About Future Projects

The assumption that the duration of assets and liabilities can be matched up to arrive at the "right" maturity mix for financing is predicated on the belief that the assets and projects of a firm are well identified and that the interest rate sensitivity of these assets can therefore be estimated easily. For some firms, this may be difficult to do, however. The firm may be in transition (it could be restructuring), or the industry may be changing. In such cases, the firm may use a financing mix that is easy to change (short-term or floating rate loans) until it feels more certain about its future investment plans.

An Alternative: The presence of derivatives provides an alternative for firms that are faced with this uncertainty. They can use the financing mix that is most appropriate given their current asset mix and use derivatives to manage changes in their risk characteristics.

Cash Flows and Inflation

If a firm has assets whose earnings increase as interest rates go up, and decrease as interest rates go down, it should finance those assets with floating rate loans. While not too many manufacturing projects have these characteristics in low-inflation economies, more do in high-inflation economies, since increase in inflation results in increases in both earnings/revenues and in interest rates.

Floating Rate Debt: The interest rate on floating rate debt varies from period to period and is linked to a specified short-term rate; for instance, many floating rate bonds have coupon rates that are tied to the London Interbank Borrowing Rate (LIBOR).

9.9 INFLATION UNCERTAINTY AND FLOATING RATE DEBT

Assume that the inflation rate increases and becomes more volatile. You would expect the use of floating rate debt to

☐ increase substantially.

☐ decrease substantially.

☐ be unaffected.

Explain.

Currency Risk and Financing Mix

Many of the points made about interest rate risk exposure also apply to currency risk exposure. If any of a firm's assets or projects create cash flows that are in a currency other than the one in which the equity is denominated, there is a currency risk. The liabilities of a firm can be issued in these currencies to reduce the currency risk. A firm that expects 20 percent of its cash flows to be in Deutsche Marks, for example, would attempt to issue DM-denominated debt, in the same proportion, to mitigate the currency risk.

In recent years, firms have used more sophisticated variations on traditional bonds to manage foreign exchange risk. For instance, Philip Morris issued a dual currency bond in 1985—coupon payments were made in Swiss Francs, while the principal payment was in U.S. Dollars. In 1987, Westinghouse issued Principal Exchange Rate Linked Securities (PERLS), whereby the principal payment was the U.S. dollar value of 70.13 New Zealand dollars. Finally, firms have issued bonds embedded with foreign currency options called Indexed Currency Option Notes (ICON), which combine a fixed-rate bullet repayment bond with an option on foreign exchange. This approach is likely to work only for firms that have fairly predictable currency flows, however. For firms that do not, currency derivatives may be a cheaper way to manage currency risk, since the currency exposure changes from period to period.

PERLS: This is a bond, denominated in the domestic currency, where the principal payment at maturity is based upon the domestic currency equivalent of a fixed foreign currency amount. For instance, this could be a dollar denominated bond with the payment at maturity set equal to the dollar value of 1600 Deutsche Marks. Thus, if the dollar strengthens against the DM during the life of the bond, the principal payment will decrease.

Other Features

As we noted in Chapter 7, several special features have been added to corporate bonds. In this section, we examine how the cash flows on assets may help determine whether any of these special features should be included in new debt issued by a firm.

Business Risk

The most controversial type of risk, in terms of whether and how it should be managed, is *business risk*. Business risk arises from changes in the underlying business that a firm operates in and its exposure to macroeconomic factors; an automobile manufacturing firm, for instance, is exposed to the risk of an economic recession. Some firms have attempted to add special features to their liabilities to reduce their exposure to business risk.

- Insurance companies, for instance, have issued bonds whose payments can be drastically curtailed if there is a catastrophe that requires payouts by the insurance company. By doing so, they reduce their debt payments in those periods when their overall cash flows are most negative, thereby reducing their likelihood of default.

- Companies in commodity businesses have issued bonds whose principal and interest payments are tied to the price of the commodity. Since the operating cash flows in these firms are also positively correlated with commodity prices, adding this feature to debt decreases the likelihood of default, and allows the firm to use more debt. In 1980, for instance, Sunshine Mining issued 15-year silver-linked bond issues, which combined a debt issue with an option on silver prices.

IN PRACTICE: CATASTROPHE BONDS

As an example of a catastrophe bond issue, consider the bond issue made by USAA Insurance Company. The company privately placed $477 million of these bonds, backed up by reinsurance premiums, in June 1997. The company was protected in the event of a hurricane that created more that $1 billion in damage to the East Coast anytime before June 1998. The bonds came in two classes; in the first class, called principal-at-risk, the company could reduce the principal on the bond in the event of a hurricane; in the second class, which was less risky to investors, the coupon payments would be suspended in the event of a hurricane, but the principal would be protected. In return, the investors in these bonds, in October 1997, were earning an extra yield of almost 1.5% on the principal-at-risk bonds and almost 0.5% on the principal-protected bonds.

9.10 SPECIAL FEATURES AND INTEREST RATES

Adding special features to bonds, such as linking coupon payments to commodity prices or catastrophes, will reduce their attractiveness to investors and make the interest rates paid on them higher. It follows then that

☐ companies should not add these special features to bonds.

☐ adding these special features cannot create value for the firm if the bonds are fairly priced.

☐ adding special features can still create value even if the bonds are fairly priced.

Explain.

Growth Characteristics

Firms vary in terms of how much of their value comes from projects or assets already in place and how much comes from future growth. Firms that derive the bulk of their value from future growth use different types of financing and design their financing differently than do those that derive most of their value from assets in place. This is because the current cash flows on "high-growth" firms will be low, relative to the market value. Accordingly, the financing approach used should not create large cash outflows early; it can create substantial cash outflows later, however, reflecting the cash flow patterns of the firm. In addition, the financing should exploit the value that the perception of high growth adds to securities, and it should put relatively few constraints on investment policies.

Straight bonds do not quite fit the bill, because they create large interest payments and do not gain much value from the high-growth perceptions. Furthermore, they are likely to include covenants designed to protect the bondholders, which restrict investment and future financing policy. Convertible bonds, by contrast, create much lower interest payments, impose fewer constraints, and gain value from higher growth perceptions. They might be converted into common stock, but only if the firm is successful.

Convertible Debt: This is debt that can be converted into equity at a rate that is specified as part of the debt.

Zero-coupon Bond: A zero-coupon bond pays no interest during the life of the bond and pays the face value of the bond at maturity. It has a duration equal to its maturity.

Step 2: Examine the Tax Implications of the Financing Mix

A firm's financing choices have tax consequences. It is possible, therefore, that the favorable tax treatment of some financing choices may encourage firms to use them more than others, even if it means deviating from the choices that would be dictated by the asset characteristics. Consider the rationale used by some companies for the use of zero-coupon bonds. Since the IRS allows firms to impute interest payment on the bonds, the firms using the zeros are able to claim a tax deduction for a non-cash expense, decreasing their tax liability in the near periods. While the imputed interest income to the buyers of these bonds may create a tax liability that affects bond prices and rates, that can be avoided by placing these bonds with tax-exempt institutions.

The danger of structuring financing with the intention of saving on taxes is that changes in the tax law can very quickly render the benefit moot and leave the firm with a financing mix that is unsuited to its asset mix.

Step 3: Consider How Ratings Agencies and Equity Research Analysts Will React

Firms are rightfully concerned about the views of equity research analysts and ratings agencies on the actions they take, though they often overestimate the influence of both groups. Analysts represent stockholders, and ratings agencies represent bondholders; consequently they take very different views of the same actions. For instance, analysts may view a stock repurchase by a company with limited project opportunities as a positive action, while ratings agencies may view it as a negative action and lower ratings in response. Analysts and ratings agencies also measure the impact of actions using very different criteria. In general, analysts view a firm's actions through the prism of higher earnings per share and by looking at the firm relative to comparable firms, using multiples such as PE or PBV ratios. Ratings agencies, on the other hand, measure the effect of actions on the financial ratios, such as debt ratios and coverage ratios, which they then use to assess risk and assign ratings.

Given the weight attached to the views of both these groups, firms sometimes design securities with the intent of satisfying both groups. In some cases, they find ways of raising funds that seem to make both groups happy, at least on the surface. To illustrate, consider the use of leasing, before generally accepted accounting principles required capitalizing of leases. Leasing increased the real leverage of the company, and thus, the earnings per share, but it did not affect the measured leverage of the company because it was not viewed as debt. To the degree that analysts and ratings agencies rely on imperfect measures and do not properly factor in the effects of firm actions, firms can exploit their limitations. In a more recent example, insurance companies in the United States have issued *surplus notes*, which are considered debt for tax purposes and equity by insurance regulators, enabling them to have the best of both worlds—they could issue debt, while counting it as equity.[8]

When securities are designed in such a way, the real question is whether the markets are fooled and if so, for how long. A firm that substitutes leases for debt may fool the ratings agency and even the debt markets for some period of time, but it cannot evade the reality that it is much more levered and hence much riskier than it seems.

Finally, ratings agencies and analysts are but two players in a game that involves many more, including stockholders and bondholders themselves, and the firm's managers. Table 9.10 summarizes the different objectives, criteria, and measurement devices used by each. It is extremely unlikely, given the conflicts in interest between some of these groups, that any one financing action will result in unanimous acceptance.

Step 4: Examine the Effects of Asymmetric Information

Firms generally have more information about their future prospects than do financial markets. This *asymmetry in information* creates friction when firms try to raise funds. In particular, firms with good prospects try to distinguish themselves from firms without such prospects by taking actions that are costly and difficult to imitate. Firms also try to reduce the effect of uncertainty in future cash flows by

---

[8]In 1994 and 1995, insurance companies issued a total of $6 billion of surplus notes in the private placement market. Surplus notes are bonds where the interest payments are made only if the firm has a profit (surplus), and are suspended in periods of losses.

Table 9.10   OBJECTIVE FUNCTIONS FOR DIFFERENT GROUPS

	Ratings Agencies	Equity Research Analysts	Existing Bondholders	Managers	Stockholders
Objective	Measure risk of default in company's bond issues (existing and new)	Evaluate whether the stock is a good buy for clients (make recommendations)	Ensure that their loans to the firm (or bonds) are protected	Maximize managerial interests without arousing too much stockholder dissatisfaction	Maximize stock price
Measurement device	Financial ratios measuring • cash flow generating capacity • degree of leverage • risk • profitability	Multiples (PE, PBV) relative to comparable firms * EPS effects * EPS growth	Financial ratios specified in covenants	EPS Effects Earnings growth Earnings stability Remuneration systems	Discounted cash flow valuation Multiples
Questions raised in analysis	How will this action affect the company's ability to meet its debt payments?	How will this action affect the company's multiples and its standing relative to comparables?	How will this action affect the security and safety of the company's existing debt?	How will this action affect • flexibility? • remuneration? • relationships with large stockholders?	How will this action affect the stock price?
What makes them happy?	1. High coverage ratios 2. Low leverage ratios 3. High profitability ratios	1. Low multiples relative to comparable firms 2. Increases in EPS 3. Increases in growth	1. Protection of cash flows and ratings on existing debt (or) 2. Capacity to cash out without loss	1. High flexibility 2. More stability 3. Increase in EPS and growth 4. Higher stock price	1. Higher stock prices

designing their securities to minimize this effect. Firms may therefore issue securities that may not be optimal from the standpoint of matching up to their asset cash flows but are specifically designed to convey information to financial markets.

A number of researchers have used this information asymmetry argument to draw very different conclusions about the debt structure firms should use. Myers (1977) argued that firms tend to underinvest as a consequence of the asymmetry of information. One proposed solution to the problem is to issue short-term debt, even if the assets being financed are long-term assets. Flannery (1986) and Kale and Noe (1990) note that while both short- and long-term debt will be mispriced in the presence of asymmetric information, long-term debt will be mispriced more. Consequently, they argue that high-quality firms will issue short-term debt, while low-quality firms will issue long-term debt.

Goswami, Noe, and Rebello (1995) analyze the design of securities and relate it to uncertainty about future cash flows. They conclude that if the asymmetry of information concerns uncertainty about long-term cash flows, firms should issue coupon-bearing long-term debt, with restrictions on dividends. In contrast, firms with uncertainty about near-term cash flows and significant refinancing risk should issue long-term debt, without restrictions on dividend payments. When uncertainty about information is uniformly distributed across time, firms should finance with short-term debt.

Information Asymmetry: Information asymmetry arises any time one party to a transaction or agreement has more or better information than the other. Thus, managers may know more about their firms than their stockholders, and stockholders may know more than do bondholders.

Step 5: Consider the Implications of Financing Mix for Agency Costs

The final consideration in designing securities is the provision of features intended to reduce agency conflicts between stockholders and bondholders. As we noted in Chapter 7, differences between bondholders and stockholders on investment, financing, and dividend policy decisions can have an impact on the capital structure either by increasing the costs of borrowing or by increasing the constraints associated with borrowing. In some cases, firms design securities with the specific intent of reducing this conflict and its associated costs:

- We argued earlier that convertible bonds are a good choice for growth companies because of their cash flow characteristics. It can also be argued that convertible bonds reduce the anxiety of bondholders about equity investors taking on riskier projects and expropriating wealth, by allowing them to become stockholders if the stock price increases enough.

- More corporate bonds today include put options that allow bondholders to put the bonds back at face value if the firm takes a specified action (such as increasing leverage) or if its rating drops. In a variation, in 1988, Manufacturers Hanover issued floating rate, rating-sensitive notes promising bondholders higher coupons if the firm's rating deteriorated over time.

- Merrill Lynch introduced LYONs (Liquid Yield Option Notes), which incorporated put and conversion features to protect against both the risk shifting and claim substitution to which bondholders are exposed.

LYONS: Liquid yield option notes are notes whose holders have the right either to put them back to the firm under specified circumstances or to convert them into equity.

In Summary

In deciding on the optimal financing mix, firms should begin by examining the characteristics of the assets that they own (Are they long term or short term? How sensitive are they to economic conditions and inflation? What currencies are the cash flows in?) and trying to match up the maturity, interest rate and currency mix, and special features of their financing to these characteristics. They can then superimpose tax considerations, the views of analysts and ratings agencies, agency costs, and the effects of asymmetric information to modify this financing mix. Figure 9.5 summarizes the discussion on the preceding pages.

ILLUSTRATION 9.5 **Coming Up with the Financing Details: Disney**

In the following extended illustration, we come up with the financing details for Disney, using two approaches. First, we use a subjective analysis of Disney's project characteristics to define the appropriate debt mix for the company. Then we use a more quantitative approach for analyzing project characteristics, and use it to come up with the financing details for the firm. Both approaches should be considered in light of the analysis done in the previous chapter, which suggested that Disney had untapped debt potential that could be used for future projects.

Intuitive Approach

In the intuitive approach, we begin with an analysis of the characteristics of a typical project taken on by Disney and use it to make recommendations for Disney's new financing. Given the significant differences between Disney's different business lines, our recommendations would vary by business:

Business	Project Cash Flow Characteristics	Type of Financing
Creative content	Projects are likely to 1. Be short term 2. Have cash outflows primarily in dollars (since Disney makes most of its movies and TV programs in the United States) but cash inflows could have a substantial foreign currency component (because of overseas revenues)	Debt should be 1. Short term 2. Primarily U.S. dollar 3. If possible, tied to the success of movies (*Lion King* Bonds?)

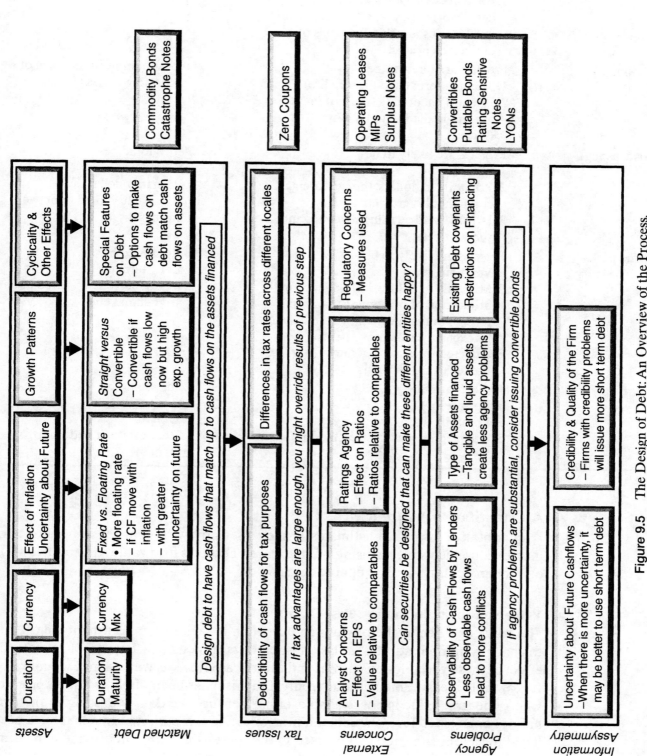

Figure 9.5   The Design of Debt: An Overview of the Process.

591

Business	Project Cash Flow Characteristics	Type of Financing
	3. Have net cash flows which are heavily driven by whether the movie or TV series is a "hit," which is often difficult to predict.	
Retailing	Projects are likely to be 1. Medium term (tied to store life) 2. Primarily in dollars (most of the stores are still in the United States) 3. Cyclical	Debt should be in the form of operating leases.
Broadcasting	Projects are likely to be 1. Short term 2. Primarily in dollars, though foreign component is growing 3. Driven by advertising revenues and show success	Debt should be 1. Short term 2. Primarily dollar debt 3. If possible, linked to network ratings
Theme parks	Projects are likely to be 1. Very long term 2. Primarily in dollars, but a significant proportion of revenues come from foreign tourists, who may be impacted by exchange rate movements 3. Affected by success of movie and broadcasting divisions	Debt should be 1. Long term 2. Mix of currencies, based upon tourist makeup
Real Estate	Projects are likely to be 1. Long term 2. Primarily in dollars 3. Affected by real estate values in the area	Debt should be 1. Long term 2. Dollars 3. Real-estate linked (mortgage bonds)

■▲▼● A Quantitative Approach

A quantitative approach estimates Disney's sensitivity to changes in a number of macroeconomic variables, using two measures: Disney's firm value (the market value of debt and equity) and its operating income.

Value Sensitivity to Factors: Past Data

The value of a firm is the obvious choice when it comes to measuring its sensitivity to changes in interest rates, inflation rates, or currency rates, because it reflects the effect of these variables on current and future cash flows as well as on discount rates. It is a viable measurement, though, only if the firm has been publicly traded. In cases where the firm value is not available, either because the data is missing or the firm has not been listed long enough, the firm values of comparable firms that have been listed for a longer period can be used in the regression. This will provide a measure of the industry characteristics.

We begin by collecting past data on firm value, operating income, and the macroeconomic variables against which we want to measure its sensitivity. In the case of Disney, we chose four broad measures (see Table 9.11):

- *Long-term Treasury bond rate,* since the sensitivity of firm value to changes in interest rates provides a measure of the duration of the projects. It also provides insight into whether the firm should be using fixed or floating rate debt; a firm whose operating income moves with interest rates should consider using floating rate loans.

- *Real GNP,* since the sensitivity of firm value to this variable provides a measure of the cyclicality of the firm.

- *Currency rate,* since the sensitivity of firm value to the currency rate provides a measure of the exposure to currency rate risk, and thus helps determine what the currency mix for the debt should be.

- *Inflation rate,* since the sensitivity of firm value to the inflation rate helps determine whether the interest rate on the debt should be fixed or floating rate debt.

This is not intended to be an all-encompassing analysis. An extended analysis might include other variables, such as industry-specific variables that may affect firm value and operating income.

Once this data has been collected, we can then estimate the sensitivity of firm values to changes in the macroeconomic variables by regressing changes in firm value each year against changes in each of the individual variables.

Sensitivity to Changes in Interest Rates

As we discussed earlier, the duration of a firm's projects provides useful information for determining the maturity of its debt. While bond-based duration measures may provide some answers, they will understate the duration of assets/projects if the cash flows on these assets/projects themselves vary with interest rates. Regressing changes in firm value against changes in interest rates over this period yields the following result (T statistics in brackets):

$$\text{Change in Firm Value} = 0.22 \quad - 7.43 \, (\text{Change in Interest Rates})$$
$$(3.09) \qquad (1.69)$$

Based upon this regression, the duration of Disney's assets collectively is about 7.43 years. In designing its debt, Disney should try to keep the duration of its debt to about 7.43 years.

9.11   REGRESSION R-SQUARED

The R-squared of the regression shown above is only 10%. This would suggest that

☐   this regression is not very useful, since good regressions have high R-squared values.

☐   this regression is useful only if it backs up your intuition.

☐   the coefficient on the regression is a noisy estimate, and you should look at longer periods or sector averages.

Explain.

Table 9.11	DISNEY'S FIRM VALUE AND MACROECONOMIC VARIABLES					
Year	Firm Value	Operating Income	Long Bond Rate	Real GNP	Weighted Dollar	Inflation Rate
1981	$1,707	$119.35	13.98%	3854	115.65	8.90%
1982	$2,108	$141.39	10.47%	3792	123.14	3.80%
1983	$1,817	$133.87	11.80%	4047	128.65	3.80%
1984	$2,024	$142.60	11.51%	4216	138.89	4.00%
1985	$3,655	$205.60	8.99%	4350	125.95	3.80%
1986	$5,631	$280.58	7.22%	4431	112.89	1.20%
1987	$8,371	$707.00	8.86%	4633	95.88	4.40%
1988	$9,195	$789.00	9.14%	4789	95.32	4.40%
1989	$16,015	$1,109.00	7.93%	4875	102.26	4.60%
1990	$14,963	$1,287.00	8.07%	4895	96.25	6.10%
1991	$17,122	$1,004.00	6.70%	4894	98.82	3.10%
1992	$24,771	$1,287.00	6.69%	5061	104.58	2.90%
1993	$25,212	$1,560.00	5.79%	5219	105.22	2.70%
1994	$26,506	$1,804.00	7.82%	5416	98.6	2.70%
1995	$33,858	$2,262.00	5.57%	5503	95.1	2.50%
1996	$39,561	$3,024.00	6.42%	5679	101.5	3.30%

(We have not considered the operating income from the Capital Cities acquisition.)

Sensitivity to Changes in the Economy

Is Disney a cyclical firm? One way of answering this question is to measure the sensitivity of firm value to changes in economic growth. Regressing changes in firm value against changes in the GNP over this period yields the following result (T statistics in brackets):

$$\text{Change in Firm Value} = 0.31 \quad - 1.71 \text{ (GNP Growth)}$$
$$(2.43) \quad (0.45)$$

Disney is only mildly sensitive to cyclical movements in the economy (The T statistic is not statistically significant). This may be because it derives so much of its revenues from overseas visitors to its theme parks, and from its strong brand name, and because of its dependency on big movie hits for financial success.

Sensitivity to Changes in the Inflation Rates

We earlier made the argument, based upon asset/liability matching, that firms whose firm value tends to move with inflation should be more likely to issue floating rate debt. To examine whether Disney fits this bill, we regressed changes in firm value against changes in the inflation rate over this period with the following result:

$$\text{Change in Firm Value} = 0.26 \quad -0.22 \text{ (Change in Inflation Rate)}$$
$$(3.36) \quad (0.05)$$

Disney's firm value is unaffected by changes in the inflation rate. Other things held equal, we would argue that Disney should be using fixed rate debt rather than floating rate debt. Since interest payments have to be made out of operating cash flows, we will also have to look at how operating income moves with inflation before we can pass final judgment on this issue.

Sensitivity to Changes in the Dollar

The question of how sensitive Disney's value is to currency rates can be answered by looking at how the firm value changes as a function of changes in currency rates. Regressing changes in firm value against changes in the weighted dollar over this period yields the following regression (T statistics in brackets):

$$\text{Change in Firm Value} = 0.26 \quad -1.01 \text{ (Change in Weighted Dollar)}$$
$$(3.46) \quad (0.98)$$

Disney's value has not been very sensitive to changes in the dollar over the last fifteen years. If this pattern continues, its debt should be primarily dollar debt. If it had been very sensitive to exchange rate changes, Disney might have considered issuing some debt denominated in other currencies to insulate itself against some of the currency risk.

Cash Flow Sensitivity to Factors: Past Data

In some cases, it is more reasonable to estimate the sensitivity of operating cash flows directly against changes in interest rates, inflation, and other variables. This is particularly the case when designing interest payments on debt, which have to be made out of operating cash flows. For instance, while the regression of firm value on inflation rates showed no relationship and led to the conclusion that Disney should not issue floating rate debt, this conclusion might be overridden if operating income turns out to be correlated with inflation rates. For Disney, we repeated the analysis using operating income as the dependent variable, rather than firm value. Since the procedure for the analysis is similar, we summarize the conclusions below (T statistics are in brackets):

- Regressing changes in operating cash flow against changes in interest rates over this period yields the following result:

$$\text{Change in Operating Income} = 0.31 - 4.99 \text{ (Change in Interest Rates)}$$
$$(2.90) \quad (0.78)$$

Disney's operating income, like its firm value, has been very sensitive to interest rates, which confirms our conclusion to use long-term debt. It yields a lower estimate of duration than the firm value measure, for two reasons—income tends to be smoothed out relative to value, and current operating income does not reflect the effects of changes in interest rates on discount rates.

- Regressing changes in operating cash flow against changes in GNP over this period yields the following regression:

$$\text{Change in Operating Income} = 0.17 + \textbf{4.06}\,(\text{GNP Growth})$$
$$(1.04)\ (0.80)$$

Disney's operating income is more sensitive to economic cycles than is the firm value, but the relationship is not statistically significant.

- Regressing changes in operating cash flow against changes in the dollar over this period yields the following regression:

$$\text{Change in Operating Income} = 0.26 - \textbf{3.03}\,(\text{Change in Dollar})$$
$$(3.14)\ (2.59)$$

Disney's operating income is much more sensitive to changes in the dollar than is Disney's firm value. In particular, a stronger dollar seems to hurt Disney's operating income, which we would attribute to its effect on tourist revenues at the theme parks.

- Regressing changes in operating cash flow against changes in inflation over this period yields the following result:

$$\text{Change in Operating Income} = 0.32 + 10.51\,(\text{Change in Inflation Rate})$$
$$(3.61)\ (2.27)$$

This is the regression where there is the biggest difference between firm value and operating income. The operating income, unlike the firm value, tends to move with inflation. Since interest payments have to be made from operating income, this would argue for the use of floating rate debt.

The question of what to do when operating income and firm value give different results can be resolved fairly simply. For issues relating to the overall design of the debt, the firm value regression should be relied on more; for issues relating to the design of interest payments on the debt, the operating income regression should be used more. Thus, for the duration measure, the regression of firm value on interest rates should, in general, give a more precise estimate. For the inflation rate sensitivity, since it affects the choice of interest payments (fixed or floating), the operating income regression should be relied on more.

Overall Recommendations

Based upon the analyses of firm value and operating income, our recommendations would essentially match those we would have given using the intuitive approach, but they would have more depth to them because of the additional information we have acquired from the quantitative analysis:

- The debt issued should be long term and should have duration of approximately 7.43 years.
- The debt should be a mix of floating rate and fixed rate debt, since operating income tends to move with inflation.

- The debt should be a mix of currencies; the exact choice of currencies will depend upon the makeup of tourist revenues at the theme parks, and Disney's overall business mix.

While this type of analysis yields useful results, those results should be taken with a grain of salt. They make sense only if the firm has been in its current business for a long time and expects to remain in it for the foreseeable future. In today's environment, in which firms find their business mixes changing dramatically from period to period as they reorganize, acquire, divest, or restructure, it may be dangerous to base too many conclusions on a historical analysis. In such cases, it might make more sense to look at the characteristics of the industry in which a firm plans to expand, rather than using past earnings or firm value as a basis for the analysis.

 There is a dataset on the Web that summarizes the results of regressing firm value against macroeconomic variables, by sector, for U.S. companies (**macro.xls**).

 ILLUSTRATION 9.5   Estimating the Right Financing Mix for Bookscape, Aracruz, and Deutsche Bank

While we will not examine the right financing type for Bookscape, Aracruz, and Deutsche Bank in the same level of detail as we did for Disney, we will summarize, based upon our understanding of their businesses, what we think will be the best kind of financing for each of these firms:

- *Bookscape:* Given Bookscape's dependency on revenues at its New York bookstores, we would design the debt to be
  - Fairly long term, since it is a long-term investment
  - Dollar-denominated, since all the cash flows are in dollars
  - Fixed rate debt, since Bookscape's lack of pricing power makes it unlikely that it can keep pace with inflation

  It is worth noting that operating leases fulfill all of these conditions, making them the right debt for Bookscape.
- *Aracruz:* Aracruz operates most of its paper plants in Brazil, but sells a significant proportion of its products overseas. More than eighty percent of its revenues in 1995 and 1996 were from outside Brazil, and the bulk of these revenues were dollar-denominated. Given this structure, we would design debt to be
  - Long term, since a typical paper plant has a life in excess of twenty years
  - Predominantly dollar-denominated, since the cash inflows are primarily in dollars
  - Floating rate debt, since paper and pulp prices are likely to reflect inflation

  The last recommendation is shaky partly because the overall inflation rate and paper/pulp inflation rates may not move together. It would be better if we could modify the debt to link coupon payments to the price of paper and pulp (similar to the silver-and gold-linked bonds described earlier).

- *Deutsche Bank:* In the case of Deutsche Bank, the recommendation is made simpler by the fact that the debt ratio we are analyzing is the long-term debt ratio. In addition to being long term, however, the debt should reflect
  - The mix of currencies in which Deutsche Bank gets its cash flows, which should lead to significant dollar (from its U.S. holdings) and British Pound (from its Morgan Grenfell subsidiary) debt issues. In future years, this would expand to include more emerging market debt issues to reflect Deutsche Bank's greater dependency on cash flows from these markets.
  - The changing mix of Deutsche Bank's business to reflect its increasing role in investment banking.

It is possible that Deutsche Bank's reputation in Europe may allow it to borrow more cheaply in some markets (say, Germany) than in others. If that is the case, it can either issue its dollar-denominated or pound-denominated debt in those markets, or issue debt in the currency of those markets (say, DM) and then swap the debt into dollar or pound debt.

IN PRACTICE: FIRM REPUTATION, INTEREST RATES AND THE ROLE OF SWAPS

Firms should try to match the currencies in which they raise financing to the currencies of their projects' cash flows. Generally, firms should raise financing in each country to fund projects in that country. In some cases, however, firms may have a much better reputation among investors in one country (usually, the domestic market in which they operate) than in other markets. In such cases, firms may choose to raise their funds domestically, even for foreign projects, because they get better terms on their financing. This creates a mismatch between cash inflows and outflows, which can be resolved using currency swaps, where a firm's liabilities in one currency can be swapped for liabilities in another currency. This may enable the firm to take advantage of its reputation effect and match cash flows at the same time.

Generally speaking, swaps can be used to take advantage of any "market" imperfections that a firm might observe. Thus, if floating rate debt is attractively priced relative to fixed rate debt, a firm which does not need floating rate debt can issue floating rate debt, and then swap it for fixed rate debt at a later date.

CONCLUSION

In this chapter, we have completed our analysis of capital structure by looking at the ways in which firms can go from identifying their optimal debt ratios to actually devising the right financial mix for themselves. In particular, we noted that:

- Some firms have to change their leverage quickly to respond to external pressure brought on by the likelihood of an acquisition (if a firm is underlevered) or the chance of bankruptcy (if a firm is overlevered). Those firms that want to increase leverage quickly can do so by borrowing money and repurchasing stock, conducting debt-for-equity swaps, or selling assets and paying large special dividends. Those firms that want to decrease leverage quickly can do so by renegotiating their debt agreements to have more of an equity component or by selling assets and paying off debt.

- Some firms have the luxury of moving to their desired leverage gradually over time. They have to decide whether to take on new projects with the financing or to change the financing mix on their existing projects. That decision should be based upon the quality of projects; firms with good projects should finance them with new debt, if they want to increase leverage, or with new equity, if they want to decrease leverage.

- Once firms have decided on new financing, they still have to decide on the maturity, interest rate structure, currency, and special features for their financing. In making these decisions, they should first look at the cash flow characteristics of the assets that will be funded by the new financing and use other factors (such as taxes, the views of analysts and ratings agencies, agency conflicts, and information factors) to modify the financing to meet their specific objectives.

PROBLEMS AND QUESTIONS

1. BMD Inc. is a firm with no debt on its books currently and a market value of equity of $2 billion. Based upon its EBITDA of $200 million, it can afford to have a debt ratio of 50%, at which level the firm value should be $300 million higher.

   a. Assuming that the firm plans to increase its leverage instantaneously, what are some of the approaches it could use to get to 50%?

   b. Is there a difference between repurchasing stock and paying a special dividend? Why or why not?

   c. If BMD has a cash balance of $250 million at this time, will it change any of your analysis?

2. MiniSink Inc. is a manufacturing company that has $100 million in debt outstanding and 9 million shares trading at $100 per share. The current beta is 1.10, and the interest rate on the debt is 8%. In the latest year, MiniSink reported a net income of $7.50 per share, and analysts expect earnings growth to be 10% a year for the next five years. The firm faces a tax rate of 40% and pays out 20% of its earnings as dividends (the Treasury bond rate is 7%).

   a. Estimate the debt ratio each year for the next five years, assuming that the firm maintains its current payout ratio.

   b. Estimate the debt ratio each year for the next five years, assuming that the firm doubles its dividends and repurchases 5% of the outstanding stock every year.

3. IOU Inc. has $5 billion in debt outstanding (carrying an interest rate of 9%), and 10 million shares trading at $50 per share. Based upon its current EBIT of $500 million, its optimal debt ratio is only 30%. The firm has a beta of 1.20, the tax rate is 40%, and the current Treasury bond rate is 7%. Assuming that the operating income will increase 10% a year for the next five years and that the firm's depreciation and capital expenditures both amount to $100 million

annually for each of the five years, estimate the debt ratio for IOU if

a. It maintains its existing policy of paying $50 million a year in dividends for the next five years.

b. It eliminates dividends.

4. DGF Corporation has come to you for some advice on how best to increase its leverage over time. In the most recent year, DGF had EBIT of $300 million, owed $1 billion in both book value and market value terms, and had a net worth of $2 billion. (The market value was twice the book value). It had a beta of 1.30, and the interest rate on its debt is 8% (the Treasury bond rate is 7%). If it moves to its optimal debt ratio of 40%, the cost of capital is expected to drop by 1%. The tax rate is 40%.

a. How should the firm move to its optimal? In particular, should it borrow money and take on projects, or should it pay dividends/repurchase stock?

b. Are there any other considerations that may affect your decision?

5. STL Inc. has asked you for advice on putting together the details of the new debt issues it is planning to make. What information would you need to obtain to provide this advice?

6. Assume now that you have uncovered the following facts about the types of projects STL takes:

a. The projects are primarily infrastructure projects, requiring large initial investments and long gestation periods.

b. Most of the new projects will be in emerging markets, and the cash flows are expected to be in the local currencies, when they do occur.

c. The magnitude of the cash flows will, in large part, depend upon how quickly the economies of the emerging markets grow in the long term.

How would you use this information in the design of the debt?

7. You are attempting to structure a debt issue for Eaton Corporation, a manufacturer of automotive components. You have collected the following information on the market values of debt and equity for the last 10 years:

Year	Market Value of Equity	Debt
1985	1,824.9	436
1986	2,260.6	632
1987	2,389.6	795
1988	1,960.8	655
1989	2,226	836
1990	1,875.9	755
1991	2,009.7	795
1992	2,589.3	833
1993	3,210	649
1994	3,962.7	1053

In addition, you have the following information on the changes in long-term interest rates, inflation rates, GNP, and exchange rates over the same period.

Year	Long Bond Rate (%)	GNP Growth (%)	Weighted Dollar	Inflation Rate (%)
1985	11.40	6.44	125.95	3.50
1986	9.00	5.40	112.89	1.90
1987	9.40	6.90	95.88	3.70
1988	9.70	7.89	95.32	4.10
1989	9.30	7.23	102.26	4.80
1990	9.30	5.35	96.25	5.40
1991	8.80	2.88	98.82	4.20
1992	8.10	6.22	104.58	3.00
1993	7.20	5.34	105.22	3.00
1994	8.00	5.97	98.6	2.60

a. Estimate the duration of this firm's projects. How would you use this information in designing the debt issue?

b. How cyclical is this company? How would that affect your debt issue?

c. Estimate the sensitivity of firm value to exchange rates. How would you use this information in designing the debt issue?

d. How sensitive is firm value to inflation rates? How would you use this information in designing the debt issue?

e. What factors might lead you to override the results of this analysis?

8. Repeat the analysis in Problem 7 for a private firm that has provided you with the following estimates of operating income for the 10 years for which you have the macroeconomic data:

Year	Operating Income
1985	463.05
1986	411.696
1987	483.252
1988	544.633
1989	550.65
1990	454.875
1991	341.481
1992	413.983
1993	567.729
1994	810.968

9. Assuming that you do the regression analysis with both firm value and operating income, what are the reasons for the differences you might find in the results, using each? When would you use one over the other?

10. Pfizer, a major pharmaceutical company, has a debt ratio of 10.30% and is considering increasing its debt ratio to 30%. Its cost of capital is expected to drop from 14.51% to 13.45%. Pfizer had earnings before interest and taxes of $2 billion in 1995 and a book value of capital (debt + equity) of approximately $8 billion. It also faced a tax rate of 40% on its income. The stock in the firm is widely held, but the corporate charter includes significant anti-takeover restrictions.
   a. Should Pfizer move to its desired debt ratio quickly or gradually? Explain.
   b. Given the choice in part (a), explain how you would move to the optimal.
   c. Pfizer is considering using the excess debt capacity for an acquisition. What are some of the concerns it should have?

11. Upjohn, another major pharmaceutical company, is considering increasing its debt ratio from 11% to 40%, which is its optimal debt ratio. Its beta is 1.17, and the current Treasury bond rate is 6.50%. The return on equity was 14.5% in the most recent year, but it is dropping, as health care matures as a business. The company has also been mentioned as a possible takeover target and is widely held.
   a. Would you suggest that Upjohn move to the optimal ratio immediately? Explain.
   b. How would you recommend that Upjohn increase its debt ratio?

12. U.S. steel companies have generally been considered mature, in terms of growth, and often take on high leverage to finance their plant and equipment. Steel companies in some emerging markets often have high risk and good growth prospects. Would you expect these companies also to have high leverage? Why or why not?

13. You are trying to decide whether the debt structure that Bethlehem Steel has currently is appropriate, given its assets. You regress changes in firm value against changes in interest rates and arrive at the following equation:

$$\text{Change in Firm Value} = 0.20\% - 6.33$$
$$\text{(Change in Interest Rates)}$$

   a. If Bethlehem Steel has primarily short-term debt outstanding, with a maturity of one year, would you deem it appropriate?
   b. Why might Bethlehem Steel be inclined to use short-term debt to finance longer term assets?

14. Railroad companies in the United States tend to have long-term, fixed rate, dollar-denominated debt. Explain why.

15. The following table summarizes the results of regressing changes in firm value against changes in interest rates for six major footwear companies:

$$\text{Change in Firm Value} = a + b$$
$$\text{(Change in Long Term Interest Rates)}$$

Company	Intercept (a)	Slope Coefficient (b)
LA Gear	−0.07	−4.74
Nike	0.05	−11.03
Stride Rite	0.01	−8.08
Timberland	0.06	−22.50
Reebok	0.04	−4.79
Wolverine	0.06	−2.42

   a. How would you use these results to design debt for each of these companies?
   b. How would you explain the wide variation across companies? Would you use the average across the companies in any way?

16. You have run a series of regressions of firm value changes at Motorola, the semiconductor company, against changes in a number of macroeconomic variables. The results are as follows:

Change in Firm Value = 0.05 − 3.87
(Change in Long-Term Interest Rate)
Change in Firm Value = 0.02 + 5.76
(Change in Real GNP)
Change in Firm Value = 0.04 − 2.59
(Inflation Rate)
Change in Firm Value = 0.05 − 3.40 ($/DM)
(Assume that all coefficients are statistically significant.)

a. Based on these regressions, how would you design Motorola's financing?

b. Motorola, like all semiconductor companies, is sensitive to the health of the high-technology sector. Is there any special feature you can add to the debt to reflect this dependence?

17. Assume that you are designing the debt that will be issued by Compaq Computer. Knowing what you do about the business—it is high-growth, high-risk and extremely volatile—what type of debt would you suggest that Compaq use? Why?

18. Heavily regulated companies in the United States, such as power and phone utilities, are governed by regulatory agencies that grant them rate increases based upon inflation. They are also restricted in terms of investment policy and cannot diversify into other businesses. What type of debt would you expect these firms to issue? Why?

19. ACM Inc. is a mining company that holds large stakes in copper, zinc, and magnesium mines around the world. Historically, its revenues and earnings have gone up in periods of high inflation and down during periods of deflation or low inflation. What type of debt would you recommend for ACM Inc.? What special features would you consider adding to this debt?

20. In this chapter, we have argued that firms with substantial cash flows in foreign currencies should consider using debt denominated in those currencies. Can you think of good reasons for such firms to continue to issue debt denominated in the local currency and in local markets?

21. A CFO of a small manufacturing firm with long-term assets argues that it is better to use short-term debt because it is cheaper than long-term debt. This in turn, he notes, reduces the cost of capital. Do you agree? Why or why not?

22. GF Technology Inc. is in the business of manufacturing disk drives for computers. While the underlying business is risky, the managers of GF Technology believe that their cash flows are much more stable than perceived by the market, largely because of several long-term contracts that the firm has with major computer manufacturers. They are considering the use of convertible bonds to raise funds for the firms. Would you concur? Why or why not?

23. VisiGen Inc. is a biotechnology firm involved in gene therapy. It is trying to raise funds to finance its research and is weighing the pluses and minuses of issuing stock versus warrants. What would your advice be?

VII. MECHANICS OF MOVING TO THE OPTIMAL

Objective: To develop a plan to get from the firm's current leverage to its optimal, and to examine the "right type" of financing for the firm.

Key Questions

- If your firm's actual debt ratio is different from its "recommended" debt ratio, how should they get from the actual to the optimal? In particular,
  a) should they do it gradually over time or should they do it right now?
  b) should they alter their existing mix (by buying back stock or retiring debt) or should they take new projects with debt or equity?
- What type of financing should this firm use? In particular,
  c) should it be short term or long term?
  d) what currency should it be in?
  e) what special features should the financing have?

Framework for Analysis

1. The Immediacy Question
- If the firm is under levered, does it have the characteristics of a firm that is a likely takeover target? (Target firms in hostile takeovers tend to be smaller, have poorer project and stock price performance than their peer groups and have lower insider holdings.)
- If the firm is over levered, is it in danger of bankruptcy? (Look at the bond rating, if the company is rated. A junk bond rating suggests high bankruptcy risk.)

2. Alter Financing Mix or Take Projects
- What kind of projects does this firm expect to have? Can it expect to make excess returns on these projects? (Past project returns is a reasonable place to start—see the section under investment returns.)
- What type of stockholders does this firm have? If cash had to be returned to them, would they prefer dividends or stock buybacks? (Again, look at the past. If the company has paid high dividends historically, it will end up with investors who like dividends.)

3. Financing Type
- How sensitive has this firm's value been to changes in macroeconomic variables such as interest rates, currency movements, inflation and the economy?
- How sensitive has this firm's operating income been to changes in the same variables?

- How sensitive is the sector's value and operating income to the same variables?
- Intuitively, what is a typical project for this firm and what financing will best fit this project?

Getting Information on Mechanics of Capital Structure

To get the inputs needed to estimate the capital structure mechanics, you can get the information on macroeconomic variables such as interest rates, inflation, GNP growth and exchange rates from my web site (**macro.xls**). You can get historical information on your own firm by looking at the Value Line page for your firm, which has information for the last 15 years on revenues and operating income.

You can get information on sector sensitivity to macroeconomic variables in the data set on my web site (**indfin.xls**).

CHAPTER 10

THE DETERMINANTS OF DIVIDEND POLICY

As a firm starts receiving cash flows from its current operations it is faced with a decision. Should it reinvest the cash back into the business, or should it pay it out to equity investors? The decision may seem simple enough, but it evokes a surprising amount of controversy. In this chapter, we look at three very different schools of thought on dividend policy. The first argues that dividends do not really matter, since they do not affect value. The second vehemently argues that dividends are bad for the average stockholder, because of the tax disadvantage they create, which results in lower value. The third argues that dividends are clearly good because stockholders like them. We will probe a series of questions to provide a groundwork for analyzing dividend policy:

- What are the ways in which a firm can return cash to its stockholders?

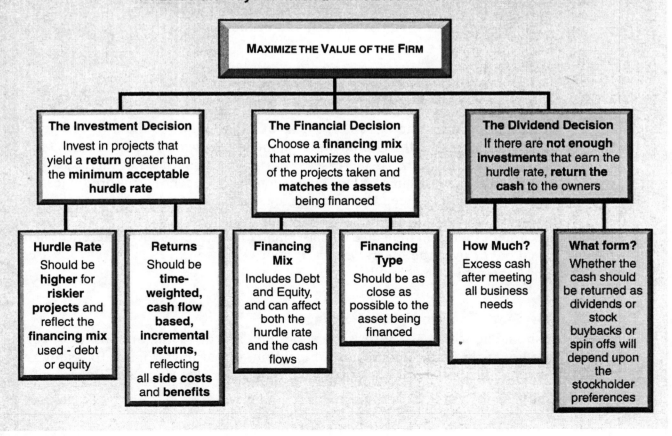

- What are some of the historical patterns that emerge from an examination of dividend policy over time (for U.S. firms)? How different is dividend policy across countries?

- What is the basis for the argument that dividend policy is irrelevant and does not affect value?

- What are the basis and evidence for the argument that dividends create a tax disadvantage?

- What is behind the notion that some stockholders like dividends?

- What do firms actually look at when they set dividend policy?

- What are the alternatives to paying dividends, and how should firms pick among these alternatives?

WAYS OF RETURNING CASH TO STOCKHOLDERS

While dividends have traditionally been considered the primary approach for publicly traded firms to return cash or assets to their stockholders, they comprise only one of many ways available to the firm to accomplish this objective. In particular, firms can return cash to stockholders through *equity repurchases,* where the cash is used to buy back outstanding stock in the firm and reduces the number of shares outstanding, or through *forward contracts,* where the firm commits to buying back its own stock in future periods at a fixed price. In addition, firms can return some of their assets to their stockholders in the form of spinoffs and splitoffs.

THE HISTORICAL EVIDENCE ON DIVIDENDS

Several interesting findings emerge from an examination of the dividend policies practiced by firms in the United States in the last 50 years. First, dividends tend to lag behind earnings; that is, increases in earnings are followed by increases in dividends, and decreases in earnings by dividend cuts. Second, firms are typically reluctant to change dividends; this hesitancy is magnified when it comes to cutting dividends, making for "sticky" dividend policies. Third, dividends tend to follow a much smoother path than do earnings. Finally, there are distinct differences in dividend policy over the life cycle of a firm, driven by changes in growth rates, cash flows, and project availability.

Dividends Tend to Follow Earnings

It should not come as a surprise that earnings and dividends are positively correlated over time, since dividends are paid out of earnings. Figure 10.1 shows the movement in both earnings and dividends between 1960 and 1996. Two trends are

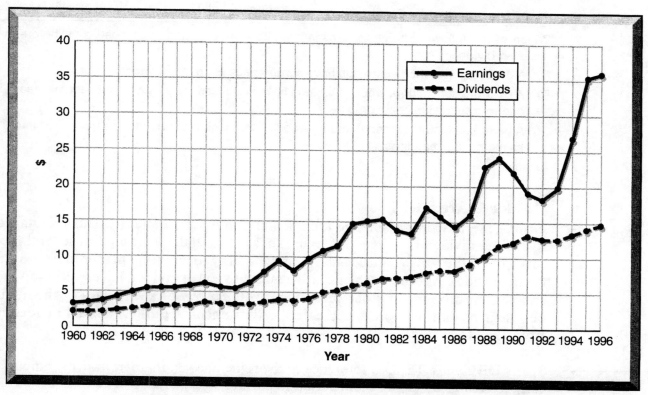

Figure 10.1 Aggregate earnings and dividends: S & P 500—1960–96.

visible in this graph. First, dividend changes tend to lag behind earnings changes over time. Second, the dividend series is much smoother than is the earnings series.

In 1956, John Lintner conducted an extensive analysis of how firms set dividends and concluded that firms have three important concerns. First, they set *target dividend payout ratios,* whereby they decide on the fraction of earnings they are willing to pay out as dividends in the long term. Second, they change dividends to match long-term and sustainable shifts in earnings, but they increase dividends only if they feel they can maintain these higher dividends. As a consequence of this concern over having to cut dividends, dividends lag earnings and have a much smoother path. Finally, managers are much more concerned about changes in dividends, rather than levels of dividends. Fama and Babiak (1968) noted the lagged effect that earnings have on dividends, by regressing changes in dividends against changes in earnings in both current and prior periods. They confirmed Lintner's findings that dividend changes tend to follow earnings changes.

Target Dividend Payout Ratio: This is the desired proportion of earnings that a firm wants to pay out in dividends.

10.1 DETERMINANTS OF DIVIDEND LAG

Which of the following types of firms is likely to wait *least* after earnings go up before increasing dividends?

☐ A cyclical firm, whose earnings have surged because of an economic boom

☐ A pharmaceutical firm, whose earnings have increased steadily over the last five years, due to a successful new drug

☐ A personal computer manufacturer, whose latest laptop's success has translated into an increase in earnings

Explain.

Dividends Are Sticky

Firms generally do not change their dollar dividends frequently. This reluctance to change dividends, which results in "sticky dividends," is rooted in several factors. One is the firm's concern about its capability to maintain higher dividends in future periods. Another is the negative market view of dividend decreases and the consequent drop in the stock price. Figure 10.2 provides a summary of the number of firms that increased, decreased, or left unchanged their annual dividends from 1981 to 1990.

Sticky Dividends This is a reference to the reluctance on the part of firms, empirically, to change dividends from period to period.

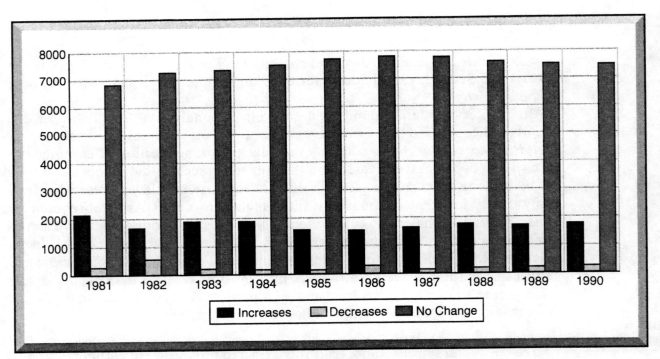

Figure 10.2 Dividend changes: Publicly owned firm—1981–90.

As you can see, in most years, the number of firms that do not change their dollar dividends far exceeds the number that do. Among the firms that change dividends, five times as many, on average, increase dividends as decrease them.

When the earnings of cyclical firms dip during recessions, you would expect to see
☐   dividends to be cut to reflect the drop in earnings.
☐   dividends to be increased to compensate for the drop in earnings.
☐   dividends to remain unchanged.
☐   dividends to be cut only if earnings drop more than expected.

Dividends Follow a Smoother Path Than Earnings

As a result of the reluctance of firms to raise dividends until they feel able to maintain them, and to cut dividends unless they absolutely have to, dividends follow a much smoother path than earnings. This stability of dividends is supported by a couple of measures. First, the variability in historical dividends is significantly lower than the variability in historical earnings. Using annual data on aggregate earnings and dividends from 1960 to 1994, for instance, the standard deviation of dividends is 5.13% while the standard deviation in earnings is 14.09%. Second, the standard deviation in earnings yields across companies is 18.57%, which is significantly higher than the standard deviation in dividend yields, which is only 3.15%. In other words, the variation in earnings yields across firms is much greater than the variation in dividend yields.

Dividend Yield   This is the dollar dividend per share divided by the current price per share.

There is a dataset on the Web that summarizes dollar earnings and dividends for U.S. companies going back to 1960 (**spearn.xls**).

A Firm's Dividend Policy Tends to Follow the Life Cycle of the Firm

A firm's life cycle can generally be graphed in terms of investment opportunities and growth. Not surprisingly, firms generally adopt dividend policies that best fit where they currently are in their life cycles. For instance, high-growth firms with great investment opportunities do not usually pay dividends, whereas stable firms with larger cash flows and fewer projects tend to pay out more of their earnings as dividends. Figure 10.3 graphs the typical path dividend payouts follow over a firm's life cycle.

This intuitive relationship between dividend policy and growth is reemphasized when payout ratios are correlated with expected growth rates. For instance, looking at all NYSE firms in 1995 and classifying them on the basis of expected growth rates, we estimated the dividend payout ratios and dividend yields by growth class; these are reported in Figure 10.4.

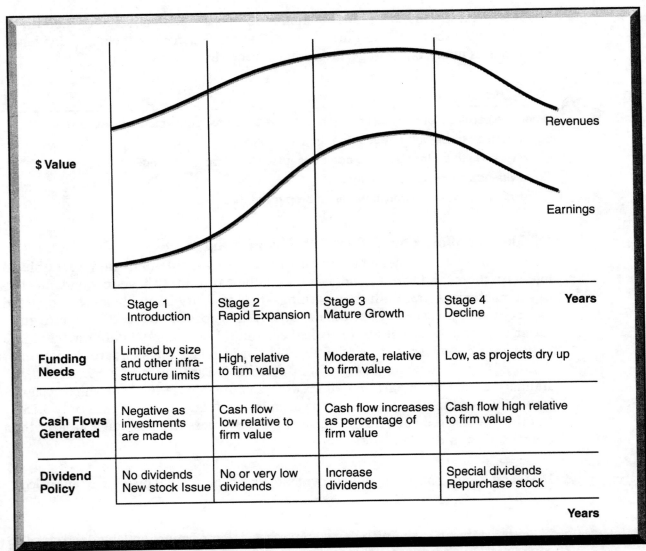

Figure 10.3 Life cycle analysis of dividend policy.

As expected growth rates increase, the dividend yields and payout ratios decrease.[1]

10.3 DIVIDEND POLICY AT GROWTH FIRMS

Assume that you are following a growth firm whose growth rate has begun easing. Which of the following would you most likely observe in terms of dividend policy at the firm?

☐ An immediate increase of dividends to reflect the lower reinvestment needs

☐ No change in dividend policy and an increase in the cash balance

☐ No change in dividend policy and an increase in acquisitions of other firms

Explain.

---

[1]These are growth rates projected by Value Line for firms in October 1995.

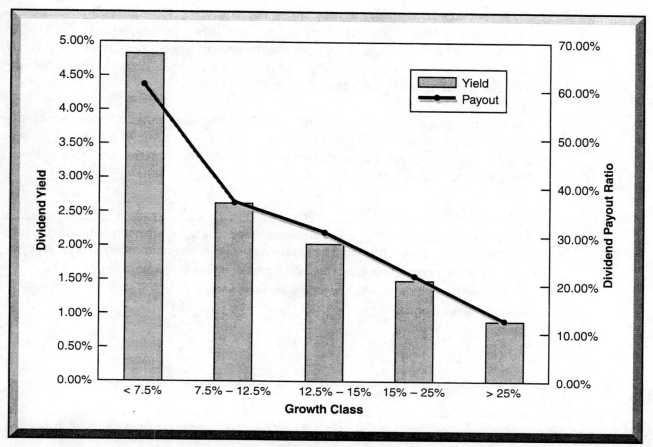

Figure 10.4   Dividend yields and payout ratios, by growth class.

DIFFERENCES IN DIVIDEND POLICY ACROSS COUNTRIES

While all of the discussion so far has focused on dividend policy in the United States, there are both commonalities and differences in dividend policy across countries. As in the United States, dividends in other countries are sticky and follow earnings. However, there are differences in dividend payout ratios across countries. Figure 10.5 summarizes the proportion of earnings paid out in dividends in the G-7 countries in 1982–84 and again in 1989–91. These differences can be attributed to a number of factors.

1. ***Differences in Stage of Growth:***   Just as higher-growth companies tend to pay out less in dividends (see Figure 10.3), countries with higher growth pay out less in dividends. For instance, Japan had much higher expected growth in 1982–84 than the other G-7 countries and paid out a much smaller percentage of its earnings as dividends.

2. ***Differences in Tax Treatment:***   Unlike the United States, where dividends are double-taxed, some of these countries provide at least partial protection against the double taxation of dividends. For instance, Germany taxes corporate retained earnings at a higher rate than corporate dividends.

3. ***Differences in Corporate Control:*** When there is a separation between ownership and management, as there is in many large publicly traded firms, and stockholders have little control over incumbent managers, the dividends paid by firms will be lower. Managers, left to their own devices, have a much greater incentive to accumulate cash than do stockholders.

Not surprisingly, the dividend payout ratios of companies in emerging markets are much lower than the dividend payout ratios in the G-7 countries. The higher growth and relative power of incumbent management in these countries contribute to keeping these payout ratios low.

10.4 FORCED DIVIDEND PAYOUTS

Some countries, such as Brazil, require all companies to pay out a minimum dividend (say 35% of earnings). Which of the following types of companies will be hurt most by such a policy?

☐ Stable-growth companies with substantial cash and low investment needs

☐ High-growth companies with significant investment needs

☐ All companies equally

Explain.

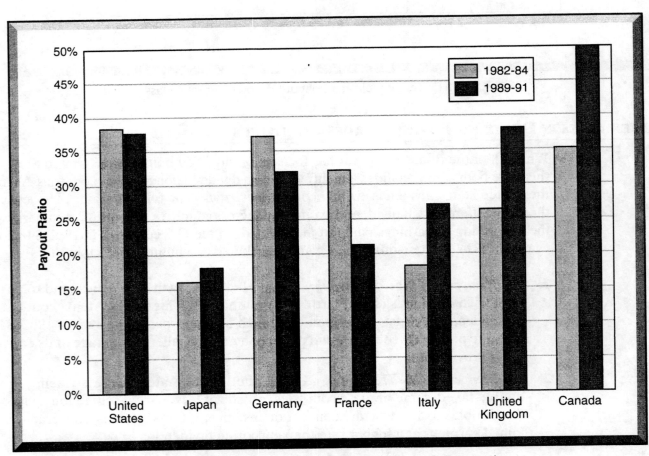

Figure 10.5 Dividend payout ratios in G-7 countries.

Measures of Dividend Policy

There are two widely used measures of dividend policy. The first is the *dividend yield,* which relates the dividend paid to the price of the stock:

Dividend Yield = Annual Dividends per Share/Price per Share

The dividend yield is significant for several reasons. First, it provides a measure of that component of the total return that comes from dividends, with the balance coming from price appreciation.

Expected Return on Stock = Dividend Yield + Price Appreciation

Second, some investors use the dividend yield as a measure of risk and as an investment screen, that is, they invest in stocks with high dividend yields. Studies indicate that stocks with high dividend yields earn excess returns, after adjusting for market performance and risk.

Figure 10.6 tracks dividend yields on stocks listed on the New York Stock Exchange in September 1997. It reveals wide differences across stocks on the exchange on dividend policy, with a large subset of stocks not paying dividends at all.

The median dividend yield of 1.76% and the average dividend yield of 2.11% are low by historical standards, as evidenced by Figure 10.7, which reports average dividend yields by year from 1960 to 1996.

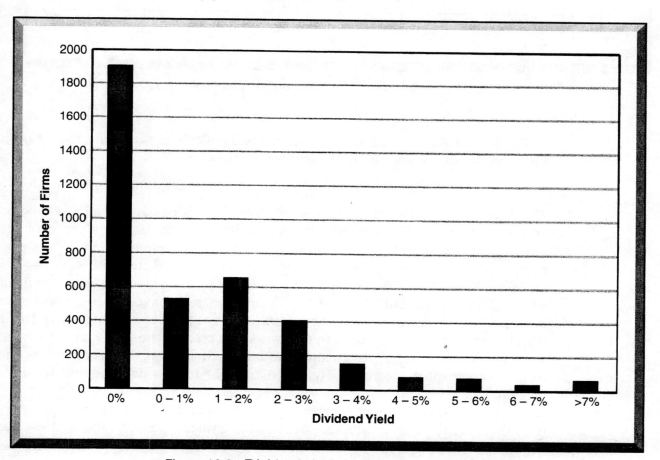

Figure 10.6 Dividend yields for U.S. firms—September 1997.

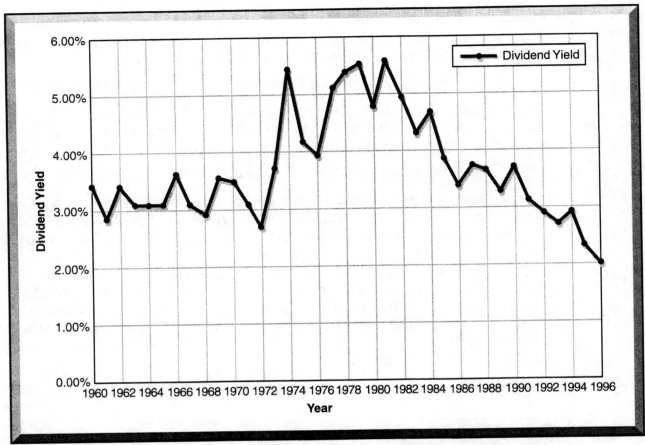

Figure 10.7 Dividend yields on S&P 500—1960–96.

The second widely used measure of dividend policy is the *dividend payout ratio,* which relates dividends paid to the earnings of the firm:

Dividend Payout Ratio = Dividends/Earnings

The payout ratio is used in a number of different settings. It is used in valuation as a way of estimating dividends in future periods, since most analysts estimate growth in earnings rather than dividends. Second, the retention ratio—the proportion of the earnings reinvested back into the firm (Retention Ratio = 1 − Dividend Payout Ratio)—is useful in estimating future growth in earnings; firms with high retention ratios (low payout ratios) generally have higher growth rates in earnings than do firms with lower retention ratios (higher payout ratios). Third, the dividend payout ratio tends to follow the life cycle of the firm, starting at zero when the firm is in high growth and gradually increasing as the firm matures and its growth prospects decrease. Figure 10.8 graphs the dividend payout ratios of U.S. firms in 1997.

The payout ratios that are greater than 100% represent firms that paid out more than their earnings as dividends. The median dividend payout ratio in 1994 was 24.93%, while the average payout ratio was 27.58%.

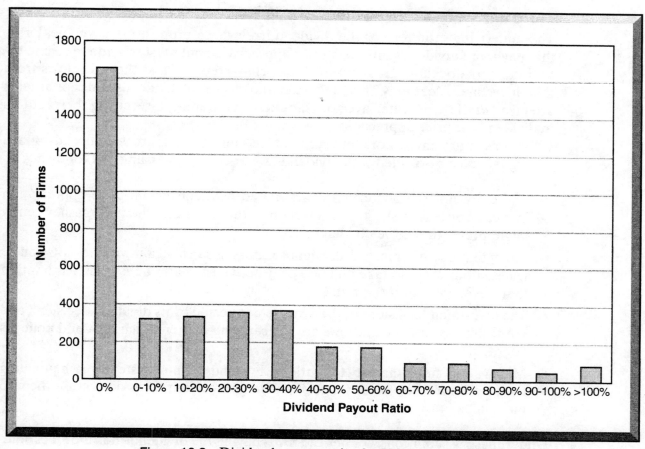

Figure 10.8   Dividend payout ratios for U.S. firms—September 1997.

 There is a dataset on the Web that summarizes dividend yields and payout ratios for U.S. companies, categorized by sector **(divend.xls)**.

 10.5   DIVIDENDS THAT EXCEED EARNINGS

Companies should never pay out more than 100% of their earnings as dividends.

☐   True

☐   False

Explain.

WHEN ARE DIVIDENDS IRRELEVANT?

There is a school of thought that argues that what a firm pays in dividends is irrelevant and that stockholders are indifferent about receiving dividends. Like the capital structure irrelevance proposition, the dividend irrelevance argument has its roots in a paper crafted by Miller and Modigliani (1961).

615

The Underlying Assumptions

The underlying intuition for the dividend irrelevance proposition is simple. Firms that pay more dividends offer less price appreciation but must provide the same total return to stockholders, given their risk characteristics and the cash flows from their investment decisions. Thus, if there are no taxes, or if dividends and capital gains are taxed at the same rate, investors should be indifferent to receiving their returns in dividends or price appreciation.

For this argument to work, in addition to assuming that there is no tax advantage or disadvantage associated with dividends, we also have to assume the following:

- There are no transactions costs associated with converting price appreciation into cash, by selling stock. If this were *not* true, investors who need cash urgently might prefer to receive dividends.

- Firms that pay too much in dividends can issue stock, again with no flotation or transactions costs, to take on good projects. There is also an implicit assumption that this stock is fairly priced.

- The investment decisions of the firm are unaffected by its dividend decisions, and the firm's operating cash flows are the same no matter which dividend policy is adopted.

- Managers of firms that pay too little in dividends do not waste the cash pursuing their own interests (i.e., managers with large free cash flows do not use them to take on bad projects).

Under these assumptions, neither the firms paying the dividends nor the stockholders receiving them will be adversely affected by firms paying either too little or too much in dividends.

10.6 DIVIDEND IRRELEVANCE

Based upon the Miller-Modigliani assumptions, dividends are least likely to affect value for the following types of firms:

☐ Small companies with substantial investment needs

☐ Large companies with significant insider holdings

☐ Large companies with significant holdings by pension funds (which are tax exempt).

Explain.

A Proof of Dividend Irrelevance

To provide a formal proof of irrelevance, assume that LongLast Corporation, an *unlevered* firm manufacturing furniture, has a net operating income after taxes of $100 million, growing at 5% a year, and a cost of capital of 10%. Further assume that this firm has net capital expenditure needs (capital expenditures in excess of depreciation) of $50 million, also growing at 5% a year, and that there are 105 million shares outstanding. Finally, assume that this firm pays out residual cash flows as dividends each year. The value of LongLast Corporation can be estimated as follows:

$$\text{Free Cash Flow to the Firm} = \text{EBIT} (1 - \text{tax rate}) - \text{Net Capital Expenditures}$$
$$= \$100 \text{ million} - \$50 \text{ million} = \$50 \text{ million}$$
$$\text{Value of the Firm} = \text{Free Cash Flow to Firm} (1 + g) / (\text{WACC} - g)$$
$$= \$ 50 (1.05) / (.10 - .05) = \$1,050 \text{ million}$$
$$\text{Price per Share} = \$1,050 \text{ million} / 105 \text{ million} = \$10.00$$

Based upon its cash flows, this firm could pay out $50 million in dividends.

$$\text{Dividend per Share} = \$50 \text{ million}/105 \text{ million} = \$0.476$$
$$\text{Total Value per Share} = \$10.00 + \$0.476 = \$10.476$$

To examine how the dividend policy affects firm value, assume that LongLast Corporation is told by an investment consultant that its stockholders would gain if the firm paid out $100 million in dividends, instead of $50 million. It now has to raise $50 million in new financing to cover its net capital expenditure needs. Assume that LongLast Corporation can issue new stock with *no flotation cost* to raise these funds. If it does so, the firm value will remain unchanged, since the value is determined not by the dividend paid but by the cash flows generated on the projects. The stock price will decrease, because there are more shares outstanding, but stockholders will find this loss offset by the increase in dividends per share. In order to estimate the price per share at which the new stock will be issued, note that after the dividend payment, the old stockholders in the firm will own only $1,000 million of the total firm value of $1,050 million.

Value of the Firm = $1,050 million
Dividends per Share = $100 million/105 million Shares = $0.953
Value of the Firm for Existing Stockholders after Dividend Payment =
   $1,000 million
Price per Share = $1,000 million / 105 million = $9.523
Value Accruing to Stockholder = $9.523 + $0.953 = $10.476

Another way of seeing this is to divide the stockholders into existing and new stockholders. When dividends are increased by $50 million, and new stock is issued for an equivalent amount, the existing stockholders now own only $1,000 million out of the firm value of $1,050 million, but their loss in firm value is offset by their gain in dividends. In fact, if the operating cash flows are unaffected by dividend policy, we can show that the firm value will be unaffected by dividend policy and that the average stockholder will be indifferent to dividend policy since he or she receives the same total value (price + dividends) under any dividend payment.

To consider an alternate scenario, assume that LongLast Corporation pays out no dividends and retains the residual $50 million as a cash balance. The value of the firm to existing stockholders can then be computed as follows:

$$\text{Value of Firm} = \text{Present Value of After-Tax Operating CF} + \text{Cash Balance}$$
$$= \$50 (1.05) / (.10 - .05) + \$50 \text{ million} = \$1,100 \text{ million}$$
$$\text{Value per Share} = \$1,100 \text{ million} / 105 \text{ million shares} = \$10.476$$

Note that the total value per share is unchanged from the previous two scenarios, as shown in Table 10.1, though all of the value comes from price appreciation.

When LongLast Corporation pays less than $50 million in dividends, the cash accrues in the firm and adds to its value. The increase in the stock price again is offset by the loss of cash flows from dividends.

It is important to note though that the irrelevance of dividend policy is grounded on the following assumptions.

- The issue of new stock is assumed to be costless and can therefore cover the cash shortfall created by paying excess dividends.

- It is assumed that firms that face a cash shortfall do not respond by cutting back on projects and thereby affecting future operating cash flows.

- Stockholders are assumed to be indifferent between receiving dividends and price appreciation.

- Any cash remaining in the firm is invested in projects that have zero net present value (such as financial investments) rather than used to take on poor projects.

Implications of Dividend Irrelevance

If dividends are, in fact, irrelevant, firms are spending a great deal of time pondering an issue about which their stockholders are indifferent. A number of strong implications emerge from this proposition. Among them, the value of equity in a firm should not change as its dividend policy changes. This does not imply that the price per share will be unaffected, however, since larger dividends should result in lower stock prices and more shares outstanding. In addition, in the long term, there should be no correlation between dividend policy and stock returns. Later in this chapter, we will examine some studies that have attempted to examine whether dividend policy is in fact irrelevant in practice.

Table 10.1   VALUE PER SHARE TO EXISTING STOCKHOLDERS FROM DIFFERENT DIVIDEND POLICIES

Value of Firm (Operating CF)	Dividends	Value to Existing Stockholders	Price per Share	Dividends per Share	Total Value per Share
$1,050	$ -	$1,100	$10.48	$ -	$10.48
$1,050	$10.00	$1,090	$10.38	$0.10	$10.48
$1,050	$20.00	$1,080	$10.29	$0.19	$10.48
$1,050	$30.00	$1,070	$10.19	$0.29	$10.48
$1,050	$40.00	$1,060	$10.10	$0.38	$10.48
$1,050	$50.00	$1,050	$10.00	$0.48	$10.48
$1,050	$60.00	$1,040	$9.90	$0.57	$10.48
$1,050	$70.00	$1,030	$9.81	$0.67	$10.48
$1,050	$80.00	$1,020	$9.71	$0.76	$10.48
$1,050	$90.00	$1,010	$9.62	$0.86	$10.48
$1,050	$100.00	$1,000	$9.52	$0.95	$10.48

The assumptions needed to arrive at the dividend irrelevance proposition may seem so onerous that many reject it without testing it. That would be a mistake, however, because the argument does contain a valuable message: A firm that has invested in bad projects cannot hope to resurrect its image with stockholders by offering them higher dividends. In fact, the correlation between dividend policy and total stock returns is weak.

THE TAXATION OF DIVIDENDS

The second school of thought on dividends argues that they create a tax disadvantage for the investors who receive them because they are taxed much more heavily than the alternative—capital gains. Carrying this rationale forward, dividend payments should decrease firm value and reduce the returns to stockholders after personal taxes. Consequently, firms will be better off either retaining the money they would have paid out as dividends or repurchasing stock.

Some History on Tax Rates

In the eyes of the Internal Revenue Service, dividends and capital gains have always been considered different types of income and, for the most part, are taxed differently (See Fig. 10.9). For several decades, until 1986, capital gains in the United States were taxed at a rate that was only 40% of the ordinary tax rate for individuals. Thus, an investor who would have paid a tax rate of 30% on ordinary income would have paid only 12% on capital gains. Under this setup, the differential advantage of capital gains is clearly a function of the investor's tax rate, with the advantage increasing with the tax rate. In 1979, for example, when the highest marginal tax rate was 70%, some investors were paying 28% on their capital gains (a tax rate differential of 42%). In 1981, a change in the tax law brought the highest marginal tax rate down to 50%, dropping the differential tax advantage to 30%.

The Tax Reform Act of 1986 was designed to simplify the tax code. One of the actions it took was to set the same tax rate on dividends and capital gains, capping the highest marginal tax rate at 28%. This simplification did not survive long in practice, however; subsequent changes in the tax law raised the highest marginal tax rate on ordinary income (dividends) to 39.6%, while leaving the capital gains tax rate at 28%. The latest changes in the tax laws, contained in the 1997 Tax Reform Act, propose to lower the capital gains tax rate even further to 20%.

The tax advantage associated with capital gains for corporations has always been lower than that associated with individuals, even though, for much of the last two decades, the capital gains tax rate has generally been lower than the ordinary tax rate. Obviously, there are no tax differences between dividends and capital gains for pension funds because their income is tax exempt.

In summary, there is a strong factual basis for the argument that historically, in the United States, capital gains have been treated more favorably under tax law than have dividends. The double taxation of dividends—once at the corporate level and once at the investor level—has never been addressed directly in U.S. tax law, but it has been dealt with in other countries in a couple of ways. In some countries, like Britain, individual

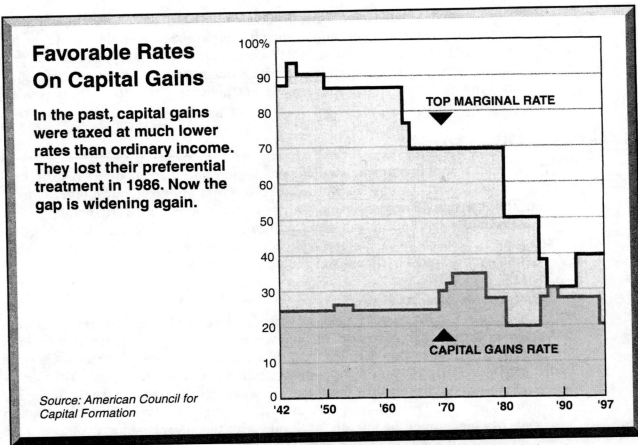

Favorable Rates On Capital Gains

In the past, capital gains were taxed at much lower rates than ordinary income. They lost their preferential treatment in 1986. Now the gap is widening again.

Source: American Council for Capital Formation

Figure 10.9 Tax rates on ordinary income and capital gains.

investors are allowed a tax credit for the corporate taxes paid on cash flows paid to them as dividends. In other countries, like Germany, the portion of the earnings paid out as dividends is taxed at a lower rate than the portion reinvested back into the firm.

Capital Gains (Losses) This is the portion of the return that an investor earns on an asset that can be attributed to the increase (decrease) in price of that asset.

10.7 TAX RATES, DOUBLE TAXATION, AND DIVIDEND POLICY

Assume now that the highest marginal tax rate for individuals is lowered to 15%. Would you expect companies to

☐ pay more in dividends?
☐ pay less in dividends?
☐ pay the same amount in dividends?

Explain.

The Tax Timing Option

When the 1986 tax law was signed into law, equalizing tax rates on ordinary income and capital gains, some believed that all the tax disadvantages associated with dividends had disappeared. Others noted that, even with the same tax rates, dividends carried a tax disadvantage because the investor had no choice on when to show the dividend as income; taxes were due when the firm paid out the dividends. In contrast, investors retained discretionary power over when to show and pay taxes on capital gains, since such taxes were not due until the asset was sold. This option allowed the investor to reduce the tax liability in one of two ways. First, by taking capital gains in periods when he or she has low income or capital losses to offset against the gain, the investor may be able to reduce the taxes paid. Second, deferring an asset's sale until an investor's death may result in tax savings.

IN PRACTICE: Estimating the Tax Disadvantage/Advantage of Dividends

The exact magnitude of the tax disadvantage associated with receiving dividends is often difficult to measure simply because different investors have different tax rates; thus, a pension fund, which does not pay any taxes, may not see any tax differences between dividends and capital gains, whereas individual investors may face different marginal tax rates on dividends and capital gains, depending upon their wealth and income levels. One simple way of estimating the differential between the tax rates of dividends and capital gains, at least to the marginal investor in a stock, is to look at the behavior of stock prices on the ex-dividend day.

If dividends and capital gains are viewed as equivalent from the investor's tax standpoint, the stock price should drop by about the same amount as the dollar dividend on the ex-dividend day to prevent arbitrage. To the degree that dividends are viewed as less attractive (because of the tax differential) than capital gains, investors will settle for a smaller capital gain, in pretax terms, as the equivalent of a dollar dividend. In other words, the price drop on the ex-dividend day will be smaller than the dollar dividend, and the magnitude of the difference will reflect the tax differential. Finally, if capital gains are taxed more heavily than dividends, the price drop on the ex-dividend day will be greater than the dollar dividend. In fact, the following relationship applies between differential tax rates and ex-dividend day price behavior:

$$\frac{P_B - P_A}{D} = \frac{(1 - t_o)}{(1 - t_{cg})}$$

where P_B is the price before the ex-dividend day, P_A is the price after the ex-dividend day, D is the dollar dividend, t_o is the tax rate on dividends and t_{cg} is the tax rate on capital gains.

Implications

There can be no argument that dividends have historically been treated less favorably than capital gains by the tax authorities. In the United States, the double taxation of dividends, at least at the level of individual investors, should create a strong disincentive to pay or to increase dividends. Other implications of the tax disadvantage argument include the following:

- Firms with an investor base composed primarily of individuals typically should have lower dividends than do firms with investor bases predominantly made up of tax-exempt institutions.

- The higher the income level (and hence the tax rates) of the investors holding stock in a firm, the lower the dividend paid out by the firm.

- As the tax disadvantage associated with dividends increases, the aggregate amount paid in dividends should decrease. Conversely, if the tax disadvantage associated with dividends decreases, the aggregate amount paid in dividends should increase. For instance, the change in the tax law in 1986 should have caused a surge in dividend payments by firms, because it eliminated the distinction between dividends and capital gains.

10.8 CORPORATE TAX STATUS AND DIVIDEND POLICY

Corporations are exempt from paying taxes on 70% of the dividends they receive from their stockholdings in other companies, whereas they face a capital gains tax rate of 20%. If all the stock in your company is held by other companies, and the ordinary tax rate for companies is 36%,

☐ dividends have a tax advantage relative to capital gains.

☐ capital gains have a tax advantage relative to dividends.

☐ dividends and capital gains are taxed at the same rate.

Explain.

SOME REASONS FOR PAYING DIVIDENDS THAT DO NOT MEASURE UP

Notwithstanding the tax disadvantages, firms continue to pay dividends and typically view such payments positively. There are a number of reasons for paying dividends, but only a few of them stand up to rational scrutiny, as we discuss below.

The Bird-in-the-Hand Fallacy

One rationalization given for why dividends are better than capital gains is that dividends are certain, whereas capital gains are uncertain; risk-averse investors, it is argued, will therefore prefer the former. This argument is severely flawed, however. The simplest counterresponse is to point out that the choice is not between certain dividends today and uncertain capital gains at some unspecified point in the future, but between dividends today and an almost equivalent amount in price appreciation today. This follows from our earlier discussion, where we noted that the stock price dropped by slightly less than the dividend on the ex-dividend day. By paying the dividend, the firm causes its stock price to drop today.

Another response to this argument is that a firm's value is determined by the cash flows from its projects. If a firm increases its dividends, but its investment policy remains unchanged, it will have to replace the dividends with new stock issues. Investors who receive the higher dividend will therefore find themselves losing, in present value terms, an equivalent amount in price appreciation.

Temporary Excess Cash

In some cases, firms are tempted to pay or initiate dividends in years in which their operations generate excess cash. While it is perfectly legitimate to return excess cash to stockholders, firms should also consider their own long-term investment needs. If the excess cash is a temporary phenomenon, resulting from having an unusually good year or a nonrecurring action (such as the sale of an asset), and the firm expects cash shortfalls in future years, it may be better off retaining the cash to cover some or all of these shortfalls. Another option is to pay the excess cash as a dividend in the current year and issue new stock when the cash shortfall occurs. This is not very practical, since the substantial expense associated with new security issues makes this a costly strategy in the long term. Table 10.2 summarizes the cost of issuing bonds, preferred stock, and common stock, by size of issue.

This said, it is important to note that some companies do pay dividends and issue stock during the course of the same period, mostly out of a desire to maintain their dividends. Figure 10.10 summarizes new stock issues by firms as a percentage of firm value, classified by their dividend yields.

Table 10.2 Issuance Cost for Securities			
	Cost of Issuing Securities		
Size of Issue	Bonds	Preferred Stock	Common Stock
Under $1 mil	14.0%	—	22.0%
$1.0–1.9 mil	11.0%	—	16.9%
$2.0–4.9 mil	4.0%	—	12.4%
$5.0–$9.9 mil	2.4%	2.6%	8.1%
$10–19.9 mil	1.2%	1.8%	6.0%
$20–49.9 mil	1.0%	1.7%	4.6%
$50 mil and over	0.9%	1.6%	3.5%

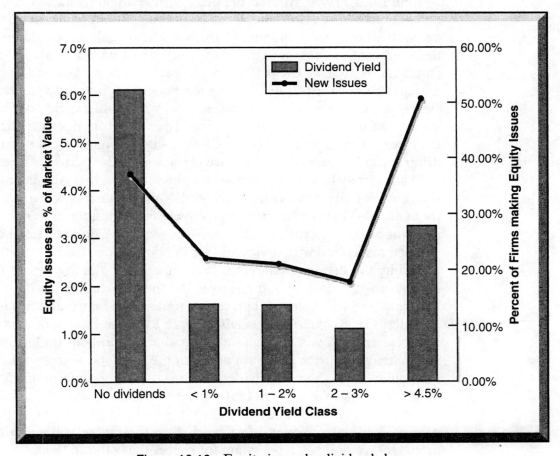

Figure 10.10 Equity issues by dividend class.

While it is not surprising that stocks that pay no dividends are most likely to issue stock, it is surprising that firms in the highest dividend yield class also issue significant proportions of new stock (approximately half of all the firms in this class also make new stock issues). This suggests that many of these firms are paying dividends, on the one hand, and issuing stock, on the other.

SOME GOOD REASONS FOR PAYING DIVIDENDS

There are several reasons why firms continue to pay dividends, ranging from investor preferences to clientele effects, to information signaling.

Some Investors Like Dividends

Many in the "dividends are bad" school of thought argue that rational investors should reject dividends due to the tax disadvantage they carry. Whatever one might think of the merits of that argument, there are some investors who have a strong preference for dividends and view large dividends positively. The most striking empirical evidence for this comes from studies of companies that have two classes of shares: one that pays cash dividends, and another that pays an equivalent amount of stock dividends; thus, investors are given a choice between dividends and capital gains.

John Long (1978) studied the price differential on Class A and B shares traded on Citizens Utility. Class B shares paid a cash dividend, while Class A shares paid an equivalent stock dividend. Moreover, Class A shares could be converted at little or no cost to Class B shares at the option of its stockholders. Thus, an investor could choose to buy Class B shares to get cash dividends, or Class A shares to get an equivalent capital gain. During the period of this study, the tax advantage was clearly on the side of capital gains; thus, we would expect to find Class B shares selling at a discount on Class A shares. The study found, surprisingly, that the Class B shares sold at a premium over Class A shares. Figure 10.11 summarizes the price differential between the two share classes over the period of the analysis.

While it may be easy to ascribe this phenomenon to irrational investors, this is not the case. Not all investors like dividends—many see its tax burden as onerous—but there are also many who view it positively, for a number of reasons. These investors may not be paying much in taxes, and consequently, do not care about the tax disadvantage associated with dividends. Or they might need and value the cash flow generated by the dividend payment. There are some who argue that the same amount can be raised in cash by selling stock, but the transactions costs and the difficulty of breaking up small holdings and selling unit shares may make this infeasible.

Bailey (1988) extended Long's study to examine Canadian utility companies that also offered dividend and capital-gains shares, and had similar findings. Table 10.3 summarizes the price premium at which the dividend shares sold. Note, once again, that, on average, the cash dividend shares sell at a premium of 7.5% over the stock dividend shares. We caution that while these findings do not indicate that *all* stockholders like dividends, they do indicate that the stockholders in these specific companies liked cash dividends so much that they were willing to overlook the tax disadvantage and pay a premium for shares that offered them.

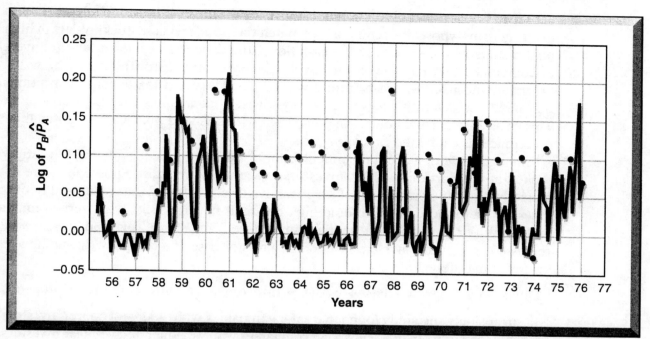

Figure 10.11   Price differential on Citizens Utility stock.

The natural log of $P_B/\hat{P}_A$ (the connected monthly observations) for the period 1956–1976. $\hat{P}_B$ is the price per share of Series B stock with dividends reinvested during each half-year prior to payment of the semi-annual Series A dividend.

Table 10.3	PRICE DIFFERENTIAL BETWEEN CASH AND STOCK DIVIDEND SHARES
Company	**Premium on Cash Dividend Shares over Stock Dividend Shares**
Consolidated Bathurst	19.30%
Donfasco	13.30%
Dome Petroleum	0.30%
Imperial Oil	12.10%
Newfoundland Light & Power	1.80%
Royal Trustco	17.30%
Stelco	2.70%
TransAlta	1.10%
Average	**7.54%**

The Clientele Effect

Stockholders in the companies covered by the studies mentioned above clearly like cash dividends. At the other extreme are companies that pay no dividends, such as Microsoft, whose stockholders seem perfectly content with that policy. Given the vast diversity of stockholders, it is not surprising that, over time, stockholders tend to invest in firms whose dividend policies match their preferences. Stockholders in high tax brackets, who do not need the cash flow from dividend payments, tend to invest in companies that pay low or no dividends. By contrast, stockholders in low tax brackets, who need the cash from dividend payments, and tax-exempt institutions that need current cash flows will usually invest in companies with high dividends. This clustering of stockholders in companies with dividend policies that match their preferences is called the *clientele effect*.

The existence of a clientele effect is supported by empirical evidence. One study looked at the portfolios of 914 investors to see if their portfolio positions were affected by their tax brackets. Not surprisingly, the study found that older and poorer investors were more likely to hold high-dividend-paying stocks than were younger and wealthier investors. In another study (see Table 10.4), dividend yields were regressed against the characteristics of the investor base of a company (including age, income, and differential tax rates):

$$\text{Dividend Yield}_t = a + b\,\beta_t + c\,\text{Age}_t + d\,\text{Income}_t + e\,\text{Differential Tax Rate}_t + \epsilon_t$$

Not surprisingly, this study found that safer companies, with older and poorer investors, tended to pay more in dividends than companies with wealthier and younger investors. Overall, dividend yields decreased as the tax disadvantage of dividends increased.

Dividend Clientele Effect This refers to the tendency of investors to buy stock in firms which have dividend policies that meet their preferences for high, low, or no dividends.

10.9 DIVIDEND CLIENTELE AND TAX EXEMPT INVESTORS

Pension funds are exempt from paying taxes on either ordinary income or capital gains, and also have substantial ongoing cash flow needs. What types of stocks would you expect these funds to buy?

☐ Stocks that pay high dividends
☐ Stocks that pay low or no dividends
Explain.

Table 10.4	DIVIDEND YIELDS AND INVESTOR CHARACTERISTICS	
Variable	**Coefficient**	**Implies**
Constant	4.22%	
Beta Coefficient	−2.145	Higher beta stocks pay lower dividends.
Age/100	3.131	Firms with older investors pay higher dividends.
Income/1000	−3.726	Firms with wealthier investors pay lower dividends.
Differential Tax Rate	−2.849	If ordinary income is taxed at a higher rate than capital gains, the firm pays less dividends.

Implications of the Clientele Effect

The existence of a clientele effect has some important implications. First, it suggests that firms get the investors they deserve, since the dividend policy of a firm attracts investors who like it. Second, it means that firms will have a difficult time changing an established dividend policy, even if it makes complete sense to do so. For instance, U.S. telephone companies have traditionally paid high dividends and acquired an investor base that liked these dividends. In the 1990s, many of these firms turned toward multimedia businesses, with much larger reinvestment needs and less stable cash flows. While the need to cut dividends in the face of the changing business mix might seem obvious, it was nevertheless a hard sell to stockholders, who had become used to the dividends.

The clientele effect also provides an alternative argument for the irrelevance of dividend policy, at least when it comes to valuation. In summary, if investors migrate to firms that pay the dividends that most closely match their needs, it can be argued that the value of any firm should not be determined by dividend policy. Thus, a firm that pays no or low dividends should not be penalized for doing so, because its investors *do not* want dividends. Conversely, a firm that pays high dividends should not have a lower value, since its investors like dividends. This argument assumes that there are enough investors in each dividend clientele to allow firms to be fairly valued, no matter what their dividend policy.

Empirical Evidence

The question of whether the clientele effect is strong enough to divorce the value of stocks from dividend policy is an empirical one. If the effect is strong enough, the returns on stocks, over long periods, should not be affected by their dividend policies. If there is a tax disadvantage associated with dividends, the returns on stocks that pay high dividends should be higher than the returns on stocks that pay low dividends, to compensate for the tax differences. Finally, if there is an overwhelming preference for dividends, these results should be reversed.

Black and Scholes (1974) examined this question by creating 25 portfolios of NYSE stocks, classifying firms into five quintiles based upon dividend yield, and then subdividing each group into five additional groups based upon risk (beta), each year for 35 years, from 1931 and 1966. When they regressed total returns on these portfolios against the dividend yields, the authors found no statistically significant relationship between the two. These findings were contested in a later study by Litzenberger and Ramaswamy (1979), who used updated dividend yields every month and examined whether the total returns in ex-dividend months were correlated with dividend yields. They found a strong *positive* relationship between total returns and dividend yields, supporting the hypothesis that investors are averse to dividends. They also estimated that the implied tax differential between capital gains and dividends was approximately 23%. Miller and Scholes (1981) countered by arguing that this finding was contaminated by the information effects of dividend increases and decreases. In response, they removed from the sample all cases in which the dividends were declared and paid in the same month and concluded that the implied tax differential was only 4%, which was not significantly different from zero.

In the interests of fairness, we must point out that most studies of this phenomenon have concluded that total returns and dividend yields are positively correlated.

While many of them contend that this is because the implied tax differential between dividends and capital gains is significantly different from zero, there are alternative explanations for the phenomenon. In particular, while one may disagree with the conclusions arrived at by Miller and Scholes, their argument that the higher returns on stocks that pay high dividends might have nothing to do with the tax disadvantages associated with dividends but may in fact be a reflection of the price increases associated with unexpected dividend increases, has both a theoretical and an empirical basis, as discussed below.

10.10 DIVIDEND CLIENTELE AND CHANGING DIVIDEND POLICY

Telephone companies in the United States have long had the following features—they are regulated, have stable earnings and low reinvestment needs, and pay high dividends. Many of these telephone companies are now considering entering the multimedia age and becoming entertainment companies, which requires more reinvestment and creates more volatility in earnings. If you were the CEO of a telephone company, which of the following would you do?

☐ Announce an immediate cut in dividends as part of a major capital investment plan.

☐ Continue to pay high dividends, and use new stock issues to finance the expansion.

☐ Something else.

Explain.

Information Signaling

Financial markets examine every action a firm takes for implications for future cash flows and firm value. When firms announce changes in dividend policy, they are conveying information to markets, whether or not they intend to. There are a couple of stories that can be told about what information dividend changes *signal* to financial markets.

Dividends as a Positive Signal

Financial markets tend to view announcements made by firms about their future prospects with a great deal of skepticism, since firms routinely make exaggerated claims. At the same time, there are some firms, with good projects, that are undervalued by markets. How do such firms convey information credibly to markets? *Signaling theory* suggests that these firms need to take actions that cannot be easily imitated by firms without good projects. Increasing dividends can be viewed as one such action. By increasing dividends, firms create a cost to themselves, since they commit to paying these dividends in the long term. The fact that they are willing to make this commitment indicates to investors that they believe that they have the capacity to generate these cash flows in the long term. This positive signal should therefore lead to a reevaluation of the cash flows and firm values and an increase in the stock price.

Decreasing dividends operates as a negative signal, largely because firms are reluctant to cut dividends. Thus, when firms take this action, markets see it as an indication that these firms are in substantial and long-term financial trouble. Consequently, such actions lead to a drop in stock prices.

The empirical evidence concerning price reactions to dividend increases and decreases is consistent, at least on average, with these stories. Figure 10.12 summarizes the average excess returns around dividend changes for firms.

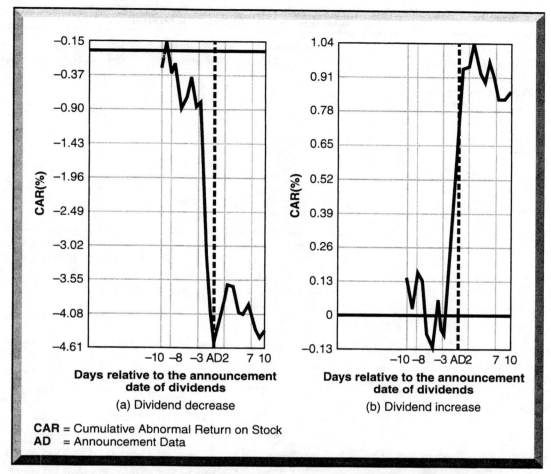

CAR = Cumulative Abnormal Return on Stock
AD = Announcement Data

Figure 10.12   Excess returns around announcements of dividend changes.

This explanation for why firms increase dividends has to be considered with some caution, however. While it is true that firms with good projects may use dividend increases as a way of conveying information to financial markets, given the substantial tax liability that it may create for stockholders, is it the most efficient way? For smaller firms, which have relatively few signals available to them, the answer might be yes. For larger firms, which have many ways of conveying information to markets, dividends might not be the least expensive or the most effective signal. For instance, the information may be more effectively and economically conveyed through an analyst report on the company.

Dividends as a Negative Signal

An equally plausible story can be told about how an increase in dividends sends a negative signal to financial markets. Consider a firm that has never paid dividends in the past, but has registered extraordinary growth and high returns on its projects. When this firm first starts paying dividends, its stockholders may consider this an indication that the firm's projects are neither as plentiful nor as lucrative as they used to be.

Table 10.5, reproduced from Palepu and Healy (1986), reports the earnings growth around dividend initiations for 151 firms from 1970 to 1979. As you can see, the earnings growth rate increases significantly after dividends are initiated,

Earnings Growth Rates in Years Surrounding First-Time Dividend Payments by 131 Firms in the Period 1970 to 1979*

Table 10.5   EARNINGS GROWTH AROUND DIVIDEND INITIATIONS

Year Relative to Dividend Initiation	Number of Firms	Mean Earnings Growth Rate	Median Earnings Growth Rate
−4	130	14.9%	17.4%
−3	129	−7.1	7.6
−2	128	12.9	10.5
−1	131	42.7**	28.0
1	130	55.0**	40.2
2	130	22.0**	35.9
3	130	35.0**	28.2
4	128	3.5	19.5

*In the original research, earnings performance was computed as earnings changes standardized by stock prices. Here these values were converted to earnings growth rates by assuming that the average price earnings ratio for the sample firms is ten.
**Significantly different from zero at the 10% level or lower.
(Palepu and Healy)

Median Earnings Growth Rates in Years Surrounding First-Time Dividend Payments*

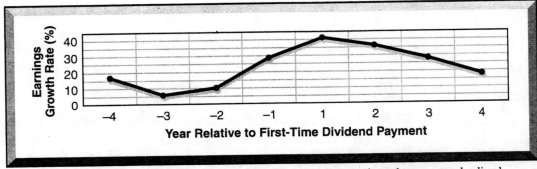

*In the original research earnings performance was computed as earnings changes standardized by stock prices. Here these values were converted to earnings growth ratios by assuming that the average price-earnings ratio for the sample firms is ten.
(Palepu and Healy)

suggesting that they operate as positive signals of future earnings growth even for these firms.

10.11   DIVIDENDS AS SIGNALS

Silicon Electronics, a company with a history of not paying dividends, high earnings growth, and reinvestment back into the company, announces that it will be initiating dividends. You would expect

☐ the stock price to go up.

☐ the stock price to go down.

☐ the stock price to remain unchanged.

Explain.

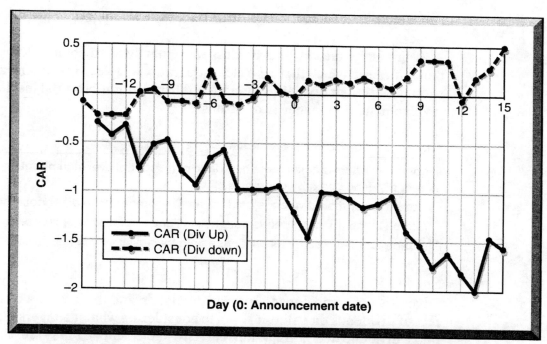

Figure 10.13 Excess returns on straight bonds around dividend changes.

STOCKHOLDERS, BONDHOLDERS, AND DIVIDENDS

The question of how much to pay in dividends is intimately connected to the financing decisions made by the firm, that is, how much debt the firm should carry. In Chapter 9, we examined how firms that want to increase or decrease leverage can do so by changing their dividend policy: Increasing dividends increases leverage, and decreasing dividends reduces leverage. In the previous chapters, we also outlined the interests of bondholders in dividend policy. Firms that increase dividends may harm bondholders by increasing their default risk, thus reducing the market value of bonds. Figure 10.13 shows the reaction of bond prices to dividend increases and decreases.

In response to this threat to their interests, bondholders often write in specific covenants into bond agreements on dividend policy, restricting the payment of dividends. These restrictions often play a role in determining a firm's dividend policy.

STOCKHOLDERS, MANAGERS, AND DIVIDENDS

In examining debt policy, we noted that one reason for taking on more debt was to induce managers to be more disciplined in their project choice. Implicit in this free cash flow argument is the assumption that cash accumulations, if left to the discretion of the managers of the firm, would be wasted on poor projects. If this is true, we can argue that forcing a firm to make a commitment to pay dividends reduces cash

631

available to managers. This, in turn, forces managers to be disciplined in project choice.

If this is the reason stockholders want managers to commit to paying larger dividends, firms in which there is a clear separation between ownership and management should pay larger dividends than should firms with substantial insider ownership and involvement in managerial decisions.

10.12 CORPORATE GOVERNANCE AND DIVIDEND POLICY

In countries where stockholders have little or no control over incumbent managers, you would expect dividends paid by companies

☐   to be lower than dividends paid by similar companies in other countries.

☐   to be higher than dividends paid by similar companies in other countries.

☐   to be about the same as dividends paid by similar companies in other countries.

Survey Results

Given the pros and cons for paying dividends, and the lack of a consensus on the effect of dividends on value, it is worth considering what managers factor in when they make dividend decisions. Baker, Farrelly, and Edelman (1985) surveyed managers on their views on dividend policy and reported the level of agreement with a series of statements. Table 10.6 summarizes their findings.

It is quite clear from this survey that, rightly or wrongly, managers believe that their dividend payout ratios affect firm value and operate as signals of future prospects. They also operate under the presumptions that investors choose firms with dividend policies that match their preferences and that management should be responsive to their needs.

Table 10.6 MANAGEMENT BELIEFS ABOUT DIVIDEND POLICY

Statement of Management Beliefs	Agree	No Opinion	Disagree
1. A firm's dividend payout ratio affects the price of the stock.	61%	33%	6%
2. Dividend payments provide a signaling device of future prospects.	52%	41%	7%
3. The market uses dividend announcements as information for assessing firm value.	43%	51%	6%
4. Investors have different perceptions of the relative riskiness of dividends and retained earnings.	56%	42%	2%
5. Investors are basically indifferent with regard to returns from dividends and capital gains.	6%	30%	64%
6. A stockholder is attracted to firms that have dividend policies appropriate to the stockholder's tax environment.	44%	49%	7%
7. Management should be responsive to shareholders' preferences regarding dividends.	41%	49%	10%

OTHER APPROACHES TO RETURNING CASH TO STOCKHOLDERS

Dividends represent just one way of returning cash to stockholders. There are other approaches that may provide more attractive options to firms, depending upon their stockholder characteristics and their objectives. These include *equity repurchases,* whereby the cash is used to buy back outstanding stock in the firm, reducing the number of shares outstanding; and *forward contracts* to buy equity in future periods, whereby the price at which the shares will be bought back is fixed.

While not strictly representing the return of cash to stockholders, we will also consider four other options: *stock dividends* and *stock splits,* which, though used by many firms to supplement cash dividends, just change the number of shares outstanding, and *spinoffs* and *splitoffs,* which can be viewed as a return of assets (rather than cash) to stockholders.

EQUITY REPURCHASES

The most widely used alternative to paying dividends is to use the cash to repurchase outstanding stock. Such *equity repurchases,* while returning cash to stockholders, provide some advantages to firms, but they also have some limitations relative to dividends.

The Process of Equity Repurchase

The process of repurchasing equity will depend largely upon whether the firm intends to repurchase stock in the open market, at the prevailing market price, or to make a more formal tender offer for its shares. There are three widely used approaches to buying back equity:

- *Repurchase Tender Offers:* In a repurchase tender offer, a firm specifies a price at which it will buy back shares, the number of shares it intends to repurchase, and the period of time for which it will keep the offer open, and invites stockholders to submit their shares for the repurchase. In many cases, firms retain the flexibility to withdraw the offer if an insufficient number of shares are submitted or to extend the offer beyond the originally specified time period. This approach is used primarily for large equity repurchases.

- *Open Market Purchases:* In the case of open market repurchases, firms buy shares in the market at the prevailing market price. While firms do not have to disclose publicly their intent to buy back shares in the market, they have to comply with SEC requirements to prevent price manipulation or insider trading. Finally, open market purchases can be spread out over much longer time periods than tender offers and are much more widely used for smaller repurchases. In terms of flexibility, an open market repurchase affords the firm much more freedom in deciding when to buy back shares and how many shares to repurchase.

- *Privately Negotiated Repurchases:* In privately negotiated repurchases, firms buy back shares from a large stockholder in the company at a negotiated price. This method is not as widely used as the first two and may be employed by managers or owners as a way of consolidating control and eliminating a troublesome stockholder.

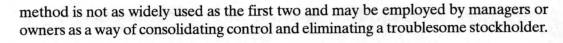 **Repurchase Tender Offer** This is an offer by a firm to buy back a specified number of shares at a fixed price during the offer period.

Open Market Purchases This is an offer to buy shares in the market at the prevailing market price.

The Rationale

In the last decade, more and more firms have used equity repurchases as an alternative to paying dividends. Figure 10.14 summarizes new equity issues and equity repurchases at U.S. corporations between 1981 and 1990.

There are several advantages to using equity repurchases as an alternative to dividend payments to return cash to stockholders:

1. Unlike regular dividends, which imply a commitment to continue payment in future periods, equity repurchases are viewed primarily as onetime returns of cash. Consequently, firms with excess cash flows that are uncertain about their ability to continue generating these cash flows in future periods should repurchase stocks rather than pay dividends. These firms could choose to pay special dividends instead of repurchasing stock, however, since special dividends also do not imply a commitment to making similar payments in the future.

2. The decision to repurchase stock affords firms much more flexibility to reverse themselves and/or to spread the repurchases over a longer period than does the decision to pay an equivalent special dividend. In fact, there is substantial evidence that many firms that announce ambitious stock repurchase plans do not carry them through to completion.

3. Equity repurchases may offer tax advantages to stockholders, since dividends are taxed at ordinary tax rates, while the price appreciation that flows from equity repurchases is taxed at capital gains rate. Furthermore, stockholders have the option not to sell their shares back to the firm and therefore do not have to realize the capital gains in the period of the equity repurchases.

4. Equity repurchases are much more focused in terms of paying out cash only to those stockholders who need it. This benefit flows from the voluntary nature of stock buybacks: Those who need the cash can tender their shares back to the firm, while those who do not can continue to hold on to them.

5. Equity repurchases may provide a way of increasing insider control in firms, since they reduce the number of shares outstanding. If the insiders do not tender their shares back, they will end up holding a larger proportion of the firm and, consequently, having greater control.

6. Finally, equity repurchases may provide firms with a way of supporting their stock prices when they are under assault. For instance, in the aftermath of the crash of 1987, many firms initiated stock buyback plans to keep stock prices from falling further.

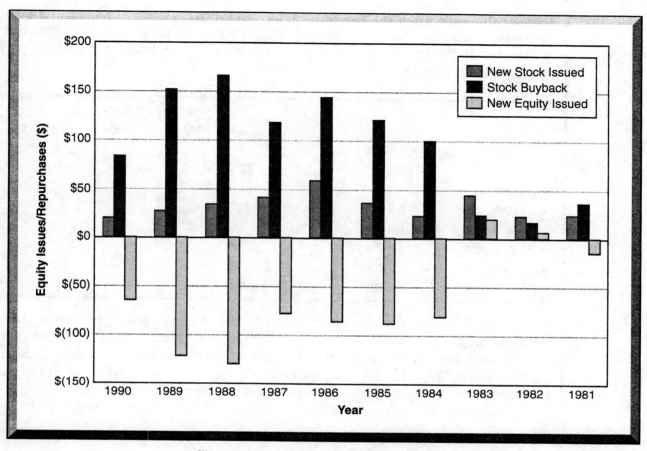

Figure 10.14 Net equity issues—1981–90.

In summary, equity repurchases allow firms to return cash to stockholders and still maintain flexibility in future periods.

IN PRACTICE: EQUITY BUYBACKS AND DILUTION

Some equity repurchases are motivated by the desire to reduce the number of shares outstanding and therefore increase the earnings per share. This argument is buttressed by assuming that the firm's price earnings ratio will remain unchanged, leading to a higher price. While the reduction in the number of shares might increase earnings per share, the effect is usually a consequence of higher leverage and not of the stock buyback per se. In other words, a special dividend of the same amount would have resulted in the same returns to stockholders. Furthermore, the increase in leverage should increase the riskiness of the stock and lower the price/earnings ratio. Whether this will increase or decrease the price per share will depend on whether the firm is moving to its optimal by repurchasing stock, in which case the price will increase, or moving away from it, in which case the price will drop.

To illustrate the effect on EPS of stock buybacks, assume that an all-equity firm in the specialty retailing business with 100 shares outstanding has $100 in earnings after taxes and a market value of $1,500. Assume that this firm borrows $300 and buys back 20 shares, using the funds. As long as the after-tax interest expense on the borrowing is less than $20, this firm will report higher earnings per share after the repurchase. If the firm's tax rate is 50%, for instance, the effect on earnings per share will be as follows:

	BEFORE Repurchase	**AFTER REPURCHASE**	
		Interest Expense = $30	**Interest Expense = $55**
EBIT	$200	$200	$200
- Interest	$0	$30	$55
= Taxable Inc.	$200	$170	$145
- Taxes	$100	$85	$72.50
= Net Income	$100	$85	$72.50
# Shares	100	80	80
EPS	$1.00	$1.0625	$0.91

If we assume that the price/earnings ratio remains at 15, the price per share will increase in proportion to the earnings per share. In this case, however, we should expect to see a drop in the price/earnings ratio, as the increase in leverage will make the firm riskier. Whether the drop will be sufficient to offset or overwhelm the increase in earnings per share will depend upon whether the firm has excess debt capacity and whether, by going to 20%, it is moving closer to its optimal debt mix.

10.13   STOCK BUYBACKS AND EPS EFFECTS

In the example above, the earnings per share increased when the firm borrowed money to buy back stock. Will this always be the case?

☐ Yes

☐ No

Explain.

Limitations of Equity Repurchases

Many critics of dividend policy would argue that equity repurchases are clearly preferable to both regular dividends (because of the tax advantages and the flexibility of the former) and special dividends (because of the tax benefits). There is a downside to this flexibility, however. To the degree that actions taken by firms signal their assurance about future cash flows, it can be argued that a firm that repurchases stock rather than instituting dividends is signaling a greater uncertainty about future cash flows. If this is the case, the increase in value that follows an equity repurchase would be smaller than the increase in value following an equivalent regular dividend payment. And if the firm fails to carry out equity repurchase plans to completion, markets will become increasingly skeptical of these plans and respond accordingly.

The Empirical Evidence

Several studies have examined the stock (and bond) price reaction to equity repurchases; most of them indicate a strong positive stock price reaction, with increases ranging from 10% to 20% around the announcements. Furthermore, this increase seems to be permanent rather than transitory, suggesting that the price increase is not just the result of liquidity effects, but of something deeper. It is not clear, however, which of the hypotheses best explains these results:

1. The increase in value seems too large to be explained away in terms of the tax benefits of equity repurchase relative to dividends. Since the typical repurchase in this sample involved a buyback of 15 to 20% of the outstanding shares, the tax savings should be roughly 5–6%, at the maximum.[2] Unless firms are expected to continue repurchasing large proportions of their equity every year—a very unlikely scenario—it is difficult to arrive at price increases of the magnitude observed in most of these studies.

2. It is also not clear that the price increase can be explained purely in terms of leverage, that is, that these firms were underleveraged to begin with and that buying back stock brings them closer to their optimal debt ratios (and higher firm values). For instance, Vermaelen (1981) reports that firms that do not issue debt to repurchase equity actually have higher price increases than firms that do.

3. The final possibility is that the increase in stock prices as a consequence of equity repurchases is the result of the information conveyed to financial markets by such buybacks; in particular, the equity repurchase may be viewed as a signal that the firm believes that its stock is significantly undervalued. Dann and DeAngelo (1983) tested this hypothesis by categorizing equity repurchases into privately negotiated buybacks (in which the motivation is usually control) and open market repurchases/tender offers (in which the motivation may include undervaluation), and concluded that stock prices actually declined slightly for the first group. This suggests that at least some of the price increase can be attributed to information effects.

It is unfair to compare the price increase associated with equity repurchases in these studies with the price increases associated with dividend increases noted in the previous chapter, because of the difference in dollar values between the two. Rather, a more appropriate comparison would look at the impact on stock prices of a given dollar change in regular dividends as opposed to the price impact an equivalent equity repurchase. In that case, we would expect the former to have a much larger impact, because dividends imply a much larger commitment on the part of the firm.

10.14 STOCK BUYBACKS AND STOCK PRICE EFFECTS

For which of the following types of firms would a stock buyback be most likely to lead to a drop in the stock price?

☐ Companies with a history of poor project choice

☐ Companies which borrow money to buy back stock

☐ Companies which are perceived to have great investment opportunities

Explain.

---

[2] A simple approximation of the tax benefit can be estimated by multiplying the equity repurchase proportion by the differential tax rate. Even taking the highest tax differential during the period (about 40%) yields a tax benefit of only 6% on an equity repurchase of 15% of the outstanding equity.

A Framework for Deciding on Equity Repurchases

While this signaling argument has some merit, it can be argued that, for most firms, the flexibility and the tax arguments will outweigh this concern. In general, however, the net benefit of equity repurchases, as opposed to dividends, will depend upon the following:

1. *Sustainability and Stability of Excess Cash Flow:*   To the degree that both equity repurchases and increased dividends are triggered by excess cash flows, the question of which course of action to take cannot be answered without looking at the sustainability of cash flows. If the excess cash flows are temporary or unstable, firms should repurchase stock; if they are stable and predictable, the signaling argument may tilt firms toward increasing dividends.

2. *Stockholder Tax Preferences:*   When capital gains and dividends are taxed at different rates, the tax preferences of the stockholders will determine whether a firm should repurchase stock or pay dividends. If stockholders are taxed at much higher rates on dividends and, consequently, are averse to dividends, the firm will be better off repurchasing stock. If, on the other hand, stockholders prefer dividends, the firm may gain by paying a special dividend.

3. *Predictability of Future Investment Needs:*   Firms that are uncertain about the magnitude of future investment opportunities are much more likely to use equity repurchases as a way of returning cash to stockholders.

4. *Undervaluation of the Stock:*   An equity repurchase makes even more sense when managers perceive their stock to be undervalued. By buying back the stock, managers can accomplish two objectives. First, if the stock remains undervalued, the remaining stockholders will benefit if managers buy back stock at less than true value. Alternatively, the stock buyback may send a signal to financial markets that the stock is undervalued, and the market will react accordingly by pushing up the price.

■▲
▼●
ILLUSTRATION 10.1   **Examining Disney's Choices**
To illustrate the choice between dividends and equity repurchases, let us consider the example of Disney. Assume, for the moment, that Disney generates $1 billion in excess cash in 1997 and that its regular dividend is only $250 million. We would argue that the excess cash should be used to buy back stock because:

1. Disney, as an entertainment company, has volatile earnings and cash flows. If Disney commits to paying higher regular dividends, it might be unable to maintain those dividends if it has a poor year.

2. Disney's stockholders have generally bought the stock for price appreciation rather than dividend yield. It is reasonable to assume, therefore, that they would much rather have the option to sell their shares back and make a capital gain, rather than receive a larger dividend (or a special dividend).

3. Disney has ambitious plans to expand its entertainment empire into Latin America and Asia. These plans create uncertainty about future investment needs; if overseas expansion goes well, future investment needs will be much higher. This uncertainty tilts the scales in favor of an equity repurchase.

FORWARD CONTRACTS TO BUY EQUITY

Many firms that announce equity repurchase plans fail to carry these plans to fruition. While this flexibility in implementation can be viewed as a benefit, it reduces the signaling benefit (and the concurrent price increase) of buying back stock. An alternative strategy, which may preserve the tax advantages of equity repurchases while also increasing the signaling benefit, is to enter into *forward contracts* to acquire stock at a fixed price. Since these contracts are commitments, the firm is forced to repurchase the shares at that price. Consequently, the market will likely view the action as concrete act and react accordingly.

Another advantage of forward contracts is that unlike regular equity repurchases, in which the number of shares that will be bought back in future periods is unknown because the stock price will be different, the number of shares that will be bought back in a forward contract is known because the purchases are at a fixed price. Consequently, the effects of the equity repurchase plans on earnings per share and related multiples can be estimated more precisely.

This certainty comes at a price, however. By agreeing to buy back shares at a fixed price, the firm increases its risk exposure, since it commits to paying this price even if the stock price drops. While it may gain an offsetting advantage if stock prices go up, the commitment to pay a higher price to buy stocks when stock prices are lower can be a burden, especially if the stock price dropped as a consequence of lower earnings or cash flows.

To summarize, the decision to cement the commitment to buying back stocks by entering into a forward contract will depend, in large part, on whether the signaling benefits are large enough to offset the higher risk and lost flexibility associated with the forward contract. The choice between paying an increased dividend or entering into a forward contract involves a tradeoff between the tax savings that may accrue from the forward contract and the increased risk associated with the forward contract.

Forward Contract This is a contract to acquire an asset (like stock) at a fixed price at a specified time in the future.

STOCK DIVIDENDS AND STOCK SPLITS

A stock dividend involves issuing to existing stockholders additional shares in the company at no cost. Thus, in a 5% stock dividend, every existing stockholder in the firm receives new shares equivalent to 5% of the number of shares currently owned. Many firms use stock dividends to supplement cash dividends; others view them as an alternative. A *stock split,* in some ways, is just a large stock dividend, since it too increases the number of shares outstanding, but it does so by a much larger factor. Thus, a firm may have a two-for-one stock split, whereby the number of shares in the firm is doubled.

The mechanics of a stock split or dividend are simple: The firm issues additional shares in the firm and distributes them to existing stockholders in proportion to their original holdings in the firm. Thus, stock splits and dividends should not alter the proportional ownership of the firm on the part of existing stockholders.

Stock Dividend (Split) These are additional shares issued at no cost to existing stockholders, in proportion to their current holdings.

Effect on Value

Since stock dividends and stock splits have no real effect on cash flows but change only the number of shares outstanding, they should not affect the cash flows of the firm, and thus should not increase the value of equity, in the aggregate. Rather, the share price will decline to reflect the increased number of shares. To illustrate, assume that a small manufacturing firm with an aggregate value of equity of $110 million and 10 million shares outstanding declares a 10% stock dividend. The aggregate value of equity will remain $110 million, but the price per share will drop from $11 per share ($110 million/10 million) to $10 per share ($110 million / 11 million). Note, though, that the stockholders in this firm are no worse off after the stock dividend, the stock price drop notwithstanding, because they receive a compensatory increase in the number of shares outstanding.

The Rationale

If the effect on stockholder wealth is in fact neutral, why do firms pay stock dividends or announce stock splits in the first place? Some firms view stock dividends as a way of fooling stockholders; thus, a firm that is in trouble and unable to pay its regular cash dividend may announce that it is "substituting" an equivalent stock dividend. It is possible that some stockholders may actually believe that these are substitutes, but it is extremely unlikely that financial markets will not see through this deception. Other firms view stock dividends as a supplement to cash dividends and use them in periods in which they have posted good results. This rationale is more defensible, because the announcement of a stock dividend may convey information to financial markets about future prospects. In fact, the use of both stock dividends and stock splits as signals of better cash flows in the future may increase the firm value.

An additional reason given (especially) for stock splits is the desire on the part of some firms to keep their stock prices within a specified trading range. Consequently, if the stock price rises above the range, a stock split may be used to bring the price back down. To illustrate, assume that a firm wants its stock to trade in the $20 to $40 range, and that the stock price rises to $45. With a two-for-one stock split, the number of shares will double and the stock price will drop back down to roughly $22.50.

The remaining question is why would a firm have a desired trading range in the first place. Firms that do argue that given restrictions on buying shares in even lots (e.g., 100 shares), a price that is too high reduces the potential market for the stock to wealthier investors and institutional investors. Bringing the price down increases the number of potential buyers for the stock, leading to a higher stock price. Furthermore, there is a control benefit to the stock being more widely held. Both of these arguments are dubious, however. The transactions costs, if one counts the bid–ask spread as one component, actually increase as a percentage of the stock price as the price drops. Thus, the firm may lose more investors than it gains by cutting the price. There is a cost to being widely held, as well, since it increases the gulf between stockholders and managers and leads to higher agency costs.

The empirical evidence on stock splits suggests that while the initial price reaction to stock splits is positive, these excess returns are not sustained if the firm cannot maintain or increase its dividends per share in following periods.

? 10.15 STOCK DIVIDENDS

A company which has a history of paying cash dividends announces that it will be doubling its dividend but paying it in the form of stock instead. As an investor, would you view this as

☐ neutral news, since stock dividends do not create value anyway?

☐ good news, since dividends were doubled?

☐ bad news, since the cash dividends were cut?

Explain.

DIVESTITURES, SPINOFFS, SPLITUPS, AND SPLITOFFS

Divestitures, spinoffs, splitups and splitoffs are other options for returning non-cash assets to stockholders. Consider a company with operations in multiple business lines, some of which are being systematically undervalued; the whole firm is therefore worth less than its parts. This firm has four options:

1. *Divest the undervalued business and pay a liquidating dividend:* One way in which this firm can deal with its predicament is through *divestiture,* which involves selling those parts that are being undervalued by the market for their true market value and then paying out the cash to stockholders in the form of either equity repurchases or dividends.

2. *Spin off the undervalued businesses:* An alternative is to spin off or create a new class of shares in the undervalued business line and to distribute these shares to the existing stockholders. Since the shares are distributed in proportion to the existing share ownership, it does not alter the proportional ownership in the firm.

3. *Split up the entire firm:* In a *splitup,* the firm splits itself off into different business lines, distributes these shares to the original stockholders, in proportion to their original ownership in the firm, and then ceases to exist.

4. *Split off the undervalued business:* A *splitoff* is similar to a spinoff, insofar as it creates new shares in the undervalued business line. In this case, however, the existing stockholders are given the option to exchange their parent company stock for these new shares, which changes the proportional ownership in the new structure.

Divestiture A divestiture is the sale of a portion or portions of a firm for cash.

Spinoff In a spinoff, shares in an asset or assets of a firm are created and distributed to stockholders in proportion to their holdings.

Splitoff In a splitoff, shares in an asset or assets of a firm are created, but existing stockholders are then given the option to exchange their parent company shares for these new shares.

The Mechanics

In terms of the mechanics, divestitures are the most straightforward to understand. The firm sells the assets to the highest bidder and then uses the cash generated by the sale to pay a special dividend or to buy back stock. In the case of spinoffs and splitups, the existing stockholders receive the new shares of stock in proportion to their existing holdings, while in the case of splitoffs, the firm offers stockholders the option to convert their existing shares for the new shares in the subsidiary. The SEC also requires that stock issued in spinoffs be registered, to prevent abuses of the process.

Spinoffs may be taxed as dividends if firms do not meet certain requirements under the tax code, which is designed to ensure that there is a business purpose for the divestiture rather than, tax avoidance. First, the parent and the subsidiary must be engaged in business for the five years preceding the spinoff, and the subsidiary must be at least 80% owned by the parent. Second, the parent has to distribute the shares in the subsidiary without a prearranged plan for these securities to be resold.

The Rationale

Firms may choose to divest or spin off assets for a number of reasons and may choose one approach over the others:

1. *Source of Undervaluation:* The initial rationale for divestitures, spinoffs, splitoffs, and splitups is the perceived undervaluation of some or all of the firm's components. The firm may be undervalued for a number of different reasons, each of which lends itself to a different response.

   - If the poor quality of incumbent management at the division or business level is one of the reasons for the low value assigned to a business, the firm will probably gain the most by selling the business, severing its connection to incumbent management. If, on the other hand, the problem lies in the quality of the management at the corporate level, a spinoff may be all that is needed.

   - If there is a broad perception that sections of the business are undervalued because of the pall created by other sections of the business, the appropriate response would be a spinoff, if only one business line is involved, or a splitup, if multiple business lines are involved. As an example of a spinoff, consider the pressure brought to bear on the tobacco firms, such as Philip Morris and RJR Nabisco, to spin off their food businesses, because of the perception that the lawsuits overhanging the tobacco businesses were weighing down the values of their food businesses as well. An example of a splitup comes from AT&T, which has split up into three business lines, each trading separate shares.

- If there is a perception on the part of some stockholders that a section of the firm is undervalued, a splitoff may make more sense because it allows these stockholders the option to exchange their shares for the new shares, maximizing the value increment to the firm.

  In the case of spinoffs, splitoffs, and splitups, the division or assets can continue to operate relatively smoothly. A sale or breakup of the assets might have a disruptive influence, however, which in turn might lower their value.

2. ***Tax and Regulatory Concerns:*** One or another of these options may provide a tax benefit, making it more favorable. For instance, Marriott spun off its real estate operations into a Real Estate Investment Trust (REIT) in the late 1980s. One reason for the spinoff might have been the perception of undervaluation. An even stronger reason might have been the tax advantages accruing from the REIT status, since REITs do not pay taxes at the entity level. A second factor is that the spun-off entity might be under fewer regulatory constraints than the parent company. For instance, AT&T may have decided to spin off its non-telephone businesses in part because the regulatory burden under which the phone business operated was constraining its other business pursuits as well.

3. ***Expropriation of Bondholder Wealth:*** Some divestitures or spinoffs are motivated by the desire to transfer wealth from bondholders to stockholders. In a divestiture, the sale of an existing asset and the payment of a liquidating dividend clearly leave bondholders worse off. In a spinoff or splitup, the results are more ambiguous, since the spun-off entities often take a share of the debt with them.

Real Estate Investment Trusts (REITs): A real estate investment trust is a real estate holding firm with traded securities, which is entitled to special tax treatment in return for restrictions on dividends and investment policy.

?

10.16 SPINOFF, SPLITOFF, OR DIVESTITURE?

MegaCorp is a conglomerate; one of its divisions, MegaOil, an oil service business, has reported declining earnings over the last five years and has underperformed other oil service companies. The other divisions of MegaCorp have all outperformed their peer groups and reported healthy earnings. The management of the company is considering a restructuring. Which of the following actions would you recommend to MegaCorp?

☐ Sell the oil service subsidiary to the highest bidder.

☐ Spin off the oil service subsidiary.

☐ Split off the oil service subsidiary.

Explain.

Empirical Evidence

Linn and Rozeff (1984) examined the price reaction to announcements of divestitures by firms and reported an average excess return of 1.45% for 77 divestitures between 1977 and 1982. Their results have been confirmed by a number of other studies of selloffs. They also note an interesting contrast between firms that announce the

	Motive Announced	
Price Announced	Yes	No
Yes	3.92%	2.30%
No	0.70%	0.37%

Table 10.7 MARKET REACTION TO DIVESTITURE ANNOUNCEMENTS

sale price and motive for the divestiture at the time of the divestiture, and those that do not: In general, markets react much more positively to the first group than to the second, as shown in Table 10.7. It appears that financial markets view firms that are evasive about the reasons for and the use of proceeds from divestitures with skepticism.

Schipper and Smith (1983) examined 93 firms that announced spinoffs between 1963 and 1981 and reported an average excess return of 2.84% in the two days surrounding the announcement. Similar results are reported in Hite and Owens (1983) and Miles and Rosenfeld (1983). Further, there is evidence that the excess returns increase with the magnitude of the spun-off entity. Finally, Schipper and Smith find evidence that the excess returns are greater for firms in which the spinoff is motivated by tax and regulatory concerns.

CHOOSING AMONG THE ALTERNATIVES

As you can see, firms have a variety of options available to them when it comes to returning cash to stockholders. They can pay out the cash as dividends—either regular or special—repurchase stock, enter into forward contracts to buy stock, or spin off businesses and distribute shares in these businesses to their stockholders. In this section, we will attempt to develop a general framework that brings together all these factors.

The Determinants

The broad determinants of which approach a firm should use to return cash to stockholders include the tax implications of each approach, the effect on a firm's flexibility on future actions, and the signaling benefits (or price effect) that may accrue from each of the actions. In addition, firms often consider how ratings agencies and analysts will view these actions, and the restrictions imposed by existing bond covenants, in making their final decisions.

Information Effects and Signaling Incentives

There is a clear information effect associated with each of the actions described above. The signaling benefit from each action will vary, however, depending upon the degree of commitment associated with it. Thus, increases in regular dividends convey a larger commitment than do equity repurchases, for example, since the former have to be maintained in future periods. Table 10.8 ranks the actions described above in terms of the commitment associated with each and the associated signaling benefit.

Table 10.8   COMMITMENT AND SIGNALING BENEFIT ASSOCIATED WITH ACTIONS

Action	Commitment	Signaling Benefit
Regular Dividend	To continue payment at the same level in future periods	High
Special Dividend	None	None
Equity Repurchase	Generally low, unless the company has a practice of buying back stock; it may, however, operate as a signal that the stock is currently undervalued	Low–Moderate
Forward Equity Contracts	To buy stock at the forward price	High
Stock Splits/Dividends	Generally none, but some firms may be expected to maintain the same dollar dividend per share (which would be an increase in dividends)	Low
Spinoffs/Splitups	May operate as a signal that the business being spun off is undervalued	Low–Moderate

Stockholder Tax Preferences

Each of the actions described above has tax consequences, in terms of both the rate at which stockholders will be taxed and the time these taxes are due. These tax consequences will vary across different types of stockholders—individual versus institutional, taxable versus tax-exempt, and wealthy versus poor. Thus, a firm needs to know who its stockholders are in order to choose an optimal approach to returning cash to stockholders. Table 10.9 summarizes the tax consequences of each action for stockholders.

Effect on Flexibility

Firms value flexibility in making investment, financing, and dividend decisions in the future. To the degree that some of the actions described above reduce flexibility more than others, firms may avoid taking them. The tradeoff, however, is between preserving flexibility and increasing the signaling benefits from a given action. Increasing dividends has a large positive signaling benefit precisely because it requires a commitment on the part of the firm and because it reduces flexibility.

Bond Covenants

In some cases, bond covenants may restrict a firm's flexibility in setting or changing dividends. In particular, these covenants may specify that no more than a specified percentage of earnings can be paid out as dividends (to prevent firms from paying out liquidating dividends) and that either equity repurchases have to be approved by bondholders, or the bonds must be puttable if the equity repurchase goes through. In fact, bond covenant restrictions on financing policy may also constrain the firm when it comes to deciding how and how much to return to stockholders.

In an interesting twist on this same principle, it can be argued that firms that do not use the freedom bond covenants grant them to set dividends may be transferring wealth to bondholders, especially if bond prices are set on the assumption that

	Table 10.9 TAX CONSEQUENCES OF ACTIONS	
Action	**Tax Consequences to Individual Investors**	
Regular Dividend	• Individual investors are taxed at ordinary tax rate.	
	• Corporate investors are exempt from paying taxes on 70% of dividends received.	
Special Dividend	• Individual investors are taxed at ordinary tax rate.	
	• Corporate investors are exempt from paying taxes on 85% of dividends received.	
Equity Repurchase	• Both individual and corporate investors are taxed at capital gains tax rate.	
Forward Equity Contracts	• Both individual and corporate investors are taxed at capital gains tax rate.	
Stock Splits/Dividends	• Generally no tax consequences for investors.	
Spinoffs/Splitups	• Not taxable if it fulfills the conditions laid out in the tax law.	

they will. To illustrate, if the bond covenant restricts dividend payments to 50% of earnings, and bond prices are set on the assumption that they will be paid, a firm that pays out only 20% of its earnings as dividends may be enriching the bondholders at the expense of the stockholders.

Ratings Agency/Analyst Views
When it comes to choosing among alternative approaches to returning cash or assets to stockholders, firms often consider the views of investors and equity research analysts, on the one hand, and of rating agencies and other representatives of bondholders, on the other. To the degree that the interests of the groups do not coincide, the firm may have to choose between them. To illustrate, a firm might be under pressure to spin off its most valuable assets if stockholders feel that the value of these assets is being dragged down by a negative perception of the rest of the firm. At the same time, the firms' bondholders may be averse to a spinoff, especially if it reduces their claim on these assets.

?

10.17 STOCK DIVIDENDS

Can a spinoff ever be viewed as good news by both bondholders and stockholders?
☐ Yes
☐ No
Explain.

A General Framework
In a general framework, firms will consider *all* of these determinants in deciding how to return cash to stockholders. Based upon the above discussion, for instance, we can draw the following conclusions:

1. Firms that want to derive the maximum signaling benefit from the return of the cash, and whose stockholders like or are indifferent to cash dividends, will likely increase regular dividends. Firms that want to derive the signaling benefit but whose stockholders are more resistant to dividends might have to enter into forward contracts to repurchase equity.

2. Firms that are unsure about their capacity to keep generating excess cash in future periods are more inclined to use special dividends, if their stockholder base likes dividends, or equity repurchases, if it does not.

3. Firms that do not have excess cash flows in the current period, but believe in their capacity to generate higher cash flows in the future may use stock splits and stock dividends, with the implicit understanding that they will be increasing dividends in future periods.

4. Firms that have assets they believe to be significantly undervalued can sell the assets and return the cash to stockholders (special dividends or equity repurchases), if the assets are liquid and the perceived quality of incumbent management is one of the reasons for the undervaluation. If the assets are not liquid, however, and it is desirable for incumbent management to stay in place, firms should consider spinoffs, whereby existing stockholders get stock in the undervalued assets.

? **10.18 STOCK BUYBACKS, DIVIDENDS, OR CASH RETENTION?**

Immunotech, Inc. is a small electronics firm whose earnings and stock price have climbed 100% over the last two years. A large one-year contract from the Defense Department has created a large cash inflow in the current year, and Immunotech does not have the capacity to take on more investments this year (due to a shortage of skilled employees). Immunotech has never paid a dividend before. Which of the following actions would you recommend?

☐ Hold the cash for projects in future years.

☐ Initiate a regular dividend to attract new investors to the company and signal.

☐ Pay a special dividend.

☐ Buy back stock.

☐ Other:

Explain.

CONCLUSION

Like investment and financing decisions, dividend decisions involve tradeoffs. Unlike the former, however, there seems to be little consensus on where the tradeoffs should lead us in terms of the "right" dividend policy. On the one hand, some believe that due to the tax disadvantages associated with receiving dividends, relative to price appreciation, firms should reduce or even eliminate dividends and consider alternative ways of returning cash to stockholders. On the other hand, many argue that dividend increases operate as positive financial signals and that there are investors who like dividends, notwithstanding the tax disadvantages. Finally, there is the school of thought that argues that dividend policy should not really affect value, as long as it does not affect the firm's investment policy. This argument maintains that, as long as there are enough investors in each dividend clientele, firms should not be penalized for adopting a particular dividend policy.

In summary, there is some truth to all of these viewpoints, and it may be possible to develop a consensus around the points on which they agree. The reality is that dividend policy requires a tradeoff between the additional tax liability it may create for some investors against the potential signaling and free cash flow benefits of making the dividend commitment. In some cases, the firm may choose not to increase or initiate dividends, because its stockholders are in high tax brackets and are particularly averse to dividends. In other cases, dividend increases may result.

Finally, firms should consider the range of alternatives to returning cash to stockholders, such as equity buybacks, forward contracts, spinoffs and splitoff, and choose the "right" way based on their own characteristics.

PROBLEMS AND QUESTIONS

1. Based on the empirical evidence that you have been presented with in this chapter, state whether the following statements are true or false.
   a. Firms are reluctant to change dividends.

      True   False
   b. Stock prices generally go up on the ex-dividend date by less than the amount of the dividend.

      True   False
   c. Increasing dividend payments to stockholders generally makes bondholders in the firm better off.

      True   False

2. Dividend policy is often described as "sticky." What is meant by this description? What might explain the sticky nature of dividends?

3. Companies are far more reluctant to cut dividends than to increase them. Why might this be the case? What are the implications for financial markets when firms announce that they will be cutting dividends?

4. Under what assumptions can the Miller–Modigliani argument that dividends are irrelevant be made? What types of firms are most likely to fit these assumptions?

5. Dividends create a tax disadvantage for investors. Is this statement true for all investors and all markets? Under what conditions is it *not* true?

6. A company that historically has had low capital investments and paid out high dividends is entering a new industry, in which capital expenditure requirements are much higher. What should the firm do to its dividends? What practical problems might it run into?

7. "An increase in dividends operates as a positive financial signal." Explain this statement. Is there empirical evidence to support it?

8. Can a dividend increase ever be a negative financial signal? Explain. Is there any evidence to support this hypothesis?

9. If Consolidated Power is priced at $50 with dividend, and its price falls to $46.50 when a dividend of $5 is paid, what is the implied marginal rate of personal taxes for its stockholders? Assume that the tax on capital gains is 40% of the personal income tax.

10. Show that, if companies are excluded from paying taxes on 85% of the dividends they receive from other corporations and if the marginal investor is a corporation, then the ex-dividend day equality becomes

$$\frac{P_B - P_A}{D} = \frac{(1 - .15t_o)}{(1 - t_{cg})}$$

11. You are comparing the dividend policies of three dividend-paying utilities. You have collected the following information on the ex-dividend behavior of these firms.

	NE Gas	SE Bell	Western Electric
Price before	$50	$70	$100
Price after	48	67	95
Dividends/share	4	4	5

If you were a tax-exempt investor, which company would you use to make "dividend arbitrage" profits? How would you go about doing so?

12. Southern Rail has just declared a dividend of $1. The average investor in Southern Rail faces an ordinary tax rate of 50%. Although the capital gains rate is also 50%, it is believed that the investor gets the advantage of deferring this tax until future years. (The effective capital gains rate will therefore be 50% discounted back to the present.) If the price of the stock before the ex-dividend day is $10 and it drops to $9.20 by the end of the ex-dividend day, how many years is the average investor deferring capital gains taxes? (Assume that the opportunity cost used by the investor in evaluating future cash flows is 10%.)

13. LMN Corporation, a real estate corporation, is planning to pay a dividend of $0.50 per share. Most of the investors in LMN Corporation are other corporations, who pay 40% of their ordinary income and 28% of their capital gains as taxes. However, they are allowed to exempt 85% of the dividends they receive from taxes. If the shares are selling at $10 per share, how much would you expect the stock price to drop on the ex-dividend day?

14. UJ Gas is a utility that has followed a policy of increasing dividends every quarter by 5% over dividends in the prior year. The company announces that it will increase quarterly dividends from $1.00 to $1.02 next quarter. What price reaction would you expect to the announcement? Why?

15. Microsoft Corporation, which has had a history of high growth and no dividends, announces that it will start paying dividends next quarter. How would you expect its stock price to react to the announcement? Why?

16. JC Automobiles is a small auto parts manufacturing firm, which has paid $1.00 in annual dividends each year for the last five years. It an-

nounces that dividends will increase to $1.25 next year. What would you expect the price reaction to be? Why? If your answer is different from the prior problem, explain the reasons for the difference.

17. Would your answer be different for the previous problem if JC Automobiles were a large firm followed by 35 analysts? Why or why not?

18. WeeMart Corporation, a retailer of children's clothes, announces a cut in dividends following a year in which both revenues and earnings dropped significantly. How would you expect its stock price to react? Explain.

19. RJR Nabisco, in response to stockholder pressure in 1996, announced a significant increase in dividends paid to stockholders, financed by the sale of some of its assets. What would you expect the stock price to do? Why?

20. RJR Nabisco also had $10 billion in bonds outstanding at the time of the dividend increase. How would you expect Nabisco's bonds to react to the announcement? Why?

21. A recent innovation in managerial incentive schemes is for the shareholders of a corporation to partially compensate management with stock options. How could such a scheme affect management's decisions concerning optimal dividend policy?

22. If the next tax reform act were to impose a flat tax of 23% on all income, how do you think this would affect corporations' dividend policies? Why?

23. This chapter has demonstrated the consequences of differential taxation of dividends and capital gains: firms have weakened incentives to pay dividends. Why would the U.S. government (acting through the tax code) want these consequences?

24. A company that has excess cash on hand is trying to decide whether to pay out the cash as a regular dividend or a special dividend or to repurchase stock with it. What are some of the considerations that would enter into this decision?

25. An equity repurchase will always provide a lesser signaling benefit than will an equivalent dollar increase in regular dividends. Explain this statement. Does it hold true if the comparison is to special dividends?

26. Suppose that a firm's management is anticipating having to make future cuts in dividends when

they unexpectedly get awarded a large cash settlement in a court decision. Could the firm conceivably reduce total dividend payments by using the surplus to repurchase shares? If so, would this be the optimal way to use the windfall?

27. In many cases, firms have offered to repurchase shares from one of their shareholders in what is called a "targeted" repurchase. In a targeted repurchase, only the shareholder named is allowed to tender shares, and the purchase price is often well above the current market price. Such repurchases are generally used to "buy off" someone who has announced the intention to take over the firm. Would such an arrangement benefit or hurt the shareholders who aren't allowed to tender shares? Why?

28. A firm is planning to borrow money to make an equity repurchase to increase its stock price. It is basing its analysis on the fact that there will be fewer shares outstanding after the repurchases, and higher earnings per share.
    a. Will earnings per share always increase after such an action? Explain.
    b. Will the higher earnings per share always translate into a higher stock price? Explain.
    c. Under what conditions will such a transaction lead to a higher price?

29. Stock repurchases can send different signals to the marketplace depending on whether or not management is allowed to tender any shares they own for repurchase. Suppose that JCL Steel has 1 million shares outstanding at a market price of $42 per share. The firm's current debt to capital ratio is 0.5 and interest payments are 10% of debt. JCL has just had a very good year and has $10 million of "extra" cash available. Management owns 5% of outstanding shares, and the firm has just announced that it will reduce debt by $5 million and buy back 100,000 shares at $50 per share. Managers will not be allowed to tender their shares, and earnings before interest and taxes are expected to be $15 million next year.
    a. If the firm's tax rate is 40%, what effect will the combined debt and equity repurchase have on EPS?
    b. Calculate JCL's current P/E ratio and determine the post-buyback price assuming that the P/E stays the same. Compare it to the $50 tender offer. Do you think

management agrees with your assumption? Why or why not?
    c. Could management have caused the stock market to reevaluate its assumption about the "correct" price for JCL stock by buying back the 100,000 shares at the current market price? Why or why not?
    d. Would your answers to (b) and (c) have changed if management had been allowed to tender shares for repurchase?

30. ABT Trucking has excess cash of $300,000 and 100,000 shares outstanding. The firm is contemplating paying this $300,000 out as an extra dividend to shareholders. Post-dividend, the price is expected to be $27 per share. Alternatively, the company is considering using the excess cash to repurchase 10,000 shares at $30 per share.
    a. If shareholders' ordinary income is taxed at 40% and their capital gains are taxed at 28%, how should the firm disburse the money?
    b. If the shareholders consist mainly of other corporations, how should the firm disburse the money?

31. JR Computers, a firm that manufactures and sells personal computers, is an all-equity firm with 100,000 shares outstanding, $10 million in earnings after taxes, and a market value of $150 million. Assume that this firm borrows $60 million at an interest rate of 8% and buys back 40,000 shares using the funds. If the firm's tax rate is 50%, estimate
    a. The effect on earnings per share of the action.
    b. What the interest rate on the debt would have to be for the earnings per share effect to disappear.

32. JK Tobacco, a diversified firm in food and tobacco is concerned about its stock price, which has dropped almost 25% over the previous two years. The managers of the firm believe that the price drop has occurred because the tobacco division is the target of lawsuits, which may result in a large liability for the firm. What action would you recommend to the firm? What might be some of the barriers to such an action?

33. The stock price of GenChem Corporation, a chemical manufacturing firm with declining earnings, has dropped from $50 to $35 over the course

of the last year, largely as a consequence of the market perception that the current management is incompetent. The management is planning to split off the firm into three businesses but plans to continue running all of them. Do you think the splitoff will cause the stock price to increase? Why or why not? What would you recommend?

34. The stock prices of firms generally increase when they announce spinoffs. How would you explain this phenomenon? On which types of firms would you expect spinoffs to have the largest positive impact, and why?

35. WeeKids, a firm that operates play arenas for children, has paid $1 as a dividend per share each year for the last five years. Because of a decline in revenues and increased competition, their earnings have plummeted this year. They substitute a $1 stock dividend for the cash dividend. What would you expect the market reaction to the stock dividend to be? Why?

36. In 1995, the Limited, a specialty retailing firm, announced that it was splitting up its businesses into three separate businesses—the Limited stores forming one business, Victoria's Secret and lingerie becoming the second business, and its other holdings forming the third business. The Limited had been struggling over the previous four years with lackluster sales and operating profits overall, and the market reacted positively to the announcement. What might be some of the explanations for this reaction?

37. JW Bell, a regulated company, also has extensive holdings in nonregulated businesses and reports consolidated income from all segments. There are severe restrictions on investment and financing policy in the regulated component of the business. Can you provide a rationale for spinning off the nonregulated businesses?

38. An article in a business periodical recently argued that the only reason for spinoffs and splitoffs was to make it easier for Wall Street to value firms. Why would a spinoff or a splitoff make it easier to value a firm? Do you agree that this is the only reason for spinoffs and splitoffs? If so, what types of firms would you expect to take these actions?

39. JC Conglo Corporation is a firm that was founded in the 1960s and grew to become a conglomerate through acquisitions. It has substantial corporate costs that get allocated over the different divisions of the firm. Analysts argue that divesting the firm of these divisions will increase value, since the buyer will not have to pay the corporate costs. Under what conditions would spinning off the divisions of the firm add to the value of the firm? Conversely, under what conditions would a spinoff have a neutral or negative effect on value?

40. RJR Nabisco, the food and tobacco giant, is waging a battle against dissident stockholders who want it to divest itself of its food division and pay a large dividend to the stockholders. RJR Nabisco offers to spin off the food division, while keeping it under incumbent management. Are stockholders likely to be satisfied? Why or why not?

LIVE CASE STUDY

VIII. DIVIDEND POLICY

Objective: To examine the firm's current dividend policy in light of its current characteristics

Key Questions

- How has this company returned cash to its owners? Has it paid dividends, bought back stock, or spun off assets?
- Given this firm's characteristics today, how would you recommend that they return cash to stockholders (assuming that they have excess cash)?

Framework for Analysis

1. Historical Dividend Policy
- How much has this company paid in dividends over the last few years?
- How much stock has this company bought back over the last few years?

2. Firm Characteristics
- How easily can the firm convey information to financial markets? In other words, how necessary is it for them to use dividend policy as a signal?
- Who is the average stockholder in this firm? Does he or she like dividends or would they prefer stock buybacks?
- How well can this firm forecast its future financing needs? How valuable is preserving flexibility to this firm?
- Are there any significant bond covenants that you know of that restrict the firm's dividend policy?
- How does this firm compare with other firms in the sector in terms of dividend policy?

Getting Information on Dividend Policy

You can get information on dividends paid and stock bought back over time from the financials of the firm. (The statement of changes in cash flows is usually the best source for both.) To see typical dividend payout ratios and yields for the sector in which this firm operates, examine the data set on industry averages on my Web site (**inddiv.xls**)

Outline

Part IV: Additional Topics

- Lecture slides on deterministic capital budgeting

- Chapter 8 of "Advanced Engineering Economics" by Park and Sharp-Bette

- Lecture slides on utility theory

- Chapter 9 of "Advanced Engineering Economics" by Park and Sharp-Bette

- Chapter 13 of "Advanced Engineering Economics" by Park and Sharp-Bette

Deterministic Capital Budgeting

- **Primal formulation**

max

$$Z = \sum_{j=1}^{J} p_j \cdot x_j$$

subject to

$$-\sum_{j=1}^{J} a_{nj} \cdot x_j \leq M_n \quad , \quad n = 0, 1, \dots, N$$

$$x_j \leq 1 \quad , \quad j = 1, 2, \dots, J$$

$$x_j \geq 0 \quad , \quad j = 1, 2, \dots, J$$

Where:

➢ p_j is the present value of project j

➢ x_j is the project selection variable

➢ M_n is the budget limit at time n

➢ N is the end of the planning period

Deterministic Capital Budgeting

- **Complementary slackness conditions**

$$\rho_n^*(M_n + \sum_{j=1}^{J} a_{nj}x_j^*) = 0 \qquad , \quad n = 0,1,...,N$$

$$x_j^*(\mu_j^* - p_j - \sum_{n=0}^{N} a_{nj}\rho_n^*) = 0 \quad , \quad j = 1,2,...,J$$

$$\mu_j^*(1 - x_j^*) = 0 \qquad\qquad , \quad j = 1,2,...,J$$

> The complementary slackness conditions hold at the optimal solution

Deterministic Capital Budgeting

Pure Capital Rationing with no lending or borrowing allowed

- **Economic interpretation: the present value of a project plus the sum of the cash flows over the horizon "discounted" by the dual variables is:**

  - Non-positive for a rejected project

  - Exactly zero for a partially funded project

  - Non-negative for a fully funded project

- **Primal formulation with one lending, one borrowing rate, and unlimited borrowing capacity**

max
$$Z = \sum_{j=1}^{J} \hat{a}_j . x_j + v_N - w_N$$

subject to
$$-\sum_{j=1}^{J} a_{0j} . x_j + v_0 - w_0 \leq M_0$$

$$-\sum_{j=1}^{J} a_{nj} . x_j - (1 + r_l) v_{n-1} + v_n + (1 + r_b) w_{n-1} - w_n \leq M_n \quad , \quad n = 1, \ldots, N$$

$$v_n, w_n \geq 0 \quad , \quad n = 0, 1, \ldots, N$$

$$0 \leq x_j \leq 1 \quad , \quad j = 1, 2, \ldots, J$$

Where:
- r_l is the lending rate
- r_b is the borrowing rate

Deterministic Capital Budgeting

- **Let us distinguish three scenarios for a project *j*. Using the dual formulation and complementary slackness, we obtain:**

  - The project is rejected

$$\hat{a}_j + \sum_{n=0}^{N} a_{nj} \rho_n^* \leq 0$$

  - The project is partially funded

$$\hat{a}_j + \sum_{n=0}^{N} a_{nj} \rho_n^* = 0$$

  - The project is fully funded

$$\hat{a}_j + \sum_{n=0}^{N} a_{nj} \rho_n^* \geq 0$$

- **Other insights from duality and complementary slackness**

  ➢ Dual variables:

$$\rho_N^* = 1$$

$$(1 + r_l)\rho_{n+1}^* \leq \rho_n^* \leq (1 + r_b)\rho_{n+1}^* \;,\;\; n = 0,1,....N - 1$$

  ➢ In period of borrowing

$$w_n > 0 \Rightarrow \begin{array}{c} v_n = 0 \\ \rho_n^* = (1 + r_b)\rho_{n+1}^* \end{array}$$

  ➢ In period of lending

$$v_n > 0 \Rightarrow \begin{array}{c} w_n = 0 \\ \rho_n^* = (1 + r_l)\rho_{n+1}^* \end{array}$$

Outline

Part IV: Additional Topics

- Lecture slides on deterministic capital budgeting

- Chapter 8 of "Advanced Engineering Economics" by Park and Sharp-Bette

- Lecture slides on utility theory

- Chapter 9 of "Advanced Engineering Economics" by Park and Sharp-Bette

- Chapter 13 of "Advanced Engineering Economics" by Park and Sharp-Bette

Deterministic Capital Budgeting Models

8.1 INTRODUCTION

In the previous chapter we determined that we should select from among multiple alternatives by choosing the one with the maximum net present value (*PV*) or by using the incremental approach with one of several criteria. There are two important characteristics of the problems solved in the previous chapter.

1. We could easily formulate and list all mutually exclusive alternatives of interest.

2. There is an underlying assumption of ability to borrow and lend unlimited amounts at a single, fixed interest rate. When budget limits are imposed, the borrowing ability at time 0 is restricted, and we are left with a single, fixed interest rate for future lending, or reinvestment.

In this chapter we relax these assumptions. We consider problems in which budget limits are imposed during several time periods, the projects have interdependencies, and there are different, but known, borrowing and lending opportunities. In short, we examine problems for which it would be exceedingly difficult to specify all mutually exclusive alternatives. This type of analysis is called capital budgeting. In keeping with the sense of Part Two of this book, we assume certainty with respect to all information. Linear programming (LP) is a convenient tool for analyzing such situations, and we give a brief introduction to its use in Section 8.2.

We will also see that *PV* maximization is not necessarily our best objective, for different reinvestment rates are possible. In the pure capital rationing model (Section 8.3), which allows no external borrowing and lending, this situation has been the focus of much academic controversy during the last twenty years. We include a brief review of the major arguments, not from the view of favoring any one of them but rather to give the reader an important historical perspective on the subject.

The inclusion of borrowing and lending opportunities (Section 8.4) leads to more realistic operational models. In some situations the previously mentioned academic controversy disappears, and in others it reappears. Weingartner's horizon model (Section 8.5) provides the analyst with a convenient way of avoiding these issues, while yielding solutions consistent with *PV* analysis of situations allowing unlimited borrowing and lending. Bernhard's general model (Section 8.6) allows for the use of dividends and other terms in the objective function, and for a variety of linear and nonlinear constraints.

In Section 8.7 we finally consider the situation of integer restrictions, which we have avoided until now because it requires more difficult mathematical analysis. Multiple objectives are discussed in Section 8.8. Following the summary, the chapter ends with a case study illustrating the application of Bernhard's general model to a dividend-terminal-wealth problem.

8.2 THE USE OF LINEAR PROGRAMMING MODELS

Because linear programming models are so widely used in capital budgeting, we present a brief introduction here. In this section we illustrate the application of LP in a typical example. A word of caution is in order here: the example given is *not* intended to represent the best principles of capital budgeting but *rather to illustrate* the use of LP. The various methods of capital budgeting (for the deterministic case) are given in the following sections.

Example 8.1

Table 8.1 presents data for Example 8.1, which concerns five investment projects. There are budget limits of $4,400 and $4,000 at time 0 and time 1, respectively; these limits do not apply to any funds generated by the projects themselves. We note the sign convention that inflows are positive and outflows negative. Most of the projects require investment during the first two years before they return any funds. All the projects are simple investments with unique, positive, real *IRR*s, and for a sufficiently low *MARR*, say 20%, all have positive *PV*s. But from the budget limits it is clear that we cannot accept all of them; hence the capital rationing problem. Moreover, project 5 starts to provide cash inflow at time 1, when all the others require outflows, so we would like to consider this advantage of project 5. (The solution to Example 8.1 follows in the text).   □

8.2.1 Criterion Function To Be Optimized
A variety of criterion functions could be optimized.

- Maximize the *PV* of the cash flows of the selected projects.
- Maximize the *IRR* of the total cash flow of the selected projects.

Table 8.1 Data for Example 8.1

Cash Flow at Time	Project				
	1	2	3	4	5
0	−$1,000	−$1,200	−$2,000	−$2,500	−$3,000
1	−2,000	−2,400	−2,100	−1,300	900
2	2,000	2,500	3,000	2,000	1,400
3	2,900	3,567	3,000	2,000	1,600
4	0	0	1,308	2,000	1,800
5	0	0	0	2,296	955
PV(20%)	$400	600	700	850	900
IRR, %	29.1	31.3	29.7	28.9	32.2

Budgets for external sources of funds: $n = 0$, $4,400; $n = 1$, $4,000

- Maximize the "utility" of the dividends that can be paid from the cash flows of the selected projects.
- Maximize the cash that can be accumulated at the end of the planning period.

Other functions could be used. The important thing is that the function is clearly expressed in terms of the decision variables for project acceptance or rejection and that it is (we hope) linear.

Let us see, for *illustration* purposes, the *PV* of the cash flows of the selected projects,

$$\text{Max} \sum_j p_j x_j \tag{8.1}$$

where p_j is the *PV* of project j, using $i = MARR$, and
x_j is a project selection variable, with $0 \le x_j \le 1$.

Using a *MARR* value of $i = 20\%$, we obtain

j	1	2	3	4	5
p_j	$400	600	700	850	900

Thus Eq. 8.1 becomes, for Example 8.1,

$$\text{max } \$400x_1 + 600x_2 + 700x_3 + 850x_4 + 900x_5 \tag{8.2}$$

The project selection variables are continuous in this linear formulation. A value of $x_j = 0$ means that the project is not selected, a value of $x_j = 1$ implies complete acceptance, and a fractional values implies partial acceptance. We will leave aside the question of the practicality of fractional acceptance. In some industries, such as oil and gas exploration, fractional acceptance is common practice; generally, though, it is not possible to accept fractional projects without changing the nature of their cash flows. (We will consider integer restrictions in Section 8.7.)

8.2.2 Multiple Budget Periods

The budget limits for Example 8.1 can be expressed by linear constraints on the selection variables,

$$-\sum_j a_{nj}x_j \le M_n, \qquad n = 0, 1, ..., N \tag{8.3}$$

where a_{nj} = cash flow for project j at time n, inflows having a plus sign, and outflows a minus sign,

M_n = budget limit on externally supplied funds at time n, and

N = end of the planning period.

Notice that M_n represents only the funds from sources other than the projects. The equation states that project outflows minus project inflows at time n must be less than the budget limit on funds from other sources at time n. A negative value for M_n implies that the set of selected projects must *generate* funds. (Equation 8.3 states that cash outflows $\le$ cash inflows + M_n). Note that the absence of a budget limit is not equivalent to M_n being zero; the former implies a positive, unbounded M_n value. Equations of the type (8.3) are usually called budget constraints or cash balance equations. Inflows and outflows for borrowing, lending, and dividend payments may also be included; these are discussed in later sections.

Applying the equation to Example 8.1, we obtain two constraints,

$n = 0$: $\quad \$1{,}000x_1 + 1{,}200x_2 + 2{,}000x_3 + 2{,}500x_4 + 3{,}000x_5 \le 4{,}400$

$n = 1$: $\quad \$2{,}000x_1 + 2{,}400x_2 + 2{,}100x_3 + 1{,}300x_4 - 900x_5 \le 4{,}000 \tag{8.4}$

The advantage of project 5 at time 1 is clearly apparent here; setting $x_5 = 1$ increases the amount available for other projects by \$900. There are no stated limits for times 2, 3, 4, and 5, so we need not write constraints for these times.

8.2.3 Project Limits and Interdependencies

The limits on the selection variables given following Eq. 8.1 are presented here again.

$$x_j \le 1, \qquad j = 1, \ldots, J \tag{8.5}$$

The nonnegativity constraints are expressed separately:

$$x_j \ge 0, \qquad j = 1, \ldots, J \tag{8.6}$$

It is also possible to have interdependencies among project selection variables. Some common types are the following.

1. Mutual exclusivity—when a subset of projects form a mutually exclusive set.

$$x_j + x_k + x_m \leqslant 1 \qquad (8.7)$$

The selection of one project precludes the selection of either of the other two in Eq. 8.7. Note that a complete interpretation is possible only if the x_j are restricted to integers.

2. Contingency—when execution of one project depends on execution of another.

$$x_j - x_k \leqslant 0 \qquad (8.8)$$

Here x_j cannot be selected unless x_k is also selected.

3. Complementary and competitive projects—when the selection of two projects changes the cash flows involved. For complementary projects inflows are greater than the sum of the individual project inflows; the opposite is true for competitive projects. Such situations can be handled by defining a new project for the combination and then establishing mutual exclusivity,

$$x_j + x_k + x_m \leqslant 1$$

where x_m is a combination of j and k. (If there are many such situations, the method becomes cumbersome.)

We will not impose interdependencies in Example 8.1, in order to keep the duality analysis simple at this point. That type of treatment is given in Section 8.5.

8.2.4 LP Formulation of Lorie–Savage Problem

In LP terminology, the *primal problem* formulation of the capital budgeting problem is given symbolically and numerically by Table 8.2. This version summarizes the relationships that have been presented so far in this chapter. This version of the problem is also designated as the LP formulation of the Lorie–Savage problem [15], after the two economists who stated the original form of the project selection problem. Their concern with the problem came from the inadequacies of the *IRR* method to deal with budget limitations and project interdependencies. Our analysis in the next section follows closely the work of Weingartner [20], who applied LP to the Lorie–Savage problem.

8.2.5 Duality Analysis

For every *primal problem* in linear programming, there is a related *dual problem* formulation. Table 8.3 presents both the symbolic and numeric versions of the dual problem for Example 8.1. The dual formulation is a minimization problem stated in terms of the ρ_n and μ_n. By making appropriate conversions from minimization to maximization and from $\geqslant$ to $\leqslant$, we can easily show that the dual formulation of the problem in Table 8.3 is the same as the formulation given in Table 8.2. In other words, the dual of the dual is the primal, and our specific designations are based on habit and convenience.

Table 8.2 *Primal Problem Formulation for Maximizing PV for Example 8.1 (Lorie–Savage Formulation)*

Symbolic

$$\text{Max} \sum_j p_j x_j \tag{8.1}$$

s.t.*

$$[\rho_n] \qquad -\sum_j a_{nj} x_j \le M_n, \qquad n = 0, 1, \ldots, N \tag{8.3}$$

$$[\mu_j] \qquad\qquad x_j \le 1, \qquad j = 1, \ldots, J \tag{8.5}$$

$$x_j \ge 0, \qquad j = 1, \ldots, J \tag{8.6}$$

where p_j = PV of project j using i = MARR,

x_j = project selection variable,

a_{nj} = cash flow for project j at time n; inflows have a plus sign, outflows have a minus sign,

M_n = budget limit on externally supplied funds at time n,

N = end of the planning period,

ρ_n, μ_j = dual variables for the primal constraints.

Numeric

$$\text{Max } \$400x_1 + 600x_2 + 700x_3 + 850x_4 + 900x_5 \tag{8.2}$$

s.t.

$$[\rho_0] \quad \$1,000x_1 + 1,200x_2 + 2,000x_3 + 2,500x_4 + 3,000x_5 \le \$4,400$$

$$[\rho_1] \quad \$2,000x_1 + 2,400x_2 + 2,100x_3 + 1,300x_4 - 900x_5 \le \$4,000 \tag{8.4}$$

$$
\begin{array}{llr}
[\mu_1] & x_1 & \le 1 \\
[\mu_2] & x_2 & \le 1 \\
[\mu_3] & x_3 & \le 1 \\
[\mu_4] & x_4 & \le 1 \\
[\mu_5] & x_5 & \le 1
\end{array}
\tag{8.5}
$$

$$\text{All } x_j \ge 0, j = 1, \ldots, 5 \tag{8.6}$$

*The abbreviation s.t. stands for subject to.

The economic interpretation of the dual problem is to establish prices for each of the scarce resources so that the minimum total possible would be paid for the consumption of the resources, while ensuring that the resources used for any project cost as much as or more than the value of the project, the project PV in this case [5]. We have two categories of resources here. The first category is cash, represented by cash at time 0 and by cash at time 1; the dual variables ρ_0 and ρ_1 represent the prices, respectively. The second category consists of the projects themselves: a project is considered a scarce resource in the sense that we have the opportunity to execute only one of each. The dual variables $\mu_1, \ldots, \mu_5$ correspond to the upper-bound constraints of the projects and represent the respective prices for the project opportunities.

Table 8.3 *Dual Problem Formulation for Example 8.1, Solution to Primal and Dual*

Symbolic

$$\text{Min} \sum_n \rho_n M_n + \sum_j \mu_j \tag{8.9}$$

s.t.

$$[x_j] \quad -\sum_n a_{nj}\rho_n + \mu_j \geq p_j, \quad j = 1, \ldots, J \tag{8.10}$$

$$\rho_n \geq 0, \quad n = 0, 1, \ldots, N \tag{8.11}$$

$$\mu_j \geq 0, \quad j = 1, \ldots, J \tag{8.12}$$

where ρ_n = dual variable for budget constraint,
μ_j = dual variable for project upper bound.

Numeric

$$\text{Min} \quad 4{,}400\rho_0 + 4{,}000\rho_1 + \mu_1 + \mu_2 + \mu_3 + \mu_4 + \mu_5 \tag{8.13}$$

s.t.

$[x_1]$	$+1{,}000\rho_0$	$+2{,}000\rho_1$	$+\mu_1$				≥ 400	
$[x_2]$	$+1{,}200\rho_0$	$+2{,}400\rho_1$		$+\mu_2$			≥ 600	
$[x_3]$	$+2{,}000\rho_0$	$+2{,}100\rho_1$			$+\mu_3$		≥ 700	(8.14)
$[x_4]$	$+2{,}500\rho_0$	$+1{,}300\rho_1$				$+\mu_4$	≥ 850	
$[x_5]$	$+3{,}000\rho_0$	$-\ \ 900\rho_1$				$+\mu_5$	≥ 900	

$$\rho_n, \mu_j \geq 0$$

Solution

Primal variables: $x_1 = 0.22$, $x_2 = 1.00$, $x_3 = 0.0$, $x_4 = 1.0$, $x_5 = 0.16$
Dual variables: $\rho_0 = 0.3130$, $\rho_1 = 0.0435$
$\mu_1 = 0.0$, $\mu_2 = 120.0$, $\mu_3 = 0.0$, $\mu_4 = 10.9$, $\mu_5 = 0.0$
Objective function value: $1,682

If the primal problem is feasible and bounded, there is an optimal solution to both problems. At such an optimum we have, from the dual constraint,

$$\mu_j^* \geq p_j + \sum_n a_{nj}\rho_n^* \tag{8.15}$$

where the asterisk refers to values of the primal and dual variables at the optimum. We know from complementary slackness [5] that if $x_j^* > 0$, the dual constraint is met exactly, and since all dual variables are nonnegative, we have

$$0 \leq \mu_j^* = p_j + \sum_n a_{nj}\rho_n^* \tag{8.16}$$

The μ_j^* represents the opportunity value of project j, and it is equal to the PV plus the cash inflows less any cash outflows evaluated by the ρ_n^*. Hence, for all projects that are accepted fractionally or completely,

$$-\sum_n a_{nj}\rho_n^* \leq p_j \qquad (8.17)$$

Equation 8.17 states that in order for a project to be accepted, its PV must be equal to or greater than the cash outflows minus cash inflows evaluated by the ρ_n^*.

Again from complementary slackness, if $x_j^* < 1$, then $\mu_j^* = 0$. So for fractionally accepted projects (8.17) becomes

$$-\sum_n a_{nj}\rho_n^* = p_j \qquad (8.18)$$

For rejected projects we also have $\mu_j^* = 0$ and, using Eq. 8.15,

$$-\sum_n a_{nj}\rho_n^* \geq p_j \qquad (8.19)$$

In other words, the cash outflows minus cash inflows, evaluated by the ρ_n^*, exceed (or equal) the PV of the project.

We can demonstrate these conditions by using the optimal values of the LP problem given in Table 8.3. For project 1, fractionally accepted, applying (8.18) gives

$$(\$1,000)(0.313) + (2,000)(0.0435) = \$400 = PV$$

The value of cash inflows minus outflows equals the PV.

For project 2, completely accepted, applying (8.16) gives

$$\mu_2^* = \$600 - (1,200)(0.313) - (2,400)(0.0435) = \$120 > 0$$

The opportunity cost of the project is $120, the difference between the PV and the cash outflows minus the cash inflows.

For project 3, rejected, applying (8.19) gives

$$(\$2,000)(0.313) + (2,100)(0.0435) = \$717 \geq \$700$$

Here the cash outflows minus inflows are worth more than the PV, which explains the rejection.

These types of project evaluation, or project pricing, with the dual variables, are fundamental to the LP modeling and analysis of capital budgeting problems. We will see more of this type of analysis in the following sections.

8.3 PURE CAPITAL RATIONING MODELS

The type of model given in Table 8.2 has been extensively analyzed, criticized, and modified during the last twenty years. In this section we attempt to summarize the major arguments so that the reader will obtain a historical perspective on the situation. We do not go into great detail, because the arguments are presented better elsewhere [21] and because the major conclusion to be drawn is that the pure capital rationing (PCR) model is of extremely limited applicability. This fact reinforces the fundamental notion that one must fully understand the assumptions embedded in any mathematical model before attempting to use it.

8.3.1 Criticisms of the PV Model

Among the first to criticize the *PV* model (as in Table 8.2) were Baumol and Quandt [3]. They identified three major flaws.

1. There is no provision in the model for investment outside the firm or for dividend payments.

2. The model does not provide for carryover of unused funds from one period to the next.

3. Assuming that we have an appropriate discount rate *i* for computing the *PV* of each project, this rate is valid in general only for the situation of unlimited borrowing and lending at that rate. Since we have borrowing limits implicitly stated in the budget constraints, an externally determined discount rate is inappropriate.

The first two objections can easily be overcome. For example, investment outside the firm, including lending activities, can easily be represented by new projects. Define project 6 to be lending from time 0 to time 1 at 15%. Then we set $a_{06} = -1$ and $a_{16} = 1.15$ and place no upper bound (or a very large bound) on x_6. Similarly, variables can be defined for divided payments and included in the budget constraints. We would also need to include dividends in the objective function, which implies knowledge of the discount rate appropriate for the owner(s) or shareholders of the firm in order to discount correctly the future dividends. Later, we will see some different methods for including dividends in the objective function.

The third objection is a serious one and requires more attention. To illustrate the difficulties arising from it, let us analyze Example 8.2.

Example 8.2

Table 8.4 presents the data for Example 8.2 along with the optimal LP solution. Example 8.2 is somewhat similar to Example 8.1: projects 1, 2, and 4 are the same; projects 3 and 5 are slightly changed so their *PV*s are negative; project 6 is added to the set; and the budget limits are changed.

Notice that projects 2 and 4 are completely accepted, as they were in

Table 8.4 *Data and Solution for Example 8.2*

Cash Flow at Time	Project					
	1	2	3	4	5	6
0	−$1,000	−$1,200	−$2,000	−2,500	−$3,000	$1,000
1	−2,000	−2,400	−2,100	−1,300	900	−700
2	2,000	2,500	3,000	2,000	1,400	−700
3	2,900	3,567	2,621	2,000	1,600	0
4	0	0	0	2,000	211	0
5	0	0	0	2,296	0	0
PV (20%)	$400	600	−150	850	−250	−70

Budgets for external sources of funds: $n = 0$, $3,000$; $n = 1$, $5,000$

Solution

Primal variables: $x_1 = 0.30$, $x_2 = 1.0$, $x_3 = 0.0$, $x_4 = 1.0$, $x_5 = 0.0$, $x_6 = 1.0$

Dual variables: $\rho_0 = 0.3189$, $\rho_1 = 0.0405$

$\mu_1 = 0.0$, $\mu_2 = 120.0$, $\mu_3 = 0.0$, $\mu_4 = 0.0$, $\mu_5 = 0.0$, $\mu_6 = 220.5$

Objective function value: $1,500

Example 8.1. The dual variables for the budget constraints, ρ_0 and ρ_1, do not have their optimal values changed much, so the pricing of projects 2 and 4 is similar.

Project 2: $\mu_2 = \$120 = \$600 - (1,200)(0.3189) - (2,400)(0.0405)$

Project 4: $\mu_4 = 0 = \$850 - (2,500)(0.3189) - (1,300)(0.0405)$

Here we have an example of a completely accepted project with $\mu_j = 0$. Project 1 is again accepted fractionally, and it prices out at zero.

Project 1: $\mu_1 = 0 = \$400 - (1,000)(0.3189) - (2,000)(0.0405)$

We can demonstrate Eq. 8.19 for a rejected project with negative *PV*.

Project 3: $(\$2,000)(0.3189) + (2,100)(0.0405) = 723 > -150$

This result is hardly surprising since project 3 has only outflows during the critical times and has a negative *PV*.

The real surprise is that project 6, with a negative *PV* of $-\$70$, is accepted. Pricing out by using Eq. 8.16 yields

Project 6: $\mu_6 = \$221 = -70 + (1,000)(0.3189) - (700)(0.0405)$

The value of the $1,000 inflow at time 0, less the value of the $700 outflow at time 1, more than overcomes the negative *PV* and makes project 6 desirable. (The $700 outflow at time 2 is worth zero since there is no constraint on money at this time.) The extra $1,000 when it is needed most enables us to select more of the other projects and thereby increase the overall *PV* of the projects selected. □

Project 6 in Example 8.2 has the cash flow pattern of a borrowing activity. Since its *IRR* = 26%, we are effectively borrowing at a periodic rate of 26% in order to maximize overall *PV* at 20%! This example clearly demonstrates the philosophical conflict in using an interest rate for *PV* maximization when we are faced with a budget limitation. If we have available a borrowing opportunity at a different, higher interest rate, we could be induced to borrow at a rate higher than that used for computing *PV*. The budget limits, in effect, invalidate the use of an externally determined discount rate. The inclusion of lending opportunities and dividend payments does not solve the difficulty, so various authors have attempted other approaches, some of which are discussed in the following.

8.3.2 Consistent Discount Factors

In reformulating the *PV* model to eliminate the incompatibility presented, Baumol and Quandt defined a model in which the discount rates between periods are determined by the model itself [3]. On the basis of our previous notation, their revised model is

$$\underset{x_j, \rho_n}{\text{Max}} \sum_n \sum_j a_{nj} \frac{\rho_n}{\rho_O} x_j \tag{8.20}$$

s.t.[1]
[ρ_n]
$$-\sum_j a_{nj} x_j \leq M_n, \qquad n = 0, 1, ..., N \tag{8.3}$$

$$x_j \geq 0, \qquad j = 1, ..., J \tag{8.6}$$

The terms ρ_n/ρ_0 represent the discount factors from time 0 to time *n*. Whenever the discount factors are so defined, we will designate them as *consistent discount factors*. Notice the absence of project upper-bound constraints (8.5).

A typical dual constraint has the form

$$-\sum_n a_{nj}\rho_n \geq \sum_n a_{nj} \frac{\rho_n}{\rho_0} \tag{8.21}$$

or

$$\left(-1 - \frac{1}{\rho_0}\right) \sum_n a_{nj}\rho_n \geq 0$$

But the dual variables are nonnegative, so

$$\sum_n a_{nj}\rho_n \leq 0$$

[1]The abbreviation s.t. stands for subject to.

In the primal objective function the term ρ_0 can be placed before the summation signs; thus each coefficient of x_j is nonpositive. The objective function must therefore have an optimal solution of zero with all $x_j = 0$. In addition, the solution to the dual objective function

$$\operatorname*{Min}_{\rho_n} \sum_n M_n \rho_n \qquad (8.22)$$

with $M_n > 0$ will be zero, with all $\rho_n = 0$. The zero value of ρ_0 in the denominator of the primal objective function (8.20) renders that function indeterminate.

With this line of reasoning, Baumol and Quandt rejected *PV* models. They then formulated a model with an objective function that is linear in dividend payments. We will not present this model here but instead examine the PCR line that was pursued by others.

Atkins and Ashton [1] criticized the approach of Baumol and Quandt because there were no upper-bound constraints on the projects and the consequent interpretation of dual variables was absent. The discount factors ρ_n/ρ_0 are determined by the marginal productivities of capital in the various time periods. In the absence of upper bounds on projects, any project that is accepted is also partially rejected. Hence, the discounted cash flow of that project *must* be zero.

The implication of this reasoning is that projects must have upper bounds placed on them to avoid the phenomenon of each accepted (and, at the same time, rejected) project having a *PV*, based on consistent discount factors $d_n = \rho_n/\rho_0$, equal to zero. In addition, the Atkins and Ashton model allows for funds to be carried forward at a lending rate of interest. The final modification is the interpretation of the discount factors when one of the ρ_n becomes zero: the equivalent form $\rho_n = d_n \rho_0$ avoids these difficulties.

The method for finding a *consistent optimal solution* (an optimal set of x_j and $d_n = \rho_n/\rho_0$) consists of identifying and evaluating the Kuhn–Tucker stationary points [17] of the problem. In the PCR model there are potentially many consistent solutions, whereas in the situation with lending there is only one solution. In general, this is a rather unsatisfactory procedure because of the large number of such points.

Freeland and Rosenblatt [8] pursued the PCR model (with project upper-bound constraints) further and obtained several interesting results.

- The value of the objective function at a consistent optimal solution equals

$$\frac{1}{2} \sum_j \mu_j^* \text{ (property 2).}$$

- For the PCR case (no lending or borrowing allowed) an objective function value different from zero can be obtained only if some of the M_n values have opposite signs.

- If the objective function value for a consistent optimal solution is not zero, there are alternative optimal discount factors d_n.

A more recent article by Hayes [12] on the same topic has further clarified the issue for the situation in which *all budgets are fully expended.* Hayes's analysis assumes upper bounds on projects and lending from one period to the next, but his major result does not depend on the lending activities. If the budgets are fully utilized in all periods except the last (the horizon), the optimal set of projects is independent of discount factors and may be obtained by maximizing the cash at the end of the last period (at the horizon). To see why this result is true, let us reexamine the *PV* model.

$$\text{Max}_{x_j} \sum_n \sum_j a_{nj} d_n x_j \qquad (8.23)$$

s.t.
$[\rho_n]$
$$-\sum_j a_{nj} x_j = M_n, \qquad n = 0, 1, ..., N-1 \qquad (8.24)$$

$[\rho_N]$
$$-\sum_j a_{Nj} x_j + l_N = M_N \qquad (8.25)$$

$$x_j \leq 1, \qquad j = 1, ..., J \qquad (8.5)$$

$$x_j \geq 0, \qquad j = 1, ..., J \qquad (8.6)$$

where d_n = discount factor for time n,
   l_n = cash left over at time N, the horizon,

and the other terms are as defined previously. Note that the budget constraints 8.24 and 8.25 are equalities, reflecting the assumption about cash being used up each period. The l_N term measures any leftover cash at time N, the horizon, the only time we are allowed to have excess cash in this model.

To obtain the desired result, let us split the objective function.

$$\text{Max}_{x_j} \sum_j a_{Nj} d_N x_j + \sum_{n=0}^{N-1} \sum_j a_{nj} d_n x_j \qquad (8.26)$$

Now we can substitute the constraints into the objective function.

$$\text{Max}_{x_j} d_N(l_N - M_N) - \sum_{n=0}^{N-1} d_n M_n = \text{Max}_{x_j} d_N l_N - \sum_{n=0}^{N} d_n M_n \qquad (8.27)$$

Since the summation in Eq. 8.27 is a constant for fixed values of d_n, it may be dropped without affecting the solution, and by dividing out the constant d_N we are left with

$$\text{Max}_{x_j} l_N \qquad (8.28)$$

subject to constraints 8.24, 8.25, 8.5, and 8.6.

Appropriate discount factors may be obtained by the usual form $d_n = \rho_n/\rho_0$ with $\rho_0 = 1$ or any positive constant. With all budget constraints at equality, it is easy to show that $\rho_{n-1} \geq \rho_n$; therefore, no possibility exists of zero dual variables. In summary, the discount factors are irrelevant for project selection!

The foregoing result is important because it emphasizes the fact that the dual variables for the budget constraints reflect the marginal productivities of capital in the respective time periods. Since all cash flows are automatically reinvested in this closed system, any consumption choices by the owner or owners of the firm have been expressed by the values set for the M_n.

In this section we appear to have presented numerous models, summarized extensive analyses, and arrived at very little in terms of a useful *PV* model. That is precisely true. All the arguments and discussion repeatedly point to the following types of conclusions and statements.

- In any *PV* model the budget constraint dual variables must reflect the marginal productivities of capital.
- Project upper-bound constraints and lending activities must be included in order to have a meaningful formulation.
- For certain types of closed systems, in which all budgets are fully expended, the projects are selected by maximizing cash at the horizon.

We will return to this last point in Section 8.5. In the meantime, we will discuss in more detail the inclusion of lending and borrowing opportunities in the *PV* model.

8.4 NET PRESENT VALUE MAXIMIZATION WITH LENDING AND BORROWING

8.4.1 Inclusion of Lending Opportunities

We can define a lending project as an outflow of cash in one period followed by an inflow, with interest, at a later period. Define v_n to be the amount lent at time n, to be repaid at time $n + 1$ with interest r_n. We then have coefficients $a_{nj} = -1$ and $a_{n+1,j} = 1 + r_n$. We will define as many lending variables as there are time periods with budget constraints. There are no limits on lending.

Notice that we have defined only one-period loans, which is the common practice. Multiple-period lending could easily be included. The following are some typical examples, all with a constant lending rate.

Period	Case 1: Lump Sum Payment	Case 2: Interest Only During Period, Principal at End of Last Period	Case 3: Equal Payments
		a_{nj}	
n	-1	-1	-1
$n + 1$	0	r	$(A/P, r, 2)$
$n + 2$	$(1 + r)^2$	$1 + r$	$(A/P, r, 2)$

The number of variables tends to become somewhat unwieldy with this approach, however, compared with the benefits derived from distinguishing between short-term and long-term lending rates. If the projects consist mainly of financial instruments, it is important to work at this level of detail [11]. Otherwise, the approximation of multiple-period lending with successive one-period lending usually suffices.

The objective function coefficients for the lending activities can be obtained by straightforward discounting at $i = MARR$. Applying this concept to case 2, we have

$$PV = -1 + \frac{r}{1 + i} + \frac{1 + r}{(1 + i)^2}$$

The resulting PV may be positive or negative, depending on whether r is greater than or smaller than i, respectively.

If one-period lending opportunities are included in the PV model, and lending is always preferred to doing nothing, we can solve an equivalent problem by simply maximizing the amount of cash at the horizon [1,8]. This result is similar to that obtained by Hayes, as described in Section 8.3.2. With attractive lending opportunities present, all budgets will be fully expended, and Hayes's result can be applied directly.

8.4.2 Inclusion of Borrowing Opportunities

We should note that the inclusion of unlimited lending opportunities still has not resolved the philosophical conflict between using an interest rate for PV maximization and having budget constraints. If borrowing opportunities are also unlimited, it appears that we have eliminated the conflict. But in that case we really do not need budget constraints and LP to solve our project selection problem. Investment projects with an IRR less than the lending rate would always be rejected, and those with an IRR greater than the borrowing rate would be accepted. The selection problem would concern only projects with an IRR between the lending and borrowing rates.

There remain two difficulties with such an approach. The first is that we rarely have unlimited borrowing opportunities at one interest rate. (In a practical sense, only an agency of the U.S. government can borrow unlimited amounts). Typically, we can borrow, but only up to a limit. Some of the models presented in the next section have this feature. The second difficulty is related to the interpretation of the interest rate used for PV calculations. If the (different) lending and borrowing rates are specified, any other discount rate must presumably reflect the time preferences of the owners of the firm. There is no philosophical conflict in having three distinct rates for lending by the firm, borrowing by the firm, and discounting to reflect the owners' time preferences. But in this case we need to include dividends in the objective function, as shown in Section 8.6 and Appendix 8.A.

We have again failed to develop a rational *PV* model. The reasons here are similar to those for the PCR case. In the face of limits on borrowing, the decisions about selecting projects must be related, through the interrelationships among project combinations and budget amounts, to the decisions for dividend payments [21]. The marginal productivities of capital from one period to the next determine the dual variables ρ_n. Any attempt to ignore these two realities in constructing a project selection model or procedure is bound to have major conceptual flaws.

8.5. WEINGARTNER'S HORIZON MODEL

Many of the conceptual issues discussed in the previous two sections can be avoided by ignoring *PV* and concentrating on accumulated cash as the objective. Such models are called horizon models. They typically include borrowing and lending activities and may have other constraints added. These models represent an empirical approach to capital budgeting and should therefore be judged mainly on this basis. The presentation in this section, which is based largely on Weingartner [20], presumes the use of LP and hence allows fractional projects.

8.5.1 Equal Lending and Borrowing Rates

The simplest type of horizon model contains budget constraints, project upper bounds, and lending and borrowing opportunities at a common, fixed rate.

Example 8.3

Table 8.5 presents the data for Example 8.3, and Table 8.6 presents both the symbolic and numeric primal formulations. The projects, 1 through 6, are the same as for Example 8.2. The budget amounts are slightly different from those in Example 8.2, being $3,000, $5,000, and $4,800 at times 0, 1, and 2, respectively. We are using 20% for both borrowing and lending, with no limits on either. The horizon is at time 2, so we are trying to maximize the accumulated cash at this time. Most of the projects, however, have cash flows after time 2, so we discount at 20% these flows back to time 2. For example, $\hat{a}_1$ represents the $2,900 inflow at time 3 for project 1, discounted at 20% for one period, or $2,900/1.2 = $2,417.

The objective function in this horizon model is $v_2 - w_2$, the accumulated cash available (for lending) at time 2, plus the value of posthorizon flows, represented by the $\hat{a}_j$. The cash balance equations 8.30 and 8.31 are similar to those for the *PV* model. A typical constraint says that cash outflows from projects, plus current lending, plus repayment with interest of previous-period borrowing, minus repayment with interest of previous-period lending, minus current borrowing must be less than or equal to the amount of externally supplied funds. The project upper bounds and nonnegativity restrictions complete the model. For simplicity, we have not included any project dependency or exclusivity constraints. (The solution to Example 8.3 follows in the text.)   □

Table 8.5 *Data for Examples 8.3 and 8.5 (Horizon Is Time 2)*

Variable Type		Project					
		1	2	3	4	5	6
Cash Flow at Time	0	−$1,000	−$1,200	−$2,000	−$2,500	−$3,000	$1,000
Same for	1	−2,000	−2,400	−2,100	−1,300	900	−700
Examples 8.3	2	2,000	2,500	3,000	2,000	1,400	−700
and 8.5	3	2,900	3,567	2,621	2,000	1,600	0
	4	0	0	0	2,000	211	0
	5	0	0	0	2,296	0	0
Example 8.3 $\hat{a}_j$		$2,417	2,973	2,184	4,384	1,480	0
Example 8.5 $\hat{a}_j$		$2,230	2,744	2,016	3,767	1,356	0

Budgets (M_n)	$n = 0$	$n = 1$	$n = 2$
Example 8.3	$3,000	5,000	4,800
Example 8.5	$1,000	2,000	4,800
Lending rates	$n = 0 \to 1$	$n = 1 \to 2$	$n = 2 \to 3$
Example 8.3	20%	20%	20%
Example 8.5	15%	15%	15%
Borrowing rates	$n = 0 \to 1$	$n = 1 \to 2$	$n = 2 \to 3$
Example 8.3	20%	20%	20%
Example 8.5	30%	30%	30%
Borrowing limits Example 8.5 only	$n = 0 \to 1$ None	$n = 1 \to 2$ 1,000	$n = 2 \to 3$ None

The LP solution of the horizon model in Example 8.3 is straightforward and quick, requiring less than one second of time for both processing and input–output on a mainframe computer. Table 8.7 contains the solution for Example 8.3. Projects 1, 2, and 4 were accepted completely, and projects 3, 5, and 6 were rejected. In addition, there was borrowing of $1,700 at time 0 and $2,740 at time 1. At time 2 a total cash accumulation of $8,012 was available for lending.

There is more to the solution of this horizon problem than the numerical results, however. We note several features of the solution.

- The dual variables ρ_n are powers of 1.2.
- The dual variables μ_j for accepted projects are equal to the *FV*(20%) of these projects.
- Projects with positive *PV*(20%) were accepted and those with negative *PV* (20%) were rejected.

These features are not coincidental but rather are characteristic of the horizon model as presented in Table 8.6. We can verify this by examining the dual formulation, given in Table 8.8.

Table 8.6 *Primal Problem Formulation For Horizon Model for Example 8.3*

Symbolic

$$\max_{x_j, v_n, w_n} \sum_j \hat{a}_j x_j + v_N - w_N \tag{8.29}$$

s.t.

$[\rho_0]$
$$-\sum_j a_{0j} x_j + v_0 - w_0 \leq M_0 \tag{8.30}$$

$[\rho_n]$
$$-\sum_j a_{nj} x_j - (1+r)v_{n-1} + v_n + (1+r)w_{n-1} - w_n \leq M_n,$$
$$n = 1, 2, \ldots, N \tag{8.31}$$

$[\mu_j]$
$$x_j \leq 1, \qquad j = 1, \ldots, J \tag{8.5}$$

$$x_j \geq 0, \qquad j = 1, \ldots, J \tag{8.6}$$

$$v_n, w_n \geq 0, \qquad j = 0, \ldots, J \tag{8.32}$$

where $\hat{a}_j$ = horizon time value of cash flows beyond horizon

x_j = project selection variable

a_{nj} = cash flow for project j at time n; inflows have a plus sign, outflows have a minus sign

v_n = lending amount from time n to time $n + 1$

w_n = amount borrowed from time n to time $n + 1$

r = interest rate for borrowing and lending

M_n = budget limit on externally supplied funds at time n

N = horizon, end of the planning period

ρ_n, μ_j = dual variables

Numeric

$$\text{Max } \$2{,}417x_1 + 2{,}973x_2 + 2{,}184x_3 + 4{,}384x_4 + 1{,}480x_5 + v_2 - w_2$$

s.t.

$[\rho_0]$
$$\$1{,}000x_1 + 1{,}200x_2 + 2{,}000x_3 + 2{,}500x_4 + 3{,}000x_5 - 1{,}000x_6$$
$$+ v_0 - w_0 \leq 3{,}000$$

$[\rho_1]$
$$\$2{,}000x_1 + 2{,}400x_2 + 2{,}100x_3 + 1{,}300x_4 - 900x_5 + 700x_6$$
$$- 1.2v_0 + v_1 + 1.2w_0 - w_1 \leq 5{,}000$$

$[\rho_2]$
$$-\$2{,}000x_1 - 2{,}500x_2 - 3{,}000x_3 - 2{,}000x_4 - 1{,}400x_5 + 700x_6$$
$$- 1.2v_1 + v_2 + 1.2w_1 - w_2 \leq 4{,}800$$

$[\mu_1]$ $\quad x_1 \qquad\qquad\qquad\qquad\qquad\qquad \leq 1$

$[\mu_2]$ $\qquad\quad x_2 \qquad\qquad\qquad\qquad\qquad \leq 1$

$[\mu_3]$ $\qquad\qquad\quad x_3 \qquad\qquad\qquad\qquad \leq 1$

$[\mu_4]$ $\qquad\qquad\qquad\quad x_4 \qquad\qquad\qquad \leq 1$

$[\mu_5]$ $\qquad\qquad\qquad\qquad\quad x_5 \qquad\qquad \leq 1$

$[\mu_6]$ $\qquad\qquad\qquad\qquad\qquad\quad x_6 \leq 1$

all $\quad x_j \geq 0, \qquad j = 1, \ldots, 6$

all $v_n, w_n \geq 0, \qquad n = 0, 1, 2$

Table 8.7 *Solution to Examples 8.3 and 8.5*

Variable Type	Objective Function	Example 8.3, $17,786	Example 8.5, $9,210
Project selection	x_1	1.0	0
	x_2	1.0	1.0
	x_3	0	0
	x_4	1.0	0.151
	x_5	0	0
	x_6	0	0.577
Lending	v_0	0	0
	v_1	0	0
	v_2	$8,012	$5,898
Borrowing	w_0	$1,700	0
	w_1	2,740	$1,000
	w_2	0	0
Budget constraint dual variable	ρ_0	1.44	1.622
	ρ_1	1.20	1.317
	ρ_2	1.00	1.0
Project upper-bound dual variable	μ_1	577	0
	μ_2	865	137
	μ_3	0	0
	μ_4	1.224	0
	μ_5	0	0
	μ_6	0	0
Borrowing limit dual variable	β_1	—	0.017

From (8.36) and (8.37) we have $\rho_n^* = 1$. The value of \$1 at time N is \$1 in the optimal solution because we do not have time to do anything with it. Similarly, from (8.34) and (8.35) we obtain

$$1 + r \leq \frac{\rho_n^*}{\rho_{n+1}^*} \leq 1 + r, \qquad n = 0, ..., N - 1 \tag{8.38}$$

or

$$\frac{\rho_n^*}{\rho_{n+1}^*} = 1 + r \tag{8.39}$$

and

$$\rho_n^* = \rho_{n+1}^*(1 + r) = \rho_{n+2}^*(1 + r)^2 = \cdots = \rho_{n+N-n}^*(1 + r)^{N-n}$$

$$= \rho_N^*(1 + r)^{N-n} = (1 + r)^{N-n} \tag{8.40}$$

The interpretation of the ρ_n^* now becomes clear: they are compound interest factors that reflect the value at the horizon, time N, of an additional dollar at time n.

Table 8.8 *Dual Problem Formulation for Horizon Model with Common, Fixed Rate for Borrowing and Lending*

$$\text{Min} \sum_n \rho_n M_n + \sum_j \mu_j \tag{8.9}$$

s.t.

$$[x_j] \qquad -\sum_n a_{nj}\rho_n + \mu_j \geq \hat{a}_j, \qquad j = 1, \ldots, J \tag{8.33}$$

$$[v_n] \qquad \rho_n - (1 + r)\rho_{n+1} \geq 0, \qquad n = 0, \ldots, N - 1 \tag{8.34}$$

$$[w_n] \qquad -\rho_n + (1 + r)\rho_{n+1} \geq 0, \qquad n = 0, \ldots, N - 1 \tag{8.35}$$

$$[v_N] \qquad \rho_N \geq 1 \tag{8.36}$$

$$[w_N] \qquad -\rho_N \geq -1 \tag{8.37}$$

$$\rho_n \geq 0, \qquad n = 0, 1, \ldots, N - 1 \tag{8.11}$$

$$\mu_j \geq 0, \qquad j = 1, \ldots, J \tag{8.12}$$

The analysis of (8.33) is similar to that of (8.10) in Section 8.2.5. If $x_j^* > 0$, the dual constraint is met exactly, and

$$0 \leq \mu_j^* = \hat{a}_j + \sum_n a_{nj}\rho_n^* \tag{8.41}$$

Substituting for ρ_n^* from (8.40), we have

$$\mu_j^* = \hat{a}_j + \sum_n a_{nj}(1 + r)^{N-n} \tag{8.42}$$

The right side of (8.42) is simply the net future value (*FV*) at time *N* of the cash flows for project *j*. The $\hat{a}_j$ term is the value of posthorizon flows discounted back to time *N*, and the summation is the forward compounding of the other cash flows. For fractionally accepted projects $\mu_j^* = 0$, and thus (8.42) equals zero. For rejected projects x_j^* and μ_j^* are both equal to zero, so

$$0 \geq \hat{a}_j + \sum_n a_{nj}(1 + r)^{N-n} \tag{8.43}$$

The horizon model with a common, fixed rate for borrowing and lending thus will accept only projects with nonnegative *FV(r)*, or *PV(r)*, and the *FV(r)* of any rejected project is nonpositive. This agreement between the LP model and the *PV* criterion reassures us that the model performs as intended. Actually, we would expect the model to perform precisely in this manner, since the unlimited borrowing and lending opportunities at interest rate r are equivalent to the assumptions underlying the *PV* criterion.

8.5.2. Lending Rates Less Than Borrowing Rates

Clearly, an LP model that yields the same answers as *PV* analysis is of little use. The true power of the LP model is the ability to represent a great variety of investment opportunities and restrictions, lending and borrowing opportunities, scarce resource restrictions, and so forth. In this section we modify the horizon model of the previous section by having a borrowing rate higher than the lending rate. The only modification needed in the model is in the cash balance equation 8.31, which becomes

$$[\rho_n] \qquad -\sum_j a_{nj}x_j - (1 + r_l)v_{n-1} + v_n + (1 + r_b)w_{n-1}$$

$$- w_n \leq M_n, \qquad n = 1, 2, ..., N \qquad (8.44)$$

where r_l = lending interest rate,
 r_b = borrowing interest rate.

The corresponding changes in the dual problem affect constraints 8.34 and 8.35, which become, respectively,

$$[v_n] \qquad \rho_n - (1 + r_l)\rho_{n+1} \geq 0, \qquad n = 0, \ldots, N-1 \qquad (8.45)$$

$$[w_n] \qquad -\rho_n + (1 + r_b)\rho_{n+1} \geq 0, \qquad n = 0, \ldots, N-1 \qquad (8.46)$$

Instead of (8.38) and (8.39), we obtain

$$1 + r_l \leq \frac{\rho_n^*}{\rho_{n+1}^*} \leq 1 + r_b, \qquad n = 0, ..., N - 1 \qquad (8.47)$$

The ratio of the dual variables for the cash balance equations is now restricted to the range (including end points) between the lending and borrowing interest factors. From complementary slackness [5] we can deduce that if we are lending money at time n ($v_n > 0$), then (8.45) and the left part of (8.47) are satisfied as equality. If we are borrowing at time n ($w_n > 0$), then (8.46) and the right side of (8.47) are satisfied as equality. This makes sense, because the lending activity implies that extra dollars at time n would also be lent, leading to 1.2 times the extra dollars at the horizon as extra dollars at time $n + 1$, and so forth.

Example 8.4

We can demonstrate these results with Example 8.4, for which both data and solution are shown in Table 8.9. There are four projects, six budget limits, a

Table 8.9 *Data and Solution for Example 8.4 (Lending Rate Less Than Borrowing Rate)*

Cash Flow at Time	Project				Budget
	1	2	3	4	
0	−600	−$1,200	−$900	−$1,500	$270
1	360	480	360	420	150
2	330	360	330	480	30
3	60	0	300	510	0
4	−150	660	270	540	−60
5	330	510	240	540	0
$\hat{a}_j$	150	300	150	330	—

$r_l = 0.2, r_b = 0.3, N = 5$

Solution

$x_1 = 1.0$	$v_0 = 0$	$w_0 = 420$	$\rho_0 = 2.754$
$x_2 = 0$	$v_1 = 0$	$w_1 = 0$	$\rho_1 = 2.119$
$x_3 = 0.1$	$v_2 = 393$	$w_2 = 0$	$\rho_2 = 1.728$
$x_4 = 0$	$v_3 = 561$	$w_3 = 0$	$\rho_3 = 1.440$
$\mu_1 = 67$	$v_4 = 490$	$w_4 = 0$	$\rho_4 = 1.200$
$\mu_2 = 0$	$v_5 = 943$	$w_5 = 0$	$\rho_5 = 1.000$
$\mu_3 = 0$			
$\mu_4 = 0$			

lending rate of 20%, a borrowing rate of 30%, and a horizon at time 5. The negative budget at time 4 means we must generate $60 to be used elsewhere in the firm. Only project 1 is accepted completely; project 3 is accepted fractionally, and the other two are rejected. There are borrowing at time 0 and lending at times 2 through 5. We can demonstrate how Eq. 8.47 indicates borrowing or lending by taking the ratios of the dual variables.

$\rho_0^*/\rho_1^* = 1.3$ borrowing at time 0

$\rho_1^*/\rho_2^* = 1.23$ neither at time 1

$\rho_2^*/\rho_3^* = 1.2$ lending at time 2

$\rho_3^*/\rho_4^* = 1.2$ lending at time 3

$\rho_4^*/\rho_5^* = 1.2$ lending at time 4   □

Everything seems to work according to theory in Example 8.4, but how do we explain the ratio ρ_1^*/ρ_2^* of 1.23, which is strictly between the limits? And if there are no restrictions on borrowing, why is project 3 accepted only fractionally? To answer these questions, let us assume two hypothetical situations in Example 8.3. First, assume everything is as before except that we borrow at time

1, forcing the ratio to be 1.3. The new dual variables can then be obtained as follows.

$\rho_5 = 1.0$

$\rho_4 = \rho_5(1.2) = 1.2$

$\rho_3 = \rho_4(1.2) = 1.44$

$\rho_2 = \rho_3(1.2) = 1.728$

$\rho_1 = \rho_2(1.3) = 2.246$

$\rho_0 = \rho_1(1.3) = 2.920$

Now let us find the corresponding value of μ_3 from Eq. 8.41. In LP terminology, we are pricing out the activity vector for project 3.

$$\$150 + (-900)(2.920) + (360)(2.246) + (330)(1.728)$$
$$+ (300)(1.44) + (270)(1.2) + (240)(1.0) = -\$103$$

The negative value means that we would not introduce project 3 into the LP solution, given the values for the ρ_r. In other words, given the other borrowing and lending activities, we are not justified in borrowing at 30% at time 1 in order to accept more of project 3.

Now assume everything is as in the original solution in Table 8.9, except that we lend at time 1, forcing the ratio to be 1.2. The new dual variables are obtained as before, and the pricing of the activity vector yields

$\rho_5 = 1.0$

$\rho_4 = \rho_5(1.2) = 1.2$

$\rho_3 = \rho_4(1.2) = 1.44$

$\rho_2 = \rho_3(1.2) = 1.728$

$\rho_1 = \rho_2(1.2) = 2.074$

$\rho_0 = \rho_1(1.3) = 2.696$

$$\$150 + (-900)(2.696) + (360)(2.074) + (330)(1.728)$$
$$+ (300)(1.44) + (270)(1.2) + (240)(1.0) = \$37$$

The positive value means that if we were lending money at time 1, given the other borrowing and lending activities, we could improve our situation by accepting project 3. The best action is to accept as much as possible without borrowing at time 1. This turns out to be 10%. What has happened is that the marginal productivity of cash at time 1 is determined by project 3.

8.5.3 Inclusion of Borrowing Limits, Supply Schedule of Funds

Another typical restriction in the horizon model is a limit on the amount borrowed at a particular time. Example 8.5 is a slight variation on Example 8.3.

Example 8.5

Table 8.5 presents the relevant data. The project cash flows are the same, the budgets at times 0 and 1 are reduced, the lending rate is 15%, the borrowing rate is 30%, and a $1,000 limit on borrowing is imposed at time 1. In anticipation of future borrowing at 30%, the $\hat{a}_j$ have been computed by using a discount rate of 30%. The solution for Example 8.5 is given in Table 8.7. Only one project, number 2, is accepted completely, and 4 and 6 are accepted fractionally. The only borrowing activity is at time 1, at the limit of $1,000. $\square$

To analyze the results of Example 8.5, we need to add one more constraint to the primal problem.

$$[\beta_1] \qquad\qquad w_1 \leq 1,000 \qquad\qquad (8.48)$$

The changes in the dual formulation are in the objective function and in Eq. 8.46.

$$\text{Min} \sum_n \rho_n M_n + \sum_j \mu_j + 1,000\beta_1 \qquad\qquad (8.49)$$

$$[w_1] \qquad\qquad -\rho_1 + (1 + r_b)\rho_2 + \beta_1 \geq 0 \qquad\qquad (8.50)$$

Instead of (8.47) we have

$$(1 + r_l)\rho_2^* \leq \rho_1^* \leq (1 + r_b)\rho_2^* + \beta_1^* \qquad\qquad (8.51)$$

The borrowing restriction at time 1 places a premium on funds at time 1 beyond that of the normal borrowing interest factor of 1.3. The nonzero value of β_1^* implies that we are borrowing the full amount and would like to borrow more. We can verify the right side of (8.51).

$$1.317 = (1.3)(1.0) + 0.017$$

What has happened in this example is as follows.

- Project 2, with the highest *IRR* of 31.26%, was accepted completely, exhausting the time 0 budget of $1,000. The cheapest method of borrowing was with partial acceptance of project 6, which is equivalent to borrowing at 26%.

- Projects 3 and 5 had negative *PV*(20%) and would not justify borrowing at 26 or 30%.

- Projects 1 and 4 have similar *IRR*s, 29.1% and 28.9%, respectively, for the original cash flows. The *IRR*s are 28.7% and 28.1%, respectively, for the $a_{0j}, a_{1j}, a_{2j}, \hat{a}_j$ flows, which is what the LP program sees. However, project 1 requires twice as much investment at time 1 as at time 0, whereas the opposite is true for project 4. Since time 1 borrowing costs 30% and the time 0 borrowing costs 26% (via project 6), preference is given to project

4. Neither project justifies borrowing at 30% in both periods, so just enough of project 4 is accepted to reach the borrowing limit of $1,000 at time 1.

It should be noted that the pricing operation with Eq. 8.41 is still valid and yields results consistent with the solution in Table 8.7.

The concept of borrowing limit can be generalized to a series of limits, each applicable to a source of loan funds at a designated rate. For example, a firm may be able to borrow an amount, say 2,000, at 22%, an additional 1,000 at 25%, and a final 1,000 at 30%, as shown in Figure 8.1. This representation is called a sloping supply schedule for funds [20]. If we let w_{kn} represent the amount borrowed at the kth step at time n, the modification to the horizon model is straightforward, as shown in Table 8.10. By convention, we order the borrowing steps in increasing order of cost r_k; the LP algorithm will naturally start borrowing at the lowest cost and move to the next step as each limit is reached.

Analysis of the dual formulation is similar to that in Example 8.5. For each w_{kn} in the primal we have a dual constraint.

$$[w_{kn}] \qquad -\rho_n + (1 + r_{kn})\rho_{n+1} + \beta_{kn} \geq 0 \qquad (8.56)$$

The dual constraint of interest is the one corresponding to the last step k at time n. If we are at the limit on the last step, we can not say anything beyond Eq. 8.56 without the actual value of β_{kn}^* from the LP solution. If we are borrowing an amount below the limit on the last step, however, we have

$$\frac{\rho_n^*}{\rho_{n+1}^*} = 1 + r_{kn} \qquad (8.57)$$

Equation 8.57 illustrates the nature of the ρ_n^* as indicators of the marginal cost of funds.

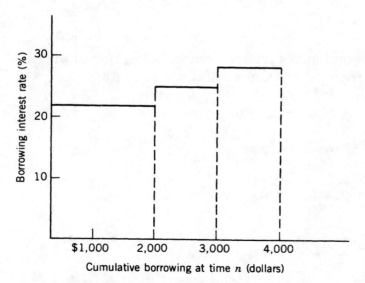

FIGURE 8.1. Sloping supply schedule of funds.

Table 8.10 *Primal Problem Formulation for Horizon Model with Sloping Supply Schedule for Funds*

$$\text{Max} \sum_j \hat{a}_j x_j + v_N - \sum_k w_{kN} \tag{8.52}$$

s.t.

$$[\rho_0] \quad -\sum_j a_{0j} x_j + v_0 - \sum_k w_{k0} \le M_0 \tag{8.53}$$

$$[\rho_n] \quad -\sum_j a_{nj} x_j - (1 + r_\ell) v_{n-1} + v_n + \sum_k (1 + r_k) w_{k,n-1}$$

$$-\sum_k w_{kn} \le M_n, \qquad\qquad n = 1, 2, \ldots, N \tag{8.54}$$

$$[\beta_{kn}] \quad w_{kn} \le B_{kn}, \quad k = 1, \ldots, m; \quad n = 0, \ldots, N \tag{8.55}$$

$$[\mu_j] \quad x_j \le 1, \qquad j = 1, \ldots, j \tag{8.56}$$

all variables ≥ 0

where w_{kn} = amount borrowed at kth step at time n,

r_k = interest rate at kth step of borrowing,

B_{kn} = limit on kth step at time n.

Other terms are as previously described

8.5.4 Dual Analysis with Project Interdependencies

The presence of project interdependencies will affect the use of (8.33) in pricing out project activity vectors in a manner consistent with the LP solution.

Example 8.6

We add a contingency relationship that project 4 cannot be performed without project 5 in Example 8.3. Then we add to the primal the form 8.8, or

$$[\nu] \qquad\qquad x_4 - x_5 \le 0$$

and the dual constraints 8.33 would become

$$-\sum_n a_{n4} \rho_n + \mu_4 + \upsilon \ge \hat{a}_4$$

$$-\sum_n a_{n5} \rho_n + \mu_5 - \upsilon \ge \hat{a}_5$$

The pricing operation would reflect a penalty being applied to project 4 and a subsidy being applied to project 5. Since project 4 is so highly favorable, both 4 and 5 would be accepted. Using (8.41), we have

$$\text{Project 4:} \quad \mu_4^* = \$4{,}384 - (2{,}500)(1.44) - (1{,}300)(1.2)$$
$$+ (2{,}000)(1.0) - 360 = \$864$$

$$\text{Project 5:} \quad \mu_5^* = \$1{,}480 - (3{,}000)(1.44) + (900)(1.2)$$
$$+ (1{,}400)(1.0) + 360 = 0$$

The value of ν is 360, just enough for project 5 to price out at zero, where it can be accepted.   □

The mutual exclusivity constraints 8.7 would be handled in a similar manner. In practice, such constraints allow more projects to be fractionally accepted, and the typical end result is use of integer programming (Section 8.7).

8.6 BERNHARD'S GENERAL MODEL

All the features of the horizon model with borrowing constraints (Section 8.5.3) are retained in Bernhard's general model for capital budgeting [4]. Bernhard also includes dividends in a nonlinear objective function, with dividends constrained by a horizon posture restriction. In the following sections we will present the model and some general results. With few exceptions, the notation will follow Bernhard's, which is largely consistent with what we have been using. Appendix 8.A presents an application of the model to a dividend–terminal-wealth problem.

8.6.1 Model Formulation

The objective function is an unspecified function of dividends and terminal wealth.

$$\text{Max } f(D_1, D_2, \ldots, D_N, G) \tag{8.58}$$

where D_n = dividend paid at time n,
  G = time N terminal wealth, to be specified in more detail later.

It is assumed that $\partial f/\partial D_n \geq 0$ and $\partial f/\partial G \geq 0$, which imply that more dividends and terminal wealth, respectively, lead to greater utility values. Typically, f is defined to be concave.

The cash balance equations, or budget constraints, contain a liquidity requirement that reflects certain banking practices. The firm is required to maintain $C_n + c_n w_n$ in a bank account. The C_n is a constant representing basic liquidity at time n, and the c_n ($0 \leq c_n < 1$) is a compensating balance fraction. The amount $C_n + c_n w_n$ earns interest at rate r_{ln}. The typical constraint is

$$[\rho_n] \qquad -\sum_j a_{nj} x_j - l_{n-1}(v_{n-1} + c_{n-1} w_{n-1} + C_{n-1})$$
$$+ (v_n + c_n w_n + C_n) + b_{n-1} w_{n-1} - w_n$$
$$+ D_n \leq M_n', \qquad n = 0, 1, \dots, N \qquad (8.59)$$

where M_n' = budget limit on externally supplied funds at time n,
l_n = lending interest rate factor at time n, $1 + r_{ln}$, and
b_n = borrowing interest rate factor at time n, $1 + r_{bn}$.

Equation 8.59 states that project outlays, minus previous-period lending, plus current lending, plus previous-period borrowing, minus current borrowing, plus current dividend cannot exceed the budget limit on externally supplied funds at time n. Regrouping terms gives

$$[\rho_n] \qquad -\sum_j a_{nj} x_j - l_{n-1} v_{n-1} + v_n + (b_{n-1} - l_{n-1} c_{n-1}) w_{n-1}$$
$$-(1 - c_n) w_n + D_n \leq M_n, \qquad n = 0, 1, \dots, N \qquad (8.60)$$

where

$$M_n = M_n' + (l_{n-1} C_{n-1}) - C_n$$

Group payback restrictions state that at time n' the net outflows on the set of selected projects are recovered.

$$[\psi] \qquad -\sum_j \sum_{n=0}^{n'} a_{nj} x_j \leq 0 \qquad (8.61)$$

Scarce material restrictions are defined for a nonmonetary resource, which could be skilled personnel, special equipment, and so forth.

$$[\nu] \qquad \sum_j d_j x_j \leq d \qquad (8.62)$$

where d_n = amount of scarce resource consumed by project j,
d = total amount of scarce resource available.

The firm is prevented from paying excessive dividends and thus jeopardizing earning capability past the horizon. This is accomplished by a terminal-wealth horizon posture restriction. First it is necessary to define the terminal wealth. After the last dividend D_N at time N, the terminal wealth is

$$G = M' + \sum_j \hat{a}_j x_j + v_N + c_N w_N + C_N - w_N$$

where M' is the value at time N of posthorizon cash flows from other sources.

With the inclusion of M' and the liquidity requirement, the definition is the same as the objective function 8.29 of the horizon model. The definition is rewritten as

$$[\phi] \qquad -\sum_j \hat{a}_j x_j - v_N + (1 - c_N)w_N + G = M \qquad (8.63)$$

where M is $M' + C_N$.

The horizon posture restriction states that the terminal wealth must exceed some functional value of the dividends,

$$G \geqslant K + g(D_1, D_2, \ldots, D_N)$$

where K = a nonnegative constant,

g = a function, typically a convex one.

Rewriting, we have

$$[\theta] \qquad -G + g(D_1, D_2, \ldots, D_N) \leqslant -K \qquad (8.64)$$

Borrowing limits for $n = 0, 1, \ldots, N-1$, project upper bounds, and nonnegativity restrictions complete the model. Table 8.11 summarizes the objective function and constraints.

8.6.2 Major Results

With a concave objective function 8.58 and a convex constraint 8.64, the Kuhn–Tucker conditions are necessary and sufficient for optimality, and they enable us to make a number of statements about optimal solutions to the general model [17]. Table 8.12 presents the Kuhn–Tucker conditions. We present only the major results that can be obtained from them; derivations are in Bernard [4].

The pricing out of a project activity vector, analogous to (8.33), gives us

$$\mu_j^* \geq A_j^* = \sum_n a_{nj}\rho_n^* + \sum_{n=0}^{n'} a_{nj}\psi - d_j v^* + \hat{a}_j \rho_N^* \qquad (8.74)$$

where we have used the substitution $\phi^* = \rho_N^*$. The role of A_j^* in (8.74) is similar to that of PV in the horizon model.

Case 1: If $\qquad x_j^* = 1, \qquad \mu_j^* = A_j^* \geq 0$

Case 2: If $\qquad 0 < x_j^* < 1, \qquad \mu_j^* = A_j^* = 0 \qquad (8.75)$

Case 3: If $\qquad x_j^* = 0, \qquad \mu_j^* = 0 \geq A_j^*$

We should oberve that absent or nonbinding group payback and scarce material contraints imply ψ and v values of zero, and A_j^* reduces to $\sum_n a_{nj}\rho_n^* + \hat{a}_j \rho_N^*$.

Table 8.11 *Bernhard's General Model*

$$\text{Max} \quad f(D_1, D_2, \ldots, D_N, G) \tag{8.58}$$

s.t.

$$[\rho_n] \quad -\sum_j a_{nj}x_j - l_{n-1}v_{n-1} + v_n + (b_{n-1} - l_{n-1}c_{n-1})w_{n-1} \tag{8.60}$$
$$- (1 - c_n)w_n + D_n \leq M_n, \quad n = 0, 1, \ldots, N$$

$$[\psi] \quad -\sum_j \sum_{n=0}^{n'} a_{nj}x_j \leq 0 \tag{8.61}$$

$$[\upsilon] \quad \sum_j d_j x_j \leq d \tag{8.62}$$

$$[\phi] \quad -\sum_j \hat{a}_j x_j - v_N + (1 - c_N)w_N + G = M \tag{8.63}$$

$$[\theta] \quad -G + g(D_1, D_2, \ldots, D_N) \leq -K \tag{8.64}$$

$$[\beta_n] \quad w_n \leq B_n, \quad n = 0, 1, \ldots, N - 1 \tag{8.65}$$

$$[\mu_j] \quad x_j \leq 1, \quad j = 1, \ldots, J \tag{8.5}$$

$$x_j, v_n, w_n, D_n \geq 0 \tag{8.66}$$

where
x_j = project selection variable
v_n = lending amount from time n to $n + 1$,
w_n = borrowing amount from time n to $n + 1$
D_n = dividend paid at time n
a_{nj} = cash flow for project j at time n (inflows $+$)
$\hat{a}_j$ = horizon time value of cash flows beyond horizon
l_n = lending interest rate factor at time n, $1 + r_{ln}$
b_n = borrowing interest rate factor at time n, $1 + r_{bn}$
B_n = borrowing limit at time n
c_n = compensating balance fraction
M_n = budget limit on externally supplied funds at time n, adjusted for basic liquidity requirement
d_j = amount of scarce resource consumed by project j
d = total amount of scarce resource available
G = terminal wealth at time N, after paying w_N
M = value at time N of posthorizon cash flows from other sources, adjusted by basic liquidity requirement
K = nonnegative constant representing the minimum acceptable terminal wealth

$\rho_n, \psi, \upsilon, \phi, \theta, \beta_n, \mu_j$ are dual variables

Table 8.12 *Kuhn–Tucker Conditions for Bernhard's General Model*

$[v_n]$ $\quad -\rho_n + l_n\rho_{n+1} \leq 0, \qquad n = 0, 1, ..., N - 1$	(8.67)
$[w_n]$ $\quad (1 - c_n)\rho_n - (b_n - l_n c_n)\rho_{n+1} - \beta_n \leq 0, \qquad n = 0, 1, ..., N - 1$	(8.68)
$[v_N]$ $\quad -\rho_N + \phi \leq 0$	(8.69)
$[w_N]$ $\quad (1 - c_N)\rho_N - (1 - c_N)\phi \leq 0$	(8.70)
$[x_j]$ $\quad \sum_n a_{nj}\rho_n + \hat{a}_j\phi - d_j v + \sum_{n=0}^{n'} a_{nj}\psi - \mu_j \leq 0, \qquad j = 1, 2, ..., J$	(8.71)
$[D_n]$ $\quad \left.\dfrac{\partial f}{\partial D_n}\right|_{D_n} - \rho_n - \theta\left.\dfrac{\partial g}{\partial D_n}\right|_{D_n} \leq 0, \qquad n = 0, 1, ..., N$	(8.72)
$[G]$ $\quad \left.\dfrac{\partial f}{\partial G}\right|_G - \phi + \theta \leq 0$	(8.73)

SOURCE: Bernard [4].

Turning to the ρ_n^*, we let

$$\hat{b}_n = \frac{b_n - l_n c_n}{1 - c_n} \tag{8.76}$$

This $\hat{b}_n$ is the effective borrowing rate. For example, if $b_n = 1.3$, $l_n = 1.2$, and $c_n = 0.2$, in order to borrow a usable \$100, we have to borrow \$125 at 30% and put $(0.2)(125) = 25$ back in the bank at 20%. Our true borrowing cost is

$$(\$125)(0.3) - (25)(0.2) = 32.5, \text{ or } 32.5\%$$

Equation 8.76 yields the equivalent factor of 1.325. In addition, let

$$\hat{\beta}_n^* = \beta_n^*/(1 - c_n) \tag{8.77}$$

Then we can manipulate (8.67) and (8.68) to yield

$$l_n\rho_{n+1}^* \leq \rho_n^* \leq \hat{b}_n\rho_{n+1}^* + \hat{\beta}_n^*, \qquad n = 0, 1, \ldots, N - 1 \tag{8.78}$$

This equation is similar to (8.51), showing that compensating balance fractions do not necessarily complicate the model once we interpret them as higher effective borrowing rates.

If $v_n^* > 0$, complementary slackness indicates that the left side of (8.77) is satisfied as equality. In this case the ratio ρ_n^*/ρ_{n+1}^* equals the lending rate factor. If the company borrows, $w_n^* > 0$, and the right side is equality. Note that the ratio of dual variables is affected by the value of $\hat{\beta}_n^*$, the dual variable of the borrowing limit. If the borrowing constraint is absent or nonbinding, the $\hat{\beta}_n^*$ drops out and

(8.78) reduces to the analogous result 8.47 for the linear horizon model with time-varying rates.

The general model is a rather flexible framework for capital budgeting. Most of the results have been extended to the cases of linear mixed-integer programming and quadratic mixed-integer programming, respectively [18, 19]. A natural consequence of using any of these models is the need for a complete programming solution; simple acceptance criteria are possible only under very restrictive and simplistic assumptions.

8.7 DISCRETE CAPITAL BUDGETING

We have carefully avoided the issue of integer solutions until now, in order to present the concepts and theory of capital budgeting in the simpler LP framework. As we turn to discrete models, two issues face us. The first is practicality. Can we solve efficiently problems with integer restrictions? The second is the question of economic interpretation. Will the dual variables, particularly the ρ_n, play the same role in pricing out project opportunities?

8.7.1 Number of Fractional Projects in LP Solution

Before we delve into these issues, we briefly review the nature of the solutions to our example problems heretofore. Recall that in Example 8.1 we had a solution vector $\mathbf{x}^* = (0.22, 1, 0, 1, 0.16)$. Two of the five project selection variables had fractional values in the optimal LP solution. There are also two budget constraints in Example 8.1, and there are no project interdependencies. Weingartner [20] proved that in the LP formulation of the Lorie–Savage problem (the *PV* maximization in Table 8.2) the number of fractional projects in the optimal solution cannot exceed the number of budget constraints. An explanation of this fact is based on the following reasoning. If there is only one budget constraint, there need be at most one fractional project. All others would be either more preferable than the fractional one and accepted fully or less preferable and rejected completely. If there are two equally preferable fractional projects, we could adjust the investment amounts until one was completely accepted or rejected. If there are two budget constraints, it may be possible that one fractional project will exhaust the monies remaining after all fully accepted projects are funded, but more than likely two fractional projects will be needed. If there are three fractional projects in the presence of two budget constraints, one will be more (or equally) preferable, and its funding can be increased until it is accepted fully or one of the remaining two is rejected completely. The LP algorithm by nature seeks extreme points and avoids alternative optima with more variables than necessary. This type of inductive reasoning can be applied to three budget constraints and so forth.

Another way to regard the problem in Table 8.2 is as an upper-bounded LP problem [14]. A basic variable is then one whose value is allowed to be between its lower (0) and upper (1) bounds at some particular iteration. The projects' upper-bound constraints are deleted from the constraint matrix in the upper-bounded LP algorithm, and the rank of the constraint matrix is two for Example 8.1. Hence, there are at most two fractional projects in the optimal solution.

In the basic horizon model, in which the lending rate is equal to the borrowing rate for each time period and there are no borrowing limits and project interdependencies, as shown in Example 8.3, there is always an integer optimum solution. This fact is related to the equivalence between this model and the *PV* criterion. When the borrowing rate is greater than the lending rate, we can have fractional projects, as demonstrated by Example 8.4. The maximum number of fractional projects that are possible because the borrowing rate is greater is equal to the number of time periods with $r_l < r_b$, minus one. Moreover, the number of fractional projects may be increased by one for each project interdependency constraint and for each time period with a borrowing limit. The reasoning behind these last results is similar to that given for the *PV* maximization problem.

8.7.2 Branch-and-Bound Solution Procedure

Various algorithms have been developed for solving the mixed-integer linear programming problem [9]. It is beyond the scope of this text to deal with them, since many algorithms are designed for special problem structures and require a high level of mathematical sophistication on the part of the user. Instead, we will demonstrate the solution of a small problem with a branch-and-bound solution procedure which can be used by anyone with access to an LP code [17].

Example 8.7

Use Example 8.5 (Table 8.5) as a starting point and obtain an optimal integer solution. Table 8.7 shows the optimal LP solution vector $\mathbf{x}^* = (0, 1, 0, 0.15, 0, 0.58)$ and objective function value $z^* = \$9,210$. We will designate this as problem 1. The presence of two fractional project selection variables, x_4 and x_6, gives us a choice in the procedure. We will arbitrarily select x_4 and create two new problems.

> Problem 2: Problem 1 with $x_4 = 0$ added as a constraint
> Problem 3: Problem 1 with $x_4 = 1$ added as a constraint

We then proceed to solve problems 2 and 3 by using an LP algorithm.

> Problem 2: $\mathbf{x}^* = (0.17, 1, 0, 0, 0, 0.37)$, $z^* = \$9,205$
> Problem 3: $\mathbf{x}^* = (0, 0.89, 0, 1, 0, 1)$, $z^* = \$9,031$

The procedure so far has not eliminated all fractional x_i values but has, in fact, created others that did not appear in problem 1. The problem 2 solution has x_1 fractional, whereas x_1 was an integer in problem 1; the problem 3 solution has a fractional value for x_2, which was an integer in problem 1.

Undeterred, we proceed by taking problem 2 and creating from it two new problems.

> Problem 4: Problem 2 with $x_1 = 0$ added
> Problem 5: Problem 2 with $x_1 = 1$ added

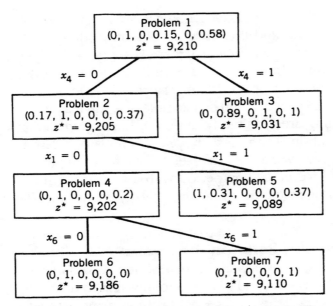

Figure 8.2. Branch-and-bound solution tree for Example 8.7. Numbers in parentheses are values of x^*, the vector of project selection variables.

Figure 8.2 shows how the problems are derived from one another. The choice of problem 2 over problem 3 is based on the LP solution values, \$9,205 versus 9,031. We know that any integer solution derived from problem 3 (with added constraints such as $x_2 = 0$ or $x_2 = 1$) cannot exceed \$9,031, since the LP solution is always an upper bound on the integer solution. We think that a better integer solution is likely to be derived from problem 2. The LP solutions are

Problem 4: $\mathbf{x}^* = (0, 1, 0, 0, 0, 0.2)$, $z^* = \$9,202$

Problem 5: $\mathbf{x}^* = (1, 0.31, 0, 0, 0, 0.37)$, $z^* = \$9,089$

Because problem 4 has a better objective function value, we create from it two new problems.

Problem 6: Problem 4 with $x_6 = 0$ added

Problem 7: Problem 4 with $x_6 = 1$ added

The LP solutions are

Problem 6: $\mathbf{x}^* = (0, 1, 0, 0, 0, 0)$, $z^* = \$9,186$

Problem 7: $\mathbf{x}^* = (0, 1, 0, 0, 0, 1)$, $z^* = \$9,110$

At this point we have two integer solutions, and we can avoid further analysis of problems 6 and 7. We select the better of the two, that from problem 6 with $z^* = \$9,186$, and designate it as the incumbent (integer) solution.

Before we decide which of problems 3 and 5 to examine further, we check to see whether either can be ruled out by comparing its upper bound, or LP objective function value, with that of the incumbent. It happens that both have upper bounds less than \$9,186, and we do not examine them further. Problems

3 and 5 have been fathomed. There are no other candidate problems to examine, so we have finished and obtained the optimal solution $\mathbf{x}^* = (0, 1, 0, 0, 0, 0)$ with $z^* = \$9,186$. Figure 8.2 depicts the entire search process in tree form.   □

In Example 8.7 the optimal integer objective function value is not much below the LP optimum, about 0.3%. However, we cannot generalize such characteristics, because so much depends on the projects, interest rates, and so forth. Note that a typical rounding process applied to the LP solution would give $\mathbf{x} = (0, 1, 0, 0, 0, 1)$, as in problem 7, which is suboptimal. We could conjecture that if we had branched first on x_6 instead of x_4, we might have reached the integer optimum sooner. Again, it is beyond our scope here to deal with such issues [9]. Our purpose has been to demonstrate an easily available integer solution procedure on a small capital budgeting problem.

8.7.3 Duality Analysis for Integer Solutions

Two basic approaches to duality analysis for mixed-integer linear programming have been presented in the literature. We will briefly discuss the first, more difficult method and then concentrate on the second, more straightforward method and its variations.

Recomputed Dual Variables.   One method for solving mixed-integer linear programs is to use the cutting-plane procedure [9]. This approach begins with the LP optimum and successively adds constraints that delete portions of the feasible LP space but do not delete any integer solutions. Each time a constraint is added, the LP is solved again. The added constraints, called cutting planes, are derived from the current LP solution. When the current LP solution is an integer in the required variables, the procedure stops. At this point we have dual variables for both the original constraint set and the added constraints.

Gomory and Baumol [10] derived a technique for taking the dual variables for the added constraints and reapportioning them among the original constraint set. The purpose is to obtain a set of dual variables for the original problem only. (Dual variables for the cutting planes would be difficult to interpret in terms of the resources expressed by the original constraint set.) The disadvantage of this approach, apart from its complexity and the need to use the cutting-plane procedure, is that the recomputed duals are not always unique. Furthermore, the interpretation of the dual variables as measuring changes in the objective function value resulting from small changes in resource limits does not always apply in the integer case. Small changes in resource limits can cause jumps in the objective function value [20].

Penalties and Subsidies.   Let us assume we have reached the LP problem corresponding to the optimal integer solution in a branch-and-bound integer procedure. (In Example 8.7 this would be problem 6, with x_1, x_4, and x_6 constrained to be zero). The LP form of the problem will contain a number of constraints that force certain project selection variables to zero and other constraints that force some project selection variables to their upper bounds. To the primal formulation of the horizon model—whether it be the basic model in Table 8.6, the model with a sloping supply schedule of funds in Table 8.10, or a model with time-dependent interest rates and project interdependencies—we would thus add

$$x_j = 0, \quad j \text{ in } J_1$$
$$x_j = 1, \quad j \text{ in } J_2 \tag{8.79}$$

where J_1 = set of projects constrained to be zero in the optimal integer solution,

J_2 = set of projects constrained to be at upper bound in the optimal integer solution.

These additional constraints will have corresponding dual variables. At first glance, the dual variables appear to be unconstrained, since the primal constraints 8.79 are equalities. We can, however, reinterpret the constraints as

$$x_j \leq \epsilon, \quad j \text{ in } J_1$$
$$x_j \geq 1 - \epsilon \quad \text{or} \quad -x_j \leq -1 + \epsilon, \quad j \text{ in } J_2 \tag{8.80}$$

where ϵ is a very small positive number. (Some LP codes check for variables set at fixed values and delete the corresponding constraints during a preprocessing stage. If this is done, it is necessary to use (8.80) instead of (8.79) to obtain information about the dual variables. An ϵ value of 0.001 or 0.0001 usually does the trick.)

In the pricing operation of a project constrained to be zero in the optimal integer solution, we then modify (8.33) as follows (assuming no project interdependencies),

$$-\sum_n a_{nj}\rho_n + \mu_j + \gamma_j \geq \hat{a}_j \tag{8.81}$$

where γ_j is a dual variable, nonnegative. Rewriting, we have

$$\mu_j^* \geq \sum_n a_{nj}\rho_n^* + \hat{a}_j - \gamma_j^* \tag{8.82}$$

But since μ_j^* for a rejected project is zero, the γ_j^* acts as a penalty (without Eq. 8.79 the μ_j^* was positive) to force rejection of project j.

If the project was constrained to be at its upper bound, Eq. 8.41 becomes

$$0 \leq \mu_j^* = \hat{a}_j + \sum_n a_{nj}\rho_n^* + \gamma_j^* \tag{8.83}$$

In this instance the γ_j^* acts as a subsidy to enable acceptance of project j. These penalties and subsidies are a natural consequence of forcing the solution to satisfy the integrality requirements. They are known only through solving the mixed-integer programming problem. If we had solved the problem by some other method, such as the cutting-plane or enumeration method, we would still have to set up an LP model with the appropriate constraints of type 8.79 in order to extract the values of the penalties and subsidies.

We can apply these concepts to our integer solution for Example 8.5. The optimal dual variables for problem 6 are

$$\rho_0^* = 1.69 \quad \mu_1^* = 0 \quad \mu_4^* = 0 \quad \gamma_1^* = 0 \quad \beta_1^* = 0$$
$$\rho_1^* = 1.3 \quad \mu_2^* = 96 \quad \mu_5^* = 0 \quad \gamma_4^* = 0$$
$$\rho_2^* = 1.0 \quad \mu_3^* = 0 \quad \mu_6^* = 0 \quad \gamma_6^* = 80$$

The ratio analysis of ρ_n indicates borrowing at times 0 and 1, so projects 1 and 4 do not require penalties. Recall that project 4 was fractionally accepted in the LP optimum; project 1 was zero in the LP optimum but was introduced at an intermediate stage in the branch-and-bound procedure. We may verify the value of $\mu_6^* = 0$, which justifies rejection of project 6 (it was fractionally accepted in the LP optimum).

$$(\$1,000)(1.69) - (700)(1.3) - (700)(1.0) - 80 = 0$$

It is possible to reformulate the dual of the horizon model for an integer solution so that

- Projects forced into acceptance receive a subsidy, and projects forced into rejection receive no penalty, *or*
- Projects forced into rejection receive a penalty, but those forced into acceptance receive no subsidy.

The interested reader is referred to Weingartner [20] for further details of this method.

8.8 CAPITAL BUDGETING WITH MULTIPLE OBJECTIVES

In many situations it is not possible or desirable to evaluate different investment alternatives by one criterion, such as *PV* or terminal wealth. There are various techniques for dealing with multiple objectives, but most fall into one of three classes: goal programming, interactive multiple-criteria optimization, and non-linear programming. In this section we provide an example of a goal-programming formulation, and we discuss the interactive approach.

Nonlinear programming can be applied if the decision maker can specify a utility function of the criteria, for example, dividends and terminal wealth. The major disadvantage of the approach seems to be the difficulty of specifying the utility function. Because each application depends so much on the utility function and on subsequent refinements in the solution algorithm, we will not discuss the approach in this section. Appendix 8.A provides an example of applying a quadratic programming algorithm to a problem involving dividends and terminal wealth.

8.8.1 Goal Programming

Goal programming is a technique that enables a decision maker to strive toward a number of objectives simultaneously. The first step consists of establishing a goal for each criterion. Next, an objective function is specified for each criterion with respect to this goal. Third, weighting factors are placed on deviations of the objective functions from their goals. Fourth, the separate objective functions are combined into one overall function to be optimized [13].

Example 8.8

Table 8.13 presents data for Example 8.8. The first-year after-tax profit and employment of specialized personnel are considered to be primary goals, and terminal wealth at time 2 is considered a secondary goal. Let us assume the goals are established, respectively, as

Goal 1, first-year after-tax profits: $2,500

Goal 2, specialized personnel needed: 700 person-hours

Goal 3, terminal wealth at time 2: $4,000

These imply

$$\$2,000x_1 + 3,000x_2 + 1,700x_3 - 500x_4 \geq \$2,500$$

$$100x_1 + 100x_2 + 300x_3 + 400x_4 = 700 \text{ person-hours}$$

$$v_2 - w_2 + \$800x_1 + 600x_2 + 3,000x_3 + 1,000x_4 \geq \$4,000$$

$$(8.84)$$

Table 8.13 Goal Programming, Example 8.8

Coefficient Type	Project			
	1	2	3	4
First-year after-tax profit	$2,000	$3,000	$1,700	−$500
Specialized personnel needed, person-hours	100	100	300	400
Cash flow at time				
0	−$1,000	−$800	−$2,000	−$200
1	300	200	1,000	100
2	400	200	1,000	200
$\hat{a}_j$	$800	$600	$3,000	$1,000

Budgets for external sources of funds: $n = 0$, $2,000; $n = 1$, −$500; $n = 2$, −$500

The inequalities for profits and terminal wealth are typical of goals that can be exceeded without penalty. We now define auxiliary variables as follows.

$$y_1 = \$2,000x_1 + 3,000x_2 + 1,700x_3 - 500x_4 - 2,500$$

$$y_2 = 100x_1 + 100x_2 + 300x_3 + 400x_4 - 700 \text{ person-hours} \qquad (8.85)$$

$$y_3 = v_2 - w_2 + \$800x_1 + 600x_2 + 3,000x_3 + 1,000x_4 - 4,000$$

We are concerned with measuring positive and negative deviations, so we define components

$$\begin{aligned} y_k^+ &= y_k \quad \text{if } y_k \geq 0 \\ y_k^- &= |y_k| \quad \text{if } y_k < 0 \end{aligned} \qquad k = 1, 2, 3 \qquad (8.86)$$

Our overall objective is to minimize some weighted sum of deviations,

$$\text{Min} \sum_k (c_k^+ y_k^+ + c_k^- y_k^-) \qquad (8.87)$$

where c_k^+ and c_k^- are weighting factors for the deviations. If a \$100 profit deviation is deemed equivalent to a deviation of one specialized employee, we might set $c_1^- = 100$, $c_2^+ = 1$, and $c_2^- = 1$. Since terminal wealth is a secondary goal, set $c_3^- = 10$, an order of magnitude lower. The positive deviations for goals 1 and 3 have no adverse consequences, so $c_1^+ = 0$ and $c_3^+ = 0$. Thus, the objective function becomes

$$\text{Min } 100y_1^- + y_2^+ + y_2^- + 10y_3^- \qquad (8.88)$$

The constraints of the problem are of two types. The first type consists of goal constraints, obtained from (8.84).

$$\$2,000x_1 + 3,000x_2 + 1,700x_3 - 500x_4 - (y_1^+ - y_1^-) = \$2,500$$

$$100x_1 + 100x_2 + 300x_3 + 400x_4 - (y_2^+ - y_2^-) = 700 \text{ person-hours}$$

$$v_2 - w_2 + 800x_1 + 600x_2 + 3,000x_3 + 1,000x_4 - (y_3^+ - y_3^-) = \$4,000$$

$$(8.89)$$

The second type consists of the original set of constraints. In this example they would be cash balance equations for $n = 0$, 1, and 2, respectively; project upper bounds; and nonnegativity constraints. An LP solution of (8.88) subject to the two types of constraints yields values for the x_j, v_n, and w_n that result in the "best" set of deviations from the goals. Assuming that lending and borrowing occur at 10%, the solution is:

$$x_1 = 0.483 \quad v_0 = 0 \qquad w_0 = 494.2 \quad y_1^+ = 1,825 \quad y_1^- = 0$$

$$x_2 = 1.0 \qquad v_1 = 0 \qquad w_1 = 93.0 \qquad y_2^+ = 0 \qquad y_2^- = 0$$

$$x_3 = 0.51 \quad v_2 = 496.5 \quad w_2 = 0 \qquad y_3^+ = 0 \qquad y_3^- = 0$$

$$x_4 = 1.0$$

objective function value = 0

The solution indicates that the first-year after-tax profit will be \$4,325, or \$1,825 above the goal of \$2,500. Goal 2, specialized personnel needed, and goal 3, terminal wealth at time 2, are met exactly. Since there is no penalty for exceeding goal 1, the objective function value is 0. ☐

A number of variations of the goal-programming technique are suitable for particular circumstances [13]. In all of them care must be taken in formulating the goals and relative weights for deviations.

8.8.2 Interactive Multiple-Criteria Optimization

Another approach is to assume the operational setting of optimizing a nonlinear function of the decision variables, *without* knowing the explicit form of the trade-off (utility) function. Instead, we assume the decision maker is able to provide information about the gradient of the function. This information is then used to guide a search process over the domain of the function [6].

To illustrate the concept, let us take the three goals in Example 8.8, described in the previous section, and convert them into three criteria. We assume that we can measure each criterion by a function f_j and that we wish to maximize an overall utility function,

$$\underset{\mathbf{x}}{Max}\ U(f_1, f_2, f_3) \tag{8.90}$$

where $f_1(\mathbf{x})$ = criterion function for first-year after-tax profits,

$f_2(\mathbf{x})$ = criterion function for specialized personnel needed, and

$f_3(\mathbf{x})$ = criterion function for terminal wealth at time 2 (let $\mathbf{v}$ and $\mathbf{w}$ be included in an extended $\mathbf{x}$ vector).

We will be careful to specify the f_j as concave, differentiable functions and assume U is increasing in each f_j. Maximization of (8.90) by a steepest-ascent procedure will then lead to a global optimum [23].

The procedure begins with an initial feasible solution $\mathbf{x}^1$. At any iteration k the direction of the search is obtained from

$$\underset{\mathbf{y}^k}{Max}\ \nabla_{\mathbf{x}^k} U(f_1(\mathbf{x}^k), f_2(\mathbf{x}^k), f_3(\mathbf{x}^k)) \bullet \mathbf{y}^k \tag{8.91}$$

by letting the search direction be $\mathbf{d}^k = \mathbf{y}^k - \mathbf{x}^k$. But (8.91) can be replaced by

$$\underset{\mathbf{y}^k}{Max}\ \sum_j c_j^k \nabla_{\mathbf{x}^k} f_j(\mathbf{x}^k) \bullet \mathbf{y}^k \tag{8.92}$$

where

$$c_j^k = \frac{(\partial U/\partial f_j)^k}{(\partial U/\partial f_1)^k} \tag{8.93}$$

In many situations (8.92) is linear and can be solved by LP. In any case, if we can express f_j, we can express (8.92). What has happened is that the ratios of the partial derivatives of U with respect to f_j (which result from the breakdown of ∇U) have been replaced by trade-offs c_j^k. Each c_j^k measures the reduction in value of criterion function j that the decision maker would tolerate for one unit of increase in the value of criterion function 1, which is taken as a reference point. The trade-offs depend on the current solution and thus are indexed by the iteration counter k. They are obtained from the decision maker by an interactive procedure.

After the direction $\mathbf{d}^k$ is determined, the interactive procedure presents a number of solutions in the form of

$$f_1(\mathbf{x}^k + a\mathbf{y}^k), \qquad f_2(\mathbf{x}^k + a\mathbf{y}^k), \qquad f_3(\mathbf{x}^k + a\mathbf{y}^k)$$

where a is the step size, which is typically incremented by one-tenth of $\mathbf{d}^k$. The decision maker provides input again by selecting the preferred combination of f_1, f_2, f_3 values, without reference to the utility function U.

Given appropriate conditions on the f_j and U, the procedure will converge to a global maximum. The great advantage of the procedure is that no explicit form of the function U is required. The decision maker instead is required to provide information about trade-offs among f_j values and to indicate preferences for $f_1, \ldots, f_n$ combinations.

8.9 SUMMARY

In this chapter we have presented a number of techniques for capital budgeting under deterministic conditions. The methods are generally designed for selecting among many different investment alternatives (too many to enumerate explicitly) in the presence of budget limits, project interdependencies, and lending and borrowing opportunities. Linear programming is a major tool in the formulation, solution, and interpretation of many of the methods, either as the primary modeling technique or as a subroutine. The pricing of activity vectors is an important concept with direct economic interpretation, and we have devoted considerable space to illustrating the concept.

The models in this chapter may be grouped into three broad classifications. The first is the class of *PV* objective functions. This type suffers from some serious conceptual problems in the reconciliation of the discount rate used and the presence of budget constraints. The second class consists of horizon models; their objective is to maximize the end cash value or the terminal wealth at the end of some planning period. A number of desirable economic interpretations can be derived from such models. Moreover, models of this type are readily extended to include borrowing limits, a sloping supply schedule of funds, and integer restrictions.

The third class is characterized by objective functions containing different types of criterion variables. Bernhard's general model is the first of this type; it includes dividends and terminal wealth in the objective function. Other types discussed are the goal-programming approach and interactive multiple-criteria optimization. Appendix 8.A presents an application of Bernhard's approach to a problem which has dividends and terminal wealth to consider.

REFERENCES

1. ATKINS, D. R., and D. J. ASHTON, "Discount Rates in Capital Budgeting: A Re-examination of the Baumol & Quandt Paradox," *The Engineering Economist*, Vol. 21, No. 3, pp. 159–171, Spring 1976.

2. BALAS, E., *Duality in Discrete Programming*, Graduate School of Industrial Administration, Carnegie-Mellon University, Pittsburgh, December 1967.

3. BAUMOL, W. J., and R. E. QUANDT, "Investment and Discount Rates under Capital Rationing—A Programming Approach," *Economic Journal*, Vol. 75, No. 298, pp. 317–329, June 1965.

4. BERNHARD, R. H., "Mathematical Programming Models for Capital Budgeting—A Survey, Generalization, and Critique," *Journal of Financial and Quantitative Analysis*, Vol. 4, No. 2, pp. 111–158, 1969.

5. DANTZIG, G. B., *Linear Programming and Extensions*, Princeton University Press, Princeton, N.J., 1963. (See Chapter 12 for a discussion of economic interpretation of dual problem.)

6. DYER, J. S., "A Time-Sharing Computer Program for the Solution of the Multiple Criteria Problem," *Management Science*, Vol. 19, No. 12, pp. 1379–1383, August 1973.

7. FISHER, I., *The Theory of Interest*, Macmillan, New York, 1930 (reprinted by A. M. Kelley, New York, 1961).

8. FREELAND, J. R., and M. J. ROSENBLATT, "An Analysis of Linear Programming Formulations for the Capital Rationing Problem," *The Engineering Economist*, Vol. 24, No. 1, pp. 49–61, Fall 1978.

9. GARFINKEL, R. S., and G. L. NEMHAUSER, *Integer Programming*, Wiley, New York, 1972.

10. GOMORY, R. E., and W. J. BAUMOL, "Integer Programming and Pricing," *Econometrica*, Vol. 28, No. 3, pp. 551–560, 1960.

11. HAMILTON, W. F., and M. A. MOSES, "An Optimization Model for Corporate Financial Planning," *Operations Research*, Vol. 21, No. 3, pp. 677–691, 1973.

12. HAYES, J. W., "Discount Rates in Linear Programming Formulations of the Capital Budgeting Problem," *The Engineering Economist*, Vol. 29, No. 2, pp. 113–126, Winter 1984.

13. IGNIZIO, J. P., *Linear Programming in Single and Multiple Objective Systems*, Prentice–Hall, Englewood Cliffs, N.J., 1982.

14. LASDON, L., *Optimization Theory for Large Systems*, Macmillan, New York, 1970. (See Chapter 6 for upper-bounded algorithm.)

15. LORIE, J. H., and L. J. SAVAGE, "Three Problems in Rationing Capital," *Journal of Business*, Vol. 28, No. 4, pp. 229–239, October 1955; also reprinted in Solomon, E. (ed.), *The Management of Corporate Capital*, Free Press, New York, 1959.

16. MURGA, P., *Capital Budgeting Objective Functions That Consider Dividends and Terminal Wealth*, M.S. thesis, School of Industrial and Systems Engineering, Georgia Institute of Technology, Atlanta, 1978.

17. RAVINDRAN, A., D. T. PHILLIPS, AND J. J. SOLBERG *Operations Research: Principles and Practice*, Wiley, New York, 1987. (See Chapter 4 for branch-and-bound technique. See Chapter 11 for Kuhn–Tucker conditions.)

18. SHARP, G. P., *Extension of Bernhard's Capital Budgeting Model to the Quadratic and Nonlinear Case,* School of Industrial and Systems Engineering, Georgia Institute of Technology, Atlanta, 1983.

19. UNGER, V. E., "Duality Results for Discrete Capital Budgeting Models," *The Engineering Economist,* Vol. 19, No. 4, pp. 237–252, Summer 1974.

20. WEINGARTNER, H. M., *Mathematical Programming and the Analysis of Capital Budgeting Problems,* Prentice–Hall, Englewood Cliffs, N.J., 1963.

21. WEINGARTNER, H. M., "Capital Rationing: n Authors in Search of a Plot," *Journal of Finance,* Vol. 32, No. 5, pp. 1403–1431. December 1977.

22. WILKES, F. M., *Capital Budgeting Techniques,* John Wiley & Sons, New York, 1983.

23. ZANGWILL, W. I., *Nonlinear Programming: A Unified Approach,* Prentice–Hall, Englewood Cliffs, N.J., 1969.

PROBLEMS

8.1. You wish to include lending activities at 8% and borrowing activities at 12% in a *PV* LP model. The interest rate used for *PV* calculations is 10%. Define the activity vectors for lending and borrowing opportunities, and write a model formulation for a time horizon of 2 years and three budget constraints.

8.2. One of the criticisms of the typical capital budgeting LP model is that only short-term (one-year) lending and borrowing is represented. Can long-term lending and borrowing be included? If so, show how by defining variables and specifying coefficients in the objective function and constraints. Would long-term lending and borrowing be more appropriate in a *PV* LP model or a horizon LP model?

8.3. In many decision environments the total number of major projects to be considered is ten or fewer. Thus, enumeration of all combinations would be feasible, since there would be $2^{10} = 1,024$ or fewer combinations. In such a case, would it make sense to use a mathematical programming approach? What information would the mathematical programming approach give that is not available from enumeration?

8.4. Formulate a *PV* LP model for selecting among the three projects described below. *MARR* = 8%. There is a budget of $13,000 at time 0, and the projects are required to generate $3,500 at time 1 and $1,200 at time 2. The life of each project is 5 years. The projects are independent except that C cannot be selected unless A is also selected. What is the value of extra budget money at time 2?

Project	Investment	Annual Cash Flow
A	$5,000	$1,319
B	7,000	1,942
C	8,500	2,300

8.5. Formulate a *PV* LP model for selecting among the three projects described below. *MARR* = 15%. There is a budget of $16,000 at time 0, and the projects are required to generate $4,000 at time 1 and $1,300 at time 2. The life of each project is 10 years. The projects are independent except that A cannot be selected unless B is also selected. What is the value of extra budget money at time 2?

Project	Investment	Annual Cash Flow
A	$8,000	$1,900
B	5,000	1,400
C	10,000	2,500

8.6. Fromulate a horizon LP model for selecting among the three projects described below, with time 2 as the horizon. There is a budget of $2,000 at time 0, and the projects are required to generate $500 at time 1 and $500 at time 2. The life of each project is 20 years. The projects are independent except that C cannot be selected unless A is also selected. The lending rate is 15% and the borrowing rate is 20%, per year. Do you see any obvious difficulty with the application of the horizon model to this particular example?

Project	Investment	Annual Cash Flow
A	$1,000	$240
B	800	190
C	1,500	310

8.7. A horizon LP model was formulated and solved for five independent projects and four budget constraints. The lending rate is 18% and the borrowing rate 25%, per year. There are no posthorizon cash flows. The solution is:

Project selection variables = (0.0, 1.0, 1.0, 0.5, 1.0)

Budget dual variables = (1.7995, 1.475, 1.25, 1.0)

Project dual variables = (10, 240, 310, 0, 110)

a. Indicate whether borrowing or lending occurs in each period.
b. Do you see any difficulty in interpreting the solution of this example?
c. Suppose you wish to evaluate a new independent project.

Time	0	1	2	3
Cash flow	−$1,000	−1,000	2,000	1,000

What would be your recommendation regarding acceptance?

8.8. A horizon LP model was formulated and solved for five independent projects and four budget constraints. The lending rate is 20% and the borrowing rate 25%, per year. There are no posthorizon cash flows. The solution is:

Project selection variables = (1.0, 0.0, 0.4, 1.0, 0.0)

Budget dual variables = (1.8, 1.44, 1.2, 1.0)

Project dual variables = (560, 0, 0, 320, 0)

a. Indicate whether borrowing or lending occurs in each period.
b. Suppose you wished to evaluate a new independent project.

Time	0	1	2	3
Cash flow	−$1,000	−1,000	2,000	1,000

What would be your recommendation regarding acceptance?

8.9. A horizon LP model was formulated and solved for five independent projects and four budget constraints. The lending and borrowing rates are

Time 0 to 1: lend at 15%, borrow at 20%

Time 1 to 2: lend at 15%, borrow at 20%

Time 2 to 3: lend at 18%, borrow at 25%

There are no posthorizon cash flows. The solution is

Project selection variables $= (1.0, 0.0, 0.4, 1.0, 0.0)$

Budget dual variables $= (1.628, 1.357, 1.18, 1.0)$

Project dual variables $= (560, 0, 0, 320, 0)$

a. Indicate whether borrowing or lending occurs in each period.

b. Suppose you wish to evaluate a new independent project.

Time	0	1	2	3
Cash flow	$-\$1,500$	$-1,500$	$3,500$	800

What would be your recommendation regarding acceptance?

c. What does the first project contribute to the objective function?

8.10. Formulate and solve a horizon LP model for selecting among the five following projects. The lending rate is 13% and the borrowing rate 17%, per year. There are no posthorizon cash flows.

			Project			
n	A	B	C	D	E	Budget
0	$-\$10,000$	$-\$5,000$	$-\$7,500$	$-\$15,000$	$-\$20,000$	$\$30,000$
1	$-5,000$	$-12,000$	$-8,500$	$-3,000$	$-5,000$	$25,000$
2	$2,000$	$15,000$	$11,000$	$2,176$	$14,000$	$30,000$
3	$4,072$	$3,761$	$1,541$	$2,176$	$16,005$	$35,000$
4	$16,000$	$1,700$	$4,000$	$2,176$	$8,000$	$10,000$
5	$18,000$	$1,700$	$12,000$	$2,176$	$10,000$	$20,000$

Verify that projects with positive future worth are accepted and those with negative future worth rejected. Verify that the ratios of the budget dual variables indicate lending or borrowing.

8.11. Rework Problem 8.10 with the inclusion of borrowing limits of $2,000 at time 0 and $2,000 at time 1, at the 17% rate. Unlimited borrowing at 20% is available at times 0 and 1.

8.12. Formulate and solve a horizon LP model for selecting among the five projects below. The lending rate is 15% and the borrowing rate 20%, per year. There are no posthorizon cash flows.

			Project			
n	A	B	C	D	E	Budget
0	$-\$10,000$	$-\$20,000$	$-\$15,000$	$+\$5,000$	$-\$15,000$	$\$25,000$
1	$4,000$	$8,000$	$-2,000$	$-1,000$	$1,300$	$2,000$
2	$5,000$	$10,000$	$5,000$	$-1,000$	$1,700$	0
3	$4,400$	$3,000$	$7,300$	$-3,200$	$6,000$	$2,000$
4	$2,800$	$7,000$	$6,000$	$-1,150$	$4,000$	$1,000$
5	$1,000$	$6,000$	$7,100$	-800	$2,700$	0

Verify that projects with positive future worth are accepted and those with negative future worth rejected. Verify that the ratios of the budget dual variables indicate lending or borrowing.

8.13. Rework Problem 8.12 with the inclusion of another activity, project F, with cash flow

n	0	1	2	3	4	5
Cash Flow	−$25,000	10,000	8,000	8,000	8,000	7,000

8.14. Rework Problem 8.13 (six projects) with the inclusion of borrowing restrictions of $10,000 per year over the planning period (5 years).

8.15. Rework Problem 8.13 (six projects) with the inclusion of a sloping supply schedule of funds. During each year the first $5,000 of borrowing is at 20% and the next $2,500 at 25%, and unlimited borrowing is available at 30%.

8.16. A horizon LP model was formulated and solved for selecting among the five projects below. The lending rate is 10% and the borrowing rate 20%, per year. There are no posthorizon cash flows.

			Project			
n	A	B	C	D	E	Budget
0	−$1,000	−$1,200	−$900	−$1,000	$1,000	$1,000
1	400	900	300	500	−400	1,300
2	800	800	500	700	−400	1,500
3	135	700	250	700	−400	200

The optimal solution contains:

Project selection variables = (1.0, 1.0, 0, 1.0, 1.0)

Budget dual variables = (1.452, 1.21, 1.1, 1.0)

a. Indicate whether lending or borrowing occurs during each time period.
b. Determine the project dual variable for project C and for Project E.
c. With a new set of budget amounts, the solution changes.

Budget amounts = ($1,000, −1,000, 1,500, 200)

Project selection variables = (0, 1.0, 0, 1.0, 1.0)

Budget dual variables = (1.584, 1.32, 1.1, 1.0)

Explain why project A is rejected here although it was accepted previously. Express your answer in LP terms, using specific numbers.

d. If you know nothing about the budget amounts, can you say *anything* specific about the acceptance or rejection of projects in this example?
e. Describe a method for determining the optimal value of the objective function for the original problem formulation, if you know the optimal values of the project selection variables and the budget dual variables.

8.17. Construct a horizon LP example with lending rate(s) less than borrowing rate(s). Demonstrate the relationships between lending or borrowing activities and the budget dual variables and the relationships between project dual variables and project future values.

8.18. Construct a horizon LP example where at least one of the projects is accepted fractionally. Explain why it is accepted fractionally by pricing out the project activity vector.

8.19. Construct a horizon LP example with a sloping supply schedule of funds. Validate the relationships between the budget dual variables and tightness of the borrowing constraints.

8.20. Construct a horizon integer programming example. Solve it by using a branch-and-bound algorithm. Determine the subsidies and penalties attached to projects that are fractionally accepted in the LP solution, in order to force them to be integer.

8.21. Solve the goal-programming example in Section 8.8.1.

8.22. Construct an example of Bernhard's general model, using a linear objective function and a linear terminal-wealth posture restriction. Use at least four time periods and different lending or borrowing rates. Try to construct the problem so that at least one project is accepted, at least one is rejected, and at least one borrowing constraint is tight.

8.23. The ABC Company has to determine its capital budget for the coming 3 years, for which data (in thousands of dollars) are given in the following table.

End of Year	Available Investment Capital	Investment Projects					
		1	2	3	4	5	6
0	300	−50	−100	−60	−50	−170	−16
1	100	−80	−50	−60	−100	−40	−25
2	200	20	−20	−60	−150	50	−40
Discounted future revenues		150	210	220	350	200	100

At the start of year 1 the company has $300,000 available for investment; in year 2 another $100,000 becomes available, and at the start of year 3 an additional $200,000 becomes available. Project 1 requires $50,000 at the start of year 1 and another $80,000 at the start of year 2; at the start of year 3, the project yields $20,000. The yield at the start of year 3 and the discounted yields for later years amount to $150,000. The company can borrow at most $50,000 plus 20% of the money invested so far in the various investment projects at an interest rate of 12% per year. If the company deposits money at the bank, the interest rate is 8%. The company has a bank debt of $10,000, on which it pays 11% interest and which may be repaid at the start of any year. Assume that the company may undertake 100% of each project or take a participation in each project of less than 100%.

a. Formulate the capital budgeting problem by using the horizon model.

b. Find the optimal capital allocations by using a linear programming package.

c. Find the optimal capital budget, assuming that no project can be undertaken partially.

8.24. The Micromegabyte Company is a small American manufacturer of microprocessors, which are vital components in many pieces of electronic equipment, including personal computers. In a recent meeting of the board of directors, the company was instructed to engage in the development of various types of software that would go with their microprocessor products. An ad hoc committee has been formed to come up with various proposals that can be initiated in the new fiscal period. The following six proposals were considered to be competitive in the market and to have good profit potentials. Because technology in this field advances rapidly, most software products will have a market life of about 3 years.

	Software Projects and Their Cash Flows*					
End of Period	1	2	3	4	5	6
0	−50	−100	−70	−130	−250	−300
1	−100	−50	−100	−50	−100	−60
2	50	100	90	−100	−60	150
3	100	50	150	260	300	200
4	50	30	100	250	150	100
5	30	30	30		100	

*All units in $1,000.

The company will have at the start of year 1 (end of period 0) $500,000 available for investment; in year 2 another $200,000 becomes available, and at the start of year 3 an additional $50,000 becomes available.

The company can borrow at most $200,000 over the planning horizon at an interest rate of 12% per year. The company has to repay an old loan of $50,000 over the planning horizon. No partial payment of this loan is allowed, but the company has to pay 13% interest at the end of each year until the loan is paid in full.

Projects 1 and 3 are considered to be mutually exclusive because both projects lead to the same software development but with application on different machines. The company does not have enough resources to support more than one type of operating system. Project 2 is contingent on project 1, and project 4 is contingent on project 3. Projects 2 and 4 are graphics softwares designed to run on the specific operating system.

The company has a total of 10,000 programming hours per year for the first 2 years that can be put into the development of these software projects. Annual programming hour requirements for the projects are estimated to be as follows.

	Project					
Year	1	2	3	4	5	6
First	2,000	3,000	3,000	5,000	4,000	4,000
Second	3,000	4,000	3,000	4,000	5,000	4,000

The company can always lend any unspent funds at an interest rate of 9%. Determine the firm's best course of action with a horizon time of 4 years.

8.25. The National Bank of Maine has $1 billion in total assets, which are offset on the balance sheet by demand deposits, time deposits, and capital accounts of $650 million, $250 million, and $100 million, respectively. The bank seeks your advice on how best to allocate its resources among the following list of assets.

Bank Assets and Their Expected Rates of Return

Asset	Expected Net Return (%)
Cash and cash equivalents	0
Loans	
Commercial loans	5.5
FHA and VA mortgages	5.0
Conventional mortgages	6.2
Other loans	6.9
Investments	
Short-term U.S. government securities	3.0
Long-term U.S. government securities	4.2

In allocating its resources, the bank is now constrained by the following legal and policy considerations.

Legal restrictions

- Cash items must equal or exceed 30% of demand deposits.

- Within the loan portfolio, conventional mortgages must not exceed 20% of time deposits.

Policy guidelines (goals)

- The management does not wish its total loans to exceed 65% of total assets. Each dollar of deviation from this target will carry a penalty of 3.5 cents per period.

- Within the loan portfolio "commercial loans" are not to exceed 45% or fall below 30% of total loans, and "other loans" are not to exceed the amount of total mortgages. Deviations of 1$ from these targets will carry uniform penalties of 0.8 cent per period.

- To ensure solvency, the management desires to limit its holdings of risk assets, defined as total assets less cash items less short-term U.S. government securities, to seven times the bank's capital accounts. Each dollar of deviation will carry a penalty of 4 cents per period.

- The management wishes to earn a target profit of $50 million. It places no premium on overattainment of this profit objective, but it places a penalty of $1 on each dollar of underattainment. Set up and solve a goal programming formulation for this problem.

Outline

Part IV: Additional Topics

- Lecture slides on deterministic capital budgeting

- Chapter 8 of "Advanced Engineering Economics" by Park and Sharp-Bette

- Lecture slides on utility theory

- Chapter 9 of "Advanced Engineering Economics" by Park and Sharp-Bette

- Chapter 13 of "Advanced Engineering Economics" by Park and Sharp-Bette

Utility Theory

- **Consider the following game:**

  ➢ A fair coin is tossed until the first time a head occurs. If it takes n tosses to obtain the first head, the payoff to the player is $\$2^n$

  ➢ What is the expected payoff?

  ➢ What is the maximum amount that you would be willing to pay to play this game?

- **Risk preference:**

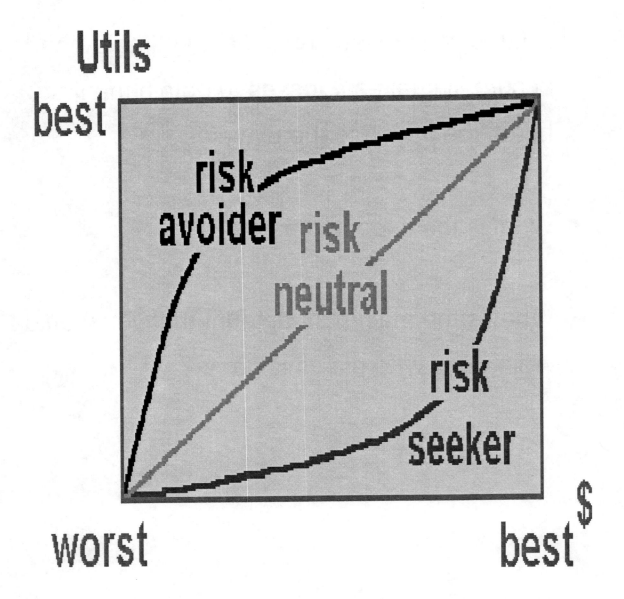

Utility Theory

- **Two famous economists: Von Neumann and Morgenstern**

  - ➢ They developed a set of axioms of behavior that lead to the existence of a utility function

  - ➢ Decision makers make decisions based on maximizing expected utility

Utility Theory

- **Risk averse investors have an *increasing concave* utility function**

    ➤ u (x) = ln (x)

    ➤ u (x) = x $^{0.5}$

    ➤ These are two examples of increasing concave

    ➤ The increasing concavity reflects a decreasing incremental value from each incremental dollar of wealth

Utility Theory

- **Expected utility:**

  ➤ $E[u(X)]$

- **Jensen's inequality using concavity of u :**

  ➤ $E[u(X)] \leq u(E[X])$

  ➤ An individual with a concave utility function u (.) would prefer to have E [X] for certain, than face the random variable X

- **Certainty Equivalent:**

  ➢ An individual will take less than E [X] for
    certain, rather than facing the random variable X

  ➢ The exact amount that the individual will take is
    called the certainty equivalent: CE

  ➢ $u (CE) = E [u (X)]$

  ➢ Or: $CE = u^{-1}(E [u (X)])$

Outline

Part IV: Additional Topics

- Lecture slides on deterministic capital budgeting

- Chapter 8 of "Advanced Engineering Economics" by Park and Sharp-Bette

- Lecture slides on utility theory

- Chapter 9 of "Advanced Engineering Economics" by Park and Sharp-Bette

- Chapter 13 of "Advanced Engineering Economics" by Park and Sharp-Bette

9
Utility Theory

9.1 INTRODUCTION

In the first two parts of this book we have assumed that decisions are made in a context of complete certainty. The decision makers are characterized as persons wishing to maximize cash flow, the present value of cash flow, or perhaps terminal cash wealth. Cash amounts at different points in time are converted to some common point in time, often time 0, by using an interest rate, and are then added to obtain *PV, FV,* and so forth.

In this third part of the book we relax these ideal assumptions in two important ways.

1. Project cash flow will no longer be regarded as certain. Instead, we will use probability concepts to describe project flows.
2. Decision makers will no longer be assumed to add (linearly) different cash flows at the same point in time or after conversion to the same point in time by use of an interest rate. Instead, small cash flows will usually be given more consideration per dollar than large cash flows.

In this chapter we give a brief introduction of the first concept, the probabilistic description of cash flows. We assume the reader is familiar with the fundamental concepts of probability theory. Probabilistic approaches to investment decisions are given extensive coverage in Chapters 10 to 13.

The principal emphasis in this chapter is on the second concept, namely the utility theory approach to combining and evaluating cash flows. Following the introduction of the concept in this section, the formal statement of utility theory is presented in Section 9.2. In Section 9.3 we discuss the properties of utility functions, followed by the procedures for assessing a utility function by empirical means in Section 9.4. An important operational method, mean–variance analysis, is shown in Section 9.5 to be based on the utility theory concept; mean–variance analysis is presented in depth in Chapters 10 and 11.

9.1.1 The Concept of Risk

We may introduce the concept of risk by asking why individual homeowners (with no outstanding mortgage or loan against their homes) would buy fire insurance. The possibility of damage from fire in a particular year is quite low, say 0.01. If the amount of damage caused by a fire is $60,000, we would say the *risk* of fire damage is a 0.01 chance (1% chance) of a $60,000 loss. If the fire insurance premium is $700 per year and the deductible amount on a loss (the amount the individual pays) is $250, then on an *expected monetary value* (*EMV*) basis an individual who buys insurance has the following yearly cost.

Event	Cost	Probability	Product
No fire occurs	$700	0.99	$693.00
Fire occurs	$700 + 250 = $950	0.01	9.50
		Expected annual cost	$702.50

Contrast this with the situation of an individual who decides *not* to buy fire insurance.

Event	Cost	Probability	Product
No fire occurs	0	0.99	0
Fire occurs	$60,000	0.01	$600.00
		Expected annual cost	$600.00

Most individual homeowners would clearly prefer to buy fire insurance in order to avoid the risk of a 0.01 chance of a $60,000 loss, even though the expected annual cost of $702.50 is greater than the expected annual cost of

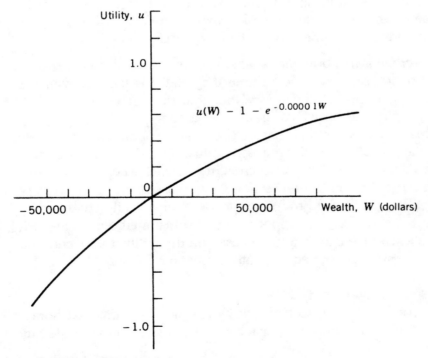

FIGURE 9.1. Example of a utility curve.

$600.00 without insurance. On the other hand, a large corporation with hundreds of retail outlets, facing similar risks and premiums at each outlet, might decide not to buy fire insurance. Such a corporation would become a *self-insurer*. The individual homeowner's way of evaluating the possible $60,000 loss is different from that of the large corporation, which can presumably make decisions regarding such amounts on an *EMV* basis. A $60,000 loss could be disastrous for an individual, whereas the large corporation would expect only one such loss per hundred retail outlets.

The individual's behavior, which is *not* based on an *EMV,* can be explained by the concept of *utility*. An example of a *utility function* for an individual, shown in Figure 9.1, has the following selected values. The function is

$$u(W) = 1 - e^{-0.00001W} \tag{9.1}$$

where W is the dollar amount of wealth.

Wealth, W	Utility Value
$100,000	0.63212
50,000	0.39347
10,000	0.09516
1,000	0.00995
0	0
−1,000	−0.01005
−10,000	−0.10517

The utility function in Figure 9.1 reflects a decreasing incremental value from each incremental dollar of wealth.

Following this line of argument, we can calculate an *expected utility* (*EU*) for our individual homeowner for the two decisions available: buy fire insurance or do not buy it. Let us assume the individual's total wealth, including the home, is $80,000. If the individual *buys* insurance, the *EU* of this decision for the next year is

Event	Resulting Wealth, W	Utility	Probability	Product
No fire occurs	$79,300	0.54751	0.99	0.54204
Fire occurs	$79,050	0.54638	0.01	0.00546

Expected utility = $E[u(W)]$ = 0.54750

If the individual *does not buy* insurance, the *EU* of this decision for the next year is

Event	Resulting Wealth, W	Utility	Probability	Product
No fire occurs	$80,000	0.55067	0.99	0.54516
Fire occurs	$20,000	0.18127	0.01	0.00181

Expected utility $E[u(W)]$ = 0.54697

Thus, on the basis of the *EU,* we can explain the decision of an individual homeowner to buy fire insurance even though the *expected annual cost* is higher. Large corporations also make decisions that do not result in the lowest expected annual costs, especially when potential losses are high. Such decisions can also be explained on the basis of *EU.* The difference is the scale of the cash flows; the corporation that is a self-insurer when losses are $60,000 per retail outlet might obtain insurance from an outside source when a single loss could be $25 million.

It is important to distinguish between *risk* and *uncertainty. Risk* applies to situations for which the outcomes are not known with certainty but about which we do have good probability information. Subsequent analysis could then be based on *EMV* or on *EU. Uncertainty* applies to situations about which we do not even have good probability information. In such situations other analysis techniques are appropriate, and the reader is referred to Luca and Raiffa [16].

9.1.2 Role of Utility Theory

In the preceding section we used utility theory to reconcile actual behavior with *EMV* decision making. This role of utility theory can be expanded to include behavior that is seemingly irrational because information is incomplete, because individuals have difficulties in establishing ordinal measurement scales, and because multiple-objective functions have been maximized [6]. Empirical behavior of individuals has prompted economists to construct some unusual utility functions. For example, an individual may buy insurance, normally an expected loss in a situation the individual feels offers no other choice. The same individual may buy lottery tickets, virtually always an expected loss in a situation in which the individual *does* have a choice. This type of observed behavior has led economists to hypothesize a compound-shaped utility function [7].

Utility theory can be used to justify the time value of money, as applied in Parts One and Two of this book. Furthermore, by including the effects of uncertainty in the future, we can argue for a discount rate *greater* than the equity rate or the weighted-average cost of capital presented in Chapter 5.

A very important role of utility theory is in the justification of the mean—variance method for analyzing risky cash flows. This is presented in Section 9.5.

It is important to remember that utility theory is both a *prescriptive* and a *descriptive* approach to decision making. The theory tells us how individuals and corporations *should* make decisions, as well as predicting how they *do* make decisions. The *hypothesis* aspect of utility theory should not be forgotten.

9.1.3 Alternative Approaches to Decision Making

Two related approaches other than utility theory, have been presented as constructs for decision making. They are based on principles other than expected value with a discount rate based on cost of capital. The first approach uses a risk-adjusted discount rate [2, 10]. Investment projects are assigned to risk classes, based on the uncertainty of the component cash flows. Investments in a "safe" risk class are evaluated by using an interest rate based on cost of capital, whereas investments with more uncertain cash flows are evaluated by using a higher interest rate.

The second approach is based on the concept of general states of wealth at different points in time and the implicit trade-offs an individual or corporation might make among these states [8, 14]. Although conceptually appealing, this choice–theoretic approach is difficult to implement.

9.2 PREFERENCE AND ORDERING RULES

In this section we present the formal definition of utility theory as it is commonly interpreted by economists. The theory consists of two parts: the hypothesis about maximizing expected utility and the axioms of behavior.

9.2.1 Bernoulli Hypothesis

The basic hypothesis of utility theory is that individuals make decisions with respect to investments in order to *maximize expected utility* [3]. This concept is demonstrated by the following example.

Example 9.1

An individual with a utility function $u(W) = 1 - e^{-0.0001W}$ is faced with a choice between two alternatives. Alternative 1 is represented by the following probability distribution.

Cash Amount	$-10,000	0	10,000	20,000	30,000
Probability	0.2	0.2	0.2	0.2	0.2

Alternative 2 is a certain cash amount of $5,000. The individual has an initial wealth of zero, and no investment is required for either alternative. Which alternative would the individual prefer?

For alternative 1 the expected utility is computed as follows.

Wealth, W	Utility	Probability	Product
−$10,000	−1.7183	0.2	−0.3437
0	0	0.2	0
10,000	0.6321	0.2	0.1264
20,000	0.8647	0.2	0.1729
30,000	0.9502	0.2	0.1900

Expected utility = $E[u(W)] = 0.1456$

For alternative 2 the utility is 0.3935. As this amount is greater than that for alternative 1, the certain cash amount of $5,000 is preferred to the risky alternative 1, which has a higher expected value of $10,000.

We can begin with the utility value of 0.1456 and determine a certain cash amount that is exactly equivalent to alternative 1.

$$0.1456 = 1 - e^{-0.0001W}$$

$$e^{-0.0001W} = 0.8544$$

Taking natural logarithms of both sides, we obtain

$$-0.0001W = -0.1574$$

$$W = \$1,574$$

The amount $1,574 is called the *certainty equivalent* (*CE*) of alternative 1. Our individual would prefer any larger certain cash amount to alternative 1, would prefer alternative 1 to any smaller certain cash amount, and would be indifferent about a certain cash amount of $1,574 and alternative 1. □

Definition. A *certainty equivalent* (*CE*) is a certain cash amount that an individual values as being as desirable as a particular risky option.

9.2.2 Axioms of Utility Theory

Individuals are assumed to obey the following rules of behavior in decision making [13, 17, 20].

Orderability. We can establish distinct preferences between any two alternatives. For example, given alternatives A and B, an individual prefers A to B, shown by A > B; prefers B to A, shown by $A < B$—we read the symbol < as "is less preferred than"; or is indifferent about choosing between the two, shown by $A \sim B$.

Transitivity. The preferences established by ordering are transitive. If A is preferred to B, and B is preferred to C, then A is preferred to C.

$$A > B \quad \text{and} \quad B > C \quad \text{imply } A > C$$

In addition,

$$A \sim B \quad \text{and} \quad B \sim C \quad \text{imply } A \sim C$$

Continuity. If A is preferred to B and B is preferred to C, there exists a probability p so that the individual is indifferent between receiving B for certain and obtaining A with chance p and C with chance $(1 - p)$. The second alternative is called a lottery involving A and C.

$$A > B > C$$

implies that there exists a p so that

$$B \sim \{(p, A), (1 - p, C)\}$$

Example 9.2

Consider the individual with utility function $u(W) = 1 - e^{-0.0001W}$. Find the probability p so that the individual is indifferent between receiving $20,000 for certain and entering a lottery with chance p of $30,000 and $(1 - p)$ of $10,000. The individual's wealth is $10,000, and there is no cost for either alternative. The comparison is between $30,000 (the initial $10,000 plus $20,000) for certain, a utility of 0.9502, and a chance p of $40,000 and chance $(1 - p)$ of $20,000.

$$u(\$40,000) = 0.9817$$

$$u(\$20,000) = 0.8647$$

$$0.9502 = (p)(0.9817) + (1 - p)(0.8647)$$

Solving for p gives 0.731. □

Monotonicity. If two lotteries involve the same two alternatives A and B, the individual prefers the lottery in which the preferred alternative has the greater probability of occurring.

$$A > B \quad \text{implies}$$

$$\{(p, A), (1 - p, B)\} > \{(p', A), (1 - p', B)\}$$

if and only if $p > p'$.

Decomposability. A risky option containing another risky option may be reduced to its more fundamental components. This axiom, often called the "no fun in gambling" axiom, is best explained by an example.

Example 9.3

Consider a two-stage lottery. In stage 1 there is a 0.5 chance of stopping and receiving nothing and a 0.5 chance of advancing to stage 2. In stage 2 there is a 0.5 chance of receiving $5,000 and a 0.5 chance of receiving nothing. This lottery may be reduced to its one-stage equivalent of

$$\$0: \quad (0.5) + (0.5)(0.5) = 0.75 \text{ chance}$$

$$\$5,000: \quad (0.5)(0.5) \qquad = 0.25 \text{ chance} \quad \square$$

Independence. A risky option A is preferred to a risky option B if and only if a $[p, (1 - p)]$ chance of A or C, respectively, is preferred to a $[p, (1 - p)]$ chance of B or C, for arbitrary chance p and risky options A, B, and C.

$$A > B$$

if and only if

$$\{(p, A), (1 - p, C)\} > \{(p, B), (1 - p, C)\}$$

for any p, A, B, and C.

The foregoing axioms have been used to derive the Bernoulli hypothesis [17, 20]. There are several different versions of the axioms. Some authors define additional ones or declare that some are embodied in others and thus superfluous.

Psychologists and behaviorally oriented economists each year write numerous papers describing experiments in which individuals systematically violate one or more of these axioms. It is not uncommon for such authors to propose a modification or elaboration of the theory [1, 4, 5, 11, 18]. This point brings us back to the *hypothesis* aspect of utility theory. The theory is an elegant mathematical way to describe real behavior, but it will always be at variance, more or less, with observed behavior.

9.3 PROPERTIES OF UTILITY FUNCTIONS

Most economists agree that an individual prefers more wealth to less. Hence, a utility function should be an *increasing*, or at the very least a *nondecreasing*, function of wealth. Other desirable properties are continuity (actually guaranteed by the axioms) and differentiability. The major question is about *risk avoidance* versus *risk seeking*.

9.3.1 Risk Attitudes

In all the examples presented so far in this chapter, the individual has been willing to accept a certain cash amount that is *less* than the *EMV* of a risky option. This type of behavior is described as *risk-averse*, or *risk-avoiding* behavior. Risk-averse utility functions, such as the one in Figure 9.1, are *concave* functions of wealth.

It has been suggested that some individuals exhibit *risk-seeking* behavior, as demonstrated by the following example.

Example 9.4

An individual is observed to buy a $5.00 lottery ticket each week. The possible prizes are represented by random variable X, and the chances of winning them are represented by probability p as follows.

$X =$		$p =$
	No prize	0.98889
	$100 prize	0.01000
	$1,000 prize	0.00100
	$10,000 prize	0.00010
	$100,000 prize	0.00001

Explain the behavior of the individual.

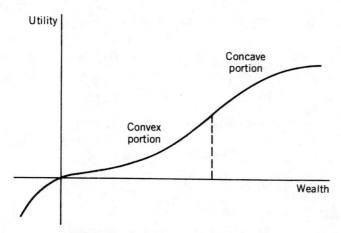

FIGURE 9.2. Utility function with a convex portion.

The *EMV* of such a lottery ticket is

$$E(X) = -5 + (0.98889)(0) + (0.01)(100) + (0.001)(1,000)$$
$$+ (0.0001)(10,000) + (0.00001)(100,000)$$
$$= -5 + 0 + 1 + 1 + 1 + 1$$
$$= -1$$

We may suggest two possible reasons for the individual to suffer the $1 expected loss each week. The first is that the purchase of a lottery ticket is a form of entertainment, similar to buying tickets to a sports event or a musical performance. The second, and more intriguing possibility, is suggested by the fact that poor people buy disproportionately more lottery tickets than middle-class and wealthy people, especially compared with other expenditures for entertainment. This fact has led many economists to suggest that the utility function for some persons may be *convex,* over a certain range of wealth, as shown in Figure 9.2. The rationale is that a poor person, in order to get out of his or her environment, is willing to take risks that a middle-class or wealthy person would not take [7]. □

We thus have a classification scheme for persons and their respective utility functions.

1. Risk-averse person: concave utility function.
2. Risk-neutral person: linear utility function.
3. Risk-seeking person: convex utility function.

Now let us reconsider the individual in Example 9.1 with utility function $u(W) = 1 - e^{-0.0001W}$. Assume that the individual has a starting wealth of $W_0 = \$20,000$ and is presented with the following lottery at no cost.

$$\{(0.5, \$10,000), (0.5, \$20,000)\}$$

The *CE* for the individual facing this lottery is obtained as follows.

Event, X	Resulting Wealth, W	Utility	Probability	Product
$10,000	$30,000	0.95021	0.5	0.47511
$20,000	$40,000	0.98168	0.5	0.49084

Expected utility $= E[u(W)] = 0.96595$

$$0.96595 = 1 - e^{-0.0001W}$$

$$e^{-0.0001W} = 0.03405$$

$$-0.0001W = -3.3798$$

$$CE = W = \$33,798$$

The difference between the *EMV* of $(0.5)(\$30,000) + (0.5)(\$40,000) = \$35,000$ and the *CE* of $33,798 is the *risk premium* (*RP*) the individual is willing to give up to avoid the risky option.

Risk premium, $RP = \$35,000 - 33,798 = \$1,202$

Definition [15]. A *risk premium* is an amount *RP* that solves Eq. 9.2.

$$E[u(W_0 + X)] = u[W_0 + E(X) - RP] \qquad (9.2)$$

where W_0 = the individual's wealth, a constant,
$\quad X$ = random variable representing the cash flow from a risky option,
$\quad RP$ = risk premium.

Here $W = W_0 + X$ is a random variable.

Let us recompute the *CE* for the previous lottery for an individual with the utility function of

$$u(W) = W - (0.00001)(W^2), \qquad 0 \le W \le 50,000 \qquad (9.3)$$

Event, X	Resulting Wealth, W	Utility	Probability	Product
$10,000	$30,000	21,000	0.5	10,500
$20,000	$40,000	24,000	0.5	12,000

Expected utility $= E[u(W)] = 22,500$

This corresponds to a *CE* of $34,190 (see Problem 9.7) and a corresponding *RP* of

$$RP = \$35,000 - 34,190 = \$810$$

The fact that the risk premium is different should not cause us much concern, since the utility functions for the two individuals are different. Let us recompute, however, the risk premiums for *both* individuals assuming an initial wealth of $W_0 = \$30,000$. For the individual with $u(W) = 1 - e^{-0.0001W}$, we have

Event, X	Resulting Wealth, W	Utility	Probability	Product
$10,000	$40,000	0.98168	0.5	0.49084
$20,000	$50,000	0.99326	0.5	0.49663

Expected utility $= E[u(W)] = 0.98747$

The *CE* is $43,796, which implies $RP = \$45,000 - \$43,796 = \$1,204$. This amount is not much different from the previous $1,202. (It actually is the same.)

For the individual with the quadratic utility function, Eq. 9.3, and an initial wealth of $W_0 = \$30,000$, we obtain

Event, X	Resulting Wealth, W	Utility	Probability	Product
$10,000	$40,000	24,000	0.5	12,000
$20,000	$50,000	25,000	0.5	12,500

Expected utility $= E[u(W)] = 24,500$

The *CE* is $42,930, with a corresponding $RP = \$45,000 - \$42,930 = \$2,070$.

The risk premium *increases* as the individual's wealth increases! In other words, the individual with the quadratic utility function is willing to give up *more* certain cash when faced with a risky option, as his or her wealth increases. Many economists argue that such behavior is not characteristic of intelligent investors. Instead, as their wealth increases, people should be willing to give up a *smaller* risk premium when faced with the same risky option.

9.3.2 Types of Utility Functions

Changes in the risk premium as a function of wealth are related to the behavior of the *risk aversion function* [21].

Definition. For a utility function u with first and second derivatives u' and u'', respectively, the *risk aversion function* is given by

$$r(W) = -u''(W)/u'(W) \qquad (9.4)$$

where W is wealth.

Specifically, if $r(W)$ is *decreasing* as a function of wealth, the risk premium (for a given risky option) decreases as a function of wealth. Similarly, an increasing $r(W)$ implies an increasing *RP*, and a constant $r(W)$ implies a constant *RP*.

A negative exponential function such as

$$u(W) = 1 - e^{-cW}, \qquad c > 0 \qquad (9.5)$$

has a constant risk aversion function, since

$$u'(W) = ce^{-cW} \tag{9.5a}$$

$$u''(W) = -c^2 e^{-cW} \tag{9.5b}$$

$$r(W) = c^2 e^{-cW}/(ce^{-cW}) \tag{9.5c}$$
$$= c$$

This property makes the function appealing to analysts. One does not have to know the wealth of the decision maker to perform analysis regarding *CE*s and *RP*s.

A quadratic function such as

$$u(W) = W - aW^2, \quad a > 0, \quad W \leq 1/(2a) \tag{9.6}$$

has an increasing risk aversion function, since

$$u'(W) = 1 - 2aW \tag{9.6a}$$

$$u''(W) = -2a \tag{9.6b}$$

$$r(W) = \frac{2a}{1 - 2aW} \tag{9.6c}$$

and the denominator of Eq. 9.6c is less than 1.0.

In Section 9.3.1 we presented the classification of utility functions as follows.

1. Risk-averse person: concave utility function,

$$u''(W) < 0 \tag{9.7a}$$

2. Risk-neutral person: linear utility function,

$$u''(W) = 0 \tag{9.7b}$$

3. Risk-seeking person: convex utility function,

$$u''(W) > 0 \tag{9.7c}$$

We can now add the subclassifications based on the risk aversion function, Eq. 9.4.

a. Decreasing risk aversion,

$$r'(W) < 0 \tag{9.8a}$$

b. Constant risk aversion,

$$r'(W) = 0 \tag{9.8b}$$

c. Increasing risk aversion,

$$r'(W) > 0 \qquad (9.8c)$$

An example of a risk-averse utility function with constant risk aversion is the negative exponential function given by Eq. 9.5. An example of a risk-averse utility function with increasing risk aversion is the quadratic function of Eq. 9.6. An example of a risk-averse function with decreasing risk aversion is the logarithmic function.

$$u(W) = \ln(W + d), \qquad d \geq 0 \qquad (9.9)$$

In addition, some utility functions have bounded functional values, and others are meaningful only over a bounded domain (range of wealth). Other characteristics are related to the *proportion* of wealth an individual would invest in a risky option [21].

Linear combinations of utility functions, where the weights are positive and all component utility functions have the same subclassification based on Eqs. 9.8a, b, and c, maintain that subclassification [21]. This property is useful when defining a utility function of present value. For example, we can define a utility function for cash F_n received in period n, when the utility is measured at time n.

$$u_n(F_n) = (F_n)^a, \qquad 0 < a < 1 \qquad (9.10)$$

A composite utility function for the vector of cash flows $(F_1, F_2, \ldots, F_n)$ can be expressed as

$$u(F_1, F_2, \ldots, F_n) = \sum_{n=1}^{N} \frac{(F_n)^a}{(1 + i)^n} \qquad (9.11)$$

Other functional forms are possible.

9.4 EMPIRICAL DETERMINATION OF UTILITY FUNCTIONS

9.4.1. General Procedure

The most popular way to determine a utility function is by the certainty equivalent method, whereby information from an individual is elicited by asking questions about lotteries [12]. Either a *numerical* or a *functional* approach can be followed. The numerical approach is presented first, for an individual with zero wealth.

The *numerical* approach requires two reference values for starting. Pick one as $0 with zero utility and one as $1,000 with utility 1.0.

$$u(0) = 0 \qquad (9.12a)$$

$$u(\$1,000) = 1.0 \qquad (9.12b)$$

Now present the individual with a lottery involving the nonzero reference point (there is no cost to play).

$$\{(p, \$1,000), (1 - p, -\$1,000)\} \qquad (9.13)$$

The value p that makes the individual indifferent to the lottery results in the following relation.

$$(p)u(\$1,000) + (1 - p)u(-\$1,000) = u(0) = 0 \qquad (9.14)$$

This is so because the individual values the lottery with p, the same as not playing, which is equivalent to the individual's current state of zero wealth. If, for example, a value of $p = 0.60$ makes the individual indifferent about playing, then substituting from Eq. 9.12, we have

$$(0.6)(1.0) + (0.4)u(-\$1,000) = 0$$

$$u(-\$1,000) = -1.5 \qquad (9.15)$$

This gives us three value points, and we continue in a similar manner.

For example, we can present the individual with a choice between a certain cash amount of \$1,000 and the following lottery.

$$\{(p, \$10,000), (1 - p, \$0)\} \qquad (9.16)$$

The value p that causes the individual to be indifferent results in

$$(p)u(\$10,000) + (1 - p)u(0) = u(\$1,000) \qquad (9.17)$$

If $p = 0.35$, for example, substituting and solving gives

$$(0.35)u(\$10,000) + (0.65)(0) = 1.0$$

$$u(\$10,000) = 2.86 \qquad (9.18)$$

Continuing in this manner, we can develop a table as shown here and graphed in Figure 9.3.

Wealth (dollars)	Utility Value
\$20,000	3.40
10,000	2.86
1,000	1.00
0	0
−1,000	−1.50
−2,000	−4.00

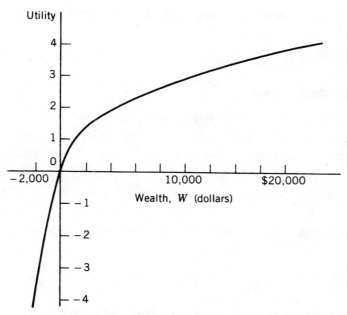

FIGURE 9.3. Typical empirically derived utility function.

The *functional* approach requires only one reference value for starting, most often $0 with zero utility. We also hypothesize the *functional* form. For example, assume the individual's utility function is Eq. 9.5,

$$u(W) = 1 - e^{-cW}, \qquad c > 0 \qquad (9.5)$$

Next, we present a lottery, such as Eq. 9.13, with no cost to play, and elicit the value p that makes the individual indifferent about playing. If the same value $p = 0.6$ is obtained, we have an equation with one unknown.

$$(0.6)[1 - e^{(-c)(1,000)}] + (0.4)[1 - e^{(-c)(-1,000)}] = 0$$

$$(0.6)(e^{-1,000c}) + (0.4)(e^{1,000c}) = 1 \qquad (9.19)$$

This can be solved by trial and error for $c = 0.0004$. Thus, the specific form of Eq. 9.5 is

$$u(W) = 1 - e^{-0.0004W} \qquad (9.20)$$

Determining utility functions must be done with extreme care, despite the apparent simplicity of these examples. Inconsistencies and irregular-shaped functions often result. Alternative forms of lotteries are recommended by some to reduce bias in the information-gathering process [19].

9.4.2 Sample Results

In this section we present empirical results for the bids in two lottery games.

Game 1: A number of individuals (more than 10) submit sealed bids for the right to play a lottery.

$$\{(0.5, \$50), (0.5, -\text{bid})\} \qquad (9.21)$$

The highest bidder *must* play the lottery.

Game 2: A number of individuals (more than 10) submit sealed bids for the right to play the St. Petersburg game [3]. The highest bidder *must* play. In the St. Petersburg game a coin is tossed repeatedly until it turns up "heads." The payoff is

$$\$(2)^{n-1} \qquad (9.22)$$

where n is the first time heads appears. This compound lottery is equivalent to the simple lottery of

$$\{(0.5, \$1), (0.25, \$2), (0.125, \$4), \ldots, [(0.5)^n, (2)^{n-1}], \ldots\} \qquad (9.23)$$

The lottery 9.23 has an infinite number of outcomes, and its *EMV* is infinity.

$$EMV = E(X) = (0.5)(1) + (0.25)(2) + (0.125)(4) + \cdots$$
$$= 0.5 + 0.5 + 0.5 + \cdots$$

Table 9.1 shows the results of the bids made by graduate engineering students during the early 1980s. The bidders are ordered by ascending game 1 bids and, for equal game 1 bids, by ascending game 2 bids. Some of the low bids clearly reflect the artificiality of a classroom situation, or perhaps the cash amount in the pocket of a student. Similar artificial distortions can exist in a corporate environment, however, where one may be trying to calibrate a utility function by posing lottery games.

Except for the very low bids of reluctant players, the game 1 bids jump in increments of $5 or more. The lack of bids in amounts of $17 and $22, for example, might lead us to question the continuity axiom. It is apparent that some game 1 bidders—those whose bids were at least $20 (bidders 25 to 31)—thought seriously about the possibility of playing the lottery. With the exception of the highest bidder (who was willing to accept an *EMV* of zero), all showed fairly strong risk aversion. This type of result was expected.

The game 2 bids are more interesting but not so much for the degree of risk aversion shown, which was also expected. Rather, it is interesting to compare the two bids made by the same individual. For example, bidder 27 bid $25 for game 1 and $0.5 for game 2. The $0.5 bid for game 2 is equal to the first payoff in *EMV* terms, so the individual either reflects an unusual utility function or has difficulties assessing probabilities and *EMV* and *EU*. Similar low bids for game 2 were made by bidders 25 and 26. Bidders 18 and 22 offered unusually large sums to play game 2—$12 and $20, respectively.

Such difficulties in assessing *EMV* and *EU,* with resulting inconsistencies, are likely to be experienced by most individuals in society. Recall that the bids

Table 9.1 *Results of Bids for*
Two Lottery Games

Bidder	Game 1 Bid	Game 2 Bid
1–5	$1	$1
6	1	2
7	1.5	1
8	2	1
9, 10	2	2
11	5	1
12, 13	5	2
14–17	5	5
18	5	12
19	10	2
20	10	4
21	10	5
22	10	20
23	15	2
24	15	4
25, 26	20	1
27	25	0.5
28	25	2.5
29	25	4
30	40	3
31	50	4

were made by engineering students with some formal training in probability
and statistics. Experiments conducted elsewhere show similar inconsistencies
[11, 19]. Thus, the application of utility theory must be performed with great care
and caution.

9.5 MEAN–VARIANCE ANALYSIS

The *EMV* and *EU* approaches are based on probabilistic expectation over the
range of possible outcomes of a risky option. In this section we present arguments for methods that are operationally different but are still based on utility
concepts. These operational methods are, in general, more popular and easier
to use. Therefore, a theoretical justification is attractive from a modeling point of
view. We outline the main arguments and refer the interested reader to detailed
sources.

9.5.1 Indifference Curves

Take the view of an investor with a quadratic utility function, as in Eq. 9.3,
facing a set of alternative lotteries,

$$\{(p, 0), (1 - p, \$X)\}$$

Table 9.2 *Lotteries Toward Which an Individual Might Be Indifferent*

p	$1 - p$	X	$E(X)$	$Var(X)$, 10^6
0	1.0	$10,000	$10,000	0
0.4375	0.5625	20,000	11,250	98.4
0.5714	0.4286	30,000	12,857	220.4
0.6250	0.3750	40,000	15,000	375.0
0.6400	0.3600	50,000	18,000	576.0

NOTES: 1. Lotteries are of type

$$\{(p, 0), (1 - p, \$X)\}$$

2. Utility function is

$$u(W) = W - (0.00001)W^2, \quad W \le 50,000$$

3. All lotteries have the same $CE = \$10,000$.

with X in the range $10,000 to $50,000. Table 9.2 shows the lotteries, along with $E(X)$ and $Var(X)$. The $Var(X)$ is the second moment about the mean. It is equal to $E(X^2) - [E(X)]^2$. (See Section 10.2.1 for a more detailed explanation.)

These $E(X)$ and $Var(X)$ values are plotted as curve U_1 in Figure 9.4. The lotteries in Table 9.2 have been constructed so that all have a CE of $10,000; each lottery has the same utility value, and the individual with utility $W - (0.00001)W^2$ would view them indifferently. Curve U_1 in Figure 9.4 can thus be interpreted as an indifference function relating $E(X)$ and $Var(X)$. Each combination of $E(X)$, $Var(X)$ on curve U_1 has the same utility value.

We could construct other sets of lotteries in which all in a set would have the same utility value. The result would be a family of curves $U_1, U_2, U_3, U_4, \ldots$, one curve corresponding to each set of lotteries. Higher curves represent higher utility values.

Points A and B on curve U_3 are valued the same by the individual. A point like C or D that is not on the same curve does not have the same utility as point A. Point C is considered less desirable than point A because it has the same $E(X)$ but a higher $Var(X)$. On the other hand, point D is preferred to point A because for the same $Var(X)$ it has a higher $E(X)$. Point B is preferred to point C because of higher $E(X)$ *and* lower $Var(X)$, but by the same reasoning point D is preferred to point B. These preference rules are specified in greater detail in Chapter 11. A formal analysis [22] along these lines shows that the mean–variance approach is justified when the investor's utility function is quadratic and the probability distributions of X can be characterized by only two parameters (e.g., normal, lognormal).

9.5.2 Coefficient of Risk Aversion

We may observe some characteristics of the utility curves in Figure 9.4. First, the intersection point of a curve with the vertical $E(X)$ axis represents the

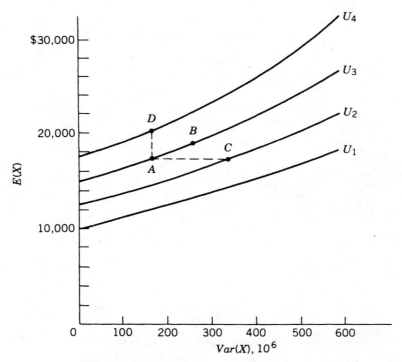

FIGURE 9.4. Utility indifference curves relating $E(X)$ and $Var(X)$.

certainty equivalent for all the points on that curve. Since such an intersection point has zero $Var(X)$, the cash outcome is certain. Second, the curves have positive slope. This reflects the fact that utility is an *increasing* function of $E(X)$ and a *decreasing* function of $Var(X)$. Third, the curves are concave. One way to explain the concavity of the indifference curves is that as risk increases, much larger increases in $E(X)$ are necessary to maintain the same level of utility for risk-averse individuals.

An approximation to the set of curves in Figure 9.4 might appear as in Figure 9.5. Here all the utility curves are linear and parallel. In Figure 9.5 we can obtain the *CE* of any point, such as Point *D,* as follows.

$$CE_D = E(D) - \lambda\, Var(D) \qquad (9.24)$$

The value λ is called the *coefficient of risk aversion* (or sometimes the *risk aversion factor*). It measures the trade-off between $E(X)$ and $Var(X)$. This means that a *CE* is easier to calculate when λ is known.

Even if the linear approximation in Figure 9.5 is not appropriate, we can define λ as the *tangent* to a utility indifference curve in Figure 9.4. The value of the coefficient of risk aversion is then reasonably valid over a restricted interval. For known functional utility forms, expressions for λ as a function of the cash outcomes can be developed [9]. In practice, if we are not confident with assuming a single value of λ, then λ is varied parametrically (see Appendix 11A).

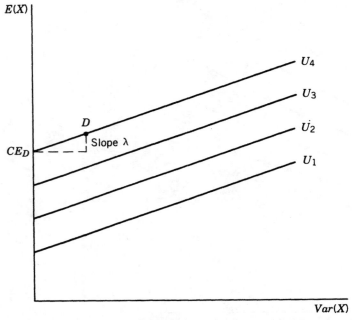

FIGURE 9.5. Approximation of indifference curves in Figure 9.4.

9.5.3 *Justification of Certainty Equivalent Method*

Applying Eq. 9.24 to a periodic cash flow F_n, which may be a random variable, we have

$$V_n = E(F_n) - \lambda \, Var(F_n) \tag{9.25}$$

For a series of cash flows from a project, we have in the simplest case, where λ is time-invariant and the F_n are independent random variables,

$$PV(i) = \sum_{n=0}^{N} \frac{V_n}{(1 + i)^n}$$

$$= \sum_{n=0}^{N} \frac{E(F_n) - \lambda \, Var(F_n)}{(1 + i)^n} \tag{9.26}$$

Here the interest rate i is a *risk-free* rate, which accounts for only the time value of money. This risk-free rate can be viewed as a rate at which the individual can always invest money in some risk-free projects (such as a short-term government bond). This is the amount forgone if the project is undertaken and a net income is received from the risk-free project. Thus, having a present value of the certainty equivalents greater than zero means that the project is acceptable to this investor.

Example 9.5

To illustrate the procedures involved in calculating the present value of certainty equivalents, let us examine a 5-year project with $E(F_n)$ and $Var(F_n)$ as shown in the tabulation. We assume that the λ value is known to be 0.02 for this investor. Then the certainty equivalents for the periodic random cash flows F_n are

n	$E(F_n)$	$Var(F_n)$	V_n	$PV(10\%)$
0	−400	400	−408	−408.00
1	120	100	118	107.27
2	120	225	115.5	95.45
3	120	400	112	84.15
4	110	900	92	62.84
5	120	2500	70	43.46

$$\sum = -\$14.83$$

Since the total present value of the certainty equivalents is negative, the investor would reject the project. □

Returning to the general case, let us assume that the utility function for cash flows distributed over time is

$$u = \sum_{n=0}^{N} c_n u_n \tag{9.27}$$

where u_n is a utility function for the random cash flow F_n occurring at time n and c_n is a constant. This expression implies that contributions to total utility are additive over time, and periodic utility values are multiplied by the constant c_n to adjust for the time preference of the events F_n. The exact form of the periodic utility functions u_n is not specified. In fact, u_n could be different functions over time or, in the simplest case, time-invariant. For our discussion, let us assume that $u_n = u_1$ for all n. A Taylor expansion can be used to generate a reasonable approximation to an expected utility function [20].

$$E(u_n) = u_n[E(F_n)] + u_n^{(2)}[E(F_n)] \, Var(F_n)/2 \tag{9.28}$$

This expression is obtained by adopting "sufficient approximation" reasoning to justify ignoring the higher moments about the mean of the cash flow in the Taylor series. If the utility function is a quadratic, however, any term $u_n^{(n)}$ (nth derivative of u_n) with $n > 3$ will be zero. Thus Eq. 9.28 becomes the exact expression of the expected utility measure. Further, the term $u_n^{(2)}$ becomes a constant for the quadratic utility function. Thus, rewriting Eq. 9.28 gives us the expression

$$E(u_n) = u_n[E(F_n)] + A_n \, Var(F_n) \tag{9.29}$$

where

$$A_n = u_n^{(2)}[E(F_n)]/2 \tag{9.30}$$

Returning to the total utility function given in Eq. 9.27 and taking the expected value of each side of the equation, we obtain

$$E(u) = \sum_{n=0}^{N} c_n E(u_n) \tag{9.31}$$

Substituting Eq. 9.29 into Eq. 9.31 yields

$$E(u) = \sum_{n=0}^{N} c_n u_n [E(F_n)] + \sum_{n=0}^{N} c_n A_n Var(F_n) \tag{9.32}$$

If a certainty equivalent can be found for each time period so that

$$u_n(V_n) = u_n[E(F_n)] + A_n Var(F_n) \tag{9.33}$$

the present value of this set of certainty equivalents will be equal to the expected utility of the cash flows from the investment project by letting $c_n = 1/(1 + i)^n$ [20].

9.6 SUMMARY

Utility theory is a very important concept because it helps to reconcile real behavior with expected monetary value in decision making. The typical individual has a concave utility function, reflecting an aversion to risk, which is usually measured by the variance of the cash flow. The axioms of utility theory can be used to derive the Bernoulli hypothesis of expected utility maximization. Validation experiments reveal, however, that this hypothesis is not perfectly true.

Operationally, the utility indifference curves that relate $E(X)$ and $Var(X)$ provide the theoretical basis for the popular mean–variance analysis presented in Chapter 11. The coefficient of risk aversion, heavily used in portfolio analysis, is the slope of the indifference curve. Finally, the discounted sum of certainty equivalents is shown to be an approximation (exact for quadratic utility) to the expected utility of a random future cash flow stream. All these results will be used in later chapters.

REFERENCES

1. BECKER, J., and R. K. SARIN, "Lottery Dependent Utility," *Management Science,* Vol. 33, No. 11, pp. 1367–1382, 1987.

2. BERNHARD, R. H., "Risk-Adjusted Values, Timing of Uncertainty Resolution, and the Measurement of Project Worth," *Journal of Financial and Quantitative Analysis,* Vol. 19, No. 1, pp. 83–99, 1984.

3. BERNOULLI, D., "Exposition of a New Theory of the Measurement of Risk," *Econometrica,* Vol. 22, No. 1, pp. 23–36, 1954. (Accessible translation of "Specimen Theoriae Novae de Mensura Sortis," 1738.)

4. BROCKETT, P. L., and L. L. GOLDEN, "A Class of Utility Functions Containing All the Common Utility Functions," *Management Science,* Vol. 33, No. 8, pp. 955–964, 1987.

5. CURRIM, I. S., and R. K. SARIN, "Prospect Versus Utility," *Management Science,* Vol. 35, No. 1, pp. 22–41, 1989.

6. EDWARDS, E., "The Theory of Decision Making," *Psychological Bulletin,* Vol. 51, No. 4, pp. 380–417, 1954.

7. FRIEDMAN, M., and L. J. SAVAGE, "The Utility Analysis of Choices Involving Risk," *Journal of Political Economy,* Vol. 56, No. 4, pp. 279–304, 1948.

8. HIRSHLEIFER, J., "Investment Decision under Uncertainty: Choice-Theoretic Approaches," *Quarterly Journal of Economics,* Vol. 79, No. 4, pp. 509–536, 1965.

9. JEAN, W. H., *The Analytical Theory of Finance,* Holt, Rinehart and Winston, New York, 1970.

10. JOHNSON, W., *Capital Budgeting,* Wadsworth, Belmont, Calif., 1970, Ch. 5.

11. KAHNEMAN, D., and A. TVERSKY, "Prospect Theory: An Analysis of Decision under Risk," *Econometrica,* Vol. 47, pp. 263–291, 1979.

12. KEENEY, R. L., and H. RAIFFA, *Decisions with Multiple Objectives; Preferences and Value Tradeoffs,* Wiley, New York, 1976.

13. KELLER, L. R., "Testing of the 'Reduction of Compound Alternatives' Principle," *OMEGA, International Journal of Management Science,* Vol. 13, No. 4, pp. 349–358, 1985.

14. LAVALLE, I. H., and P. C. FISHBURN, "Decision Analysis under States-Additive SSB Preferences," *Operations Research,* Vol. 35, No. 5, pp. 722–735, 1987.

15. LEVY, H., and M. SARNAT, *Portfolio and Investment Selection: Theory and Practice,* Prentice–Hall, Englewood Cliffs, N.J., 1984.

16. LUCE, D. R., and H. RAIFFA, *Games and Decisions: Introduction and Critical Survey,* Wiley, New York, 1957.

17. MACHINA, M. J., "A Stronger Characterization of Declining Risk Aversion," *Econometrica,* Vol. 50, No. 4, pp. 1069–1079, 1982.

18. MACHINA, M. J., "Decision-Making in the Presence of Risk," *Science,* Vol. 236, pp. 537–543, 1 May 1987.

19. McCORD, M., and R. DE NEUFVILLE, "'Lottery Equivalents' Reduction of the Certainty Effect Problem in Utility Assessment," *Management Science,* Vol. 32, No. 1, pp. 56–61, 1986.

20. NEUMANN, J. V., and O. MORGENSTERN, *Theory of Games and Economic Behavior,* 2nd edition, Princeton University Press, Princeton, N.J., 1947.

21. PRATT, J. W., "Risk Aversion in the Small and in the Large," *Econometrica,* Vol. 32, No. 1–2, pp. 122–136, 1964.

22. TOBIN, J., "Liquidity Preference as Behavior toward Risk," *Review of Economic Studies,* No. 67, pp. 65–85, February 1958.

PROBLEMS

9.1. Consider the homeowner in Section 9.1.1 with the utility function given by Eq. 9.1. If the deductible amount on a loss is higher than $250, the homeowner might prefer not to buy fire insurance, on an *EU* basis. Using the data in Section 9.1.1 for other factors, determine the deductible amount that would make the homeowner *indifferent* about choosing between buying and not buying insurance, on an *EU* basis.

9.2. For an individual with zero initial wealth and a utility function

$$u(W) = 1 - e^{-0.0001W}$$

find the *CE* for each of the following alternatives (probabilities of the outcomes are given).

Alternative	Cash Amount				
	−$10,000	0	$10,000	$20,000	$30,000
1	0.1	0.2	0.4	0.2	0.1
2	0.1	0.2	0.3	0.3	0.1
3	0	0.3	0.4	0	0.3
4	0	0.15	0.65	0	0.2
5	0.5	0	0	0	0.5

9.3. Solve Example 9.2 for the situation in which the individual's initial wealth is $20,000. Would you expect the probability to change as the initial wealth changes?

9.4. Consider a three-stage lottery. In the first stage there are a 0.2 chance of receiving $1,000 and a 0.8 chance of going on to stage 2. In stage 2 there are a 0.5 chance of receiving $2,000 and a 0.5 chance of going on to stage 3. In stage 3 there are a 0.2 chance of receiving $1,000, a 0.3 chance of receiving $2,000, and a 0.5 chance of receiving $5,000. Reduce this three-stage lottery to an equivalent one-stage lottery.

9.5. Construct a compound lottery and reduce it to its equivalent one-stage lottery.

9.6. Obtain information about a lottery. Calculate the *EMV* of the act of purchasing a ticket.

9.7. Derive the *CE* for an individual with initial wealth $20,000 and a quadratic utility function as given by Eq. 9.3, when facing the lottery {(0.5, $10,000), (0.5, $20,000)}. There is no cost for the lottery. Show all computations.

9.8. Can you specify a risk-seeking utility function with decreasing risk aversion? With constant risk aversion? With increasing risk aversion?

9.9. Conduct a lottery game of the type described in Section 9.4.2. Analyze the results for consistency.

9.10. Construct a set of lotteries, each with the same *CE* and similar to the ones in Table 9.2, to derive one of the higher utility curves in Figure 9.4.

9.11. Construct a set of lotteries, each with the same *CE* and similar to the ones in Table 9.2, but using the utility function given by Eq. 9.1. What is the shape of the indifference curve?

9.12. Using the worksheet provided, develop your utility function. In doing so, consider the following steps.

Step 1: Find the certainty equivalent amount *B* for a given lottery (*A* or zero with 0.5 probability each). Once the amounts *A* and *B* are specified, find the certainty equivalent amount *C* for a new lottery (*B* or zero with 0.5 probability each). Continue this procedure for the remaining lotteries. You are likely to find some inconsistencies in the certainty equivalent amounts assessed. Resolve these inconsistencies by reassessing the certainty equivalent amounts.

Step 2: Scale the certainty equivalent amounts (*A* through *J*) as a percentage of *A*. For example, if *A* = $1,000 and *B* = $300, then *A* = 100% of *A* and *B* = 30% of *A*.

Step 3: Plot the scaling preferences on the chart provided and smooth the curve when connecting the points plotted.

WORKSHEET FOR DETERMINING THE UTILITY FUNCTION

Certainty Equivalent

1	A_____ or zero	vs.	B_____
2	B_____ or zero	vs.	C_____
3	C_____ or zero	vs.	D_____
4	A_____ or E_____	vs.	zero
5	E_____ or zero	vs.	F_____
6	F_____ or zero	vs.	G_____
7	A_____ or F_____	vs.	H_____
8	C_____ or E_____	vs.	J_____

Scaling Preference

	Amount	%A	U
A			+8
B			+4
C			+2
D			+1
E			−8
F			−4
G			−2
H			+2
J			−3

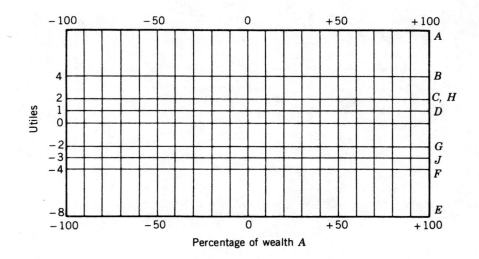

747

13

Decision Tree Analysis

13.1 INTRODUCTION

Another class of investment problems that will be described in this chapter consists of multiple-stage investment problems. This class is characterized by a series of decisions to be made, at various time intervals, with each decision influenced by the information that is available at the time it is made. Decision problems with more than a single stage introduce another source of complexity. It is the sequence of decisions and uncertain events that links the initial decision to the consequences. With this added complexity, direct choice among the initial decisions is very difficult. One popular method for dealing with such a multiple-stage problem is the decision tree method. The decision tree technique facilitates project evaluation by enabling the firm to write down all the possible future decisions, as well as their monetary outcomes, in a systematic manner.

We will take the experience of a retail chain outlet to demonstrate the selection of optimal investment strategies, given substantial market uncertainty. Section 13.2 explains a simple decision analysis model. The situation illustrated is a forecasting event, although the model could be used for any step-by-step selection of alternatives in any uncertain problem environment. Section 13.3 considers the cost of uncertainty and the value of additional information. We also discuss how sensitivity analysis may help to limit the consequences of uncertain measurements. Section 13.4 presents an example of the investment sampling process in which an investment, although initially not desirable, may appear acceptable in view of the consequent opportunity of obtaining additional information.

13.2 SEQUENTIAL DECISION PROCESS

A characteristic of the investment problems described up to this point has been that a single decision is made and, as a consequence of this decision, estimated revenues may be earned and estimated costs may be incurred. But in a sequential decision problem, in which the actions taken at one stage depend on actions taken in earlier stages, the evaluation of investment alternatives can become very complicated. In these situations the decision tree method provides a valuable tool for organizing the information needed to make the decision.

13.2.1 Structuring the Decision Tree

Before introducing a multiple-stage decision problem, we will work with a single-stage decision tree to illustrate the terminology used in decision tree analysis [4]. Then later we will expand the decision tree to include a multiple-stage decision problem. Perhaps the best way to explain the decision tree is to demonstrate its use by a specific example.

Retail Convenience Store Problem. A large chain of retail convenience stores is considering the expansion of one of its Orlando outlets. Continuation of the current rate of growth will require increasing the hours of operation and paying overtime if substantial business is not to be lost. As an alternative, the company is considering enlarging the store. This expansion may be accomplished in either of two ways.

Option 1: Expand Large. Because there is a possibility of substantial growth in the neighborhood, the first plan is to expand the current store by leasing additional floor space and then to remodel the entire store. This would nearly double its floor space. This plan will cost $150,000 initially, consisting of the remodeling expense of $70,000 and the purchase of new equipment worth $80,000. The equipment is expected to have a residual value of $15,000 at the end of 5 years. Leasing additional floor space will cost the store $10,000 annually. This large-scale expansion requires an $18,000 investment in working capital that is recovered at the end of planning horizon.

Option 2: Expand Small. A less costly plan is to redo the layout of the store and make a small addition on one side. It is thought that this small expansion will be sufficient for 5 years, the usual planning period for the company, and will cost $50,000. No residual value is expected at the end of this period.

A preliminary analysis indicates the estimated incremental revenues (compared with the no-expansion alternative) affected by each of the three assumed classes of business conditions.

Business Conditions	Estimated Probability of Occurrence	Incremental Net Revenues under Each Option	
		Option 1, Expand Large	Option 2, Expand Small
Good	0.25	$100,000	$40,000
Moderate	0.60	75,000	30,000
Poor	0.15	35,000	10,000

Here the net revenue means the incremental revenue caused by expansion less regular operating and maintenance but excluding depreciation and lease expenses. For tax purposes the store will expense all remodeling costs, but the expenditures on the equipment must be capitalized. The installed equipment would be classified in the 5-year personal property class. The chain store's *MARR* is known to be 15% after tax, and the store has a marginal tax rate of 40%, which is expected to remain the same for the investment period.

Decision Tree for the Orlando Store Expansion Problem. To illustrate the basic ideas, we will develop the decision tree for the Orlando store expansion problem. Recall that the decision is between investment options, and the decision point is represented by a decision node (□) in Figure 13.1. The decision alternatives are represented as branches from the decision node. The direction of the arrows refers to the time flow of the decision process.

Suppose that the store manager selects a particular alternative, say option 1. There are three chance events that can happen, each event representing a business condition that can prevail. These are shown in Figure 13.1 as branches emanating from a circle node (○). (In a decision tree analysis, we always use the convention of a square box for a decision node and a circle for an event or chance node.) Notice that these chance nodes represent events over which the store manager has no control. In our example the chance nodes represent the business conditions over the planning horizon. We must assign probabilities to each event in Figure 13.1.

Generally, traversing each branch on the decision tree will bring some reward, positive or negative, to the decision maker. At the end of each branch is the conditional profit associated with the selected action and given event. The conditional profit thus represents the profit associated with the decisions and events along the path from the first part of the tree to the end. For our example the incremental annual revenue of $100,000 in Figure 13.1 is associated with the action that leads to investment in option 1, and the store experiences a good business condition over the planning horizon.

Relevant Net After-Tax Cash Flow. Once the structure of the decision tree is determined, the next step is to find the relevant cash flow (monetary value)

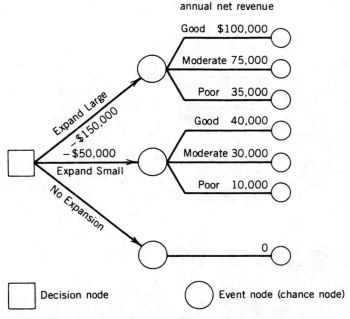

FIGURE 13.1 The decision tree for the Orlando store expansion problem.

associated with each of the decision alternatives and the possible chance outcomes. As we have emphasized throughout this book, the decision has to be
made on an after-tax basis. Therefore, the relevant monetary value should be on
an after-tax basis. Since the costs and revenues occur at different points in time
over the study period (5 years), we also need to convert the various amounts on
the tree's branches to their equivalent amounts (present value). For the problem
being considered, the after-tax *MARR* is 15%, and Figure 13.2 shows the costs
and revenues on the branches transformed to their present equivalents.

To illustrate, if the store adopts option 1 and a good business condition
prevails over the planning horizon, the net cash flows after taxes are as computed in Table 13.1a. Then the present value of this branch is

$$PV(15\%) = -140{,}000 + 60{,}400(P/F, 15\%, 1) + 64{,}240(P/F, 15\%, 2)$$

$$+ 60{,}144(P/F, 15\%, 3) + 57{,}686(P/F, 15\%, 4)$$

$$+ 86{,}529(P/F, 15\%, 5)$$

$$= \$76{,}645$$

and the internal rate of return is 35.42%. This amount of $76,645 is entered at
the end of the corresponding branch tip. This procedure is repeated for the
remaining two branches associated with option 1, and the resulting amounts are
shown in Figure 13.2.

For option 2 the net cash flow calculation is rather simple, as shown in
Table 13.1b. Again we repeat the procedure for the remaining two branches
originating from "Expand Small," and the computed *PV*s are entered at the tips
of the respective branches.

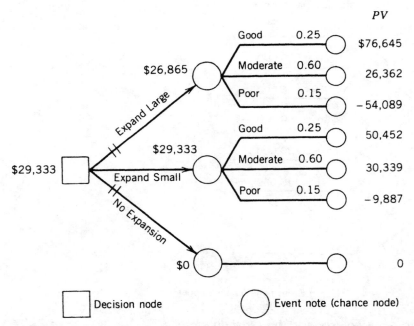

FIGURE 13.2 Present-value amounts of after-tax cash flows for
each outcome and solution of decision tree.

Table 13.1 *Net Cash Flows after Taxes for Decision Paths 1 and 4*

	0	1	2	3	4	5
a. *Decision path 1—expand large under good business conditions*						
Incremental revenue		$100,000	100,000	100,000	100,000	100,000
Lease expense		10,000	10,000	10,000	10,000	10,000
Depreciation		16,000	25,600	15,360	9,216	9,216
Remodeling	$70,000					
Taxable income	−70,000	74,000	64,400	74,640	80,784	80,784
Income taxes	−28,000	29,600	25,760	29,856	32,314	32,314
Net income	−42,000	44,400	38,640	44,784	48,470	48,470
Add depreciation		60,400	64,240	60,144	57,686	57,686
Investment	−80,000					
Salvage						15,000
Gains tax						−4,157
Working capital	−18,000					18,000
Net cash flow	−$140,000	60,400	64,240	60,144	57,686	86,529
b. *Decision path 4—expand small under good business conditions*						
Incremental revenue		$40,000	40,000	40,000	40,000	40,000
Remodeling	$50,000					
Taxable income	−50,000	40,000	40,000	40,000	40,000	40,000
Income taxes	−20,000	16,000	16,000	16,000	16,000	16,000
Net income	−30,000	24,000	24,000	24,000	24,000	24,000
Net cash flow	−$30,000	24,000	24,000	24,000	24,000	24,000

13.2.2 Expected Value as a Decision Criterion

At this point we can analyze the decision tree to determine which alternative should be undertaken. To analyze a decision tree, we begin at the end of the tree and work backward—the *averaging out and folding back* procedure [6]. In other words, starting at the tips of the decision tree's branches and working toward the initial node, we use the following two rules.

1. For each chance node we calculate the expected monetary value (*EMV*) by multiplying probabilities by conditional profits associated with branches emanating from that chance node and summing these conditional profits. We then place the *EMV* next to the node to indicate that it is the expected value calculated over all branches emanating from this node.

2. At each decision node we select the alternative with the highest *EMV* (or minimum cost). Then we eliminate from further consideration the decision alternatives that are not selected. On the decision tree diagram we draw a mark across the nonoptimal decision branches, indicating that they are not to be followed.

This procedure is illustrated in Figure 13.2 for our store expansion example. First, we calculate the *EMV*s for the event nodes associated with the larger-scale store expansion. For example, the *EMV* of option 1 represents the sum of the product of probabilities for good, moderate, and poor business conditions times the respective conditional profits.

$$EMV = (\$76,645)(0.25) + (26,362)(0.60) - (54,089)(0.15)$$
$$= \$26,865$$

For option 2 the *EMV* is simply

$$EMV = (\$50,452)(0.25) + (30,339)(0.60) - (9,887)(0.15)$$
$$= \$29,333$$

In Figure 13.2 the expected monetary values are shown next to the event nodes. The store manager must choose which action to take, and this would be the one with the highest *EMV,* namely option 2 (Expand Small) with *EMV* = \$29,333. We indicate this expected value in the tree by putting \$29,333 next to the decision node at the beginning of the tree. Notice that the decision tree uses the idea of maximizing expected monetary value that was developed in the previous section.

13.3 OBTAINING ADDITIONAL INFORMATION

In this section we introduce a general method for evaluating the possibility of obtaining more information. Most of the information we can obtain is imperfect in the sense that it will not tell us exactly which event will occur. Such imperfect information may have value if it improves the chances of making a correct decision, that is, if it improves the expected monetary value. The problem is whether the reduced uncertainty is valuable enough to offset its cost. The gain is in the improved efficiency of decisions that may become possible with better information.

We will use the term *experiment* in a broad sense here. An experiment may represent a market survey to predict sales volume for a typical consumer product, statistical sampling of production quality, or a seismic test to give a well-drilling firm some indications of the presence of oil [4].

13.3.1 The Value of Perfect Information

Let us take the prior decision of Expand Small as a starting point. How do we determine whether further strategic steps would be profitable? We could do more to obtain additional information about the future business condition, but such steps cost money. Thus, we have to balance the monetary value of reducing uncertainty with the cost of securing additional information. In general, we can evaluate the worth of a particular experiment only if we can estimate the reliability of the resulting information. In our store expansion problem an expert's opinion may be helpful in deciding whether or not to expand the store. This opinion can be of value, however, only if management can say beforehand how closely the expert can predict the future business condition. An example will make this clear.

Orlando Retail Store Expansion Problem Revisited. Suppose that the store manager knows an expert who can be called in as a consultant on the store expansion described as option 1. The expert will charge a fee to provide the store with a report that the business condition is *good, moderate,* or *poor.* This expert is not infallible but can provide a market survey that is pretty reliable. From past experience management estimates that, when the business condition is relatively good (A), the survey predicts a favorable business condition (F) with probability 0.80, an inconclusive business condition (I) with probability 0.10, and an unfavorable business condition (UF) with probability 0.10. Such probabilities would reflect past experience with surveys of this nature, modified perhaps by the judgment of the store manager. The probabilities shown in Table 13.2 express the reliability or accuracy of a survey of this type.

How much are the consultant's services worth to the manager? Should the store manager hire the expert as a consultant? To answer these questions, we will first introduce the *opportunity loss* concept and illustrate how this loss concept is related to the *value of perfect information.*

The Opportunity Loss Concept. The best place to start a decision improvement process is with a determination of how much we might improve incremental profit by removing uncertainty. Although we probably could not obtain perfect information, its value is worth computing as an upper bound to the value of additional information.

We can easily calculate the value of perfect information. Merely note the difference between the incremental profit from an optimal decision based on perfect information and the incremental profit from the original decision of Expand Small, made without foreknowledge of the actual business condition. We call this difference *opportunity loss,* and we must compute it for each potential degree of business condition.

For our store expansion example, the decision may hinge on the future

Table 13.2 *Conditional Probabilities of Survey Prediction*

Survey Outcome	For a Given Business Condition		
	Good (A)	Moderate (B)	Poor (C)
Favorable (F)	0.80	0.30	0.10
Inconclusive (I)	0.10	0.40	0.20
Unfavorable (UF)	0.10	0.30	0.70
Sum	1.00	1.00	1.00

business condition. The only unknown, subject to a probability distribution, is the business condition. Recall that the business condition was assumed to be good, moderate, or poor. The opportunity loss table for this prior decision is shown in Table 13.3. For example, the conditional net present value of $76,645 is the net profit associated with option 1 should the potential business condition be good. Recall also that, without receiving any information, the indicated action (prior optimal decision) was to select option 2 (Expand Small). Under a good business condition this option will yield a net present value of $50,452. Therefore, for a good business condition with perfect information, the prior decision to Expand Small is inferior to the decision to Expand Large to the extent of $76,645 − $50,452 = $26,193. When decision strategies with and without perfect information are the same (in this case for Expand Small with a moderate business condition), the value of opportunity loss must be zero. If a poor business condition prevails, the No Expansion alternative becomes the best strategy. The opportunity loss under this situation would be $0 − (−$9,887) = $9,887.

Being reluctant to give up a chance to make $76,645, however, the store manager may wonder whether to obtain further information before action. As with the prior decision, we need a single figure to represent the expected value of perfect information (*EVPI*). Again, an average weighted by the assigned chances is used, but this time weights are applied to the set of opportunity losses (regrets) in Table 13.3.

Business Condition	Opportunity Loss	Probability
Good	$26,193	0.25
Moderate	0	0.60
Poor	9,887	0.15

$$EVPI = (0.25)(26,193) + (0.60)(0) + (0.15)(9,887) = \$8,031$$

This figure represents the maximum expected amount that could be gained in incremental profit from perfect knowledge. This *EVPI* places an upper limit on the sum the manager would be willing to pay for additional information.

Table 13.3 *Conditional Value Table for Store Expansion Decison Problem*

Business Condition	Probability	Optimal Choice with Perfect Information		Prior Decision (Expand Small)	Opportunity Loss
		Decision	Outcome		
Good	0.25	Expand Large	$76,645	$50,452	$26,193
Moderate	0.60	Expand Small	30,339	30,339	0
Poor	0.15	No Expansion	0	−9,887	9,887
		EPPI* =	$37,365	$29,333	$8,031
Expected value			Prior optimal		
				Expected opportunity losses	

*EPPI = Expected profit with perfect information.

Updating Conditional Profit. Thus, there is (potentially at least) some value to be obtained from additional information. The store manager can perform an experiment in this situation. Recall that the experiment takes the form of receiving a market survey from a consultant.

There are three possible outcomes from the survey: (1) the survey may predict a good business condition, (2) the survey may be inconclusive, or (3) the survey may predict a poor business condition. The manager's alternatives are to employ this service or simply to expand the store on a small scale, as previously decided.

If the store manager takes a survey before acting, the decision can be based on the survey outcomes. We can express this problem in terms of a decision tree, as shown in Figure 13.3. The upper part of the tree shows the decision process if no survey is taken. This is the same as Figure 13.2, with probabilities of 0.25, 0.60, and 0.15 for good, moderate, and poor conditions and an expected profit of $26,865 for Expand Large that is less than the expected profit from Expand Small. Thus the optimal decision had an expected value of $29,333 based on the Expand Small strategy. (Note that all of Figure 13.2 has been repeated as the top part of Figure 13.3 for completeness, but only the earlier "best decision" is actually needed at this point.)

The lower part of the tree, following the branch Take Survey, displays the results and the subsequent decision possibilities in Figure 13.3. Using a forecasting service allows for two stages of events—the survey prediction and the actual level of business condition. After each of the three possible survey outcomes, a decision about whether or not to expand the store must be made.

13.3.2 Determining Revised Probabilities[1]

In Figure 13.3 market survey outcomes precede actual business conditions because the former are obtained as additional information before actual business conditions are known. To complete the analysis of Figure 13.3, we need the revised probabilities for the various events after additional information has been obtained. Recall that the store manager estimates the probabilities shown in Table 13.2. These are the conditional probabilities for the various survey outcomes, given the potential business condition. For example, when the actual business is good, the survey predicts a good business condition with a probability of 0.80, the survey results are inconclusive with a probability of 0.10, and the survey predicts a poor business condition with a probability of 0.10.

In fact, the probabilities in Table 13.2 express the reliability or accuracy of the experiment. It is a question of counting the number of times the survey was "on target" or had a "complete miss" for each of the three actual levels of business condition. We may convert the counts into proportions, entered as decimal fractions (probabilities) in Figure 13.4. With these estimates the store manager can evaluate the economic worth of the service. Without these reliability estimates, no specific value can be attached to taking the survey.

[1]This discussion of revised probabilities has been considerably influenced by an excellent presentation of decisions and revision of probabilities by Bierman, Bonini, and Hausman [1].

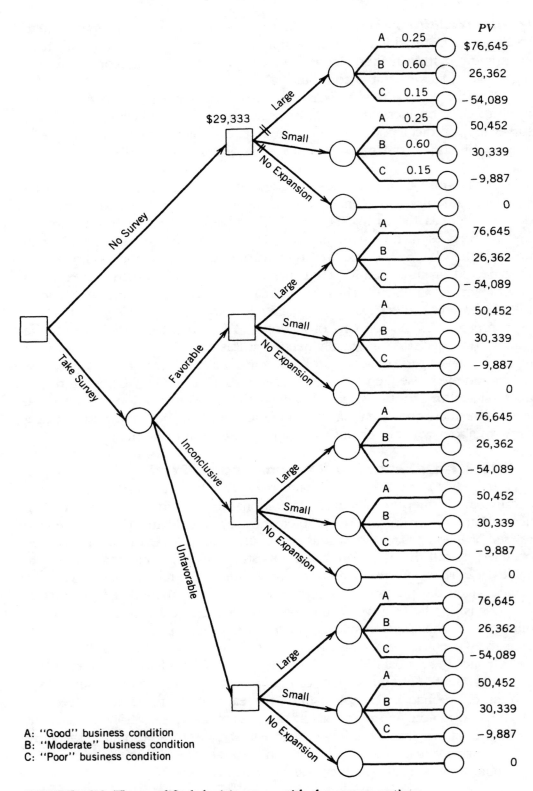

A: "Good" business condition
B: "Moderate" business condition
C: "Poor" business condition

FIGURE 13.3 The modified decision tree with the survey option.

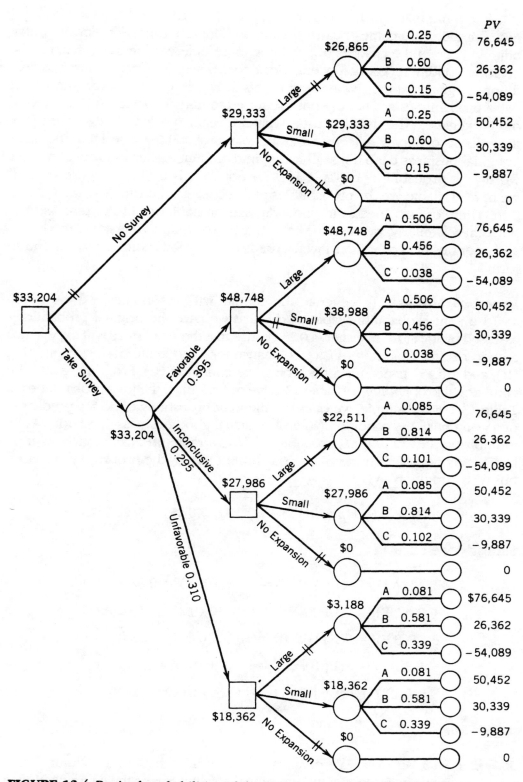

FIGURE 13.4 Revised probabilities of the decision tree with the survey option.

Now the manager has information on (1) the chances for particular business condition outcomes before getting additional information (prior probabilities) and (2) the chances of obtaining three different forecast levels for the business condition (good, moderate, or poor), given three actual business conditions. A glance at the sequence of events in Figure 13.4, however, shows that these probabilities are not the ones required to find "expected" values of various strategies in the decision path. What are really needed are the chances of three levels of survey outcomes and the total probabilities of each of the three potential business conditions, all taking into account earlier estimates. In other words, the probabilities of Table 13.2 are not directly useful in Figure 13.4. All we have available are the probabilities of three levels of business market condition. Therefore, we need the unconditional probabilities of the three survey outcomes. Similarly, we need the conditional probabilities of a good, moderate, and poor business condition, given a prediction of good business market, and so forth.

Joint Probabilities. To generate the conditional probabilities, we must construct a joint probabilities table. Recall that we have the original probabilities assessed by the store manager: a 0.25 chance that the retail store will experience a good market condition (A), a 0.60 chance for a moderate business condition (B), and a 0.15 chance for a poor business condition (C). From these and the conditional probabilities of Table 13.2, we can calculate the joint probabilities of Table 13.4. For example, we calculate the joint probability of both a prediction of a good business condition (F) and an actual good business condition (A) by multiplying the conditional probability of a favorable prediction, given a good business condition (which is 0.80 from Table 13.2), by the probability of a good business condition (A):

$$P(A,F) = P(F \mid A)P(A) = (0.80)(0.25) = 0.200$$

Similarly, we calculate

$$P(A,I) = P(I \mid A)P(A) = (0.10)(0.25) = 0.025$$
$$P(A,UF) = P(UF \mid A)P(A) = (0.10)(0.25) = 0.025$$
$$P(B,F) = P(F \mid B)P(B) = (0.30)(0.60) = 0.180$$
$$P(B,I) = P(I \mid B)P(B) = (0.40)(0.60) = 0.240$$
$$P(B,UF) = P(UF \mid B)P(B) = (0.30)(0.60) = 0.180$$

and so on.

Marginal Probabilities. We obtain the marginal probabilities of future business conditions in Table 13.4 by summing the values across the columns. Notice that these are in fact the original probabilities for good, moderate, and poor business conditions, and they are called prior probabilities because they were assessed before any information from the survey was obtained. In interpreting

Table 13.4 *Probabilities for Joint Events and Revised Probabilities (Store Expansion Problem)*

Potential Business Condition	Survey Prediction			Marginal Probabilities of Business Condition
	Favorable (F)	Inconclusive (I)	Unfavorable (UF)	
Good (A)	0.200	0.025	0.025	0.25
Moderate (B)	0.180	0.240	0.180	0.60
Poor (C)	0.015	0.030	0.105	0.15
Marginal probabilities of survey prediction	0.395	0.295	0.310	1.00

Given Survey Outcome	Actual Business Condition			Probability Sum
	Good (A)	Moderate (B)	Poor (C)	
Favorable (F)	0.506	0.456	0.038	1.00
Inconclusive (I)	0.085	0.814	0.101	1.00
Unfavorable (UF)	0.081	0.581	0.339	1.00

the marginal probabilities, we will borrow the analogy by Bierman, Bonini, and Hausman [1].

It is useful to think of Table 13.4 as representing the results of 1,000 past situations identical to the one under consideration. The probabilities then represent the frequency with which the various outcomes occurred. For example, in 250 of the 1,000 cases, the actual business condition turned out to be good; and in these 250 good cases, the survey predicted a favorable condition in 200 instances [that is, $P(A, F) = 0.20$], a moderate one in 25 instances, and an unfavorable one in 25 instances, respectively.

We can then interpret the marginal probabilities of survey predictions in Table 13.4 as the relative frequencies with which the survey predicted favorable, moderate, and unfavorable conditions. For example, the survey predicted favorable 395 out of 1,000 times—200 of these times when business conditions actually were good, 180 times when business conditions were moderate, and 15 times when business conditions were poor.

These marginal probabilities of survey prediction are critical in our analysis, because they provide us the probabilities associated with the information received by the store manager before the decision to invest in the store expansion is made. The probabilities are entered beside the appropriate branches in Figure 13.4.

Posterior Probabilities. What we need now, after receiving the survey information, is to calculate the probabilities for the branches labeled A (good), B (moderate), and C (poor). Clearly, we cannot use the values of 0.25, 0.60, and 0.15 for these events, because these probabilities were calculated *prior* to taking the survey. The required probabilities are the conditional probabilities for the various levels of business condition given the survey result—for our example

$P(A \mid F)$, the probability of a good business condition (A) given that the survey predicts a favorable market condition (F). We can easily compute this from the definition of conditional probability, using the data from Table 13.4.

$$P(A \mid F) = P(A,F)/P(F) = 0.200/0.395 = 0.506$$

The probabilities of moderate and poor conditions, given a prediction of favorable condition, are

$$P(B \mid F) = P(B,F)/P(F) = 0.180/0.395 = 0.456$$

$$P(C \mid F) = P(C,F)/P(F) = 0.015/0.395 = 0.038$$

We call these probabilities *posterior* probabilities because they come after receiving the information from the survey. To understand the meaning of the foregoing calculations, think again of Table 13.4 as representing 1,000 past identical situations. Then, in 395 cases [since $P(F) = 0.395$], 200 actually had a good business condition. Hence, the posterior probability for good business condition is, as calculated, $200/395 = 0.506$.

The posterior probabilities after survey predictions of other situations can be calculated similarly.

$$P(A \mid I) = P(A,I)/P(I) = 0.025/0.295 = 0.085$$

$$P(B \mid I) = P(B,I)/P(I) = 0.240/0.295 = 0.814$$

$$P(C \mid I) = P(C,I)/P(I) = 0.030/0.295 = 0.101$$

$$P(A \mid UF) = P(A,UF)/P(UF) = 0.025/0.310 = 0.081$$

$$P(B \mid UF) = P(B,UF)/P(UF) = 0.180/0.310 = 0.581$$

$$P(C \mid UF) = P(C,UF)/P(UF) = 0.105/0.310 = 0.339$$

These values are also shown in Figure 13.4 at the appropriate points in the decision tree.

13.3.3 Expected Monetary Value after Receiving Sample Information

As we have all the necessary information, we can analyze Figure 13.4, starting from the right and working backward. The expected values are shown next to the circles. For example, follow the branches Take Survey, Favorable Prediction, and Expand Large. The expected value of $48,748 shown next to the circle at the end of these branches is calculated as

$$(0.506)(\$76,645) + (0.456)(26,362) + (0.038)(-54,089) = \$48,748$$

Thus, the manager can expect a profit of $48,748 (before survey cost) if the store is doubled in size after a prediction of favorable business market conditions is received. Since this is better than the $38,988 associated with the smaller-scale expansion, the decision to expand the store on a larger scale is made, and the Expand Small and No Expansion branches are marked to indicate that they are not optimal.

There will be an expected loss of $27,986 − $22,511 = $5,475 if the survey gives a moderate market prediction, but the manager nevertheless goes ahead with the larger store expansion. Therefore, the Expand Small option becomes a better option, and the Expand Large branch is marked out. We also observe a situation similar to this when the survey indicates an unfavorable business condition.

We now reduce the part of the decision tree related to taking the survey to three chance events ($48,748, $27,986, and $18,362). We also calculate the expected value next to the circle node as

$$(0.395)(\$48,748) + (0.295)(\$27,986) + (0.310)(\$18,362) = \$33,204$$

Thus, if the survey is taken at *no cost* and the manager acts on the basis of the information received, the expected profit is $33,204.

Suppose the market survey is available at a cost of $1,000. Since this survey cost is deductible from income as a business expense, the net after-tax survey cost is ($1,000)(1 − 0.40) = $600. Subtracting this $600 from $33,204 yields $32,604, which is still greater than the $29,333 profit that would be obtained without taking the survey, so we conclude that it is worth spending $1,000 to receive some additional information from the market survey.

13.3.4 Value of the Market Survey

Taking the survey in the foregoing example is a means of obtaining additional information. The information is not perfect, because the survey cannot tell exactly whether the business condition will be good, moderate, or poor. Recall that the expected profit with the survey was $33,204. In fact, this is the expected profit with *free* information. The difference between the profit with information and without it is $33,204 − $29,333 = $3,871. In this situation, the value of the sample information is simply $3,871. This implies that the market survey would be worth taking as long as its cost did not exceed this amount. (In our example, taking the survey costs $600 after taxes, which is less than $3,871, and we conclude that it is worth taking.)

Compared with the *EVPI* ($8,032), the value of the survey is substantially lower, reflecting the fact that the survey can give inconclusive or incorrect information as indicated in Table 13.4. In other words, taking a sample is a means of obtaining information, but it is imperfect, since the sample is not likely to represent exactly the population from which it is taken [1].

13.4 DECISION TREE AND RISK

To simplify the decision analysis in the store expansion example, we made the rather unrealistic assumption that the manager seeks to maximize the expected

PV, by ignoring the risk incurred in each of the possible courses of action. Conceptually, risk can be incorporated in the analysis simply by assigning a utility to each monetary outcome and then choosing the branch that maximizes the expected utility. Such a procedure provides an acceptable theoretical solution to the problem but, as we have already noted, is rather difficult to implement in practice. Alternatively, answers to "what if" questions can be obtained with relative ease by using sensitivity analysis. With this general approach we could evaluate many possible "what if" situations merely by repetitively solving the tree with different values of parameters. In this section we will illustrate both approaches, sensitivity analysis and utility theory.

13.4.1 Sensitivity Analysis

Sensitivity analysis deals with the consequences of incremental change. How much could the manager's subjective assessment of chances be altered before the optimal decision would shift? In our store expansion example, just how far could chances shift before Expand Small would replace Expand Large as the optimal value? Formally, this amounts to establishing the values of chances at the break-even condition. Here the expected values of the two strategies are equal because this is the crossover point of indifference between strategies.

Example 13.1

Suppose the probability of a moderate business condition is held around a neutral level at 0.60 and the chances of good and poor business conditions are calculated to equate the two strategies Expand Large and Expand Small. If p symbolizes the chance of good business condition, then $(1 - 0.60 - p)$ or $(0.40 - p)$ is the chance of poor demand. This follows because the chances for all possible levels of business condition must sum to 1.

From the values of strategies in Figure 13.2, we can determine the break-even probability of

Expected value of Expand Large = expected value of Expand Small

or

$$p(76{,}645) + (0.60)(26{,}362) + (0.4 - p)(-54{,}089)$$
$$= p(50{,}452) + (0.60)(30{,}339) + (0.4 - p)(-9{,}887)$$

or

$$70{,}395p = 20{,}067$$

Solving this equation for p yields 0.285.

At this chance level the manager would be indifferent to choosing between Expand Large and Expand Small because the expected values of both strategies are equal. Even so, the manager might prefer one strategy over the other on the basis of other information not included in this quantitative analysis. □

13.4.2 Decision Based on Certainty Equivalents

Recall from the discussion of expected utility in Chapter 9 that expected monetary value is not an appropriate decision criterion when the conditional profits or losses are so large that the decision maker views the alternatives as having different amounts of risk. In such situations utility values are used in the decision tree in place of conditional monetary profits. Recall also that the preference curve takes into account an individual's attitude toward risk. The probabilities take into account the individual's beliefs about the uncertain events. The mechanics of the calculation are as follows.

1. For each branch outcome, convert the evaluation units (usually in dollars) to preference scale values (utile values).
2. Calculate the expected values of the preference numbers for each branch.
3. At each decision node, compare the expected values of the preference numbers and select the decision alternative with the largest expected utile value.
4. When the optimal decision path for the decision tree is reached, use the preference curve to obtain the *certainty equivalent amount* corresponding to the expected utile value of the optimal decision path.

Example 13.2

This example illustrates how the procedure we have discussed is used in a sequential analysis. In applying this procedure, reconsider the store expansion problem shown in Figure 13.4. Suppose that the manager's preference curve as a function of monetary outcome (X) can be described by

$$U(X) = 1 - e^{-X/30,000}$$

For example, the monetary outcome of \$76,645 associated with the first branch has an equivalent preference (utility) value of

$$U(76,645) = 1 - e^{-76,645/30,000}$$

$$= 0.922$$

The remaining *PV*s of all branch monetary outcomes in Figure 13.4 are replaced by the preference values, and these are summarized in Figure 13.5. Then the expected utility values are calculated for event nodes. For example, the expected utility value of -0.179 at the topmost right circle in Figure 13.5 represents the sum of the products of probabilities for good (A), moderate (B), and poor (C) business conditions times the respective conditional utility values.

$$E[U(X)] = (0.25)(0.922) + (0.60)(0.585) + (0.15)(-5.068) = -0.179$$

The other expected utility values are computed similarly.

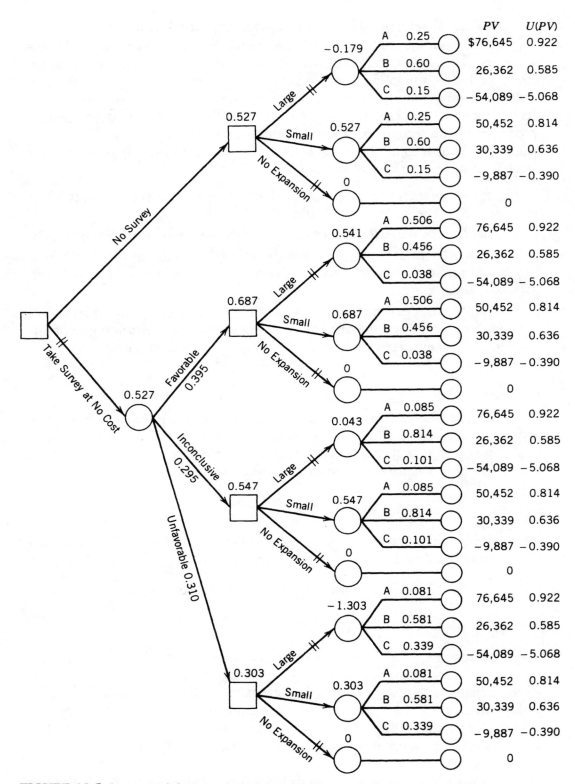

FIGURE 13.5 Sequential decision based on preference values (utilities). The $U(X) = 1 \cdot - e^{-X/30,000}$ calculation is based on a free sample. If the sampling cost is not zero, the cost must be subtracted before computing U(X).

Notice that the expected utility value for both options (Take Survey at No Cost versus No Survey) are the same (0.527). This is purely coincidental. Based on the expected-utility principle, the branch Take Survey at Some cost is no longer the optimal decision path. It appears that the Expand Small option becomes the ultimate choice, even if the survey is taken and the manager acts on the basis of the information received. To calculate the actual expected utility value for the Take Survey at Some Cost option, *we must subtract the sampling cost from each branch outcome before calculating the equivalent utile value for the branch.* □

13.5 INVESTMENT DECISIONS WITH REPLICATION OPPORTUNITIES

Consider situations in which a single type of equipment can be installed in many different locations, and it is possible to obtain additional information by trying the equipment in one location before deciding what to do about the other locations. This class of decision problem is known as investment decisions with replications [1,2]. In this section we will emphasize that an apparently good individual investment might be delayed when considered in the broader context of subsequent investments. For the same reason, an apparently poor individual investment might be good after obtaining additional information and having the opportunity to make sequential decisions.

13.5.1 The Opportunity to Replicate

We may observe the situations in which multiple-plant firms have an opportunity to innovate sequentially or a single plant has multiple production lines. Consider the introduction of new manufacturing technology (such as a flexible manufacturing system) in a multiple-plant company. The analysis for a single unit of the manufacturing system indicates a negative *PV*. But there is some probability that the manufacturing system would be successful and would have a positive *PV* in any subsequent use. In other words, there is uncertainty about the outcome, but there is some probability that the investment would be desirable. In such a situation the possibility that the firm may miss out on a technological breakthrough may be sufficient motivation for trying the new technology as a sample investment [3].

If one unit of a manufacturing system has a positive expected *PV*, some may argue that all the units should be installed for the entire firm. On an expected-value basis this is true. Under conditions of uncertainty and risk aversion, however, trying the investment on a small scale may help to determine whether the forecasted good result will actually occur. If the result is good, the remaining units can be installed. The cost of this policy is delay of the investments, however, which may be a disadvantage.

13.5.2 Experiment Leading to Perfect Information[2]

We will assume initially that undertaking one investment would allow perfect information about what could happen if all the identical investments

[2]This section is based on an article by Bierman and Rao [2].

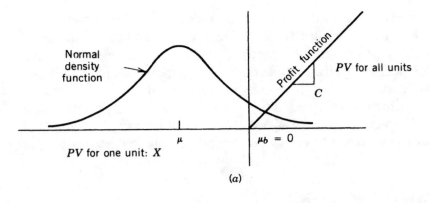

Normal
density
function

Profit function

PV for all units

C

μ

$\mu_b = 0$

PV for one unit: *X*

(a)

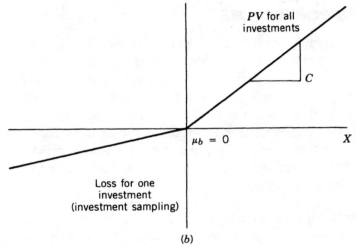

PV for all
investments

C

$\mu_b = 0$

X

Loss for one
investment
(investment sampling)

(b)

FIGURE 13.6 Expected value of perfect information and investment sampling. (a) Net present value lost by not undertaking investment; (b) Net present value if investment is undertaken.

were undertaken. Figure 13.6*a* shows the basic model with the *PV* of the profits lost by not undertaking the investment. Here *X* is the continuous random variable *PV* with mean μ for one unit of investment, and μ_b is the break-even present value. Under the expected value criterion, μ_b is the value when *X* is equal to zero.

Since μ is to the left of μ_b, the correct decision seems to be to reject the investment. If the investment is rejected, the present value is zero. But *X* is a random variable with a probability density function. This is a "prior distribution." If we are certain that the *PV* of the investment is $X = \mu$ (the variance of the distribution is zero), the investment would be rejected. If there is some probability that $X > \mu_b$, then further analysis is required.

The slope *C* of the *PV* curve for all units of investment depends on the number of units in which the firm can feasibly invest. The more units of investment, the steeper the slope. Thus, the profit potential for multiple investments, given an undesirable single investment, is a function of the slope of the *PV* line, the variance of the probability density function, and the distance between μ and μ_b.

If μ is less than 0 and if the value of X is positive, the expected profits are

$$C\int_0^\infty xf(x)\,dx$$

where $f(x)$ is the probability density function of X. The expected loss from undertaking one unit of investment if X is less than μ_b is

$$\int_{-\infty}^0 (-x)f(x)\,dx$$

If the expected present value is positive, the investment would be tried. If we have a discrete random variable, the integral would be replaced by the summation but the basic principle remains unchanged.

Figure 13.6*b* shows the *PV* if we undertake one investment and then we undertake the remaining investments should the actual value of X be greater than μ_b. If the actual value of X is less than μ_b, no additional investments are undertaken.

Example 13.3[3]

In converting a job shop operation to a flexible cellular manufacturing operation, we often face a decision whether to convert the whole factory or convert gradually. Normally, it costs less to convert the whole factory than do the conversion partially over periods. The gradual conversion, however, is a less risky investment because we can dictate the level of automation as we see fit. Moreover, this gradual automation can serve as an investment sampling process; the investment (automating the whole factory), although initially desirable, may appear unacceptable after obtaining additional information and being able to make sequential decisions. To structure this decision problem, consider the situation in which we can convert the whole factory with six identical manufacturing cells. We may convert just one cell and see how economical it is, then convert another cell, and so forth.

To make the problem simple, we assume that the level of performance of the converted cell can be described by a discrete set of three outcomes.

Probability (excellent performance) = $P(\theta_1)$ = 0.5
Probability (fair performance) = $P(\theta_2)$ = 0.3
Probability (poor performance) = $P(\theta_3)$ = 0.2

The cash flow information related to each performance level is summarized as follows.

Cell conversion costs (from job shop to cellular manufacturing): $1,000 per cell

[3]This problem was suggested by George Prueitt.

Annual returns after tax over 10 years,

$$\text{if } \theta_1 \quad \$250$$
$$\text{if } \theta_2 \quad 170$$
$$\text{if } \theta_3 \quad 50$$

The expected *PV* at *MARR* of 10% over a planning horizon of 10 years, is

$$
\begin{aligned}
E(X) &= 0.5[-1,000 + 250(P/A, 10\%, 10)] \\
&\quad + 0.3[-1,000 + 170(P/A, 10\%, 10)] \\
&\quad + 0.2[-1,000 + 50(P/A, 10\%, 10)] \\
&= 0.5(536) + 0.3(45) + 0.2(-693) \\
&= \$143 > 0
\end{aligned}
$$

$$
\begin{aligned}
Var(X) &= 0.5(536 - 143)^2 + 0.3(45 - 143)^2 + 0.2(-693 - 143)^2 \\
&= (469)^2
\end{aligned}
$$

Since the expected *PV* is positive, we would accept on an expected present value basis. However, there is 0.5 probability that each unit cell will perform to produce a *PV* of $536 or $3,216 in total. There is 0.3 probability that each unit cell will produce $45 per unit or $270 in total, and there is 0.2 probability that each unit will lose $693 or $4,158 in total. The expected value is still positive ($858). The variance of the total *PV* is then

$$Var(6X) = 36Var(X) = (2,814)^2$$

indicating a significant risk in the problem.

At this point we may compute the value of perfect information. For each possible event (θ_j), the optimal act would be as follows.

Event	Optimal Act	Based on Prior Belief	Opportunity Loss
θ_1	Convert	Convert	0
θ_2	Convert	Convert	0
θ_3	Do not convert	Convert	$4,158

The expected opportunity loss would be

$$
\begin{aligned}
E(\text{loss}) &= 0.50(0) + 0.3(0) + 0.2(\$4,158) \\
&= \$832
\end{aligned}
$$

Therefore, the *EVPI* is $832.

We can eliminate the uncertainty by converting just one cell for a maximum cost of $693. We will assume that, at the end of year 1, converting one cell would allow perfect information about what could happen if all the identical cells were converted. The firm will convert the five additional cells only if event θ_1 or event θ_2 occurs and the process proves to be feasible. If the process is feasible, each investment adds $536 or $45 of net present value, depending on the performance level. The sampling procedure (trying one investment before proceeding with the remainder) will delay the other investments and adversely affect their present value if they have positive present values. Multiplying the $536 by the five cells, we find $2,680. Since these five cells are converted a year later, the PV is $2,680(P/F, 10\%, 1) = \$2,436$. Therefore, the total PV associated with the five-cell conversion after successful performance of the first cell is $536 + $2,436 = $2,972. Similarly, if we observe θ_2, we go ahead and convert the remaining five cells. This will result in $45 + $225(P/F, 10\%, 1) = \$250$. Therefore, the expected value corresponding to the two favorable outcomes is $(0.50)(\$2,972) + (0.30)(\$250) = \$1,561$.

If event θ_3 is observed, the firm will make no further conversions, thereby limiting the loss to the one cell. The expected cost (in present value) of obtaining this information is equal to $(0.2)(\$693) = \$254$, the net expected opportunity loss associated with conversion of one cell, that will occur if the event is θ_3. (If the firm returned to the job shop operation after observing the first year's operation, the net cost would depend on the disposal value of the installed cell. In this example we assume that there would be no market for this used and unsuccessful manufacturing equipment, so the abandonment cost of the already installed cell would be greater than that of the retaining option.) Figure 13.7 shows the decision tree that evolves.

Because the expected value of $1,561 exceeds the expected cost of $254, we advocate undertaking the single cell conversion in the hope that we will find out that either event θ_1 or event θ_2 is the true state of the world.

If the alternative were to make all the investments now or do nothing, the firm would convert all the cells. If the delay of other conversions is allowed, the firm certainly wants to obtain information as cheaply as possible, which is accomplished by undertaking a minimum-sized investment. The fact that the other investments will be delayed is unfortunate, but it does not affect the basic sampling strategy. Delaying the investments decreases their PV, but it also enables the firm to avoid investing funds in undesirable investments. On balance, it is a desirable strategy if the investment would otherwise be rejected. □

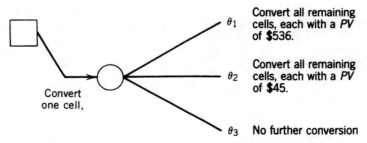

FIGURE 13.7 Decision tree with perfect information.

Example 13.3 illustrates a situation in which the investment appeared to be acceptable on the expected-value criterion, but it was worth buying perfect information before implementing the investment. We can apply the same investment sampling process even when the investment, although initially *not* desirable, may appear acceptable after we obtain additional information and are able to make sequential decisions. In general, we will observe that the greater the uncertainty, the better it is to obtain additional information, perhaps by trying an investment if the investment can be replicated.

13.5.3 Sampling Leading to Imperfect Information

Now assume in Example 13.3 that after the first investment is made and the results are observed, we still cannot be certain of the desirability of the investment; that is, the information obtained is imperfect. Suppose we are able to assign a set of probabilities reflecting the reliability of the information as shown in Table 13.5a. If the conversion actually is excellent, there is still a 0.05 proba-

Table 13.5 *Calculation of Joint and Posterior Probabilities*

a. *Conditional Probabilities*

	Actual State		
Observed Event from Sample Investment	θ_1	θ_2	θ_3
Conversion seems to be excellent (E)	0.80	0.20	0.10
Conversion seems to be fair (F)	0.15	0.60	0.20
Conversion seems to be bad (B)	0.05	0.20	0.70

b. *Joint Probabilities*

Joint Probabilities	Sample Prediction Outcome			Marginal Probabilities (Performance)
	E	F	B	
θ_1	0.400	0.075	0.025	0.50
θ_2	0.060	0.180	0.060	0.30
θ_3	0.020	0.040	0.140	0.20
Marginal Probabilities (Sample)	0.480	0.295	0.225	1.00

c. *Revised (Posterior) Probabilities*

Conditonal Outcome	Posterior Probabilities for a Given Survey Prediction		
	E	F	B
θ_1	0.833	0.254	0.111
θ_2	0.125	0.610	0.267
θ_3	0.042	0.136	0.622

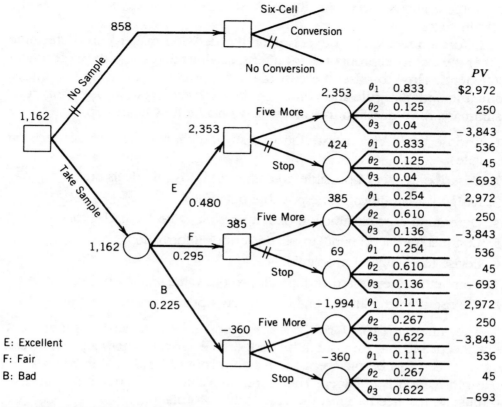

FIGURE 13.8 Decision tree with imperfect information.

bility that it may not appear profitable. If the conversion actually is not good, there are a 0.10 probability that it may appear excellent, a 0.20 probability that it may appear fair, and so forth.

The problem that has to be solved is whether or not it is desirable to go ahead and make the initial cell conversion. The computations of the relevant revised probabilities are shown in Table 13.5c. Figure 13.8 shows the probabilities and the outcomes if one cell conversion is undertaken to obtain information and then the decision is whether or not to undertake the conversions of the remaining cells. In Figure 13.8 we find that the one-unit conversion as a means of obtaining information is still desirable, even with imperfect information. The delayed investment strategy results in an expected net present value of $1,162, which is $304 more than that of the no-delay situation.

13.6 SUMMARY

The decision tree is another technique that can facilitate investment decision making when uncertainty prevails, especially when the problem involves a sequence of decisions. In decision tree analysis a decision criterion is chosen—say, to maximize expected profit. If possible and feasible, an experiment is conducted. The earlier probabilities of the states of nature are revised on the basis of the experimental results. The expected profit of each possible decision is computed, and the act with the highest expected profit is chosen as the optimum action.

Before undertaking an experiment, the decision maker must determine whether the expected profit of acting after receiving the result of the experiment is sufficiently large to offset the cost of the experiment. The analysis requires finding the optimum rule and evaluating the expected profit by using this rule. In summary, for a decision tree analysis, we may follow eight steps.

1. Choose the decision criterion (we suggest the expected-value decision rule).
2. Describe the set of possible outcomes and possible decisions.
3. Assign probabilities to the possible outcomes.
4. Determine a profit function or net present value for each branch node.
5. Conduct an experiment (to obtain further information).
6. Revise the assigned probabilities.
7. Compute the expected profit (net present value) for each decision.
8. Choose the act with the highest expected profit (net present value).

The inherent project risk raises the possibility that an investment that seems acceptable may turn out to be undesirable. On the other hand, an investment that seems to be unacceptable may turn out to be desirable when additional information is obtained. Therefore, the value of the additional information must be balanced against the cost of the information.

REFERENCES

1. BIERMAN, H., JR., C. P. BONINI, and W. H. HAUSMAN, *Quantitative Analysis for Business Decisions,* 5th edition, Richard D. Irwin, Homewood, Ill., 1977.
2. BIERMAN, H., JR., and V. R. RAO, "Investment Decisions with Sampling," *Financial Management,* Vol. 7, No. 3, pp. 19–24, Autumn 1978.
3. BIERMAN, H., JR., and S. SMIDT, *The Capital Budgeting Decision—Economic Analysis of Investment Projects,* 7th edition, Macmillan, New York, 1988.
4. MAGEE, J. F., "Decision Trees for Decision Making," *Harvard Business Review,* Vol. 42, No. 4, pp. 126–138, July–August 1964.
5. NEWENDORP, P. D., *Decision Analysis for Petroleum Exploration,* Pennwell Publishing Company, Tulsa, Okla., Chs. 4 and 10, 1975.
6. RAIFFA, H., *Decision Analysis—Introductory Lectures on Choices under Uncertainty,* Addison–Wesley, Reading, Mass., 1970.

PROBLEMS

13.1. Urn 1 contains 3 red balls and 2 black balls; urn 2 contains 11 red balls and 10 black balls. You are going to be given a sample of 2 balls and on this basis decide from which urn the sample came. The sample is equally likely to come from either urn. A correct decision gives you nothing; a wrong decision costs you one dollar. You wish to choose your guess so as to minimize your expected losses.

a. You are allowed to choose whether the sample will be drawn with or without replacement. Find your better strategy and expected loss.

b. You are allowed to decide whether the sample will be drawn with or without replacement after you have seen the first ball. Find the better strategy and expected loss.

13.2. You must decide whether to buy or lease a car. You have gathered some data on the costs of buying, operating, and leasing a vehicle for 3 months under two circumstances.

Use	Buy	Lease
Light use	$1,200	$950
Intensive use	1,600	1,700

These figures include all quantifiable costs. The unknown factor is whether the car will have light use or intensive use. This factor is beyond your control, but you estimate a 0.6 probability of intensive use and a 0.4 probability of light use.

a. Draw a decision tree for this problem.

b. What action do you recommend? Why?

c. You think that you can determine with 95% accuracy whether your car will be subject to light or intensive use. This will require about 4 hours of work on your part. You value your time at $200 per 8-hour working day. Should you spend more time investigating the matter? Why?

13.3. Jones wishes to buy a loom. The dealer offers Jones a choice between a new, perfect loom for $44 and an old, possibly defective model costing $30. Jones estimates that the old loom has probability $1/3$ of being defective and requiring $30 worth of repairs.

a. Which loom should Jones buy to minimize this expected cost?

b. Jones can hire a loom inspector who always passes good looms but catches bad looms with probability $3/4$. Jones will buy the old loom if it passes inspection and the new loom if it does not. How much are the inspector's services worth to Jones?

13.4. You are evaluating the development of an information system (IS) to forecast sales volumes. You will decide the staffing of a manufacturing line on the basis of this forecasted volume. The system may forecast sales as (1) increasing, (2) stable, or (3) decreasing. You respond with either (1) single-shift or (2) double-shift staff levels. Each of the six possible combinations provides an estimated dollar payoff.

	States of Nature		
Actions	Increasing Sales	Stable Sales	Decreasing Sales
Single shift	$11,000	$10,000	$2,000
Double shift	18,000	8,000	−3,000

If an IS is used, it provides a sales volume forecast (prediction); then the manager chooses a staff level (strategy), and finally an actual sales level (state of nature) occurs, yielding its associated payoff. States of nature are uncontrollable but occur with a probability that can be estimated, sometimes from historical data. In our example sales historically increased 30% of the time, were stable 45% of the time, and decreased 25% of the time.

Next, the manager must estimate the accuracy of the IS in forecasting sales levels. If the IS is infallible, it is called a perfect information system. Most ISs are imperfect, and the conditional probabilities in the following table reflect this fact.

	Given Actual Sales		
Predicted Sales	Increase	Stable	Decrease
Increase	65%	10%	10%
Stable	20	80	15
Decrease	15	10	75
Historical Probability:	30	45	25

The value 65% in the northwest corner means that when sales actually increase in the future period, the IS will have predicted the increase 65% of the time. Note that the sum of any column must equal 100%.

a. Is it worth using the IS system?
b. What is the expected value of perfect information without the IS?
c. What is the expected value of perfect information with the IS?
d. What is the value of the sample information?

13.5. Suppose you are the manager of a frozen-food factory and you have to decide on the annual production volume of brussels sprouts. The nature of the product dictates that you produce all the annual volume during a short harvest season and then store and market the frozen brussels sprouts during the entire year. Merchandise that has not been sold after a year is disposed of; on the other hand, if you are short of finished goods, you might lose customers in the long run. Since you have to contact possible vendors (farmers), you have to decide on production volume at the beginning of the year. Unfortunately, you do not know the demand for frozen brussels sprouts in the coming year. Your experience indicates that demand can be low (4,000 units of volume), medium (6,000 units), or high (8,000 units). Moreover, according to past experience, the prior probabilities of low, medium, and high demand are 0.3, 0.5, and 0.2, respectively.

Payoff Matrix and Expected Payoffs (in PV)

		Event (Actual Demand)			
		Low 4,000	Medium 6,000	High 8,000	
	Prior Probability:	0.3	0.5	0.2	Expected Payoff ($)
Decision (Production Volume)		Payoff Matrix			
Low	4,000	$2,000	0	−2,000	200
Medium	6,000	−$8,000	8,000	6,000	2,800
High	8,000	−$18,000	−2,000	14,000	−3,600

Suppose a market survey is available with the following reliability (values obtained from past experience where actual demand was compared with predictions made by the market survey).

Given Actual Demand	Survey Prediction		
	Low	Medium	High
Low	0.70	0.25	0.05
Medium	0.20	0.60	0.20
High	0.05	0.25	0.70

a. Determine the strategy that maximizes the expected payoff before taking the market survey.

b. Compute the expected value of perfect information.

c. Compute the expected value of sample information.

d. If the market survey costs $5,000, is it worth taking?

13.6. The Football University contemplate expanding their current 70,000-seat football stadium. The question of optimal seating capacity is being debated at a board of trustees' meeting. Mr. Hagan, the board member in charge of the university's athletic program, argues that since the demand for the season tickets is uncertain, a 5,000-seat expansion should be considered at this time. Mr. Smith, the head football coach, is in favor of adding 10,000 seats now. Mr. Smith argues that it costs less to add 10,000 seats all at once than to expand piecemeal. Both Hagan and Smith agree, however, that the future ticket demands are highly correlated with the university's postseason recruiting results and how the team performed in the previous seasons. Mr. White, the university president, expresses his opinion that, without support from student fees, no stadium expansion should be considered at this time because of difficulty in obtaining bond money at a fair market rate. "Students are already paying too much in other building programs, and they do not favor this stadium project," says the president. Mr. White feels that the university should postpone the decision for a year. If the university continues to have a strong football program for the next two seasons, he points out, then the current facility can easily be expanded to provide either 5,000 or 10,000 additional seats. The work can start right after the second season and be completed before the third season starts.

Mr. Jones, the director of the university's alumni association, has presented the results of a brief telephone survey of possible season ticket buyers. The survey shows that the probability of a light ticket demand is 0.2, of a high demand 0.4, and of a moderate demand 0.4. Depending on these demand levels, over the next 8 years the following *additional* annual receipts are expected to be received from the two alternatives that require an investment now.

		Additional Annual Receipts		
	Investment	Light	Moderate	High
Add 5,000 capacity	$10*	0	$2	$3
Add 10,000 capacity	18	0	3	5

*Unit: million dollars.

Take the interest rate as 6% for simplicity. If the decision to construct 10,000 capacity is postponed, the cost of expanding the stadium 2 years from now is expected to be

Adding 5,000 capacity $12 million

Adding 10,000 capacity $20 million

For example, if the university adds 5,000 seats now and adds another 5,000 at the end of 2 years, the total investment will be $22 million.

a. Draw the decision tree that describes the decision problem.

b. On the basis of expected net revenue, how should the university make the capacity expansion decision?

c. One board member has proposed that a full survey be taken to establish the actual demand to be experienced. What is the maximum value of such a survey?

13.7. Consider the following case story.

"How to pick a peach instead of a lemon. There is a bumper crop of used cars around, and plenty of lemons. Picking a peach instead of a lemon isn't all that difficult if you know the telltale signs of good and bad. Starting out, arm yourself with the peach picker's secret weapon: patience. . . ." (From *Motor Trend,* June 1977.) Now put yourself in the market for a used car and imagine the following conversation with a used-car dealer named John. Let's say he is an honest and good friend of yours:

John: This used-car business is a tough racket. I have a customer interested in the MODEL-X on our lot, but the practices of our business prevent me from warning him that he may get stuck if he buys it.

You: What do you mean? I came here to look at the MODEL-X, which you have been advertising for the last week.

John: I worked at a MODEL-X dealer when that car first came on the market. As you may know, the MODEL-X company made 20% of its cars in a new plant where they were still having production problems; those cars were lemons. The remaining 80% of MODEL-X for that year were made at other plants and they were good cars.

You: Oh boy! What you are saying is that you have been advertising a lemon. I can hardly believe this!

John: Well, you shouldn't feel so bad: maybe the MODEL-X on our lot doesn't have any defects, or its defects may already have been fixed.

You: Hey, John. Is there any way you can tell a peach from a lemon by a simple inspection?

John: That's the trouble. I personally don't know much about the car itself. But if you are really interested in the car, it's worth having a mechanic check what the average buyer usually can't.

You: Do you know any good mechanic from your service department who can look it over?

John: Sure I do, but you can hardly expect the mechanic to go through all the trouble of examining the car and getting dirty without some financial consideration. Furthermore, you must accept the fact that he may not provide you with perfect information about the true state of the car, even if he works on the car for 5 hours for a complete test. But I am not sure either that you need this perfect information at that kind of expense.

Let us now begin the analysis of the decision problem just described. Suppose the probability that, after a simple inspection (for 30 minutes), the mechanic will say the car is a peach, when the actual state of the car is a peach, is 0.75. The probability that he will find a lemon when the car is a lemon is 0.73. Further, he charges at the rate of $20 per hour. If you buy the car and it turns out to be a lemon, it will cost you $600 to fix the car. The asking price of the car is $2,500, which is about $300 less than the price quoted by other dealers. [The other dealers sell the cars with a guarantee (anti-lemon), so no repair cost is expected.]

  a. What is the probability that the suspected car is actually a lemon, even if the mechanic tells you it is a peach?
  b. If you buy the car with your own judgment but it turns out to be a lemon, it will cost you $600 to fix the car. What is the expected value of perfect information?
  c. Is it worth having the mechanic give the car a simple inspection?

d. Suppose the probability that the mechanic will find the true state of the car is a linear function of the testing time. He says the car is a peach with the following probability when the car is a peach.

$$0.6 + 0.3t, \qquad 0 \leq t \leq 1$$

$$0.875 + 0.025t, \qquad 1 \leq t \leq 5$$

where t is the testing time in hours. He says the car is a lemon with the following probability when it is a lemon.

$$0.7 + 0.06t, \qquad 0 \leq t \leq 5$$

How long would you let him check the car?

e. In part d, express the expected value of perfect information as a function of t.

Acknowledgments

- Problem 13.4 is based on an article by G. P. Schell, "Establishing the Value of Information Systems," *Interfaces,* Vol. 16, No. 3, pp. 82–89, 1986.

- Problem 13.5 is based on an article by N. Ahituv and Y. Wand, "Information Evaluation and Decision Makers' Objectives," *Interfaces,* Vol. 11, No. 3, pp. 24–33, 1981.

ISBN 0-471-76971-1

DATE DUE